PHYSICS
and
ASTRONOMY *of*
the MOON

PHYSICS
and
ASTRONOMY *of*
the MOON

Edited by
ZDENĚK KOPAL
Department of Astronomy
University of Manchester

1962
ACADEMIC PRESS, New York and London

ACADEMIC PRESS INC.

111 Fifth Avenue
New York 3, New York

U.K. Edition published by
ACADEMIC PRESS INC. (LONDON) LIMITED
Berkeley Square House, Berkeley Square, London, W.1.

Copyright © 1961 by Academic Press Inc.

Library of Congress Catalog Card Number: 60-16985

Printed in Great Britain by
J. W. ARROWSMITH, LIMITED, WINTERSTOKE ROAD, BRISTOL 3

List of Contributors

DIRK BROUWER, *Yale University Observatory, New Haven, Connecticut, U.S.A.*

AUDOUIN DOLLFUS, *Observatoire de Paris, Section d'Astrophysique, Meudon (Seine et Oise), France.*

J. V. EVANS, *Massachusetts Institute of Technology, Lincoln Laboratory, Lexington, Massachusetts, U.S.A.*

V. G. FESSENKOV, *Committee for Meteorites, U.S.S.R. Academy of Sciences, Moscow, U.S.S.R.*

J. F. GRAINGER, *Department of Astronomy, University of Manchester, England.*

GORDON W. GROVES, *Universidad Nacional de Mexico, Instituto de Geofisica, Mexico.*

GEN-ICHIRO HORI, *Yale University Observatory, New Haven, Connecticut, U.S.A.*

ZDENĚK KOPAL, *Department of Astronomy, University of Manchester, England.*

KAROL KOZIEL, *Astronomical Observatory, University of Cracow, Cracow, Poland.*

N. A. KOZYREV, *Pulkovo Observatory, Leningrad, U.S.S.R.*

FRANTIŠEK LINK, *Astronomical Institute of the Czechoslovak Academy of Sciences, Prague, Czechoslovakia.*

J. RING, *Department of Physics, University of Manchester, England.*

EUGENE M. SHOEMAKER, *United States Department of the Interior, Geological Survey, Menlo Park, California, U.S.A.*

WILLIAM M. SINTON, *Lowell Observatory, Flagstaff, Arizona, U.S.A.*

HAROLD C. UREY, *University of California, School of Science and Engineering, La Jolla, California, U.S.A.*

Preface

After spending several decades in astronomical semi-obscurity, the Moon—our nearest celestial neighbour—has of late suddenly emerged to claim renewed interest and attention on the part of physical scientists as well as of their fellow men all over the world; and the reasons which brought this about are indeed of historical significance.

From time immemorial, astronomy has been debarred from the status of a genuine experimental science by the remoteness of its objects of study. With the exception of the meteors—those small freaks of cosmic matter intercepted by the Earth on its perpetual journey through space—the properties of all celestial bodies outside the Earth could be studied only at a distance—from the effects of attraction exerted by their masses, and from the ciphered message of their light brought to us by nimble-footed photons across the intervening gaps of space.

The dramatic emergence of long-range rockets in recent years bids fair to bring about a change in this time-honoured picture. On September 13th of 1959—a memorable date in the annals of human endeavour—a man-made missile sent out from trans-Caucasian steppes to the Moon crash-landed on the surface of our satellite, and thus ended already the age-long separation of these two bodies. Moreover, the continuing advances in rocket engineering make it a virtual certainty that this first flight will soon be followed by others carrying instruments—and, eventually, men—to the Moon, thus inaugurating an era of direct exploration of this first one of the heavenly bodies outside the gravitational confines of our Earth.

At the dawn of this new age, which the current technological advances have so suddenly thrust upon us, it may be both timely and appropriate to take stock of our present knowledge of the astronomy and physics of our satellite, gathered by all preceding generations of astronomers by more conventional methods, and to offer it as a votive gift to the explorers of the forthcoming space age. In the present volume, fifteen authors—all authorities in their respective fields—have combined their efforts to this end.

The general plan underlying this book should be apparent at a glance from its contents. Its first three chapters contain a comprehensive account of the dynamics of the Moon—its best explored property so far—describing for the technical reader the methods and results of the study of the Moon through space (Chapter 1) as well as around its own centre of gravity (Chapter 2), and its dynamical interaction with the Earth (Chapter 3). The next three chapters expound an analysis of the light of the Moon: i.e. the photometry of sunlight scattered by the lunar surface (Chapter 4) and its polarization properties (Chapter 5), together with an exhaustive discussion of the photometry of lunar eclipses (Chapter 6).

Chapter 7 contains an account of the methods of lunar topography and charting, while in the subsequent Chapter 8 an attempt has been made to explain the existence of the principal features of lunar landscape in terms of the forces which must have been operative there since time immemorial. In Chapters 9 to 11 we return again to the properties of moonlight: but this time to its fluorescent and infrared component, the study of which can reveal many additional properties (thermal, chemical, etc.) of the lunar surface. Chapter 12 then treats the radio-observations of the Moon—both of its thermal emission as well as of the surface reflections at radar frequencies–while its concluding Chapter 13 takes stock of our present knowledge and views on the origin, past history, and present structure, of the lunar globe as a whole.

In perusing the contents of this volume, the reader will doubtless learn to appreciate that an investigation of any celestial body at a distance must leave many questions unanswered, and others subject to some uncertainty. The authors cooperating on this volume deliberately avoided any effort to minimize such difficulties by attempting to present a "united front" in the face of issues which may still hang in balance; thus they intend to share with the reader not only the main fruits of their knowledge, but also at least some of their perplexities.

They do so in anticipation of the fact that many of the present lacunae in our knowledge will be filled, and many doubts resolved, by the measurements and soundings on the actual lunar surface, secured by means of instruments to be landed on the Moon by space probes in the relatively near future. The results of such experiments —marking the beginnings of true experimental astronomy—will no doubt correct many conclusions based on previous observations at a distance. In particular, a reliable knowledge of the detailed structure and composition of lunar rocks will probably have to await—albeit not too long—the hammer of the geologist on the spot; and he alone may eventually settle the time-honoured problem of the origin of lunar craters, and other surface features, to everyone's satisfaction.

There is no room for doubt that, in the next decade, our knowledge of the properties of our only natural satellite is due to take a great and unprecedented leap ahead. It is, however, equally certain that

this leap can be successfully accomplished only from the springboard
of our past and present achievements in this field—which by themselves represent a remarkable triumph of the human mind—and of
which the present volume attempts to give a full and faithful account.

"Greenfield", Parkway,
Wilmslow, Cheshire,   *Zdeněk Kopal.*
October 1961.

Contents

LIST OF CONTRIBUTORS v

PREFACE vii

CHAPTER 1

The Motion of the Moon in Space

DIRK BROUWER AND GEN-ICHIRO HORI

I.	Introductory Remarks	1
II.	The Principal Methods	8
III.	Hill's Equations of Motion	14
IV.	Non-Solar Perturbations	19
V.	Comparison with the Observations	22
VI.	The Improved Lunar Ephemeris	23
VII.	Radar Distances of the Moon	24
	References	25

CHAPTER 2

Libration of the Moon

KAROL KOZIEL

I.	Rotation of the Moon and the Laws of Cassini	27
II.	Optical Libration of the Moon	27
III.	Physical Libration of the Moon	31
IV.	Physical Libration in Longitude	33
V.	Physical Libration in Inclination and Node	43
VI.	Influence of Solar Attraction	46
VII.	Determination of the Constants of the Moon's Physical Libration from Observations	46
VIII.	Comparison of Heliometric Observations of the Moon with Theory	47
IX.	Adjustment of Heliometric Observations of the Moon's Libration	50
X.	Remarks Concerning the Figure of the Moon	54
XI.	Values of the Constants of the Moon's Physical Libration and Conclusion	56
	References	58

CHAPTER 3

Dynamics of the Earth-Moon System

GORDON W. GROVES

I.	Introduction	61
II.	Kinematical and Dynamical Relationships	63
III.	Tidal Deformation	70

IV. Rotation of the Earth 76
V. Secular Variation: the Evidence............................. 80
VI. The Tidal Couple 88
VII. Inclination and Eccentricity.............................. 92
References 96

CHAPTER 4

Photometry of the Moon

V. G. FESSENKOV

I. Introduction 99
II. Integral Brightness as a Function of the Phase-Angle.......... 100
III. Absolute Magnitude and Albedo of the Moon 106
IV. Brightness of Surface Details.............................. 111
V. Laws of Reflection 113
VI. Colorimetric Characteristics............................... 121
VII. Conclusions 125
References 128

CHAPTER 5

The Polarization of Moonlight

AUDOUIN DOLLFUS

I. Introduction 131
II. Polarization of Light from the Whole Disk 132
III. Polarization by Different Regions of the Disk 133
IV. Polarization of Light by Mineral Substances................. 134
V. Substances with Vitreous Surfaces.......................... 134
VI. Slightly Absorbing Powdered Substances..................... 137
VII. Substances with Rough or Diffusing Surfaces 141
VIII. Powdered Opaque Substances.............................. 143
IX. The Interpretation of the Polarization of the Light from the Moon 144
X. Origin of the Powdery Nature of Lunar Ground............... 146
XI. Polarization of the Ashen Light of the Moon 148
XII. The Study of the Polarization of Ashen Light................ 150
XIII. Origin of the Polarization of the Ashen Light 151
XIV. Polarization Curve of the Earth............................ 151
XV. The Nature of the Lunar Ground 153
XVI. The Investigation of an Atmosphere Surrounding the Moon...... 154
References 159

CHAPTER 6

Lunar Eclipses

FRANTIŠEK LINK

I. Introduction 161
II. The History of Lunar Eclipses............................. 162

III.	The Basic Characteristics of the Eclipses	164
IV.	Future Eclipses	166
V.	Increase of the Earth's Shadow	167
VI.	The Photometric Model of the Eclipses	170
VII.	General Transmission Coefficient	172
VIII.	Computation of the Refraction and of the Air-mass	175
IX.	Brightness of the Solar Elementary Ring	177
X.	Structure of the Auxiliary Shadow	179
XI.	Normal Densities of the Shadow	180
XII.	The Eclipse on the Moon	184
XIII.	Geographic Circumstances of Eclipses	186
XIV.	Effects of Light Scattering	188
XV.	Photometry of Lunar Eclipses	190
XVI.	Comparison between Theory and Observations	193
XVII.	Atmospheric Ozone	194
XVIII.	High Absorbing Layer	198
XIX.	Meteorological Analysis of the Eclipse	206
XX.	Lunar Luminescence	209
XXI.	Possible Manifestations of Lunar Luminescence Outside the Eclipses	213
XXII.	The Variations in Brightness of the Eclipse	217
XXIII	Further Phenomena during Lunar Eclipses	222
XXIV.	Allied Phenomena	224
XXV.	Conclusions	225
	References	226

CHAPTER 7

Topography of the Moon

ZDENĚK KOPAL

I.	Lunar Topography: a Survey	231
II.	Lunar Coordinates	246
III.	Determination of Altitudes on the Moon	251
IV.	Formations of the Lunar Surface	265
	References	281

CHAPTER 8

Interpretation of Lunar Craters

EUGENE M. SHOEMAKER

I.	Introduction	283
II.	Crater-forming Processes	285
III.	Maars	291
IV.	Impact Craters	307
V.	Ballistics of Copernicus	323
VI.	History of the Copernicus Region	344
	References	351

CHAPTER 9

Physical Observations of the Lunar Surfaces

N. A. KOZYREV

I. Introduction 361
II. Observations by Dinsmore Alter 363
III. Spectral Observations of Alphonsus on 3rd November, 1958 363
IV. Spectral Observations of Alphonsus on 23rd October, 1959 375
V. Conclusions 382

CHAPTER 10

The Luminescence of the Lunar Surface

J. F. GRAINGER AND J. RING

I. Introduction 385
II. Historical Survey 385
III. Observations of Line Profiles 393
IV. Photometric Accuracy Requirements 397
V. The Ideal Luminescence Spectrophotometer 399
VI. Conclusions 404
References 404

CHAPTER 11

Temperatures on the Lunar Surface

WILLIAM M. SINTON

I. Early Infrared Measurements of the Moon 407
II. Infrared Measurements of Lunar Temperatures 407
III. Temperature of Moon in Eclipse 411
IV. Theoretical Analysis of the Surface Temperature Variation 413
V. Analysis of the Surface Temperature Variation During an Eclipse 417
VI. Temperature Dependence of Thermal Conductivity and Specific
Heat 418
VII. Microwave and Millimetre-wave Observations................ 419
VIII. Interpretation of Microwave Temperatures 421
IX. Comparison of Measurements at Different Wavelengths 424
X. Departures of Observations from the Theory and Model......... 426
References 427

CHAPTER 12

Radio Echo Studies of the Moon

J. V. EVANS

I. Introduction: the Radar Equation............................ 429
II. Factors Influencing the Intensity of the Echoes................ 435
III. The Directivity Factor g 439

IV.   The Librations of the Moon 441
 V.   Pulse Length Considerations.............................. 444
VI.   The Early Experiments.................................... 446
VII.   The Later Experiments.................................... 452
VIII. Summary of the Results 468
IX.   Discussion of the Results................................ 469
 X.   The Lunar Ionosphere 477
XI.   Conclusion 477
       References 478

CHAPTER 13

Origin and History of the Moon

HAROLD C. UREY

 I.   Introduction 481
 II.   Origin of the Lunar Craters 482
III.   The Imbrium Collision................................... 484
IV.   Time of Formation of the Lunar Surface 489
 V.   The Figure of the Moon 491
VI.   The Heat Balance of the Moon 495
VII.   Density and Composition of the Moon 505
VIII. The Chemical Composition of the Surface Regions.......... 510
IX.   The Origin of the Moon.................................. 513
 X.   Conclusions 521
       References 521

AUTHOR INDEX   525

SUBJECT INDEX   533

Chapter 1

The Motion of the Moon in Space

Dirk Brouwer and Gen-Ichiro Hori

I. Introductory Remarks... 1
   A. The Equations of Motion for the Main Problem................. 2
   B. Change of Notation.. 5
II. The Principal Methods.. 8
   A. Methods with the True Longitude as Independent Variable....... 8
   B. Perturbations in Polar Coordinates with the Time as Independent
      Variable.. 9
   C. The Method of the Variation of Arbitrary Constants............. 9
   D. Hansen's Method.. 10
   E. The Method using Rectangular Coordinates.................... 13
III. Hill's Equations of Motion...................................... 14
   A. The Principal Part of the Motion of the Perigee................. 16
   B. Contributions by J. C. Adams............................... 18
   C. Brown's Extension to Higher Orders......................... 18
   D. Numerical Verification of the Lunar Theory................... 18
IV. Non-Solar Perturbations.. 19
   A. Planetary Perturbations.................................... 19
   B. Perturbations Produced by the Figure of the Earth and the Moon 20
   C. Secular Acceleration.. 20
V. Comparison with the Observations................................ 22
VI. The Improved Lunar Ephemeris.................................. 23
VII. Radar Distances of the Moon................................... 24
   References... 25

I. Introductory Remarks

Accounting for the Moon's motion in space on the basis of gravitational theory constitutes a complex problem in dynamical astronomy. The construction of a complete lunar theory for the purpose of comparison with observations requires the solution of the differential equations of the Moon's relative motion about the Earth's centre in which the attractions by the Earth, the Sun, and the principal planets are included and allowance is made for the deviations from sphericity of the bodies of the Earth and the Moon. In addition, the constants of integration present in the solution must be evaluated by comparison with observations, and a choice must be made with regard to the values of various parameters to be used in the numerical evaluation of the theory. Examples are the values of the solar parallax, the Moon's mass, the Earth's dynamical oblateness and the parameters that specify the figure of the Moon. All these are to be incorporated in the tables of the Moon's motion that serve for the calculation of the lunar ephemeris.

E. W. Brown's "Tables of the Moon", Yale University Press, 1919, represent the most exhaustive solution of the lunar problem ever made. It is the outcome of Brown's investigations covering a period of almost thirty years.

The nucleus of any attempt at representing the Moon's motion is the solution of the so-called "main problem" of the lunar theory, in which the Moon, the Earth, and the Sun are the only bodies considered, and it is assumed that they attract each other as point masses. The designation "main problem" is due to E. W. Brown, but the concept is much older.

A. THE EQUATIONS OF MOTION FOR THE MAIN PROBLEM

In an inertial coordinate system let the masses and coordinates be designated as follows:

$$
\begin{array}{llll}
\text{for the Moon,} & m_1, & \xi_1,\ \xi_2,\ \xi_3; \\
\text{for the Sun,} & m_4, & \xi_4,\ \xi_5,\ \xi_6; \\
\text{for the Earth,} & m_7, & \xi_7,\ \xi_8,\ \xi_9.
\end{array}
$$

Let

$$
\eta_j = m_1 \frac{d\xi_j}{dt}, \qquad \eta_{j+3} = m_4 \frac{d\xi_{j+3}}{dt}, \qquad \eta_{j+6} = m_7 \frac{d\xi_{j+6}}{dt},
$$

be the momenta conjugate to ξ_j, ξ_j+3, ξ_j+6 ($j = 1, 2, 3$). Then the equations of motion for the three bodies are

$$
\frac{d\xi_j}{dt} = \frac{\partial H}{\partial \eta_j}, \qquad \frac{d\eta_j}{dt} = -\frac{\partial H}{\partial \xi_j}, \quad (j = 1, 2, \ldots, 9) \qquad (1)
$$

with the Hamiltonian

$$
H = \frac{1}{2m_1} \sum_{j=1}^{3} \eta_j^2 + \frac{1}{2m_4} \sum_{j=1}^{3} \eta_{j+3}^2 + \frac{1}{2m_7} \sum_{j=1}^{3} \eta_{j+6}^2 - U.
$$

The force function U is

$$
U = k^2 \left[\frac{m_1 m_4}{r_{14}} + \frac{m_4 m_7}{r_{47}} + \frac{m_7 m_1}{r_{71}} \right],
$$

in which the denominators are the distances between the masses indicated by the double subscripts.

The equations (1) form a system of canonical equations of nine degrees of freedom. By making use of Jacobi's coordinates with reduced masses the number of degrees of freedom may be reduced to six while retaining the canonical form of the equations. Let, therefore,

$$
\left.
\begin{aligned}
x_j &= \xi_j - \xi_{j+6}, \\
x_{j+3} &= \xi_{j+3} - \frac{m_1\xi_j + m_7\xi_{j+6}}{m_1 + m_7}, \qquad (i = 1, 2, 3) \\
x_{j+6} &= 0,
\end{aligned}
\right\} \quad (2)
$$

so that the Moon is referred to the centre of the Earth, the Sun to the barycentre of the Earth-Moon system. With the determining function

$$
\begin{aligned}
S &= S(\xi_1, \xi_2, \ldots, \xi_9, y_1, y_2, \ldots, y_9) \\
&= \sum_{j=1}^{3} (\xi_j - \xi_{j+6}) y_j + \sum_{j=1}^{3} \left(\xi_{j+3} - \frac{m_1\xi_j + m_7\xi_{j+6}}{m_1 + m_7} \right) y_{j+3},
\end{aligned}
$$

the transformation is given by

$$
x_j = \frac{\partial S}{\partial y_j}, \qquad \eta_j = \frac{\partial S}{\partial \xi_j} \qquad (j = 1, 2, \ldots, 9) .
$$

These expressions for x_j are identical with Eq. (2), while those for η_j yield for the transformation of the momenta

$$
\left.
\begin{aligned}
\eta_j &= y_j - \frac{m_1}{m_1 + m_7} y_{j+3}, \\
\eta_{j+3} &= y_{j+3}, \qquad\qquad\quad (j = 1, 2, 3) \\
\eta_{j+6} &= -y_j - \frac{m_7}{m_1 + m_7} y_{j+3}.
\end{aligned}
\right\} \quad (3)
$$

The new equations are

$$
\frac{dx_j}{dt} = \frac{\partial H}{\partial y_j}, \qquad \frac{dy_j}{dt} = -\frac{\partial H}{\partial x_j}, \qquad (j = 1, 2, \ldots, 6) \quad (4)
$$

with the same Hamiltonian as in Eq. (1) but expressed in the new variables.

Thus,

$$H = \frac{1}{2m_1'}\sum_{j=1}^{3} y_j^2 + \frac{1}{2m_4'}\sum_{j=1}^{3} y_{j+3}^2 - U,$$

in which

$$m_1' = \frac{m_1 m_7}{m_1 + m_7}, \qquad m_4' = \frac{m_4(m_1 + m_7)}{m_1 + m_4 + m_7}$$

are the reduced masses.

If now

$$r_1^2 = x_1^2 + x_2^2 + x_3^2,$$
$$r_4^2 = x_4^2 + x_5^2 + x_6^2,$$

so that $r_1 \ (= r_{71})$ is the geocentric distance of the Moon, while r_4 is the distance of the Sun from the barycentre of the Earth-Moon system, the force function may be developed into

$$U = k^2 \left[\frac{m_1 m_7}{r_1} + \frac{m_4(m_1 + m_7)}{r_4} + m_1 m_4 \left(\frac{1}{r_{14}} - \frac{1}{r_4} \right) + m_4 m_7 \left(\frac{1}{r_{47}} - \frac{1}{r_4} \right) \right]$$

$$= k^2 \left[\frac{m_1 m_7}{r_1} + \frac{m_4(m_1 + m_7)}{r_4} + \frac{m_1 m_4 m_7}{m_1 + m_7} \frac{r_1^2}{r_4^3} P_2(\cos \sigma) \right.$$

$$+ \frac{m_1 m_4 m_7 (m_7 - m_1)}{(m_1 + m_7)^2} \frac{r_1^3}{r_4^4} P_3(\cos \sigma)$$

$$\left. + \frac{m_1 m_4 m_7 (m_7^2 - m_7 m_1 + m_1^2)}{(m_1 + m_7)^3} \frac{r_1^4}{r_4^5} P_4(\cos \sigma) + \cdots \right],$$

in which σ is the angle at the barycentre of the Earth-Moon system between the directions to the Sun and the Moon, and P_2, P_3, P_4 are Legendre polynomials.

Substitution of the approximate numerical values,

$$\frac{r_1}{r_4} \sim \frac{1}{400}, \qquad \frac{m_4}{m_1 + m_7} \sim \frac{10^6}{3}, \qquad \frac{m_1}{m_7} \sim \frac{1}{80},$$

shows that in the Moon's motion the ratio between the coefficients of the second harmonic and the principal term is

$$\frac{m_4}{m_1 + m_7} \left(\frac{r_1}{r_4} \right)^3 \sim \frac{10^6}{3} \left(\frac{1}{400} \right)^3 \sim \frac{1}{200};$$

the third harmonic and the principal term is

$$\sim \frac{1}{200} \times \frac{1}{400} = \frac{1}{80,000};$$

and the fourth harmonic and the principal term is

$$\sim \frac{1}{200} \times \left(\frac{1}{400}\right)^2 = \frac{1}{32,000,000}.$$

In the case of the Sun's motion relative to the barycentre of the Earth-Moon system the ratio between the coefficients of the second harmonic and the principal term is

$$\frac{m_1 m_7}{(m_1+m_7)^2} \left(\frac{r_1}{r_4}\right)^2 \sim \frac{1}{80} \left(\frac{1}{400}\right)^2 \sim \frac{1}{13,000,000}.$$

Thus the Sun's motion relative to the barycentre of the Earth-Moon system can be approximated by a Keplerian motion to a high degree of accuracy.

According to Hill (1878) the principal deviation of the Sun's orbit from a Keplerian ellipse, for instance, in radius vector is

$$\Delta r_4 = a_4[0 \cdot 00000\ 00200 + 0 \cdot 00000\ 00003 \cos 2(\lambda_1 - \lambda_4)],$$

in which λ_1, λ_4 are the mean longitudes of the Moon and the Sun, respectively. This can be allowed for as a small correction at the very end of the solution of the problem of the Moon's motion and was actually included in Brown's "Tables of the Moon".

The entire solution of the main problem may, therefore, be developed as if the deviation from Keplerian motion in the Sun's orbit did not exist. The simplification thereby introduced is of great value: the coordinates of the Sun relative to the barycentre of the Earth-Moon system may be considered to be known functions of the time and the elements of the Sun's orbit. Hence, the equations of motion for the Moon may be separated from those for the Sun.

B. CHANGE OF NOTATION

If the following change of notation is effected,

$$x_1', x_2', x_3', r', m', r, E, M,$$

for

$$x_4, x_5, x_6, r_4, m_4, r_1, m_7, m_1,$$

the system of equations for the solution of the main problem becomes

$$\frac{dx_j}{dt} = \frac{\partial H_{\mathbb{C}}}{\partial y_j}, \qquad \frac{dy_j}{dt} = -\frac{\partial H_{\mathbb{C}}}{\partial x_j}, \qquad (j = 1, 2, 3)$$

$$H_{\mathbb{C}} = \frac{E+M}{2EM}(y_1^2 + y_2^2 + y_3^2) - U_{\mathbb{C}},$$

$$U_{\mathbb{C}} = k^2 \left[\frac{EM}{r} + \frac{m'EM}{E+M} \frac{r^2}{r'^3} P_2(\cos \sigma) + \frac{m'EM(E-M)}{(E+M)^2} \frac{r^3}{r'^4} P_3(\cos \sigma) \right.$$

$$+ \frac{m'EM(E^2-EM+M^2)}{(E+M)^3} \frac{r^4}{r'^5} P_4(\cos \sigma)$$

$$\left. + \ldots \right],$$

with

$$rr' \cos \sigma = x_1 x_1' + x_2 x_2' + x_3 x_3'.$$

Since

$$\frac{dy_j}{dt} = \frac{\partial U_{\mathbb{C}}}{\partial x_j}, \qquad \frac{dx_j}{dt} = \frac{E+M}{EM} y_j, \qquad (j = 1, 2, 3)$$

these equations may be written as second-order differential equations

$$\frac{d^2 x_j}{dt^2} = \frac{E+M}{EM} \frac{\partial U_{\mathbb{C}}}{\partial x_j} = \frac{\partial F}{\partial x_j},$$

with

$$F = \frac{k^2(E+M)}{r} + k^2 m' \left[\frac{r^2}{r'^3} P_2(\cos \sigma) + \frac{E-M}{E+M} \frac{r^3}{r'^4} P_3(\cos \sigma) \right.$$

$$\left. + \frac{E^2-EM+M^2}{(E+M)^2} \frac{r^4}{r'^5} P_4(\cos \sigma) + \ldots \right].$$

By introducing

$$\mu = k^2(E+M)$$

and

$$n'^2 a'^3 = k^2(m' + E + M)$$

(from Kepler's third law for the Sun's orbit), F can be written

$$F = \frac{\mu}{r} + \frac{m'}{m'+E+M} n'^2 r^2 \left[\frac{a'^3}{r'^3} P_2(\cos \sigma) + \frac{E-M}{E+M} \frac{r}{a'} \frac{a'^4}{r'^4} P_3(\cos \sigma) \right.$$

$$+ \frac{E^2-EM+M^2}{(E+M)^2} \frac{r^2}{a'^2} \frac{a'^5}{r'^5} P_4(\cos \sigma)$$

$$\left. + \ldots \right].$$

It has been customary to develop the solution of the main problem with two further simplifications. The first consists of replacing the factor $m'/(m' + E + M)$ by unity. The effect on the periodic terms in the Moon's longitude produced by the disturbing function is about 5000″. Since the correction involves a common factor $1 - 3{\cdot}0 \times 10^{-6}$ in the disturbing function, this correction factor can be applied to the principal periodic terms at the very end of the development of the theory. It is seen that, to a coefficient 5000″, the correction is 0·″015.

It is more difficult to ascertain how this simplification affects the secular motions, which are of particular interest. According to Brown (1897a, 1908, p. 82) the corrections are $-0{\cdot}″69$ and $+0{\cdot}″19$ to the annual motions of the perigee and node, respectively.

The second simplification is to replace the mass factor of the fourth harmonic by $(E-M)^2/(E+M)^2$. The advantage of this change is the following: the ratio between the coefficients of P_3 and P_2 is

$$\frac{E-M}{E+M}\,\frac{r}{a'}\,\frac{a'}{r'} = \frac{E-M}{E+M}\,\frac{a}{a'}\,\frac{r}{a}\,\frac{a'}{r'},$$

if a is a properly defined mean distance of the Moon from the Earth. Thus the P_3 part of the disturbing function introduces the factor

$$\alpha = \frac{E-M}{E+M}\,\frac{a}{a'}$$

as a parameter into the theory. By writing the coefficient of the P_4 part in the simplified form, the small factor of this part of the disturbing function becomes α^2. Thus a single parameter α will serve instead of two separate parameters—one for P_3 and one for P_4.

Actually, in the development of a literal theory, the factor $(E-M)/(E+M)$ is replaced by unity, and a/a' is used to designate α. The proper allowance for the mass factor is made at the very end of the work, when a/a' is changed into α.

The neglected portion of the P_4 part is 1/80 of its whole amount. Its ratio to the P_2 part of the disturbing function is

$$\frac{EM}{(E+M)^2}\left(\frac{r}{r'}\right)^2 \sim \frac{1}{80}\left(\frac{1}{400}\right)^2 \sim \frac{1}{13{,}000{,}000}.$$

The largest periodic terms produced by P_2 do not exceed 5000″. It is, therefore, unlikely that the neglected 1/80 of the P_4 part of the disturbing function will have any significant effect. It is ignored in Brown's lunar theory.

II. The Principal Methods

The work by Newton on the Moon's motion in the "Principia" is, of course, of historical interest only. Newton succeeded in showing that the then known principal periodic perturbations and some additional ones in the Moon's motion can be ascribed to the action of the Sun. He also derived values for the mean motions of the perigee and node. The derivations are given in a geometrical form, but it is generally accepted that Newton used his method of fluxions for obtaining many of his results.

Since Newton, many authors have occupied themselves with the problem of the Moon's motion. For the solution of the main problem of the lunar theory a variety of methods has been used. A convenient classification is:

A. METHODS WITH THE TRUE LONGITUDE AS INDEPENDENT VARIABLE

The first to choose this method was Clairaut (1752); he was followed by d'Alembert (1754), Laplace (1802), Damoiseau (1827) and Plana (1832). The reason for the choice of this method is that the equations are simpler if stated in terms of the true longitude. One of the principal results of the theory is an expression for the time in terms of the true longitude. This expression must eventually be inverted, which becomes a task of considerable magnitude if it is applied to an elaborate theory. A further complication is that the coordinates of the Sun, which are easily expressed in terms of the Sun's mean anomaly, must be expressed in terms of the Moon's true longitude. Thus a heavy price is paid for the advantage of having the equations of motion in a convenient form.

The methods differ, of course, in various respects. For example, Laplace's theory is semi-algebraic. A numerical value is adopted for $m = n'/n$; similarly, numerical values are adopted for the other constants, but the "characteristic" is kept with each term, so that small corrections to the constant can be made. Damoiseau and Plana followed Laplace's method, extending it to higher approximations; the former in purely numerical form, the latter algebraically.

There is an interval of over eighty years between the beginning of Clairaut's work on the lunar theory and the publication of Plana's theory in 1832. During this period the requirements had increased considerably. While Clairaut was satisfied with a result that was only in part carried to the second power in the disturbing force, Plana's development was in general complete to the fifth powers in m, e, e', γ, a/a', but some coefficients were obtained to higher powers. It is of interest to note that the true longitude as independent variable was not used in later efforts when still higher approximations were required.

B. PERTURBATIONS IN POLAR COORDINATES WITH THE TIME AS INDEPENDENT VARIABLE

Lubbock (1834–61) and de Pontécoulant began their investigations independently by essentially the same method, about 1830. Lubbock did not complete his work as a whole beyond the second approximation; P. G. de Pontécoulant published his results in his "Théorie analytique du système du monde", volume 4, Paris, 1846.

C. THE METHOD OF THE VARIATION OF ARBITRARY CONSTANTS

This method appears first in the appendix to Euler's first theory (1753), and was explored more fully by Poisson (1835). For the complete development of the solar perturbations in the Moon's motion the method is not practical; Poisson limited himself to the calculation of some important terms. The principal merit of the method is in the calculation of the planetary perturbations in the Moon's motion.

Delaunay (1860, 1867) cast the method of the variation of arbitrary constants into a form that permits carrying it forward systematically to a high order of approximation. He used a canonical set of variables, $L = \sqrt{(\mu a)}$, $G = L\sqrt{(1-e^2)}$, $H = G\cos I$, $l = $ mean anomaly, $g = $ argument of the perigee, $h = $ longitude of the ascending node. The equations are of the form

$$(d/dt)(L,\,G,\,H) = \partial F/\partial(l,g,h),$$

$$(d/dt)(l,\,g,h\,) = -\,\partial F/\partial(L,\,G,\,H),$$

in which

$$F = \mu^2/2L^2 + R,$$

R being the disturbing function which, for the main problem, is developed as a series of cosine terms of the form

$$R = \sum \text{coeff.} \cos(p_1 l + p_2 g + p_3(h - \varpi') + p_4 l'),$$

in which l' is the Sun's mean anomaly, ϖ' the longitude of the Sun's perigee. The coefficients are developed in powers of e, $\gamma = \sin\tfrac{1}{2}I$, e', a/a' and have n'^2a^2 as a factor, while p_1, p_2, p_3, p_4 are integers, positive or negative, zero included; without affecting the generality, it is permissible to consider p_1 positive or zero.

Delaunay considers the equations in which F is replaced by

$$F_1 = \mu^2/2L^2 - B - A\cos\theta,$$

in which $-B$ is the collection of all the terms of R for which $p_1 = p_2 = p_3 = p_4 = 0$; while $-A\cos\theta$ is a single periodic term; thus,

$$\theta = p_1 l + p_2 g + p_3(h - \varpi') + p_4 l'.$$

The essence of Delaunay's method is that it provides a solution for the problem with F replaced by F_1 in the form of a canonical transformation, which transforms to new variables,

$$L^*,\ G^*,\ H^*,\ l^*,\ g^*,\ h^*,$$

such that after the transformation F_1 becomes a function of L^*, G^*, H^* only. The transformation applied to the complete equation yields the new equation

$$(d/dt)(L^*,\ G^*,\ H^*)\ =\ \partial F^*/\partial(l^*,\ g^*,\ h^*),$$
$$(d/dt)(l^*,\ g^*,\ h^*)\ =\ -\,\partial F^*/\partial(L^*,\ G^*,\ H^*),$$

in which F^* is obtained by expressing F in terms of the new variables.†

In the new F^* the term $-A\cos\theta$ has disappeared, while the equations in the new variables have the same form as the equations before the transformation.

The solution consists of the successive elimination of one term after another. After each transformation the Hamiltonian F must be expressed in terms of the new variables.

Delaunay completed the application of his method to the solution of the main problem. Hill (1884) provided the calculation of the terms arising from the non-sphericity of the Earth, while Radau (1895) calculated the planetary perturbations. The complete theory was used in the *Connaissance des Temps* for the computation of the lunar ephemeris during the years 1915–1925.

One of the merits of Delaunay's solution of the main problem is the fact that it gives a solution in which the constants and parameters of the problem are explicitly present in literal form. The solution is therefore applicable to other satellite problems in which the principal perturbations are those due to the Sun.

The explicit expression of the coefficients of all the terms as power series in n'/n, e, e', γ, a/a' has the drawback that in many of the coefficients, and especially in the expression for the motion of the perigee, the convergence of the series according to powers of n'/n is extremely slow.

D. Hansen's Method

Euler's first theory (1753) bears a certain resemblance to Hansen's method; otherwise, Hansen's theory stands by itself. It was originally designed for applications to planetary theory as in his "Untersuchung

---

†If t is present explicitly through l' in the argument θ, F is actually modified, but this does not affect the essence of the method.

über die gegenseitigen Störungen des Jupiter und Saturn", Berlin 1831, but soon Hansen decided to apply his method to the lunar problem. The method is exhibited in provisional form in his "Fundamenta" (1838). His "Darlegung" (1862, 1864), which contains the details of the method actually applied in the construction of his lunar theory, appeared in two parts after the publication of Hansen's "Tables of the Moon" in 1857 by the British Admiralty.

The principle of the method is as follows: the motion of the orbital plane and the motion in the orbital plane are dealt with separately. The former can be treated by dealing with the instantaneous inclination and longitude of the ascending node, but Hansen prefers to cast these into a different form which will not be examined further. For the motion in the orbital plane the equations are the same as in a fixed coordinate system, provided the longitudes in the orbit are reckoned from a "departure point". The nature of the departure point is evident if it is considered that the only change in the instantaneous plane can be an infinitesimal rotation of the plane about the instantaneous radius vector. This rotation moves the departure point along an infinitesimal arc which is perpendicular to the instantaneous orbital plane. If σ is the angle measured from the departure point to the instantaneous ascending node with the fixed xy plane, θ the angle from the x-axis to the ascending node I, the instantaneous inclination, then

$$\frac{d\sigma}{dt} = \cos I \frac{d\theta}{dt},$$

so that σ must be found by the solution of this differential equation.

Hansen's theory for the motion in the orbital plane may be presented by starting from the variation of arbitrary constants. The Moon's position and velocity at time t are completely defined by the knowledge of the instantaneous values of a, e, l, χ, where a and e have their usual meaning, l is the mean anomaly, χ the longitude of the perigee reckoned from the departure point. Instead of obtaining the four quantities explicitly, Hansen deals only with two functions of them that suffice to specify the position in the orbit. For this purpose he introduces a reference ellipse with a constant eccentricity and a uniform motion of the perigee (reckoned from the departure point). Let the osculating elements at the time t give the true anomaly f; the true anomaly in the reference orbit $\bar{f}$ must then satisfy the equation

$$f+\chi = \bar{f}+n_0 y t+\varpi_0,$$

where ϖ_0 is a constant, n_0 the constant mean motion in the reference ellipse, and y a function to be determined by imposing the condition that no terms having t as a factor should appear in the solution. Now $\bar{f}$ in the reference orbit is appropriate for a time z different from t. The relations between the quantities in the osculating orbit and the reference orbit yield an equation for dz/dt. Finally, let the radius vector corresponding to $\bar{f}$ in the reference orbit be designated by $\bar{r}$, the osculating value by r. The position in the orbit is therefore completely defined by knowing z or $z-t$ and the ratio $1 + v = r/\bar{r}$. Both z and v are obtained by the integration of differential equations. It can be shown that the number of constants of integration introduced is four, as required.

Associated with Hansen's theory are certain ingenious devices that the author introduced in order to economize on the labour required to apply the theory. Only a single function, designated by $\overline{W}$, is necessary in order to obtain both z and v. An additional labour-saving device is the following: the function $\overline{W}$ has the form

$$\overline{W} = L_1 + L_2\bar{r} + L_3\bar{r}\cos\bar{f} + L_4\bar{r}\sin\bar{f},$$

in which L_1, L_2, L_3, L_4 do not depend on $\bar{r}$ and $\bar{f}$, but on the osculating elements only. Thus

$$\overline{W} = \int \frac{dL_1}{dt}dt + \bar{r}\int\frac{dL_2}{dt}dt + \bar{r}\cos\bar{f}\int\frac{dL_3}{dt}dt + \bar{r}\sin\bar{f}\int\frac{dL_4}{dt}dt.$$

Now, let $\bar{r}$ be replaced by $\bar{\rho}$, $\bar{f}$ by $\bar{\phi}$ and let it be understood that $\bar{\rho}$ and $\bar{\phi}$ are to be treated as constants during the integration, but should be replaced by $\bar{r}$ and $\bar{f}$ after the integration. This is equivalent to considering $\bar{\rho}$, $\bar{\phi}$ as functions of τ, which is to be treated as a constant during the integration and to be replaced by t after the integration. It follows that $\overline{W}$ may be written

$$\overline{W} = \left[\int\left(\frac{dL_1}{dt} + \bar{\rho}\frac{dL_2}{dt} + \bar{\rho}\cos\bar{\phi}\frac{dL_3}{dt} + \bar{\rho}\sin\bar{\phi}\frac{dL_4}{dt}\right)dt\right]_{\tau\to t}.$$

If the integrand is designated by dW/dt, the result is

$$\overline{W} = \left[\int\frac{dW}{dt}dt\right]_{\tau\to t},$$

so that the only function to be developed is dW/dt.

The derivatives dL_j/dt, $j = 1, 2, 3, 4$, are known functions of the two components of the disturbing acceleration, R along the radius vector, S perpendicular to the radius vector in the orbital plane. These can be expressed in terms of the perturbed coordinates. Hence the integration of dW/dt must be performed by a process of successive approximations or iteration. This process constitutes the elaboration of the lunar theory. Hansen adopts a purely numerical type of development, assuming numerical values for all of the constants and parameters of the problem; thereby the cause of the slow convergence present in some of the literal expansion of Delaunay's form of the lunar theory is avoided.

The derivation of the formulas upon which Hansen's theory is based has an inescapable degree of complexity that is further enhanced by the peculiar devices without which the method would lose much of its merit. Once these are fully appreciated and the method is adequately mastered, the whole structure appears as a remarkably ingenious creation. Nevertheless, there remains a contradiction: Hansen originally developed his theory for application to planetary problems in which the principal terms of long period arise in the mean longitude. It is therefore important in planetary theory to have the mean longitude as one of variables of the problem. In order to introduce this feature and yet to have only two quantities in the orbital plane to deal with, Hansen devised his variables z and v, so that $n_0(z-t)$ corresponds essentially to the perturbation in mean longitude, and v to the remainder of the perturbation $\delta r/r$ after the effect on r due to the pertubation in the mean longitude has been removed by computing $\bar{r}$ with the perturbed mean anomaly.

In the main problem of the lunar theory small divisors that cause large terms in the mean longitude play no significant role. It would appear, therefore, that for the main problem of the lunar theory Hansen's method forces upon the solution an unnecessary complexity that, however, does not affect the quality of the theory. The situation is different with the planetary perturbations, for which Hansen's method has some excellent merits.

However this may be, Hansen's "Tables of the Moon" constituted an immense advance in the representation of the Moon's motion by a gravitational theory.

E. The Method using Rectangular Coordinates

Euler's second theory (1772) was the first attempt to employ rectangular coordinates in a rotating coordinate system for the solution of the main problem of the lunar theory. Euler's work antedates, therefore, Hill's celebrated papers (Hill, 1877, 1878a) by just over a century. An important difference between the two treatments is that Euler adopts a coordinate system rotating about the z axis (perpendicular to the ecliptic) with the Moon's mean angular velocity, while in Hill's work the coordinate system rotates with the Sun's mean motion. Thus, if a is the mean distance of the Moon from the Earth, and if the x axis is directed toward the Moon's mean position, Euler's $(x-a)/a$, y/a, will be small quantities that in elliptic motion have the eccentricity as a factor, while z/a is a small quantity that has the sine of the inclination as a factor. Hill's choice of rotating coordinate system has the advantage that, if the eccentricity of the Sun's orbit is ignored, the equations of motion possess the Jacobian integral, a property of which Hill takes full advantage.

An important difference between the treatments by Euler and Hill is the fact that the former adopts the observed value of the motion of the perigee, while Hill's theoretical determination of the principal part of this motion is one of the most profound and elegant contributions to celestial mechanics.

A significant similarity between the two developments is that both authors adopt the plan of dividing up the inequalities into classes. They consider first the terms that are independent of e, e', $\sin I$, a/a'; next the terms having e as a factor are determined, etc. Thus the problem may be broken up into a series of separate problems, in each of which the solution is obtained by the method of undetermined coefficients. This plan was adopted by Brown and carried out with eminent success.

Tisserand called this "une idée heureuse", but remarked, concerning both Euler's work and Hill's work that he foresaw complications with this type of expansion owing to the presence of parts having e^2, e'^2, $\sin^2 I$ as factors in the motions of the perigee and node. Brown's application of the method for the solution of the main problem (cf. Brown, 1897b, 1899, 1900, 1905, 1908) proves that such apparent difficulties can be overcome and do not impair the effectiveness of the method.

III. Hill's Equations of Motion

If X, Y, Z are the rectangular coordinates in a coordinate system rotating with the Sun's mean motion, n', and if the eccentricity of the Sun's orbit, the inclination of the Moon's orbit, and the ratio a/a' are put equal to zero, the equations of motion become

$$\frac{d^2X}{dt^2} - 2n'\frac{dY}{dt} = \frac{\partial\Omega'}{\partial X},$$

$$\frac{d^2Y}{dt^2} + 2n'\frac{dX}{dt} = \frac{\partial\Omega'}{\partial Y},$$

with

$$\Omega' = \frac{\mu}{r} + \frac{3}{2}n'^2 X^2,$$

$$\mu = k^2(E+M).$$

These equations possess the Jacobian integral

$$\frac{1}{2}\left[\left(\frac{dX}{dt}\right)^2 + \left(\frac{dY}{dt}\right)^2\right] = \Omega' - C'.$$

Although the equations are remarkably simple, they contain the solution of the main problem for the special case $e' = \sin I = a/a' = 0$.

The general solution requires the introduction of four constants of integration. Hill first deals with a special class of solutions that depends on two constants of integration. In order to obtain orbits that belong to this class, let for $t = 0$ the coordinates and velocity components be

$$X = a, \qquad Y = 0, \qquad \dot{X} = 0, \qquad \dot{Y} = b,$$

in which b is to be so determined that after a synodic period T the co-ordinates and velocity components are the same as $t = 0$. The synodic period is $T = 2\pi/(n-n')$, if n is the Moon's mean motion in a non-rotating coordinate system.

If now a new independent variable τ is introduced by

$$d\tau = (n-n')dt,$$

the equations become

$$\frac{d^2X}{d\tau^2} - 2\mathrm{m}\frac{dY}{d\tau} = \frac{\partial\Omega}{\partial X},$$

$$\frac{d^2Y}{d\tau^2} + 2\mathrm{m}\frac{dX}{d\tau} = \frac{\partial\Omega}{\partial Y},$$

(5)

with

$$\Omega = \frac{\kappa}{r} + \frac{3}{2}\mathrm{m}^2 X^2,$$

$$\kappa = \mu/(n-n')^2, \qquad \mathrm{m} = n'/(n-n'),$$

and the Jacobian integral

$$\frac{1}{2}\left[\left(\frac{dX}{d\tau}\right)^2 + \left(\frac{dY}{d\tau}\right)^2\right] = \Omega - C.$$

The equations do not change if the signs of Y and τ are changed and X is left unchanged, nor if the signs of X and τ are changed and Y is left unchanged. From these properties it follows that the orbit must be an oval that is symmetrical with respect to both the X axis and the Y axis. Let τ be zero when the orbit crosses the positive X axis. The representation of the orbit is then

$$X = A_0 \cos \tau + A_1 \cos 3\tau + A_2 \cos 5\tau + \ldots ,$$

$$Y = B_0 \sin \tau + B_1 \sin 3\tau + B_2 \sin 5\tau + \ldots ,$$

in which the coefficients A, B depend on m and κ only, the latter determining the scale of the orbit. The orbit is called the "variation orbit". Hill obtained the variation orbit for the lunar theory by using m = 0·08084 89338 08312, developing the coefficients both analytically in powers of m and numerically to fifteen decimal places.

The variation orbit is an example of periodic orbit of the first kind, in Poincaré's terminology (cf. Poincaré, 1892). The existence of this class of orbits for the problem of three bodies was later rigorously established by Poincaré.

A basic principle of Hill's approach to the lunar theory, adopted by Brown (1897b, 1899, 1900, 1905, 1908) in the complete solution of the main problem, is that a numerical value of m is adopted at the very beginning and all functions of the coordinates and their derivatives with respect to τ that may be needed are obtained as periodic series with numerical coefficients. Thus the development in powers of m, or in $m = \text{m}/(1+\text{m})$ as in Delaunay's theory, is avoided throughout, and the principal source of slow convergence in the solution is not present.

Hill (and Brown) actually used complex coordinates, $u = X + \sqrt{(-1)}Y$, $s = X - \sqrt{(-1)}Y$, but the exposition of the method could be performed equally well in ordinary rectangular coordinates.

A. THE PRINCIPAL PART OF THE MOTION OF THE PERIGEE

Let the coordinates in the variation orbit be $X_0(\tau)$, $Y_0(\tau)$, and let the coordinates of an orbit that satisfies the equations (5) be $X_0 + \delta X$, $Y_0 + \delta Y$. To the first order in δX, δY the equations become

$$\frac{d^2 \delta X}{d\tau^2} - 2m \frac{d \delta Y}{d\tau} = \Omega_{xx} \delta X + \Omega_{xy} \delta Y ,$$

$$\frac{d^2 \delta Y}{d\tau^2} + 2m \frac{d \delta X}{d\tau} = \Omega_{xy} \delta X + \Omega_{yy} \delta Y ,$$

(6)

while the Jacobian integral for orbits with the same value of C as in the variation orbit gives

$$\frac{dX_0}{d\tau}\frac{d\delta X}{d\tau}+\frac{dY_0}{d\tau}\frac{d\delta Y}{d\tau}-\Omega_x\delta X-\Omega_y\delta Y = 0,$$

in which Ω_{xx}, etc., are the partial derivatives of Ω in which X and Y are replaced by their values in the variation orbit.

A particular solution of these equations is

$$\delta X = \frac{dX_0}{d\tau}, \qquad \delta Y = \frac{dY_0}{d\tau}.$$

A change of variables to p and q, defined by

$$\delta X = p\frac{dX_0}{d\tau} - q\frac{dY_0}{d\tau},$$

$$\delta Y = q\frac{dX_0}{d\tau} + p\frac{dY_0}{d\tau},$$

leads to equations in p and q with the particular solution

$$p = 1, \qquad q = 0.$$

Since the equations are homogeneous, it follows that p is present only through $dp/d\tau$ and $d^2p/d\tau^2$. Consequently, by the elimination of the first and second derivatives of p, there results an equation

$$\frac{d^2q}{d\tau^2}+H(\tau)\frac{dq}{d\tau}+K(\tau) = 0.$$

By a final change of variables this equation is transformed into

$$\frac{d^2\rho}{d\tau^2}+\Theta(\tau)\rho = 0,$$

in which Θ is a cosine series with arguments that are even multiples of τ. This is known as Hill's equation (cf. Hill, 1877).

In Hill's discussion of this equation he used the method of undetermined coefficients, by which an infinite set of linear equations with an infinite number of unknowns is obtained. These equations he solved by introducing an infinite determinant for the first time into the mathematical literature. From this infinite determinant Hill obtained in an elegant manner the principal part of the motion of the perigee to fifteen decimal places. After the motion of the perigee is obtained

c

from Hill's equation, the solution of δX, δY is readily obtained by returning to the original equations. Since the equations are homogeneous, an arbitrary constant is present as a common factor. This corresponds to the eccentricity constant in elliptic motion.

B. Contributions by J. C. Adams

Nearly simultaneously with Hill, investigations on the motion of the Moon were pursued by J. C. Adams (1878) in Cambridge, England, by a method that is closely related to Hill's method. While Hill chose rotating rectangular coordinates, Adams used polar coordinates to obtain the variation orbit. While Hill determined the principal part of the motion of the perigee, Adams obtained the principal part of the motion of the node. In the case of the motion of the node, the equations are immediately available in the desired form; the solution yields the terms in Z that have the first power of the inclination as a factor.

C. Brown's Extension to Higher Orders

The solution of the main problem of the lunar theory by Brown (1897b, 1899, 1900, 1905, 1908) constitutes a systematic development of the solution ordered according to "characteristics". The terms of the first order are those having successively e, e', k (corresponding to $\sin I$), and $\alpha = a/a'$ as a factor. The terms having e' and a/a' as a factor require the addition of new parts of the disturbing function.

Next the terms of the second order, successively having e^2, ee', e'^2, k^2, $e\alpha$, $e'\alpha$, α^2, ke, ke', $k\alpha$ are determined. The equations for the new parts of δX, δY are of the same form as equations (6) with additional non-homogeneous parts containing only squares and products of first-order terms. The solution of the new parts of δX, δY is then obtained by the method of undetermined coefficients.

The procedure is next continued for the terms of the third order. Again, the equations for the new parts of δX, δY have the same form and the additional, non-homogeneous parts depend on the earlier approximations, but here a new feature appears: corrections to the motions of the perigee and node having e^2, e'^2, α^2, k^2 as factors must be evaluated in order to avoid terms having t as a factor outside the trigonometric terms; further corrections arise when the fifth-order terms are obtained.

D. Numerical Verification of the Lunar Theory

An attempt at a numerical verification of the solution of the main problem of the lunar theory was made by Airy (1886). Airy's plan was to substitute into the perturbational accelerations in the equations of motion numerical values based on Delaunay's solution of the main problem, with the object of improving the solution. An important result of the process of iteration would be the improvement of the numerical values of the motions of the perigee and node. The failure of Airy's attempt has been ascribed primarily to the fact, that, in Delaunay's theory, the radius vector is obtained with lower accuracy than the longitude and latitude.

During the last few years of his life, Brown—in cooperation with Dr. W. J. Eckert—occupied himself with this problem. Brown's solution of the main problem was obtained in rectangular coordinates; hence, the drawback of the lower accuracy in radius vector is not present, and the use of Brown's solution in the iteration process has an important advantage over the use of Delaunay's solution. The work has recently been carried forward by Dr. Eckert with the aid of high-speed calculators. Dr. Eckert reports that he hopes to be able to publish the results of his calculations in the near future.

IV. Non-Solar Perturbations

A. PLANETARY PERTURBATIONS

After the main problem has been solved, the next most important perturbations to be considered are those produced by the attractions of the principal planets. They can, in general, be treated separately; the problem is, therefore, a problem of four bodies: the Sun, the Earth, the Moon and, (say) Venus.

It may, for the purposes of the solution, be assumed that the orbit of Venus is Keplerian and that the effects of the attraction of Venus upon the coordinates of the Sun relative to the centre of mass of the Earth-Moon system are known. In this sense, the problem reduces to a "disturbed" three-body problem.

The complete solution of the problem requires, therefore, the solution of the equations of motion of the Moon relative to the Earth with the addition of the attraction by Venus upon the Moon. The solar coordinates (or elements) to be used in the solution of the equations should include the perturbations by Venus.

The effects of the additional terms in the equations produced by the attraction by Venus are the direct planetary perturbations. They can be evaluated by substituting into the disturbing functions the elliptic coordinates of Venus and the principal terms of the solution of the main problem. In order to allow for the perturbations of Venus on the Sun's orbit, it is necessary to consider the modifications of the main problem, necessary to allow for the fact that the coordinates of the Sun may no longer be considered to be those of a fixed ellipse. They produce indirect perturbations.

Significant work on the subject was done by Hansen (1864), Adams (1853, 1880), Delaunay (1867), and Hill (1885), especially in connection with the secular acceleration in the mean longitude. An exhaustive evaluation of the planetary perturbations, both direct and indirect, was carried out by Radau (1895). Almost simultaneously, Brown (1908) and Newcomb (1907) completed independent evaluations. Brown gave a comparison of his own results with both Radau and Newcomb, showing excellent agreement for all of the significant terms.

B. Perturbations Produced by the Figure of the Earth and the Moon

These perturbations are, in general, much smaller than the principal planetary perturbations and their calculations present no serious difficulties. Of particular interest is Hill's evaluation of the perturbation by the non-sphericity of the Earth (Hill, 1884), in which Delaunay's method was used. The perturbations caused by the Moon's figure are small, and uncertain on account of the limited knowledge of the constants that specify the Moon's gravitational potential.

According to Brown, the contributions of the various types of perturbations to the secular motions of the perigee and node are:

Mean annual motion of the	Perigee	Node
Principal solar action	$+146426.''92$	$-69672.''04$
Mass of the Earth	$-$ $\cdot68$	$+$ $\cdot19$
Direct planetary action	$+$ $2\cdot69$	$-$ $1\cdot42$
Indirect planetary action	$-$ $\cdot16$	$+$ $\cdot05$
Figure of the Earth	$+$ $6\cdot41$	$-$ $6\cdot00$
Figure of the Moon	$+$ $\cdot03$	$-$ $\cdot14$
	$+146435\cdot21$	$-69679\cdot36$

The agreement with the observed motions is, on the whole, satisfactory. De Sitter (1917) evaluated the relativity effect on the secular motions of the perigee and node, the results being $+1.''97$/century and $+1.''91$/century, respectively.

C. Secular Acceleration

The secular part of the Moon's mean longitude has an acceleration term cT^2. When T is measured in units of the Julian century from some convenient epoch (say, $1850\cdot0$), c is called the coefficient of the secular acceleration. The observed value of c may be considered as the combined effect of three contributions: (negative) acceleration caused by energy dissipation of the Earth-Moon system due to tidal friction of the Earth, (apparent) acceleration due to slow-down of the Earth's rotational velocity, and acceleration caused by secular decrease of the Sun's eccentricity. The first two will be discussed in Chapter 3 by Groves. We shall discuss the last as a contribution of the indirect planetary perturbations.

Owing to planetary actions on the Earth, the eccentricity of the Sun suffers a long-period perturbation of a period of about 24,000 years. This term is, however, more conveniently treated as a secular term of the form

$$e' = e'_0 + \alpha t + \ldots (\alpha < 0)$$

for a discussion extending over several thousand years. When this expression is substituted in the Sun's eccentricity in the indirect part of the disturbing function, there appear, after developing by the small parameter α, the terms

$$\beta t, \quad \text{and} \quad \gamma t \cos (at+b).$$

The solution for the mean longitude may, in general, be carried out by successive approximations in a similar way as in the other indirect planetary perturbations. The coefficient c is developed in powers of n'/n, in the form

$$c = n\left[c_1\left(\frac{n'}{n}\right)^2 + c_2\left(\frac{n'}{n}\right)^3 + c_2\left(\frac{n'}{n}\right)^4 + \ldots \right],$$

where n, n' are the mean motions of the Moon and the Sun respectively. The evaluation of c is rather laborious because of slow convergence of the series. In the first approximation, only the secular term in the disturbing function contributes to c through c_1. In 1787, Laplace determined the value $10.''2$ for c in the first approximation. This value being, by accident, very close to the observational value $10''—11''$, he thought a higher approximation would produce little effect. In higher approximations, however, mixed secular terms in the disturbing function are found to contribute significantly to c through $c_2, c_3, \ldots$. Adams, estimating the higher terms in 1853, found that Laplace's value should be halved. Brown (1897, 1908) obtained the value $5.''82$ based on his theory. According to Spencer Jones (1932, 1939), the discrepancy between the observational value and Brown's theoretical value is $5.''22$. Attempts have been made to attribute this discrepancy to the effect of tidal friction in shallow seas (Jeffreys, 1920, 1959; Taylor, 1920), but with some ambiguity because of the difficulty of estimating it with high precision.

V. Comparison with the Observations

Brown's theory of the Moon's motion may be considered to be free from serious errors or omissions. Nevertheless, the comparison with observations showed discrepancies of the same general character as previous theories, which amount to tens of seconds of arc over a period of several centuries. When Newcomb (1875, 1912) compared Hansen's tables with observations from about the middle of the 17th century to the end of the 19th century, he introduced a "great empirical term" in the Moon's mean longitude with coefficient 10·″71 and period 257 years. For a time it was thought that a planetary perturbation term that had been overlooked might be responsible for this empirical term. Nevertheless, as early as 1870, Newcomb suspected the existence of irregular changes in the Earth's rotational velocity, but warned that for a definite proof it would be necessary to have more positive know-ledge of the inequalities that may be produced in the Moon's motion by gravitational action. Brown's theory may now be considered to supply this positive knowledge.

From a comprehensive analysis of the observational data, Spencer Jones (1932, 1939) found for the deviation from Brown's tables

$$\Delta L_{\mathbb{C}} = \text{const.} + \text{linear term in } T + 5 \cdot ''22T^2 + B,$$

where B stands for the fluctuation. Spencer Jones also found for the deviation from Newcomb's tables of the Sun

$$\Delta L_{\odot} = \text{const.} + \text{linear term in } T + 1 \cdot ''23T^2 + 0 \cdot 0748B.$$

In this expression, $1 \cdot ''23T^2$ represents the secular acceleration in the Sun's mean longitude, the existence of which was discovered by Cowell in 1905. The factor $0 \cdot 0748$ represents the ratio between the mean motions of the Sun and the Moon. The expressions for the planets are entirely similar, with the coefficients of T^2 and B changed in proportion to the mean motions. (The term $5 \cdot ''22T^2$ in $\Delta L_{\mathbb{C}}$ is exceptional due to the contribution of the true secular retardation in the Moon's orbital motion).

These results clearly revealed that the deviations from theory are the reflections of the changes of the Earth's rotational velocity of an irregular character. Brouwer (1952) and van Woerkom (1953) showed that the fluctuation was compatible with the hypothesis that the Earth's rotational velocity is affected by cumulative random changes. In this analysis it was assumed that there is no restriction on the amount by which the accumulation of these random changes may affect the Earth's rotational velocity. On the other hand, van der Waerden (1959) presented a discussion of the data in which the accumulation is restricted by the presence of a friction couple. Over many centuries even a weak friction couple has a significant effect. The physical interpretation of the random changes is an interesting geophysical problem (cf. Chapter 3).

It is important to note that with the evaluation of ephemeris time, now based upon the comparison of the Improved Lunar Ephemeris with observations, it is in effect assumed that the lunar ephemeris represents a perfect solution of the problem of the Moon's motion. Ever since it was recognized that the observed fluctuations in the Moon's mean longitude are caused by irregularities in the Earth's rate of rotation, no direct check on the accuracy of the lunar theory by comparison with observations has been available. The drawback is, of course, that in the motions of the Sun and the inner planets, (including Mercury) the fluctuations cannot be observed with the same accuracy as in the Moon's motion. It is to be hoped that this disadvantage may be overcome in the future when, conceivably, suitable artificial satellites can be observed for an evaluation of ephemeris time independent of the observations of the Moon. Such a check on ephemeris time would be important even if further advances in the field of atomic clocks should yield thoroughly reliable determinations of "atomic" time over long intervals.

VI. The Improved Lunar Ephemeris

Beginning with the year 1960 the lunar ephemeris is no longer based on Brown's "Tables of the Moon", but it is computed directly from Brown's theory. With the use of high-speed calculators, this procedure has advantages over the use of the "Tables", which were designed to simplify the ephemeris calculations in the time when desk calculators and logarithmic tables were the only computing aids available. The data in the ephemeris are now given to an extra decimal place in all three quantities tabulated: right ascension, declination, and parallax. The principal difference from the "Tables" is that the great empirical term has been eliminated. In addition, various imperfections of the "Tables" have been improved upon. As a consequence, the comparison of the Improved Lunar Ephemeris with observations now yields the reduction from Universal Time to Ephemeris Time more directly than was formerly possible with Brown's "Tables". For the years 1952–1959 the "Improved Lunar Ephemeris" was published in a separate volume†. It contains an extensive explanation of its composition.

VII. Radar Distances of the Moon

Until recently all available information on the Moon's orbit was derived from optical observations of the Moon's position on the celestial sphere. The Moon's distance was not observed directly, but appeared only in the reduction of the ephemeris position of the Moon to topocentric position. In very recent years direct measurements of the Moon's distance have become possible by the application of radar techniques. These measurements consist of the evaluation of the time needed for a radar signal to return after reflection by the Moon's surface.

From a series of such observations during October and November 1957 at the United States Naval Research Laboratory, Bruton, Craig, and Yaplee (1959) obtained for the mean distance of the Moon's centre from the centre of the Earth the value 384,402 km with a mean error estimated to be between 1 and 2 km. The principal sources of the uncertainty are the radius of the Moon used in the reductions, and the fact that the mean distance derived from the observations shows a variation that appears to have a periodic character with a period of approximately a month and a semi-amplitude of 1·4 km.

It is likely that this periodic change is principally a topographic effect, caused by the varying elevation of the centre of the Moon's disk in the course of a month, but further observations are needed for a more definitive interpretation of the observations. An extended later series of observations was made at the Naval Research Laboratory, the results of which will probably be available soon.

An important application of the measured radar distances of the Moon can be made by substituting the observed mean distance in the well-known formula for the Moon's dynamical parallax. This formula gives a relation among the equatorial radius of the Earth, the acceleration of gravity at the equator, the Earth's oblateness, and the Moon's mass. A provisional calculation based on the best available data shows that the observed mean distance of the Moon yields for the equatorial radius of the Earth

$$a_{\oplus} = 6,378,280 \text{ metres}$$

---

† "Improved Lunar Ephemeris", 1952–1959. A joint supplement to the American Ephemeris and the British Nautical Almanac, U.S. Naval Observatory 1954.

with a mean error of about 40 metres. This result is provisional and can be improved by a more definitive discussion of more abundant observational data. For the present it is important to note that with lunar radar distances it is possible to obtain the Earth's equatorial radius with an accuracy that compares favourably with that of the best direct geodetic measurements†.

References

Adams, J. C. (1853). *Phil. Trans.* **143**, 397.

Adams, J. C. (1878). *Mon. Not. Roy. Astr. Soc.* **38**, 460.

Adams, J. C. (1880). *Mon. Not. Roy. Astr. Soc.* **40**, 472.

Airy, G. B. (1886). "Numerical Lunar Theory". London.

Brouwer, D. (1952). *Astr. J.* **57**, 126.

Brown, E. W. (1897). *Mon. Not. Roy. Astr. Soc.* **57**, 342; (1897a) *ibid.* **57**, 566.

Brown, E. W. (1897b). *Mem. Roy. Astr. Soc.* **53**, 39; (1899) *ibid.* **53**, 163; (1900) *ibid.* **54**, 1; (1905) *ibid.* **57**, 51; (1908) *ibid.* **59**, 1.

Brown, E. W. (1919). "Tables of the Motion of the Moon". Yale Univ. Press, New Haven.

Bruton, R. H., Craig, K. J., and Yaplee, B. S. (1959). *Astr. J.* **64**, 325.

Clairaut, A. C. (1752). "Théorie de la Lune". Paris.

Cowell, P. H. (1905). *Mon. Not. Roy. Astr. Soc.* **66**, 3.

Damoiseau, M. C. T. (1827). "Mémoire sur la Théorie de la Lune". *Mém. Inst. France*, **1**, 313.

D'Alembert, J. (1754). Recherches sur différents points importants du Système du Monde, Pt. 1. "Théorie de la Lune". Paris.

Delaunay, C. E. (1860). *Mém. Acad. Sci., Paris*, **28**; (1867) *ibid.* **29**.

De Sitter, W. (1917). *Mon. Not. Roy. Astr. Soc.* **77**, 155.

Euler, L. (1753). "Theoria Motus Lunae exhibens omnes eius inaequalitates". Petropolis.

Euler, L. (1772). "Theoria Motum Lunae nova methodo pertractata ...". Petropolis.

Hansen, P. A. (1838). "Fundamenta Nova Investigationis Orbitae verae quam Luna perlustrat". Gotha.

Hansen, P. A. (1862). "Darlegung der theoretischen Berechnung der in den Mondtafeln angewandten Störungen". *Abh. Sächs. Ges.(Akad.) Wiss.* **6**, 91; (1864) *ibid.* **7**, 1.

Hill, G. W. (1877). "On the Part of the Motion of the Lunar Perigee which is a Function of the Mean Motions of the Sun and Moon". John Wilson & Son, Cambridge, Mass. (Privately printed). Reprinted (1886) in *Acta. Math. Stockh.* **8**, 1, and in "Collected Mathematical Works", Vol. 1, p. 243.

Hill, G. W. (1878). *Analyst*, **5**, 33. "Collected Mathematical Works", Vol. 1, p. 336.

---

† The paper by Bruton, Craig, and Yaplee (1959) gave

$$a_{\oplus} = 6{,}378{,}125 \text{ metres}$$

from the same data. This result was evidently affected by an error of calculation. We are indebted to Mr. Yaplee and also to Dr. John A. O'Keefe for valuable discussions on the interpretation of the radar measurements and their geodetic application.

Hill, G. W. (1878a). *Amer. J. Math.* **1**, 5, 129, 245. "Collected Mathematical Works", Vol. 1, p. 284.

Hill, G. W. (1884). *Astr. Pap. Wash.* **3**, 201. "Collected Mathematical Works", Vol. 2, p. 179.

Hill, G. W. (1885). *Astr. Pap. Wash.* **3**, 373. "Collected Mathematical Works", Vol. 2, p. 321.

Jeffreys, H. (1920). *Mon. Not. Roy. Astr. Soc.* **80**, 309.

Jeffreys, H. (1959). "The Earth", 4th ed., Ch. 8. Cambridge Univ. Press.

Jones, H. Spencer (1932). *Ann. Cape Obs.* **13**, 1.

Jones, H. Spencer (1939). *Mon. Not. Roy. Astr. Soc.* **99**, 541.

Laplace, P. S. (1787). *Mém. Acad. Sci., Paris.*

Laplace, P. S. (1802). "Mécanique Céleste", Vol. 2, Book 7. Paris.

Lubbock, J. W. "On the Theory of the Moon and on the Perturbations of the Planets", Pt .1 (1834); Pt. 2 (1836); Pt. 3 (1837); Pt. 4 (1840); Pt. 10 (1861).

Newcomb, S. (1875). Researches on the motion of the Moon, Pt. 1. *Washington Obs. App. 2.*

Newcomb, S. (1907). Investigation of Inequalities in the Motion of the Moon produced by the action of the planets. *Carnegie Inst. Publ.*, p. 72.

Newcomb, S. (1912). Researches on the motion of the Moon, Pt. 2. *Astr. Pap. Wash.* **9**, 1.

Plana, J. (1832). "Théorie du Mouvement de la Lune". Turin.

Poincaré, H. (1892). "Méthodes Nouvelles de la Mécanique Céleste", Vol. 1, p. 97. Paris.

Poisson, S. P. (1835). *Mém. Acad. Sci., Paris*, **13**, 209.

Radau, R. (1895). *Ann. Obs. Paris*, 21, B 1.

Taylor, G. I. (1920). *Mon. Not. Roy. Astr. Soc.* **80**, 308.

Van der Waerden, B. L. (1959). *Astr. J.*, **64**, 96.

Van Woerkom, A. J. J. (1953). *Astr. J.* **58**, 10.

CHAPTER 2

Libration of the Moon

KAROL KOZIEL

I.	Rotation of the Moon and the Laws of Cassini	27
II.	Optical Libration of the Moon	27
III.	Physical Libration of the Moon	31
IV.	Physical Libration in Longitude	33
V.	Physical Libration in Inclination and Node	43
VI.	Influence of Solar Attraction	46
VII.	Determination of the Constants of the Moon's Physical Libration from Observations	46
VIII.	Comparison of Heliometric Observations of the Moon with Theory	47
IX.	Adjustment of Heliometric Observations of the Moon's Libration	50
X.	Remarks Concerning the Figure of the Moon	54
XI.	Values of the Constants of the Moon's Physical Libration and Conclusion	56
	References	58

I. Rotation of the Moon and the Laws of Cassini

The rotation of the Moon around the centre of its mass is characterized with good approximation by three empirical laws put forward by J. D. Cassini in the 17th century and known under the name of Cassini's laws. The first of them states that the Moon rotates eastward, on an axis fixed in its body, with a constant angular velocity, and the period of rotation is exactly the same as that of the Moon's sideral revolution around the Earth. The next two laws state that the inclination of the Moon's axis of rotation to the ecliptic is constant and that the poles of the Moon's equator, of the ecliptic and of the Moon's orbit, are all lying in one great circle in the successive order, just given.

Towards the end of the 18th century the founders of modern celestial mechanics, Lagrange (1780) and Laplace (1798), worked out the theory of the Moon's rotation and interpreted, on the basis of the law of universal gravitation, the empirical laws of Cassini concerning this rotation.

II. Optical Libration of the Moon

The first of Cassini's laws results from the observed fact that, to an observer on the Earth, the Moon shows always the same "face"; this is, however, only approximately true. Actually, there are to be noticed, in the course of a month, slight displacements of objects on the Moon's limb, which are called the *optical libration*. We distinguish the optical libration in longitude, the optical libration in latitude and the diurnal or parallactic libration.

The *optical libration in longitude* results from the fact that the Moon rotates in the course of a month uniformly and, at the same time, it revolves in its orbit around the Earth with a variable angular velocity. The maximum angular displacements of the lunar objects caused by optical libration in longitude may amount to $\pm$ 7·9°, selenocentrically reckoned.

Since the Moon's axis of rotation is not perpendicular to the plane of its orbit, at one time the north pole, and at another the south pole of the Moon, is turned towards the Earth in the course of a month. This effect, the so called *optical libration in latitude*, causes displacements of lunar objects amounting, selenocentrically reckoned, up to $\pm$ 6·8°. Finally, the displacements of the observer situated on the Earth's surface, enable him to see some additional portions of the Moon, resulting from the rotation of the Earth, and this effect constitutes what we call the *diurnal* or *parallactic libration*. These three geometrical librations enable the terrestrial observer to see more than a half—namely, 59%—of the lunar surface.

For a mathematical treatment of the effects just described, a system of selenographic coordinates, referred to the Moon's equator, will be used. In this system the *selenographic longitudes* λ—taken anticlockwise for a fictitious observer situated in the Moon's centre—are reckoned along the lunar equator from the point in which the first radius intersects the equator on that portion of the lunar globe, which is visible from the Earth. This *first radius*, through which T. Mayer made his zero meridian on the Moon pass, may be obtained as the intersection of the plane of the lunar meridian passing through the Earth's centre with the plane of the lunar equator, at the moment when the Moon's mean longitude equals the longitude of the ascending node of its orbit. The *selenographic latitude* β is counted, as usual, positively in the northern hemisphere of the Moon, i.e. in the hemisphere containing Mare Serenitatis.

The optical libration in longitude and latitude is specified by: λ_M —the selenographic longitude and β_M—the selenographic latitude of the centre M of the Moon's visible disc. To facilitate the somewhat intricate computation of the quantities λ_M and β_M, the astronomical almanacs give certain auxiliary quantities, introduced first by Encke in the "Berliner Jahrbuch" for the year 1843. For instance, the Astronomical Ephemeris contains formulae for the computation of the auxiliary angles

$$\lambda_M = L_{\mathbb{C}} + \mu + A\beta_M - l_{\mathbb{C}},$$
$$\beta_M = B - B_{\mathbb{C}}, \qquad\qquad (2.01)$$

where $L_{\mathbb{C}}$ and $B_{\mathbb{C}}$ are the longitude and latitude of the Moon, $l_{\mathbb{C}}$ its mean longitude, and A, B and μ are tabulated as functions of $L_{\mathbb{C}} - \Omega$, Ω denoting the longitude of the ascending node of the Moon's orbit.

Jointly with the quantities λ_M and β_M, characterizing the optical libration, we often determine the position angle of the Moon's axis C, i.e. the angle between the lunar meridian passing through the centre of the Moon's visible disc, and the declination circle passing through that centre. The position angle C is given by the formula:

$$\sin C = -\sin i \, \cos(\alpha - \Omega') \sec \beta_M, \qquad (2.02)$$

where i denotes the inclination of the Moon's equator to that of the Earth, α the Moon's right ascension and Ω' the angular distance of the ascending node of the lunar equator, reckoned on the terrestrial equator, from the equinox.

In order to facilitate the solution of many problems concerning the Moon's rotation and figure, Banachiewicz (1929a) published selenographic tables that may serve also for the determination of the quantities λ_M, β_M and C. First we find from Banachiewicz's selenographic tables, as functions of Ω, the elements of the cracovian L:

$$L = \begin{Bmatrix} L_{11} & L_{21} & L_{31} \\ L_{12} & L_{22} & L_{32} \\ L_{13} & L_{23} & L_{33} \end{Bmatrix} = p(-\epsilon) . r(180° + \Omega) . p(I) . r(180° - \Omega), \quad (2.03)$$

and then we find the cracovian A from the formula:

$$A = r(l_{\mathbb{C}}) . L . r(\alpha) . q(-\delta), \qquad (2.04)$$

where α and δ are the equatorial coordinates of the Moon; ϵ, as usual, the inclination of the terrestrial equator to the ecliptic; and I, the mean inclination of the lunar equator to the ecliptic; p, q and r denote rotational cracovians introduced by Banachiewicz (1929a):

$$p(n) = \begin{Bmatrix} 1 & 0 & 0 \\ 0 & \cos n & -\sin n \\ 0 & \sin n & \cos n \end{Bmatrix}, \; q(n) = \begin{Bmatrix} \cos n & 0 & \sin n \\ 0 & 1 & 0 \\ -\sin n & 0 & \cos n \end{Bmatrix}, \; r(n) = \begin{Bmatrix} \cos n & -\sin n & 0 \\ \sin n & \cos n & 0 \\ 0 & 0 & 1 \end{Bmatrix},$$

$$(2.05)$$

the multiplication of matrices-cracovians being performed column by column. The quantities characterizing the optical libration of the Moon λ_M, β_M and C may then be found from the formula:

$$r(-\lambda_M) \cdot q(\beta_M) \cdot p(C) = A, \qquad (2.06)$$

by virtue of which we obtain finally for their determination the following expressions:

$$
\left.
\begin{aligned}
\cos \lambda_M \cdot \cos\beta_M &= A_{11} \\
\sin \lambda_M \cdot \cos \beta_M &= A_{21} \\
\sin \beta_M &= -A_{31},
\end{aligned}
\right\} \qquad (2.07)
$$

giving a unique solution for λ_M and β_M within the intervals of their variability, and

$$
\left.
\begin{aligned}
\sin C \cdot \cos \beta_M &= A_{32} \\
\cos C \cdot \cos \beta_M &= A_{33},
\end{aligned}
\right\} \qquad (2.08)
$$

giving a unique solution of C. It is of advantage to apply formulae (2·07) and (2·08) for λ_M, β_M and C in case when the cracovian A has already been determined for some other purpose in lunar calculations.

Besides the values of the auxiliary quantities A, B and μ, tabulated by astronomical almanacs to facilitate the determination of the optical libration, these almanacs give an ephemeris of the quantities λ_M, β_M and C for each day of the year. This ephemeris refers, of course, to geocentric coordinates of the Moon. Thus, when applied in practice, it requires corrections depending on the topocentric coordinates of the Moon.

The corresponding differential formulae, easy to obtain from geometrical considerations, were given by Banachiewicz (1929b) in the form:

$$
\left.
\begin{aligned}
\begin{Bmatrix} \Delta\lambda \\ \Delta\beta \end{Bmatrix} &= \begin{Bmatrix} \cos \delta_0 \cdot \Delta\alpha \\ \Delta\delta \end{Bmatrix} \begin{Bmatrix} \cos C_0 & -\sin C_0 \\ -\sin C_0 & -\cos C_0 \end{Bmatrix}, \\
\{\Delta C\} &= \begin{Bmatrix} \Delta\lambda \\ \Delta\alpha \end{Bmatrix} \begin{Bmatrix} \sin \beta_0 \\ \sin \delta_0 \end{Bmatrix}.
\end{aligned}
\right\} \qquad (2.09)
$$

The corrections $\Delta\lambda$, $\Delta\beta$ and ΔC to quantities characterizing the optical libration, the geocentric values of which are denoted by λ_0, β_0 and C_0, correspond to parallactic changes of the Moon's equatorial coordinates $\Delta\alpha$ and $\Delta\delta$.

On using his (1949a) differential formulae of spherical polygonometry, Koziel (1957) obtained other differential formulae for the optical libration of the Moon:

$$\left.\begin{array}{c} \left\{\begin{array}{c} \Delta\beta \\ \cos\beta_0 . \Delta C \end{array}\right\} = \left\{\begin{array}{c} n_1 \\ n_2 \end{array}\right\} \left\{\begin{array}{cc} \sin\lambda_0 & -\cos\lambda_0 \\ \cos\lambda_0 & \sin\lambda_0 \end{array}\right\} \\ \Delta\lambda = \sin\beta_0 . \Delta C - n_3, \end{array}\right\} \qquad (2.10)$$

where

$$\{n_1\} = \Lambda_2 . \Delta . \Lambda_3, \quad \{n_2\} = \Lambda_1 . \Delta . \Lambda_3, \quad \{n_3\} = \Lambda_1 . \Delta . \Lambda_2, \quad (2.11)$$

Λ_1, Λ_2 and Λ_3 denoting the first, the second and the third column of the cracovian $\Lambda = r(l_{\mathbb{C}})$, L, and

$$\Delta = \left\{\begin{array}{ccc} 0 & -\Delta\alpha & -\cos\alpha_0 . \Delta\delta \\ \Delta\alpha & 0 & -\sin\alpha_0 . \Delta\delta \\ \cos\alpha_0 . \Delta\delta & \sin\alpha_0 . \Delta\delta & 0 \end{array}\right\}. \qquad (2.12)$$

Formulae (2.10), containing rigorous analytical values of the first derivatives as coefficients at the corresponding differentials, may be used with advantage when the cracovian Λ or L is already known from other lunar calculations. Formulae of another kind for topocentric librations were given by Atkinson (1951).

III. Physical Libration of the Moon

The empirical laws of Cassini describe only approximately the rotation of the Moon. Thus, the irregularities of this rotation, treated as deviations from the laws of Cassini, are called the *physical libration* of the Moon. This latter libration consists of some oscillations performed by the Moon about its mean position and results from differences between its principal moments of inertia. These oscillations are mainly due to the irregularities in the Moon's orbital motion. Before proceeding to a mathematical treatment of the physical libration, it is worth noting that, in the past century, efforts were made to discuss the Moon's physical libration mathematically by the use of methods admitting of a simple geometrical interpretation and appealing to the imagination, but involving a great loss in accuracy. Today, strictly analytical-numerical methods are applied instead. Their intricate mathematical transformations do not admit of any neglect of even the smallest terms, which play a significant rôle in the final determination of the physical libration, not so much because of their initial amplitudes, but because of their periods.

Proceeding now to the mathematical investigation of the Moon's rotation, let us consider a rectangular system of coordinates $(x, y, z,)$ with its origin at the centre of mass of the Moon. Direct the $+x$ axis along the Moon's first radius towards the Earth, the $+z$ axis to the

Moon's north pole, and let the $+y$ axis make with the $+x$ axis an angle of $+90°$ reckoned eastward. The position of this system of coordinates, as referred to the ecliptic, is specified by three Eulerian angles: ϕ—the angular distance of the positive part of the x axis from the descending node of the Moon's equator, ϑ—the inclination of the lunar equator to the ecliptic and ψ—the longitude of the descending node of the lunar equator. Denoting, as before, by $l_{\mathbb{C}}$ the mean longitude of the Moon, by I the mean inclination of the lunar equator to the ecliptic and by Ω the longitude of the ascending node of the Moon's orbit, the laws of Cassini may assume the following mathematical form:

$$\phi = 180° + l_{\mathbb{C}} - \psi, \quad \vartheta = I, \quad \psi = \Omega. \qquad (2.13)$$

In order to get a faithful representation of the actual rotation of the Moon, let us introduce three functions of time τ, ρ and σ, defined as perturbations of the quantities occurring in relations (2.13) by the equations:

$$\phi = 180° + (l_{\mathbb{C}} + \tau) - \psi, \quad \vartheta = I + \rho, \quad \psi = \Omega + \sigma. \qquad (2.14)$$

Cassini's laws, as we know from the observations, are actually valid to a good approximation. Thus, the quantities τ, ρ and σ, constituting the deviations from these laws, may be regarded as small quantities of the first order. Let τ be called the *physical libration in longitude*, ρ the *physical libration in inclination* and σ the *physical libration in node*.

In order to determine these quantities let us regard the Moon as a rigid body and apply Euler's equations, of which right-hand sides (being combinations of the derivatives of the potential) were expanded to a sufficient accuracy to give

$$\left.\begin{array}{l} \dfrac{dp}{dt} + \alpha qr = \quad 3M\alpha R^{-5}yz, \\[2em] \dfrac{dq}{dt} - \beta pr = -3M\beta R^{-5}xz, \\[2em] \dfrac{dr}{dt} + \gamma pq = \quad 3M\gamma R^{-5}xy, \end{array}\right\} \qquad (2.15)$$

where α, β and $\dot{\gamma}$ are defined by the relations:

$$\alpha = \frac{C-B}{A}, \quad \beta = \frac{C-A}{B}, \quad \gamma = \frac{B-A}{C}, \qquad (2.16)$$

and A, B and C denote the principal moments of inertia referred to the x, y and z axes, respectively; p, q and r are components of the angular velocity of the Moon on these axes; M, the mass of the Earth; R, the distance Earth–Moon; and x, y, z, the coordinates of the Earth's centre of mass. The components of velocity p, q and r are related with the Eulerian angles ϕ, ϑ and ψ by the well-known equations, expressed by Koziel (1948a) in the cracovian form:

$$\begin{pmatrix} p \\ q \\ r \end{pmatrix} = \frac{d}{dt} \begin{Bmatrix} \psi \\ \vartheta \\ \phi \end{Bmatrix} \cdot \left[\boldsymbol{r}(\phi - 90°) \cdot \begin{Bmatrix} -\sin \vartheta & 0 & 0 \\ 0 & 1 & 0 \\ \cos \vartheta & 0 & 1 \end{Bmatrix} \right]. \quad (2.17)$$

In order to integrate the system of differential equations (2.15), their right-hand sides must first be expressed as functions of the time t. Denoting, as before, the true longitude and latitude of the Moon by $L_{\mathbb{C}}$ and $B_{\mathbb{C}}$, we get for the true longitude of the Earth v—as seen from the Moon and reckoned from the descending node of the Moon's equator—the expression

$$v = L_{\mathbb{C}} + 180° - \psi, \quad (2.18)$$

and for the true latitude, $-B_{\mathbb{C}}$. The equations of transformation of the ecliptical coordinates into the coordinates (x, y, z) in the cracovian form (Koziel 1948a) will be:

$$\begin{Bmatrix} x \\ y \\ z \end{Bmatrix} = \begin{Bmatrix} R \cos B_{\mathbb{C}} \cos v \\ R \cos B_{\mathbb{C}} \sin v \\ -R \sin B_{\mathbb{C}} \end{Bmatrix} \cdot \boldsymbol{p}(-\vartheta) \cdot \boldsymbol{r}(\phi) = R \cos B_{\mathbb{C}} \begin{Bmatrix} \cos v \\ \sin v \\ -\tan B_{\mathbb{C}} \end{Bmatrix} \cdot [\boldsymbol{r}(\phi) \cdot \boldsymbol{p}(\vartheta)]. \quad (2.19)$$

By means of these relations the right-hand sides of the equations (2.15) may be expressed as functions of the time, since except for the perturbations τ, ρ and σ which are negligible in the first approximation, the expressions for the quantities R, $B_{\mathbb{C}}$, v, $l_{\mathbb{C}}$ and Ω are known as functions of the time t from the theory of the Moon's motion in its orbit.

IV. Physical Libration in Longitude

In order to find the physical libration in longitude τ, we shall use the third of the equations (2.15), taking the values for x and y from equations (2.19) and putting after Hayn (1902):

$$1 - \cos I + \tan i \sin I = \mu, \quad (2.20)$$

D

where i denotes the inclination of the Moon's orbit to the ecliptic. The third equation of the system (2.15) will then assume the form

$$\frac{dr}{dt} + \gamma pq = 3M\gamma R^{-3}\cos^2 B_{\mathbb{C}}[\tfrac{1}{2}\sin(2v-2\phi)(1-\mu)-\tfrac{1}{2}\mu\sin 2\phi]. \quad (2.21)$$

The solution of this equation has, in recent decades been thoroughly discussed in several papers: first by Hayn (1902, 1920), who on the basis of Hansen's (1857) lunar theory and tables obtained two different solutions in the years 1902 and 1920; and then by Jönsson (1917) who, applying in his computations Brown's (1919) tables and a theory of physical libration developed by the use of rectangular coordinates and of Lagrange's equations, obtained results disagreeing with those of Hayn. Finally, Koziel (1948a) discussed this problem afresh, applying Brown's lunar theory and tables. He found that the disagreement between the results of Hayn and Jönsson cannot be explained by the slight discrepancies between the developments of Brown and Hansen and obtained results confirming in principle, with but insignificant changes, those of Hayn from the year 1920. In what follows we shall refer to the theory of physical libration in longitude given by Koziel (1948a).

In order to solve the equation (2.21), its right-hand side should be expanded as a function of the time t. Brown's tables constituting the basis of our discussion, give the true longitude of the Moon $L_{\mathbb{C}}$, the latitude $B_{\mathbb{C}}$ and the sine of its parallax as function of time by means of the arguments: l, l', D and F. However, in order to refer to Hayn's discussion, we shall use here the arguments of Hansen: namely, g, g', ω and ω', related to the arguments of Brown by the formula

$$\begin{Bmatrix} l \\ l' \\ D \\ F \end{Bmatrix} = \begin{Bmatrix} g \\ g' \\ \omega \\ \omega' \end{Bmatrix} \begin{pmatrix} 1 & 0 & 1 & 1 \\ 0 & 1 & -1 & 0 \\ 0 & 0 & 1 & 1 \\ 0 & 0 & -1 & 0 \end{pmatrix}, \quad (2.22)$$

where g denotes the mean anomaly of the Moon; g' the mean anomaly of the Sun; ω the angular distance of the Moon's perigee from the ascending node of its orbit, and ω', the distance of the Sun's perigee from the ascending node of the orbit of the Moon.

First let us develop the expression in brackets [ ] in the equation (2.21). The brackets [ ] contain the true longitude of the Moon $L_{\mathbb{C}}$ which enters through v, the true longitude of the Earth, as seen from the Moon (2.18). But

$$L_{\mathbb{C}} = l_{\mathbb{C}} + \Sigma \text{ of periodic terms.} \quad (2.23)$$

From the development given by Brown's tables for $L_{\mathbb{C}}$, 61 terms were taken into account in the sum $\underline{\Sigma}$. Of the solar terms, all having co-efficients greater than $1''$ were retained; and of the remaining ones all those were kept which, owing to the periods of their arguments, will play a part in the integral of equation (2.21). It should be added that, in the coefficients of two such terms with arguments $-g+2\omega$ and 2ω, further decimal places were added (printed in pearl type) directly from Brown's tables. Of the planetary terms only one, depending on perturbations produced by Jupiter, has an argument greater than $1''$. Since, however, it does not combine itself with solar terms, it has no significance—within the limits of the required accuracy—in the integral of the equation (2.21). Also the empirical terms figuring in $L_{\mathbb{C}}$, being rather uncertain, were omitted in the sum $\underline{\Sigma}$.

For the purpose of illustration we are giving in Table I a list of the periodical terms of the sum $\underline{\Sigma}$, accepted in further calculations:

$$
\begin{aligned}
&\underline{\Sigma} = \Sigma_i a_i \sin \alpha_i, \\
\text{where} \qquad &\alpha_i = c_1^{(i)} g + c_2^{(i)} g' + c_3^{(i)} \omega + c_4^{(i)} \omega', \\
&c_1^{(i)}, c_2^{(i)}, c_3^{(i)}, c_4^{(i)} = 0, \pm 1, \pm 2, \ldots \\
&i = 1, 2, \ldots
\end{aligned}
\qquad (2.24)
$$

The first column of Table I gives the number of each term after Brown. The second column, arranged according to a scheme which helps to avoid errors in computation and to save time in the operations on these series, gives the arguments α_i of the individual terms. The third column contains the values of the coefficients a_i rounded off to $0\cdot''1$; and the fourth, the same values in radians.

So large a number of terms—even though their amplitudes may be small—must be introduced into our computations if we are to obtain the coefficients of the periodical terms in the integral of equation (2.21), i.e. in the physical libration in longitude τ, with an accuracy up to $1''$. *Ex post* it turned out that, in the process of the multiplication of trigonometrical series, even terms apparently quite negligible attained significance later. Thus, in order to obtain the required accuracy, the computations must be carried out to 6 decimal places (the coefficients a_i being expressed in radians) and in the calculation of the brackets [ ] of equation (2.21) all terms listed in Table I must be taken into account.

From the relations (2.14), (2.18) and (2.23) we have

$$
v - \phi = \underline{\Sigma} - \tau;
$$

TABLE I

Ref. No.	Arg. α_i	Coeff. a_i''	Coeff. a_i
		$''$	
7	g	$+\ 22639{\cdot}5$	$+\ 0{\cdot}109759$
25	$2g$	$+\ 769{\cdot}0$	$+\ 3728$
66	$3g$	$+\ 36{\cdot}1$	$+\ 175$
142	$4g$	$+\ 1{\cdot}9$	$+\ 9$
73	$-2g-g'$	$+\ 7{\cdot}6$	$+\ 37$
32	$-g-g'$	$+\ 109{\cdot}7$	$+\ 532$
15	$-g'$	$+\ 668{\cdot}1$	$+\ 3239$
39	$g-g'$	$+\ 147{\cdot}7$	$+\ 716$
80	$2g-g'$	$+\ 9{\cdot}7$	$+\ 47$
85	$-g-2g'$	$+\ 1{\cdot}2$	$+\ 6$
45	$-2g'$	$+\ 7{\cdot}5$	$+\ 36$
91	$g-2g'$	$+\ 2{\cdot}6$	$+\ 13$
268	$-g\quad +2\omega$	$+\ 0{\cdot}0_{55}$	$+\ 0_{27}$
182	$+2\omega$	$+\ 1{\cdot}2_{98}$	$+\ 6_{29}$
104	$g\quad +2\omega$	$-\ 39{\cdot}5$	$-\ 192$
51	$2g\quad +2\omega$	$-\ 411{\cdot}6$	$-\ 1995$
99	$3g\quad +2\omega$	$-\ 45{\cdot}1$	$-\ 219$
176	$4g\quad +2\omega$	$-\ 4{\cdot}0$	$-\ 19$
113	$-g'\quad -2\omega'$	$-\ 1{\cdot}4$	$-\ 7$
52	$-2g'\quad -2\omega'$	$+\ 55{\cdot}2$	$+\ 267$
103	$g-2g'\quad -2\omega'$	$-\ 6{\cdot}4$	$-\ 31$
111	$-3g'\quad -2\omega'$	$+\ 2{\cdot}2$	$+\ 10$
129	$+\omega-\omega'$	$+\ 1{\cdot}1$	$+\ 5$
61	$g\quad +\omega-\omega'$	$+\ 18{\cdot}0$	$+\ 87$
123	$2g\quad +\omega-\omega'$	$+\ 1{\cdot}3$	$+\ 6$
119	$-g-g'+\omega-\omega'$	$-\ 1{\cdot}8$	$-\ 8$
56	$-g'+\omega-\omega'$	$-\ 18{\cdot}6$	$-\ 90$
21	$g-g'+\omega-\omega'$	$-\ 125{\cdot}2$	$-\ 607$
55	$2g-g'+\omega-\omega'$	$-\ 8{\cdot}5$	$-\ 41$
92	$g\quad +2\omega-2\omega'$	$-\ 2{\cdot}5$	$-\ 12$
81	$-g'+2\omega-2\omega'$	$+\ 2{\cdot}5$	$+\ 12$
40	$g-g'+2\omega-2\omega'$	$-\ 28{\cdot}5$	$-\ 138$
14	$2g-g'+2\omega-2\omega'$	$-\ 24{\cdot}4$	$-\ 118$
31	$3g-g'+2\omega-2\omega'$	$-\ 2{\cdot}9$	$-\ 14$
67	$-g-2g'+2\omega-2\omega'$	$+\ 13{\cdot}2$	$+\ 64$
26	$-2g'+2\omega-2\omega'$	$+\ 211{\cdot}7$	$+\ 1026$
8	$g-2g'+2\omega-2\omega'$	$+\ 4586{\cdot}4$	$+\ 22236$
3	$2g-2g'+2\omega-2\omega'$	$+\ 2369{\cdot}9$	$+\ 11490$
6	$3g-2g'+2\omega-2\omega'$	$+\ 192{\cdot}0$	$+\ 931$
24	$4g-2g'+2\omega-2\omega'$	$+\ 14{\cdot}4$	$+\ 70$
65	$5g-2g'+2\omega-2\omega'$	$+\ 1{\cdot}1$	$+\ 5$
74	$-3g'+2\omega-2\omega'$	$+\ 8{\cdot}6$	$+\ 42$
33	$g-3g'+2\omega-2\omega'$	$+\ 206{\cdot}0$	$+\ 999$
16	$2g-3g'+2\omega-2\omega'$	$+\ 165{\cdot}1$	$+\ 801$
38	$3g-3g'+2\omega-2\omega'$	$+\ 14{\cdot}6$	$+\ 71$
79	$4g-3g'+2\omega-2\omega'$	$+\ 1{\cdot}2$	$+\ 6$
86	$g-4g'+2\omega-2\omega'$	$+\ 7{\cdot}4$	$+\ 36$
46	$2g-4g'+2\omega-2\omega'$	$+\ 8{\cdot}1$	$+\ 39$

TABLE I (continued)

Ref. No.	Arg. α_i	Coeff. a_i''		Coeff. a_i	
			$''$		
105	$3g - 2g' + 4\omega - 2\omega'$	$-$	9·4	$-$	45
50	$4g - 2g' + 4\omega - 2\omega'$	$-$	5·7	$-$	28
120	$g - 3g' + 3\omega - 3\omega'$	$-$	1·2	$-$	6
57	$2g - 3g' + 3\omega - 3\omega'$	$-$	3·2	$-$	16
68	$g - 4g' + 4\omega - 4\omega'$	$+$	1·2	$+$	6
27	$2g - 4g' + 4\omega - 4\omega'$	$+$	30·8	$+$	149
9	$3g - 4g' + 4\omega - 4\omega'$	$+$	38·4	$+$	186
2	$4g - 4g' + 4\omega - 4\omega'$	$+$	13·9	$+$	67
5	$5g - 4g' + 4\omega - 4\omega'$	$+$	2·0	$+$	10
75	$2g - 5g' + 4\omega - 4\omega'$	$+$	2·7	$+$	13
34	$3g - 5g' + 4\omega - 4\omega'$	$+$	4·4	$+$	21
17	$4g - 5g' + 4\omega - 4\omega'$	$+$	1·9	$+$	9

hence, for computations to the required accuracy we expand

$$\tfrac{1}{2}\sin(2v - 2\phi) = \tfrac{1}{2}\sin 2\left(\underline{\Sigma} - \tau\right) = \underline{\Sigma} - \tfrac{2}{3}\underline{\Sigma}^3 + \tfrac{2}{15}\underline{\Sigma}^5 - \tau(1 - 2\underline{\Sigma}^2 + \tfrac{2}{3}\underline{\Sigma}^4).$$
(2.25)

The second part of the latter expression, depending on τ, will, of course, be taken into account only in the second approximation, when we integrate equation (2.21). For the computation of the first part to the requisite accuracy we shall use the development:

$$\begin{aligned}
\underline{\Sigma} - \tfrac{2}{3}\underline{\Sigma}^3 + \tfrac{2}{15}\underline{\Sigma}^5 = {} & \Sigma a_i \sin \alpha_i - \tfrac{1}{2}\Sigma a_i^3(\sin \alpha_i - \tfrac{1}{3}\sin 3\alpha_i) - \\
& - \Sigma a_i^2 a_j[\sin \alpha_j - \tfrac{1}{2}\sin(2\alpha_i + \alpha_j) + \tfrac{1}{2}\sin(2\alpha_i - \alpha_j)] + \Sigma a_i \cdot a_j \cdot a_k \cdot \\
& [\sin(\alpha_i + \alpha_j + \alpha_k) - \sin(\alpha_i + \alpha_j - \alpha_k) - \sin(\alpha_i - \alpha_j + \alpha_k) + \sin(\alpha_i - \alpha_j - \alpha_k)] + \\
& + \tfrac{1}{12}\Sigma a_i^5(\sin \alpha_i - \tfrac{1}{2}\sin 3\alpha_i) + \tfrac{1}{2}\Sigma a_i^4 a_j[\tfrac{1}{2}\sin \alpha_j - \tfrac{1}{3}\sin(2\alpha_i + \alpha_j) + \\
& + \tfrac{1}{3}\sin(2\alpha_i - \alpha_j)].
\end{aligned}$$
(2.26)

The second part of the brackets [ ] in equation (2.21) has a much simpler form. For, using (2.14) and the relation

$$l_{\mathbb{C}} = g + \omega + \Omega,$$
(2.27)

we obtain

$$-\tfrac{1}{2}\mu \sin 2\phi = -\tfrac{1}{2}\mu \sin(2g + 2\omega) - \mu(\tau - \sigma)\cos(2g + 2\omega).$$
(2.28)

From (2.20) it follows that

$$\mu = 0.002779$$

if we accept for I the value given by Hayn

$$I = 1° 32' 20'',$$

and for i Brown's value

$$i = 5° 8' 43''.$$

From computations carried out according to formulae (2.26) and (2.28), we obtain the brackets [ ] of equation (2.21) in the form of a development containing 54 terms with coefficients $\geqslant 10^{-5}$ and 2 terms with coefficients smaller than 10^{-5}, but such as will become significant in the further process of calculations on account of the term with the argument 2ω.

A similar proceeding will be applied to the expression $\cos^2 B_{\mathbb{C}}$ which, on the assumption that the latitude $B_{\mathbb{C}}$ is expressed by the expansion

$$B_{\mathbb{C}} = \Sigma a_i \sin \alpha_i,$$

can be computed according to the formula (Koziel 1948a)

$$\cos^2 B_{\mathbb{C}} = 1 - \tfrac{1}{2}\Sigma a_i{}^2(1 - \cos 2\alpha_i) + \Sigma a_i\, a_j\,[\cos(\alpha_i+\alpha_j) - \cos(\alpha_i-\alpha_j)] +$$
$$+ \tfrac{1}{24}\Sigma a_i{}^4(3 - 4\cos 2\alpha_i + \cos 4\alpha_i) + \tfrac{1}{6}\Sigma a_i{}^3 a_j \ . \tag{2.29}$$
$$[3\cos(\alpha_i-\alpha_j) - 3\cos(\alpha_i+\alpha_j) - \cos(3\alpha_i-\alpha_j) + \cos(3\alpha_i+\alpha_j)].$$

In a similar way, we obtain also R^{-1} using the development of the sine of the parallax given in Brown's tables, which (after dividing it by its constant $3422 \cdot 7''$) yields

$$R^{-1} = 1 + \Sigma a_i \cos \alpha_i.$$

Hence we have with sufficient accuracy (Koziel 1948a)

$$R^{-3} = 1 + 3\Sigma a_i \cos \alpha_i + \tfrac{3}{2}\Sigma a_i{}^2(1 + \cos 2\alpha_i) + 3\Sigma a_i a_j \ .$$
$$[\cos(\alpha_i+\alpha_j) + \cos(\alpha_i-\alpha_j)] + \tfrac{1}{4}\Sigma a_i{}^3(3\cos \alpha_i + \cos 3\alpha_i) + \tfrac{3}{2}\Sigma a_i{}^2 a_j \ .$$
$$[\cos \alpha_j + \tfrac{1}{2}\cos(2\alpha_i+\alpha_j) + \tfrac{1}{2}\cos(2\alpha_i - \alpha_j)] + \tfrac{3}{2}\Sigma a_i a_j a_k \ . \tag{2.30}$$
$$[\cos(\alpha_i+\alpha_j+\alpha_k) + \cos(\alpha_i+\alpha_j-\alpha_k) + \cos(\alpha_i-\alpha_j+\alpha_k) + \cos(\alpha_i-\alpha_j-\alpha_k)].$$

An ordinary multiplication of trigonometrical series will lead us now to the determination of the right-hand side of equation (2.21), i.e. of the expression

$$R^{-3}\cos^2 B_{\mathbb{C}} \cdot [\ ],$$

given in Table II in the form of a development with 69 terms having coefficients $\geqslant 10^{-5}$. Let us denote this development briefly by

$$\Sigma H_i \sin h_i,$$

where

$$h_i = k_1^{(i)}g + k_2^{(i)}g' + k_3^{(i)}\omega + k_4^{(i)}\omega',$$
$$\left.\begin{array}{l} k_1^{(i)},\ k_2^{(i)},\ k_3^{(i)},\ k_4^{(i)} = 0,\ \pm 1,\ \pm 2,\ \ldots \end{array}\right\} \qquad (2.31)$$
$$i = 1, 2, \ldots$$

TABLE II

h_i (sin)	H_i	h_i (sin)	H_i
		$2g - g' + 2\omega - 2\omega'$	− 207
g	+ 0·108248	$3g - g' + 2\omega - 2\omega'$	− 68
$2g$	+ 12477	$4g - g' + 2\omega - 2\omega'$	− 14
$3g$	+ 1403	$-2g - 2g' + 2\omega - 2\omega'$	+ 41
$4g$	+ 145	$- g - 2g' + 2\omega - 2\omega'$	+ 300
$5g$	+ 15	$-2g' + 2\omega - 2\omega'$	+ 1200
$-3g - g'$	+ 24	$g - 2g' + 2\omega - 2\omega'$	+ 21546
$-2g - g'$	+ 169	$2g - 2g' + 2\omega - 2\omega'$	+ 14672
$- g - g'$	+ 814	$3g - 2g' + 2\omega - 2\omega'$	+ 3610
$- g'$	+ 3193	$4g - 2g' + 2\omega - 2\omega'$	+ 602
$g - g'$	+ 938	$5g - 2g' + 2\omega - 2\omega'$	+ 82
$2g - g'$	+ 194	$-3g' + 2\omega - 2\omega'$	+ 47
$3g - g'$	+ 28	$g - 3g' + 2\omega - 2\omega'$	+ 1007
$- 2g'$	+ 37	$2g - 3g' + 2\omega - 2\omega'$	+ 1004
$g - 2g'$	+ 19	$3g - 3g' + 2\omega - 2\omega'$	+ 277
$+ 2\omega$	− 11$_{65}$	$4g - 3g' + 2\omega - 2\omega'$	+ 50
$g + 2\omega$	− 692	$g - 4g' + 2\omega - 2\omega'$	+ 37
$2g + 2\omega$	− 3483	$2g - 4g' + 2\omega - 2\omega'$	+ 48
$3g + 2\omega$	− 289	$2g - 2g' + 4\omega - 2\omega'$	− 17
$4g + 2\omega$	− 23	$3g - 2g' + 4\omega - 2\omega'$	− 67
$-2g - 2g' - 2\omega'$	+ 22	$4g - 2g' + 4\omega - 2\omega'$	− 55
$- g - 2g' - 2\omega'$	+ 140	$2g - 3g' + 3\omega - 3\omega'$	− 34
$- 2g' - 2\omega'$	+ 326	$3g - 3g' + 3\omega - 3\omega'$	− 20
$g - 2g' - 2\omega'$	− 16	$3g - 3g' + 4\omega - 4\omega'$	− 10
$- 3g' - 2\omega'$	+ 14	$2g - 4g' + 4\omega - 4\omega'$	+ 458
$g + \omega - \omega'$	+ 87	$3g - 4g' + 4\omega - 4\omega'$	+ 698
$2g + \omega - \omega'$	+ 20	$4g - 4g' + 4\omega - 4\omega'$	+ 369
$- g - g' + \omega - \omega'$	− 20	$5g - 4g' + 4\omega - 4\omega'$	+ 98
$- g' + \omega - \omega'$	− 93	$6g - 4g' + 4\omega - 4\omega'$	+ 16
$g - g' + \omega - \omega'$	− 599	$2g - 5g' + 4\omega - 4\omega'$	+ 41
$2g - g' + \omega - \omega'$	− 136	$3g - 5g' + 4\omega - 4\omega'$	+ 79
$3g - g' + \omega - \omega'$	− 21	$4g - 5g' + 4\omega - 4\omega'$	+ 48
$g + 2\omega - 2\omega'$	− 13	$3g - 6g' + 6\omega - 6\omega'$	+ 10
$- g' + 2\omega - 2\omega'$	+ 17$_6$	$4g - 6g' + 6\omega - 6\omega'$	+ 20
$g - g' + 2\omega - 2\omega'$	− 181	$5g - 6g' + 6\omega - 6\omega'$	+ 14

The right-hand side of equation (2.21) in its final form, still contains terms depending on τ and σ through the expressions (2.25) and (2.28), or

$$R^{-3}\cos^2 B \left[-\tau(1 - 2\underline{\Sigma}^2 + \tfrac{2}{3}\underline{\Sigma}^4)(1-\mu) - \mu(\tau - \sigma)\cos(2g + 2\omega) \right]. \quad (2.32)$$

To the requisite accuracy we then have

$$2\underline{\Sigma}^2 - \tfrac{2}{3}\underline{\Sigma}^4 = \Sigma a_i{}^2 - \tfrac{1}{4}\Sigma a_i{}^4, \tag{2.33}$$

where a_i are the coefficients of the development $\underline{\Sigma}$. Finally, the right-hand side of (2.21) will assume the form

$$3M\gamma[\Sigma H_i \sin h_i - 0{\cdot}9853\tau - 0{\cdot}161\tau \cos g + 0{\cdot}103 I\sigma \cos(2g + 2\omega)]; \tag{2.34}$$

in the sum $\Sigma H_i \sin h_i$ we also included the term with the argument Ω, which of all empirical terms figuring in $L_{(\!(}$ appears to be the most reliable.

If we now solve for dr/dt from the third equation of the system (2.17) and substitute in equation (2.21) we obtain

$$\frac{d^2\tau}{dt^2} + 0{\cdot}9853M'\gamma\tau = M'\gamma\Sigma H_i \sin h_i - \gamma pq +$$
$$+ M'\gamma[-0{\cdot}161\tau \cos g + 0{\cdot}103 I\sigma \cos(2g + 2\omega)] + \frac{I}{2} \cdot \frac{d^2 I\sigma}{dt^2}, \tag{2.35}$$

where we abbreviated $3M = M'$. In the integration of the latter equation we shall omit, in the first approximation, all terms on its right-hand side except for the development $M'\gamma\Sigma H_i \sin h_i$. The general integral τ of this equation, thus simplified, and known in mechanics as the equation of forced oscillations, will be

$$\tau = A \sin[a + t\sqrt{(0{\cdot}9853M'\gamma)}] - \Sigma\frac{M'\gamma H_i \sin h_i}{h_i'{}^2 - 0{\cdot}9853M'\gamma}, \tag{2.36}$$

where A and a denote the constants of integrations; t, the time expresed in mean days; and h_i', the daily motion of the argument h_i.

The first term of the formula (2.36) for the physical libration in longitude, represents the so called *free libration in longitude*. All attempts at determining the constants of the free libration in longitude from observations hitherto have merely shown that the amplitude of this libration A is insignificant (Yakovkin 1952a).

The second portion of the expression (2.36) for τ in the form of a sum of periodic terms, arising from the irregularity of the Moon's motion in its orbit, is called the *forced libration in longitude*. It is already evident from the analytical form of the periodic terms of the forced libration that the terms of importance in the integral (2.36), will be not only those with large H_i, but also such terms for which $h_i'{}^2 - k\gamma$ ($k = 0{\cdot}9853M'$) will be near zero. These are first of all, the term with the argument 2ω; thus from the very beginning of the study of our problem, much attention has been paid to an accurate determination of the amplitude H_i corresponding to this term.

In order to determine the numerical values of the coefficients at the terms of the integral τ (2.36), let us introduce the so called *mechanical ellipticity of the Moon f*, characterizing the ratio

$$f = \frac{\alpha}{\beta} = \frac{B(C-B)}{A(C-A)} \tag{2.37}$$

of its principal moments of inertia. It is easily seen from the definitions (2.16) that the quantities α, β and γ satisfy the identity

$$\alpha - \beta + \gamma - \alpha\beta\gamma = 0. \tag{2.38}$$

Since, moreover, by integrating the first two equations (2.15) and setting, with Hayn (1923) $I = 1°32'20''$, we obtain—as will be seen later (p. 44–45)—the relation:

$$\beta = 0{\cdot}000\,6328 - 0{\cdot}000\,00293 \cdot f, \tag{2.39}$$

all three quantities α, β and γ can be expressed in terms of f. Considering, moreover, that the product $\alpha\beta\gamma$ is insignificant we obtain with sufficient accuracy from the relations (2.37) and (2.38):

$$\gamma = \beta(1-f). \tag{2.40}$$

The computation of the coefficients of the terms in the expression for the forced libration (2.36) still necessitates the knowledge of the numerical values of h_i' which can be found by (2.31) from the values

$$\frac{dg}{dt}, \quad \frac{dg'}{dt}, \quad \frac{d\omega}{dt}, \quad \frac{d\omega'}{dt}, \quad \frac{d\Omega}{dt},$$

as given in Brown's tables.

After evaluating from the latter data the coefficients of the forced libration in longitude, we proceed immediately to the second approximation in the integration of the equation (2.35) for τ. The term γpq is negligible, as it can be shown *ex post* with the aid of formula (2.17). From the expression for $I\sigma$ to be given later (p. 45) it may be verified that the terms contained in the brackets [ ] of equation (2.35), give rise to small terms which can be added to the terms of $\Sigma\,H_i \sin h_i$ with arguments g and $2g$, as illustrated in Table III for two particular values of f.

Finally, the numerical values of the coefficients—together with the corresponding arguments—of the forced libration in longitude τ (Koziel 1948a), computed from formulae (2.35) and (2.36) in the second, and within the required accuracy, final approximation, are given in Table IV. All eleven terms with coefficients greater than $0{\cdot}''5$ were taken into account for several values of f.

As has already been said, the integral τ (2.36) contains behind the sign Σ a term with the argument 2ω and with a coefficient whose denominator $h_i'^2 - k\gamma$ vanishes for some value of γ corresponding to $f = 0.662$. It is evident that in the immediate neighbourhood of this

TABLE III

Arg.		$f =$	0·5	0·73
g	H_i I approx.		+ 0·108248	+ 0·108248
	Corr. II ,,		+ 6143	+ 13640
	H_i II ,,		+ 0·114391	+ 0·121888
$2g$	H_i I approx.		+ 0·012477	+ 0·012477
	Corr. II ,,		+ 9	+ 5
	H_i II ,,		+ 0·012486	+ 0·012482

TABLE IV

Arg. (sin)	$f = 0.25$	0·5	0·6	0·7	0·73	0·8
	"	"	"	"	"	"
g	− 32·9	− 22·5	− 18·3	− 14·2	− 12·9	− 10·0
$2g$	− 0·9	− 0·6	− 0·5	− 0·4	− 0·3	− 0·2
$- g'$	−219·7	−131·8	−101·4	− 73·2	− 65·2	− 47·1
$+2\omega$	− 4·4	− 7·5	− 15·7	+ 19·3	+ 9·7	+ 3·5
$-2g' \qquad -2\omega'$	− 4·0	− 2·6	− 2·1	− 1·6	− 1·4	− 1·0
$- g' + \omega - \omega'$	+ 8·9	+ 5·2	+ 3·9	+ 2·8	+ 2·5	+ 1·8
$- g' + 2\omega - 2\omega'$	− 2·6	− 1·4	− 1·0	− 0·7	− 0·6	− 0·5
$-2g' + 2\omega - 2\omega'$	− 21·4	− 13·9	− 11·0	− 8·1	− 7·3	− 5·4
$g - 2g' + 2\omega - 2\omega'$	− 8·5	− 5·6	− 4·5	− 3·4	− 3·0	− 2·2
$2g - 2g' + 2\omega - 2\omega'$	− 1·2	− 0·8	− 0·7	− 0·5	− 0·4	− 0·3
Ω	+ 7·4	+ 7·5	+ 7·5	+ 7·6	+ 7·6	+ 7·7

peculiar point, within which the coefficient in question increases infinitely, the physical libration in longitude τ cannot be expressed by the equation (2.36), since the latter was deduced on the assumption (wholly justified by observations) that τ was a small quantity.

V. Physical Libration in Inclination and Node

The integration of the first two equations (2.15) gives the physical libration in inclination ρ and that in node σ. A detailed discussion of the determination of ρ and σ, undertaken in the present century by Hayn (1902, 1920) and Jönsson (1917), led both authors to the same final results. In what follows we shall, therefore, confine ourselves to a brief exposition of this problem as given in Hayn's treatise of 1923.

Let us introduce, instead of the desired functions ρ and σ, the auxiliary unknowns x and y by means of the relations

$$x = \sin\phi \sin\vartheta \quad \text{and} \quad y = \cos\phi \sin\vartheta. \tag{2.41}$$

Then, on the basis of (2.14) and (2.27), to a sufficient approximation, it follows that

$$\left.\begin{array}{l} x = -I\sin(g+\omega)-\rho\sin(g+\omega)-I\tau\cos(g+\omega)+I\sigma\cos(g+\omega), \\ y = -I\cos(g+\omega)-\rho\cos(g+\omega)+I\tau\sin(g+\omega)-I\sigma\sin(g+\omega). \end{array}\right\} \tag{2.42}$$

In terms of these variables the first two equations (2.15) now assume the form:

$$\left.\begin{array}{l} \dfrac{d^2y}{dt^2} + \dfrac{dx}{dt}l_{\mathbb{C}}'(1-\alpha)+\alpha l_{\mathbb{C}}'^2 y = M'\alpha S+U, \\[2mm] \dfrac{d^2x}{dt^2} - \dfrac{dy}{dt}l_{\mathbb{C}}'(1-\beta)+(\beta l_{\mathbb{C}}'^2+0{\cdot}9938\beta M')x = \\[2mm] \qquad\qquad = M'\beta(T+0{\cdot}9938x)+W, \end{array}\right\} \tag{2.43}$$

where

$$\left.\begin{array}{l} U = -\dfrac{dx}{dt}\dfrac{d\tau}{dt} - x\dfrac{d^2\tau}{dt^2} + \dfrac{d}{dt}\left(\tfrac{1}{2}I^2\cos(g+\omega)\dfrac{d\rho}{dt}\right), \\[3mm] W = \dfrac{dy}{dt}\dfrac{d\tau}{dt} + y\dfrac{d^2\tau}{dt^2} + \dfrac{d}{dt}\left(\tfrac{1}{2}I^2\sin(g+\omega)\dfrac{d\rho}{dt}\right), \end{array}\right\} \tag{2.44}$$

and

$$S = -R^{-5}yz, \qquad T = -R^{-5}xz; \tag{2.45}$$

S and T being developed into series in function of the time t similarly as it was done above (p. 33–34) with the expression $R^{-5}xy$. The same can, moreover, be done with the expressions for U and W.

In this manner, the right-hand sides of the system of equations (2.43) assume, to a first approximation (in which the terms containing ρ, σ and τ may be neglected) the forms

$$\sum_i F_i \cos g_i \quad \text{and} \quad \sum_i G_i \sin g_i,$$

where

$$\left.\begin{aligned}
g_i &= m_1^{(i)}g + m_2^{(i)}g' + m_3^{(i)}\omega + m_4^{(i)}\omega', \\
m_1^{(i)}, m_2^{(i)}, m_3^{(i)}, m_4^{(i)} &= 0, \pm 1, \pm 2, \dots
\end{aligned}\right\} \tag{2.46}$$

$$i = 1, 2, \dots$$

Equating the right-hand sides of equations (2.43) temporarily to zero, we find by their solution that

$$\left.\begin{aligned}
x &= B \sin(b + \lambda_1 t) + C \sin(c + \lambda_2 t), \\
y &= B \cos(b + \lambda_1 t) - \sqrt{(\epsilon\beta/\alpha)}\, C \cos(c + \lambda_2 t),
\end{aligned}\right\} \tag{2.47}$$

where
$$\lambda_1 = l_{\mathbb{C}}'[1 + (\epsilon - 1/2)\beta], \quad \lambda_2 = l_{\mathbb{C}}'\sqrt{(\epsilon\alpha\beta)}, \quad \epsilon = 3{\cdot}9450.$$

In order to obtain the general integrals of the system of equations (2.43) let us point out that these equations are also satisfied by expressions of the type:

$$x = X \sin g_i, \qquad y = Y \cos g_i; \tag{2.48}$$

the definition of g_i being given by (2.46). Substituting the expressions (2.48) in the equations (2.43) we get

$$\left.\begin{aligned}
X &= \frac{-G_i(g_i'^2 - \alpha l_{\mathbb{C}}'^2) - F_i g_i' l_{\mathbb{C}}'(1-\beta)}{(g_i'^2 - \beta l_{\mathbb{C}}'^2\epsilon)(g_i'^2 - \alpha l_{\mathbb{C}}'^2) - g_i'^2 l_{\mathbb{C}}'^2(1-\alpha)(1-\beta)}, \\
Y &= \frac{-F_i(g_i'^2 - \beta l_{\mathbb{C}}'\epsilon) - G_i g_i' l_{\mathbb{C}}'(1-\alpha)}{(g_i'^2 - \beta l_{\mathbb{C}}'^2\epsilon)(g_i'^2 - \alpha l_{\mathbb{C}}'^2) - g_i'^2 l_{\mathbb{C}}'^2(1-\alpha)(1-\beta)},
\end{aligned}\right\} \tag{2.49}$$

where g_i' is the daily motion of the argument g_i. Finally, the general integrals of the system (2.43) may be found from the formulae (2.47) and (2.49); the constants of integration B, b, C and c constituting jointly the constants of the *free libration in inclination and in node*.

Returning now through (2.41) to the original unknowns ρ and σ, we find that, to a sufficient accuracy,

$$\left.\begin{aligned}
I + \rho &= -x \sin(g+\omega) - y \cos(g+\omega), \\
I\sigma - I\tau &= x \cos(g+\omega) - y \sin(g+\omega).
\end{aligned}\right\} \tag{2.50}$$

Hence, considering that ρ consists of periodic terms only, we have for $g_i = g + \omega$ identically

$$X_{g+\omega} + Y_{g+\omega} + 2I = 0, \tag{2.51}$$

which on account of (2.37) and (2.38) yields the relation (2.39). Finally, then, the desired expressions for the physical libration in inclination ρ and in node σ assume, according to Hayn (1923), for $f = 0.73$ the following forms:

$$\rho = -B \cos(b - 146 \cdot ''6t)$$
$$+ 0.662C \cos(c + 50 \cdot ''8t - g - \omega)$$
$$+ 1.662C \cos(c + 50 \cdot ''8t + g + \omega)$$
$$- 106'' \cos g$$
$$+ 35'' \cos(g + 2\omega)$$
$$- 11'' \cos(2g + 2\omega)$$
$$- 3'' \cos(2g' + 2\omega')$$
$$- 2'' \cos(g - 2g' + 2\omega - 2\omega'),$$

$$I\sigma = I\tau + B \sin(b - 146 \cdot ''6t)$$
$$- 0.662C \sin(c + 50 \cdot ''8t - g - \omega)$$
$$+ 1.662C \sin(c + 50 \cdot ''8t + g + \omega)$$
$$- 108'' \sin g$$
$$+ 35'' \sin(g + 2\omega)$$
$$- 11'' \sin(2g + 2\omega)$$
$$- 3'' \sin(2g' + 2\omega')$$
$$- 2'' \sin(g - 2g' + 2\omega - 2\omega').$$

$$(2.52)$$

As regards the *forced librations in inclination* and *in node* only, they are given in Table V (Hayn 1920) for several selected values of f.

TABLE V

	$f = 0.5$	0.6	0.7	0.8	
	$''$	$''$	$''$	$''$	
$\rho =$	-87.9	-95.6	-103.3	-111.0	$\cos g$
	$+ 0.5$	$+ 0.2$	$- 0.2$	$- 0.5$	$\cos 2\omega$
	$+ 8.8$	$+20.2$	$+ 32.0$	$+ 43.3$	$\cos (g + 2\omega)$
	-11.1	-11.1	$- 11.1$	$- 11.1$	$\cos(2g + 2\omega)$
	$- 0.6$	$- 0.6$	$- 0.6$	$- 0.7$	$\cos(3g + 2\omega)$
	$- 3.1$	$- 3.2$	$- 3.3$	$- 3.4$	$\cos(-2g' - 2\omega')$
	$- 1.9$	$- 2.1$	$- 2.3$	$- 2.5$	$\cos(g - 2g' + 2\omega - 2\omega')$
	$''$	$''$	$''$	$''$	
$I\sigma =$	-89.8	-97.5	-105.3	-113.0	$\sin g$
	$+ 0.5$	$+ 0.2$	$- 0.2$	$- 0.5$	$\sin 2\omega$
	$+ 8.8$	$+20.2$	$+ 32.0$	$+ 43.3$	$\sin(g + 2\omega)$
	-11.1	-11.1	$- 11.1$	$- 11.1$	$\sin(2g + 2\omega)$
	$- 0.6$	$- 0.6$	$- 0.6$	$- 0.7$	$\sin(3g + 2\omega)$
	$+ 3.1$	$+ 3.2$	$+ 3.3$	$+ 3.4$	$\sin(-2g' - 2\omega')$
	$- 1.9$	$- 2.1$	$- 2.3$	$- 2.5$	$\sin(g - 2g' + 2\omega - 2\omega')$

VI. Influence of Solar Attraction

In our discussion on the Moon's physical libration we have so far taken explicitly into account only the perturbations of the Moon by the Earth. There is no doubt, however, that the influence of the Sun is also involved in our investigations through terms with solar arguments g' and ω', giving evidence of the perturbing influence of the Sun on the Moon's orbit. Nevertheless, the direct effect of the solar attraction on the rotating Moon should be examined as well. This problem was discussed in detail by Hayn (1902, 1923), who found the effect to be negligible. This may be illustrated by the fact that, according to Hayn's computations, the inclination I of the Moon's axis would change merely by $7''$ if the direct attraction on the part of the Sun were also taken into account. If we consider that the mean error of I, even if determined from long series of observations, exceeds $7''$, it is evident that the immediate effect of the Sun on the Moon's rotation is negligible.

VII. Determination of the Constants of the Moon's Physical Libration from Observations

The rotation of the Moon is described by equations (2.14) and the quantities occurring in these equations—namely, the physical libration in longitude τ, in inclination ρ and in node σ—are expressed as functions of the time t by the relation (2.36) and Table IV, as well as by relations (2.47), (2.50) and (2.52) and Table V. All these relations contain the quantities I and f as well as the integration constants A, a, B, b, C, c. Thus, in order to specify the position of the lunar ellipsoid at an arbitrary epoch, it is necessary to determine from observations the eight constants just mentioned.

This problem was attacked over a hundred years ago in a promising manner by the founder of modern astrometry, Bessel (1839). He used for this purpose the heliometer, new at that time and improved by him, which has since become the standard instrument to be applied to the determination of the constants of the Moon's physical libration. The method of reduction of these observations was worked out in detail by Bessel himself. His pupils Schlüter and Wichmann (1846, 1847), left two series of observations, the first of which has been reduced as much as three times (Franz 1889; Stratton 1909; Hayn 1914b). In the second half of the past century, the heliometric observations were undertaken by the assiduous observer, Hartwig. He observed the Moon for nearly half a century, and left among his scientific papers three series of observations. The first one, the Strasbourg series from the years 1877–1879 containing 42 observation evenings, was reduced by Hartwig himself (1880). The second one, made at Dorpat in the years 1884–1885 and covering 36 evenings, was reduced by Koziel (1948a, b, c, 1949b, c, d) in Krakow; while the third one, constituting the most extended series ever made by a single observer and comprising 266 evenings from the years 1890–1922, was partly reduced and published by Naumann (1939) of Leipzig.

A fair share of work in this domain of lunar research is due to the Engelhardt Observatory in Kazan where, with but short intervals, heliometric observations of the Moon's physical libration were carried out from 1895 until recent years by the following observers: Krassnov (1895–1898), Michailovsky (1898–1905), Banachiewicz (1910–1915), Yakovkin (1916–1931), Belkovich (1932–1942) and Nefediev (1936 until recently). During this period the Kazan observers attained the impressive total of over 800 published observation evenings. This vast observational material has been worked out in Kazan by Yakovkin (1928, 1939, 1945), Belkovich (1936, 1949) and Nefediev (1951, 1955).

An attempt to attack the problem of determination of libration constants by the way of photography undertaken in Paris by Puiseux (1925) who—from some 6,000 photographs of the Moon—selected 40 of the best secured over a period of 15 years. This attempt proved, however, a failure, because the reduction of these observations contained considerable errors. Only Weimer (1949)—after unsuccessful attempts on the part of Mrs. Chandon (1941)—obtained from the photographical observations of Puiseux results comparable with those from heliometric observations. Recently the constants of the Moon's physical libration were also obtained successfully by means of photography by Habibullin (1958) of Kazan.

VIII. Comparison of Heliometric Observations of the Moon with Theory

In order to determine the Moon's physical libration constants we choose a well-defined point on its surface—mostly the crater Mösting A—situated near the centre of the Moon's disc visible from the Earth, which owing to the motion of our satellite, changes its apparent position periodically with respect to the centre of the Moon's mass. In heliometric measurements—which constitute as yet the vast majority of the libration measurements of the Moon—it has been customary to refer the crater Mösting A to the Moon's illuminated limb. This is done by measuring the distance s_0 (s observatum) of this crater from the limb in specified position angles p, in order to determine the position of Mösting A as referred to the centre of mass of the lunar ellipsoid. The utilization of these measurements requires an application of many instrumental corrections (Koziel 1948*b*), as well as of precise reductions bringing the observations of a given evening strictly to one moment T_0 (Koziel 1948*c*) in order to facilitate their comparison with theory.

If we take some approximate initial values for the constants I and f and for the selenographic coordinates of the crater Mösting A: λ_0, β_0, as well as for the Moon's radius to the crater h and neglect, for the moment, the free libration, we can compute for the given position angles p, the corresponding distances of the crater from the limb s_c (*s calculatum*), in order to compare the heliometric observations of the Moon's libration with the theory. In this computation we have to find first the angular distance of the crater from the centre $\bar{\sigma}$ of the apparent disc of the Moon, and the position angle $\bar{\pi}$ of this distance, referred to the hour circle passing through the centre of the lunar disk.

For this purpose we solve a spherical pentagon, the vertices of which on the selenographic sphere are (Fig. 1): the terrestrial north pole P,

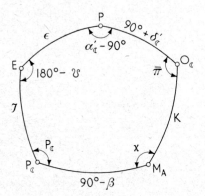

Fig. 1

the north pole of the ecliptic E, the projection on the selenographic sphere of the Moon's north pole $P_{\mathbb{C}}$, a similar projection of the crater Mösting A: M_A and the centre of the Moon's disc $O_{\mathbb{C}}$. On applying cracovian formulae (Banachiewicz 1927) of spherical polygonometry, Koziel (1949*b*), obtained for the angular distance K (selenocentrically reckoned) of crater Mösting A from the disc's centre $O_{\mathbb{C}}$ and for the position angle $\bar{\pi}$ the following relation—solving the spherical pentagon, just referred to, and constituting at the same time a ready scheme for calculations:

$$\begin{Bmatrix} \cos K \\ \sin K \cos \bar{\pi} \\ \sin K \sin \bar{\pi} \end{Bmatrix} = \begin{Bmatrix} \sin \beta \\ \cos \beta \end{Bmatrix} \cdot \begin{Bmatrix} 1 & 0 & 0 \\ 0 & -\sin(\mho - l_{(\!(} - \lambda) & -\cos(\mho - l_{(\!(} - \lambda) \end{Bmatrix}.$$

$$\begin{Bmatrix} \cos I & \sin I & 0 \\ -\sin I & \cos I & 0 \\ 0 & 0 & 1 \end{Bmatrix} \cdot \begin{Bmatrix} 1 & 0 & 0 \\ 0 & \cos \mho & \sin \mho \\ 0 & -\sin \mho & \cos \mho \end{Bmatrix} \cdot \begin{Bmatrix} \cos \epsilon & \sin \epsilon & 0 \\ -\sin \epsilon & \cos \epsilon & 0 \\ 0 & 0 & 1 \end{Bmatrix}. \quad (2.53)$$

$$\begin{Bmatrix} 1 & 0 & 0 \\ 0 & -\sin \alpha'_{(\!(} & -\cos \alpha'_{(\!(} \\ 0 & \cos \alpha'_{(\!(} & -\sin \alpha'_{(\!(} \end{Bmatrix} \cdot \begin{Bmatrix} -\sin \delta'_{(\!(} & \cos \delta'_{(\!(} & 0 \\ -\cos \delta'_{(\!(} & -\sin \delta'_{(\!(} & 0 \\ 0 & 0 & 1 \end{Bmatrix}.$$

In the latter formula let us take into account after Hayn (1923) the physical libration, taking for the coordinates of crater Mösting A the expressions:

$$\lambda = \lambda_0 + \Delta\lambda, \quad \beta = \beta_0 + \Delta\beta, \quad (2.54)$$

where

$$\Delta\lambda = -\rho\tan\beta_0\cos(g + \omega + \lambda_0) - I\sigma\tan\beta_0\sin(g + \omega + \lambda_0) + \tau,$$
$$\Delta\beta = \rho\sin(g + \omega + \lambda_0) - I\sigma\cos(g + \omega + \lambda_0). \quad \quad (2.55)$$

The quantity $\bar{\sigma}$ is then given by the formula:

$$\tan \bar{\sigma} = \frac{\sin h' \sin K}{1 - \sin h' \cos K}, \quad (2.56)$$

where h' denotes the topocentric value of the radius h. After computing π'' from the formula (Fig. 2):

$$\sin \pi'' = \frac{\bar{\sigma}}{R'_{(\!(}} \sin(p - \bar{\pi}), \quad (2.57)$$

where $R'_{(\!(}$ denotes the topocentric value of the Moon's radius, we finally get:

$$s_c = [R'_{(\!(} - \bar{\sigma} \cos(p - \bar{\pi} - \pi'')] \sec \pi''. \quad (2.58)$$

The s_c, thus computed, may be checked by the formula (Koziel 1949b):

$$s_c[s_c + 2\bar{\sigma} \cos(p - \bar{\pi})] = R'^2_{(\!(} - \bar{\sigma}^2 = \text{const.} \quad (2.59)$$

for a given observation evening.

E

IX. Adjustment of Heliometric Observations of the Moon's Libration

Until recently, the adjustment of the observations of the Moon's libration was being done in two stages: first, the auxiliary unknowns of the problem (i.e. the corrections to the rectangular (plane) co-ordinates of crater Mösting A on the disc) were found, and only the second adjustment gave the proper unknowns of the problem (i.e. the corrections to the coordinates λ_0, β_0 and h of the crater Mösting A as well as the corrections to the constants I and f. From the very beginning this manner of treatment created great difficulties in the choice of weights of the right-hand sides of the observation equations in the second adjustment. Banachiewicz (1940) pointed out that the method in question, involving in the second stage an adjustment of dependent equations, is incorrect from the point of view of the least squares method and that therefore no choice of weights can secure here a correct solution. Therefore, Banachiewicz and Koziel developed a new method for simultaneous adjustment of the observations of the Moon's libration, which was published in *Acta Astronomica* **4** (Koziel, 1949c).

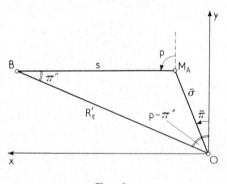

Fɪɢ. 2

The more recent form of this method can be summarized as follows. Let us consider a system of plane rectangular coordinates, with its origin at the Moon's centre O and the axes (Fig. 2) oriented so that the direction $+x$ is tangent to the parallel of declination and pointing eastwards, and $+y$ directed along the hour circle towards the north. If B denotes the point of the Moon's limb to which we refer the crater Mösting A and π'' the angle $\measuredangle$ $(M_A BO)$, the equations containing the corrections dx and dy of the crater's positions in this system of coordinates may be written as

$$\sec \pi'' \cdot \begin{Bmatrix} -\sin{(p-\pi'')} \\ -\cos{(p-\pi'')} \\ 1 \end{Bmatrix} \begin{Bmatrix} dx \\ dy \\ dR'_{\mathbb{C}} \end{Bmatrix} = \{s_0 - s_c\}, \tag{2.60}$$

where $dR'_{\mathbb{C}}$ stands for the correction of the Moon's radius for the given observation evening.

In our subsequent discussion we shall employ—instead of the desired corrections $d\lambda$, $d\beta$ and dh, to the space coordinates of crater Mösting A —the corrections $d\xi$, $d\eta$, $d\zeta$ to the rectangular (space) coordinates of this crater, a step which simplifies considerably the formulae for the differential coefficients of the observation equations of the libration problem. The transformation of one kind of corrections into the other is easily done by the formulae (Koziel 1949c)

$$\begin{Bmatrix} dh \\ h\cos\beta d\lambda \\ hd\beta \end{Bmatrix} = \begin{Bmatrix} d\xi \\ d\eta \\ d\zeta \end{Bmatrix} \cdot [\boldsymbol{q}(-\beta) \cdot \boldsymbol{r}(180° - \lambda)] =$$

$$= \begin{Bmatrix} d\xi \\ d\eta \\ d\zeta \end{Bmatrix} \cdot \begin{Bmatrix} -\cos\lambda\cos\beta & \sin\lambda & \cos\lambda\sin\beta \\ -\sin\lambda\cos\beta & -\cos\lambda & \sin\lambda\sin\beta \\ \sin\beta & 0 & \cos\beta \end{Bmatrix}. \tag{2.61}$$

Other unknowns in our problem are: the correction to the inclination of the Moon's rotation axis to the perpendicular to the ecliptic dI; the correction to the mechanical ellipticity of the Moon df, which constitutes the fundamental unknown of the problem; and, finally, the correction to the mean value of the Moon's radius dR_0, which formerly was not taken into account. As the linear dependence of the corrections dx, dy, $dR'_{\mathbb{C}}$ on the corrections $d\xi$, $d\eta$, $d\zeta$, dI, df, dR_0 is given by

$$\begin{Bmatrix} dx \\ dy \\ dR'_{\mathbb{C}} \end{Bmatrix} = \begin{Bmatrix} d\xi \\ d\eta \\ d\zeta \\ dI \\ df \\ dR_0 \end{Bmatrix} \cdot \begin{Bmatrix} A & A' & 0 \\ B & B' & 0 \\ C & C' & 0 \\ D & D' & 0 \\ E & E' & 0 \\ 0 & 0 & \dfrac{R'_{\mathbb{C}}}{R_0} \end{Bmatrix}, \tag{2.62}$$

after a substitution of (2.62) in (2.60), the final form of the observation equations of the libration problem, permitting the performance of the whole adjustment in one step, emerges as

$$
\begin{Bmatrix} d\xi \\ d\eta \\ d\zeta \\ dI \\ df \\ dR_0 \end{Bmatrix} \cdot \left[\sec \pi'' \cdot \begin{Bmatrix} -\sin(p-\pi'') \\ -\cos(p-\pi'') \\ 1 \end{Bmatrix} \begin{Bmatrix} A & B & C & D & E & 0 \\ A' & B' & C' & D' & E' & 0 \\ 0 & 0 & 0 & 0 & 0 & \dfrac{R'_\text{C}}{R_0} \end{Bmatrix} \right] = \{s_0 - s_c\}. \quad (2.63)
$$

The differential coefficients $A, A', B, B', C, C', D, D', E, E'$, occurring in equations (2.63) can be found from simple cracovian formulae (2.64) and (2.65) obtained by Koziel (1949c) on the basis of his (1949a) differential formulae of spherical polygonometry

$$
\begin{Bmatrix} A & A' \\ B & B' \\ C & C' \end{Bmatrix} = \frac{1}{\Delta} \frac{R'_\text{C}}{R_0} \begin{Bmatrix} A_{12} & A_{13} \\ A_{22} & A_{23} \\ A_{32} & A_{33} \end{Bmatrix} \quad (2.64)
$$

where $\Delta = 1 - \sin h' \cos K$ and A_{ij} $(i = 1, 2, 3; j = 2, 3)$ denote the elements of the cracovian $\boldsymbol{A}$ defined by formula (2.04). Furthermore,

$$
\begin{Bmatrix} D & E \\ D' & E' \end{Bmatrix} = \frac{1}{\Delta} \cdot \begin{Bmatrix} \bar{a} & \bar{a} \\ \bar{b} & \bar{b}' \\ \bar{c} & \bar{c}' \end{Bmatrix} \cdot \begin{Bmatrix} A_{12} & A_{13} \\ A_{22} & A_{23} \\ A_{32} & A_{33} \end{Bmatrix}, \quad (2.65)
$$

where

$$
\begin{Bmatrix} \bar{a} \\ \bar{b} \\ \bar{c} \end{Bmatrix} = h' \begin{Bmatrix} -\cos\beta \cos\lambda \\ -\cos\beta \sin\lambda \\ \sin\beta \end{Bmatrix} \begin{Bmatrix} 0 & 0 & -\sin(l_\text{C} - \Omega) \\ 0 & 0 & -\cos(l_\text{C} - \Omega) \\ \sin(l_\text{C} - \Omega) & \cos(l_\text{C} - \Omega) & 0 \end{Bmatrix}, \quad (2.66)
$$

and

$$
\begin{Bmatrix} \bar{a}' \\ \bar{b}' \\ \bar{c}' \end{Bmatrix} = h' \begin{Bmatrix} \dfrac{d\lambda}{df} \\ \dfrac{d\beta}{df} \end{Bmatrix} \begin{Bmatrix} \cos\beta \sin\lambda & -\cos\beta \cos\lambda & 0 \\ \sin\beta \cos\lambda & \sin\beta \sin\lambda & \cos\beta \end{Bmatrix}. \quad (2.67)
$$

In order to compute $d\lambda/df$ and $d\beta/df$ we have to find the derivatives of the physical libration τ, ρ and σ relative to f. For $dI\sigma/df$ and $d\rho/df$ it suffices to take the expressions obtained by numerical differentiation from Table V; while for finding $d\tau/df$, use should be made of the expression given by Koziel (1948a):

$$\frac{d\tau}{df} = -\sum_i \tau_i \left[\frac{\beta}{\gamma} - \frac{1}{H_i}\frac{dH_i}{df} + \frac{k\beta}{h_i'^2 - k\gamma} \right],$$

where

$$\tau_i = -\frac{M'\gamma H_i}{h_i'^2 - k\gamma} \cdot \sin h_i.$$

$$(2.68)$$

The manner of treating the adjustment of the libration observations, represented by the observation equations (2.63) having on their left-hand side the fundamental unknowns of the problem and, on the right-hand side, the independent quantities s_0—s_c, permits the carrying out of the adjustment in accordance with the principles of the least-squares method. This process, applied to the Dorpat heliometric series of Hartwig, gave the unknowns of the problem with smaller mean errors than those obtained by alternative ways of adjustment, and rendered it possible to obtain a strict value of the mean error of one observation (Koziel 1949d), which could not be obtained by Bessel's method. Moreover, the form of the observation equations (2.63) enables use to be made of even the so-called "quite incomplete observation evenings" —i.e. such evenings as, in the extreme case, consist of only one measurement of the distance of crater Mösting A from the illuminated limb of the Moon's disc. A further advantage of observation equations of the type (2.63) is that they allow an introduction, into their right-hand sides, of the corrections to s_0 for the irregularities of the Moon's limb —or any other corrections—according to Hayn's (1914a) charts, to Weimer's (1952) atlas, or other data, and then to carry out a parallel adjustment—without changing the left-hand sides of (2.63)—with and without taking into account the corrections for the irregularities of the limb.

Whenever the observation evenings consist of at least three measurements—according to Bessel's instructions, there should be 7 measurements; and it is worth noting that, with some observers, the number of these measurements was as large as 15—the adjustment may be carried out somewhat differently. From the auxiliary observation equations (2.60) belonging to one evening, normal equations are formed, and from the table of their coefficients its cracovian square root (Banachiewicz 1938) can be extracted without, of course, finding the intermediate unknowns. The triangular normal equations, thus

obtained, possessing the same weights as the observation equations
(2.60), may be written in the form:

$$\begin{Bmatrix} dx \\ dy \\ dR'_{\mathbb{C}} \end{Bmatrix} \begin{pmatrix} a & 0 & 0 \\ b & b' & 0 \\ c & c' & c'' \end{pmatrix} = \begin{Bmatrix} \alpha \\ \beta \\ \gamma \end{Bmatrix}. \tag{2.69}$$

By use of the formula (2.62) we get for the proper observation equations
of the problem the equation given by Koziel (1949c):

$$\begin{Bmatrix} d\xi \\ d\eta \\ d\zeta \\ dI \\ df \\ dR_0 \end{Bmatrix} \cdot \left[\begin{Bmatrix} a & 0 & 0 \\ b & b' & 0 \\ c & c' & c'' \end{Bmatrix} \begin{pmatrix} A & B & C & D & E & 0 \\ A' & B' & C' & D' & E' & 0 \\ 0 & 0 & 0 & 0 & 0 & \dfrac{R'_{\mathbb{C}}}{R_0} \end{pmatrix} \right] = \begin{Bmatrix} \alpha \\ \beta \\ \gamma \end{Bmatrix}, \tag{2.70}$$

the differential coefficients A, A', B, B', C, C', D, D', E, E', being
given by formulae (2.64) and (2.65).

The formulae (2.63) for the observation equations of the libration
problem may be successfully applied when using the electronic calculators.

X. Remarks concerning the Figure of the Moon

The problem of the figure of our satellite is to some extent connected
with the adjustment of the heliometric libration observations. Thus,
in the year 1934, Yakovkin (1934) suggested that the mean radius
of the Moon R_0 depends on the optical libration in latitude β_M and put
his hypothesis into the following mathematical form:

$$dR_0 = x + \beta_M \cdot y, \tag{2.71}$$

where dR_0 denotes, as before, the correction to the Moon's mean
radius; and x and y, the coefficients characterizing Yakovkin's hypothesis. For the coefficient y, which is of particular interest to us,
Yakovkin (1952b) obtained the value:

$$y = 0 \cdot ''04. \tag{2.72}$$

Koziel (1949d) found, however, that this result was primarily dependent
on the method of adjustment of the heliometric libration observations.
For if, in accordance with the process formerly employed, we satisfy
ourselves with the determination of the correction dR_0 with merely
the first stage of adjustment, and take into consideration only a part

of the observational material represented by the third reduced (triangular) normal equations (2.69) for each evening, by writing them in the form

$$\left(c'' \cdot \frac{R'_{\mathbb{C}}}{R_0} \right) \cdot dR_0 = \gamma, \tag{2.73}$$

then, according to Yakovkin's hypothesis (2.71), we obtain for the determination of x and y the following equations:

$$\left(c'' \frac{R'_{\mathbb{C}}}{R_0} \right) \cdot x + \left(c'' \frac{R'_{\mathbb{C}}}{R_0} \right) \beta_M \cdot y = \gamma. \tag{2.74}$$

The adjustment of equations of the type (2.74) gave for the Dorpat series of Hartwig (Koziel 1949d):

without limb corrections, $y = +0.''027 \pm 0.''027,$

with Hayn's corrections, $y = +0.''040 \pm 0.''014,$

$$\left. \right\} \tag{2.75}$$

and for the Strasbourg series of Hartwig in the rereduction of Koziel:

without limb corrections, $y = +0.''055 \pm 0.''019,$

with Hayn's corrections $y = +0.''042 \pm 0.''013.$

$$\left. \right\} \tag{2.76}$$

The results (2.75) and (2.76), particularly those obtained by taking into account the irregularities of the limb (according to Hayn's charts) seem to confirm Yakovkin's hypothesis. It should, however, be pointed out that they were obtained by using merely a part of the observational material.

Having at our disposal the new method of adjustment of the libration observations (p. 50), we can determine Yakovkin's coefficients x and y from the whole observational material. For this purpose, instead of the unknown dR_0 occurring in the observation equations of the problem (2.63) or (2.70), according to Yakovkin's hypothesis (2.71) we should set

$$dR_0 = x + \beta_M \cdot y.$$

The system (2.63) will then assume the form of the following system of observation equations, with 7 unknowns,

$$\begin{Bmatrix} d\xi \\ d\eta \\ d\zeta \\ dI \\ df \\ x \\ y \end{Bmatrix} \cdot \left[\sec \pi'' \cdot \begin{Bmatrix} -\sin(p-\pi'') \\ -\cos(p-\pi'') \\ 1 \end{Bmatrix} \begin{pmatrix} A & B & C & D & E & 0 & 0 \\ A' & B' & C' & D' & E' & 0 & 0 \\ 0 & 0 & 0 & 0 & 0 & \frac{R'_{\mathbb{C}}}{R_0} & \beta_M \cdot \frac{R'_{\mathbb{C}}}{R_0} \end{pmatrix} \right] =$$
$$= \{s_0 - s_c\}, \tag{2.77}$$

which, in a case where the given observation evening contains more than three measurements of the crater, may be transformed into a corresponding system of observation equations similar to (2.70):

$$
\begin{pmatrix} d\xi \\ d\eta \\ d\zeta \\ dI \\ df \\ x \\ y \end{pmatrix} \cdot \left[\begin{pmatrix} a & 0 & 0 \\ b & b' & 0 \\ c & c' & c'' \end{pmatrix} \begin{pmatrix} A & B & C & D & E & 0 & 0 \\ A' & B' & C' & D' & E' & 0 & 0 \\ 0 & 0 & 0 & 0 & 0 & \dfrac{R'_{\mathbb{C}}}{R_0} & \beta_M \cdot \dfrac{R'_{\mathbb{C}}}{R_0} \end{pmatrix} \right] = \begin{pmatrix} \alpha \\ \beta \\ \gamma \end{pmatrix}. \quad (2.78)
$$

After the adjustment of all the observations of the Dorpat and Strasbourg series of Hartwig by use of (2.78), Koziel (1949d, 1958), obtained:

Dorpat: without limb corrections, $y = -0 \cdot ''018 \pm 0 \cdot ''015,$
      with Hayn's corrections, $y = -0 \cdot ''011 \pm 0 \cdot ''010,$ (2.79)

Strasbourg: without limb corrections, $y = +0 \cdot ''018 \pm 0 \cdot ''013,$
      with Hayn's corrections, $y = +0 \cdot ''018 \pm 0 \cdot ''010.$ (2.80)

The results above show that if the correction to the Moon's radius dR_0 is determined from an adjustment of the whole of the heliometric libration observations then—having to do really with the mean radius of the Moon—we find no longer any enigmatic dependence of this radius on the optical libration in latitude β_M. Apart from the results (2.79) and (2.80), this fact was independently confirmed by Nefediev (1954); and the supposed indications in favour of Yakovkin's hypothesis on the part of another kind of lunar observations, also seem to be uncertain.

XI. Values of the Constants of the Moon's Physical Libration and Conclusion

The preliminary determinations of the constants of the Moon's physical libration carried out in the 19th century have already shown that the constants characterizing the amplitudes of the free libration,— i.e. A, B and C in equations (2.36), (2.47)—are very small and that, therefore, the terms containing the free libration may be neglected at the first stage of the libration research. Thus, from that time on, the investigations aimed first of all at determining—in addition to the constants specifying the position of the observed crater Mösting A—

the fundamental constants of the problem, such as the mechanical ellipticity f of the Moon and the mean inclination I of the Moon's equator to the ecliptic. From the very beginning up to the present time the constant f has been found to be the most troublesome.

Simple theoretical considerations lead to the conclusion that

$$0 < f < 1, \tag{2.81}$$

where the extreme values zero and 1 cannot be attained by f. The values of f obtained in the reductions of libration series in the 19th century were in the neighbourhood of $\frac{1}{2}$. At the beginning of the 20th century, Hayn (1914b) obtained for f values nearer $\frac{3}{4}$. Since then Hayn's values were generally being accepted for the initial value of f in the adjustments of heliometric libration series; thus Yakovkin (1928, 1939, 1945), Belkovich (1936, 1949) and Nefediev (1951) adopted $f = 0 \cdot 75$; Naumann (1939) and Nefediev (1955), $f = 0 \cdot 73$. In his paper on the Moon's libration, completed in 1944, Koziel (1949d) pointed out that Hayn's passage from the value $f = \frac{1}{2}$ to $f = \frac{3}{4}$ over the critical point $f = 0.662$—where according to formula (2.36) the physical libration in longitude τ ceases to be a small quantity—is not quite justifiable from the mathematical point of view. For that reason Koziel (1948a, 1949d) carried out the adjustment of Hartwig's Dorpat series twice: once for the initial value $f = 0 \cdot 73$, and the second time for the value $f = 0 \cdot 50$, thus finally obtaining as result two values for f lying on the two sides of the critical point $0 \cdot 662$. The existence of a double solution for f was stated later also by Belkovich (1952) and Nefediev (1951), and attempts were at once undertaken to find a way of discriminating between these solutions. With this problem were connected also the investigations of Habibullin (1955, 1958) and Schrutka-Rechtenstamm (1955) who indicated independently a way of determining the value of f near the critical point $0 \cdot 662$, where the adjustment of the libration observations offers difficulties on account of the nonlinearity of the problem. Both these astronomers are inclined to accept the value of f near $0 \cdot 6$.

Settlement of the choice between the two solutions for f could also be attempted by examining the effects of the figure of the Moon on the motion of our satellite. However, the investigations of the constants characterizing the system Earth–Moon, as carried out by Jeffreys (1936, 1941) and Spencer Jones (1937), did not so far settle the question in favour of f lying in the proximity of either value. In the computation of I, mostly together with f (e.g. Watts 1955) we do not encounter similar difficulties as in the case of f. The values of I cluster around $I = 1°32'$.

The 19th century determinations of the free libration constants had rather an orientational character. In the 20th century we encountered the first attempt at determining the free libration in longitude, undertaken by Yakovkin (1928) on the basis of the Kazan series by Banachiewicz. Yakovkin's method consisted in an examination of the residuals after the determination of the forced libration constants. Further investigations by Yakovkin (1952) and a recent attempt of Freedland (1959) did not as yet lead to sufficiently satisfying results, owing to difficulties arising from the fact that the periods of the free libration in longitude and of the term with the argument 2ω in the forced libration in longitude have, near the critical point $0\cdot662$, very similar values. Thus, for the time being, we can merely state that, for an observer on the Earth, the amplitude of the free libration in longitude is a quantity of the order of a few tenths of a second of arc.

In conclusion, it is perhaps worth while to quote the resolution, still valid today, taken by the Commission 17 (Motion and Figure of the Moon) of the International Astronomical Union at the VIIth Congress in Zürich (1948): "La Commission est unanime à estimer qu'il serait important d'entreprendre la réduction de l'ensemble des observations relatives à la libration de la lune par une méthode rigoureuse."

References

Atkinson, R. d'E. (1951). *Mon. Not. R. Astr. Soc.* **111**, 448.

Banachiewicz, T. (1927). *Circ. Obs. Cracovie*, **25**.

Banachiewicz, T. (1929a). *Bull. Acad. Polon. Sci. Sér.* **A 1**; *Cracow Repr.* **2**.

Banachiewicz, T. (1929b). *Acta Astr. Cracoviae*, c, **1**, 127.

Banachiewicz, T. (1938). *Bull. Acad. Polon. Sci. Sér.* **A 402**.

Banachiewicz, T. (1940). Scientific Meeting, Cracow Observatory, August 16th, 1940.

Belkovich, I. V. (1936). *Bull. Engelhardt Obs.* **10**.

Belkovich, I. V. (1949). *Izv. Obs. Engelhardt*, **24**.

Belkovich, I. V. (1952). *Trans. I.A.U.* **8**, 221, 224.

Bessel, F. W. (1839). *Astr. Nachr.* **16**, 257.

Brown, E. W. (1919). "Tables of the Motion of the Moon". New Haven.

Chandon, E. (1941). *C. R. Acad. Sci., Paris*, **212**, 1026.

Franz, J. (1889). *Astr. Beob. Königsberg*, **38**.

Freedland, M. V. (1959). *Bull. Inst. Theor. Astr., Leningrad*, **7**, 293.

Habibullin, S. T. (1955). *Bull. Inst. Theor. Astr., Leningrad*, **6**, 255.

Habibullin, S. T. (1958). *Izv. Obs. Engelhardt*, **31**,

Hansen, P. A. (1857). "Tables de la Lune". London.

Hartwig, E. (1880). "Beitrag zur Bestimmung der Physischen Libration des Mondes". Karlsruhe.

Hayn, F. (1902). *Abh. Sächs. Ges. Wiss.* **27**, 861; (1914a) *ibid.* **33**, 1.

Hayn, F. (1914b). *Astr. Nachr.* **199**, 261; (1920) *ibid.* **211**, 311.

Hayn, F. (1923). *Encykl. Math. Wiss.* **6**, 2, 20a, 1020.

Jeffreys, H. (1936). *Mon. Not. R. Astr. Soc.* **97**, 3; (1941) *ibid.* **101**, 34.

Jones, H. Spencer. (1937). *Mon. Not. R. Astr. Soc.* **97**, 406.

Jönsson, A. (1917). *Medd. Lunds Astr. Obs.* II, **15**.

Koziel, K. (1948a). *Acta Astr. Cracoviae*, a, **4**, 61; (1948b) *ibid.* **4**, 83; (1948c) *ibid.* **4**, 99.

Koziel, K. (1949a). *Bull. Acad. Polon. Sci. Sér.* A, **1**.

Koziel, K. (1949b). *Acta. Astr. Cracoviae*, a, **4**, 141; (1949c) *ibid.* **4**, 153; (1949d) *ibid.* **4**, 179; (1957) *ibid.* **7**, 228.

Koziel, K. (1958). Draft Reports I.A.U., Cambridge, 144.

Lagrange, J. L. (1780). *Mém. Acad. Berlin.*

Laplace, P. S. (1798). "Traité de Mécanique Céleste", Vol. 2. Paris.

Naumann, H, (1939). *Abh. Sächs. Akad. Wiss.* **43**, 1.

Nefediev, A. A. (1951). *Izv. Obs. Engelhardt*, **26**. (1955). *ibid.* **29**.

Nefediev, A. A. (1954). *Astr. Circ., Kazan*, **147**, 13.

Puiseux, M. (1925). *Ann. Obs. Paris, Mém.* **32**.

Schrutka-Rechtenstamm, G. (1955). *S.B. Öst. Akad. Wiss.* **164**, 323.

Stratton, F. J. M. (1909). *Mem. R. Astr. Soc.* **59**, Pt. IV.

Trans. I.A.U. (1948), **7**, 63.

Watts, C. B. (1955). *Astr. J.* **60**, 443.

Weimer, Th. (1949). *C.R. Acad. Sci., Paris*, **229**, 105.

Weimer, Th. (1952). "Atlas de profils lunaires". Observatoire de Paris.

Wichmann, M. (1846). *Astr. Nachr.* **26**, 289; (1847) *ibid.* **27**, 53, 81, 97, 211.

Yakovkin, A. A. (1928). *Publ. Obs. Engelhardt*, **13**; (1939) *ibid.* **21**; (1945) *ibid.* **23**.

Yakovkin, A. A. (1934). *Bull. Engelhardt Obs. Kazan*, **4**.

Yakovkin, A. A. (1952a). *Trans. I.A.U.* **8**, 231; (1952b) *ibid.* **8**, 229.

CHAPTER 3

Dynamics of the Earth-Moon System

GORDON W. GROVES

I. Introduction.. 61
II. Kinematical and Dynamical Relationships.......................... 63
III. Tidal Deformation... 70
IV. Rotation of the Earth.. 76
V. Secular Variation: the Evidence................................... 80
VI. The Tidal Couple.. 88
VII. Inclination and Eccentricity...................................... 92
References.. 96

I. Introduction

One might consider the dynamics of the Earth-Moon system in four stages: (1) The Earth and Moon (and Sun and planets) are taken as point masses. This is usually referred to as the "gravitational" theory, but of course the subsequent refinements are also based on Newton's universal law of gravitation. (2) The finite size of Earth and Moon is considered, but these are taken as rigid bodies. (3) Non-dissipative tidal deformation is considered, and finally (4) dissipation is considered.

The "point-mass" or "gravitational" theory comes remarkably close to characterizing the Moon's motion precisely enough for practical astronomy except for precession and nutation. According to this theory, there is no true secular variation in the eccentricity or inclination of the Moon's orbit, nor in its mean distance. (Long-period variations may be considered as secular over a relatively short time-span—for example, the "secular" acceleration in the Moon's mean longitude arising from long-period variation in the eccentricity of the Earth's orbit). This is a result worthwhile to keep in mind while considering the effects of further generalizations of the theory.

Finite size not only complicates the motion of the centres of mass of the Earth and Moon but also introduces new phenomena to study: motion (rotation) relative to their centres of mass. Insofar as the bodies do not depart from rigid, spherically-symmetrical mass distributions, there is no additional effect on motion of the centres of mass, and the angular velocities remain constant. Earth's largest departure from spherical symmetry is related to its equatorial bulge, upon which the Moon's (and Sun's) gravity exerts a torque. This gives rise to an irregular westward movement of the pole of the Earth's rotation about the pole of the ecliptic. This motion is considered as consisting of two components: the *precession*, manifested by a uniform westward motion of the equinoxes, making a complete revolution in about 26,000 years, in which the obliquity of the Earth's equatorial plane to the ecliptic is taken to be constant; and the *nutation*, consisting of a series of small periodic terms in both the obliquity and the longitude (relative to a fixed point) of the equinoxes, superimposed on the steady precession. The positions of celestial bodies are observed relative to the Earth's fluctuating instantaneous axis of rotation. When the Moon's position is referred to a coordinate system based on this axis, terms representing precession and nutation are necessarily included, although these do not represent "true" motion relative to an inertial system. The torque exerted by the Earth on the aspherical distribution of mass within the Moon causes the libration (see Chapter 2).

If the rigidity assumption is discarded, the resulting modification of the motion seems to depend critically on the details of the deformation. In Munk and MacDonald's (1960) recent discussion of the Earth's rotation, selection of the appropriate form of stress-strain relationship plays a central role. The effect on the Earth's material of small stress increments (to the high hydrostatic pressure) acting over long periods of time is of utmost interest. But this effect is very difficult to evaluate, either theoretically or by laboratory studies on rocks. Studies of the motion of Earth and Moon have taught us more about the properties of the Earth's materials than vice versa, and this state of affairs is likely to continue for some time.

In the Earth-Moon system's present configuration, tidal dissipation of energy within the Earth slows its rotation and increases the Moon's distance and period of revolution. The effect was first observed by Halley in 1695 as an acceleration in the Moon's longitude as referred to Universal Time (based on the Earth's rotation). A historical account is given in Chapter 1. Tidal friction is also responsible for a secular variation in the eccentricity and inclination of the Moon's orbit and in the obliquity of the Earth's rotation, but these effects are too small to have been observed during historical time. Near the end of the 19th century G. H. Darwin published a remarkable series of theoretical papers attempting to evaluate these secular effects taking the Earth as a viscous fluid. He then proposed a theory of the evolution of the Earth-Moon system since its origin. No one has yet been able to repeat Darwin's study under less restrictive assumptions. Tidal effects on the motion of the Moon's node and perigee are drowned out by several orders of magnitude by the large solar perturbations.

As for precession and nutation, the equatorial bulge, of course, over-shadows the tidal effect.

It should be emphasized that the tidal effects on the length of day, length of month, eccentricity, inclination and obliquity are probably the only true secular effects. It does not matter that the variation is slow—the effect will be important after enough time has elapsed. The problem is very pertinent to the question of the initial (and final) state of the solar system.

II. Kinematical and Dynamical Relationships

The Moon's position is conveniently referred to the same coordinate system as used in Chapter 1: the fixed ecliptic as of a certain epoch is taken as the xy plane, with the positive z direction towards the north. The positive x axis points toward the fixed mean equinox of the same epoch, with the positive y axis pointing 90° to the east. The origin is at the Earth's centre of mass, and so although this system is non-rotating it is not inertial. Specification of the Earth's orientation in space is more complicated. Let x', y', z' be a right-handed coordinate system imbedded, in some way, within the Earth, with the origin taken at the centre of mass. In the relationships that follow it makes no difference how the x', y', z' axes are imbedded in the Earth or how they move relative to the Earth, or whether the Earth is deformable or rigid. For the time being we are interested only in the relations linking the two coordinate systems. The x', y', z' system has three degrees of freedom relative to the x, y, z system, since their origins coincide. The three parameters needed to specify the orientation are usually taken to be the Eulerian angles ϵ, ϑ, ψ; evidently there is no uniformity in the literature in the way these are reckoned, but here we shall follow Condon (1958) with a slight change of symbols.

Let $\mathbf{i}$, $\mathbf{j}$, $\mathbf{k}$ and $\mathbf{i}'$, $\mathbf{j}'$, $\mathbf{k}'$ be unit vectors in the x, y, z and the x', y', z' systems, respectively. Then ϵ is the angle between $\mathbf{k}$ and $\mathbf{k}'$, so that $\cos \epsilon = \mathbf{k} \cdot \mathbf{k}'$. The xy and $x'y'$ planes intersect in a line known as the *line of nodes;* the vector $\mathbf{k} \times \mathbf{k}'$ lies in this line and determines a positive sense along it. The angle ϑ is reckoned from $\mathbf{i}$ to $\mathbf{k} \times \mathbf{k}'$ in the direction toward $\mathbf{j}$. Thus ϵ and ϑ fix the orientation of the z' axis and it only remains to specify the amount of rotation about this axis. Finally ψ is the angle between $\mathbf{k} \times \mathbf{k}'$ and $\mathbf{i}'$ according to the relations $\mathbf{i}' \cdot (\mathbf{k} \times \mathbf{k}')$ $= \sin \epsilon \cos \psi$, $\mathbf{j}' \cdot (\mathbf{k} \times \mathbf{k}') = -\sin \epsilon \sin \psi$. Later we shall associate ϵ with the obliquity of the Earth's rotation, ϑ with the longitude of the true equinox of date and ψ with sidereal time. If a vector is expressed relative to one coordinate system and we wish to find its components in the other, the nine scalar products between the unit vectors in each system are needed. In terms of the Eulerian angles, these are

$$
\left.
\begin{aligned}
\alpha_1 &= \mathbf{i}\cdot\mathbf{i}' = \cos\vartheta\,\cos\psi - \sin\vartheta\,\sin\psi\,\cos\epsilon \\
\alpha_2 &= \mathbf{i}\cdot\mathbf{j}' = -\cos\vartheta\,\sin\psi - \sin\vartheta\,\cos\psi\,\cos\epsilon \\
\alpha_3 &= \mathbf{i}\cdot\mathbf{k}' = \sin\epsilon\,\sin\vartheta \\
\beta_1 &= \mathbf{j}\cdot\mathbf{i}' = \sin\vartheta\,\cos\psi + \cos\vartheta\,\sin\psi\,\cos\epsilon \\
\beta_2 &= \mathbf{j}\cdot\mathbf{j}' = -\sin\vartheta\,\sin\psi + \cos\vartheta\,\cos\psi\,\cos\epsilon \\
\beta_3 &= \mathbf{j}\cdot\mathbf{k}' = -\sin\epsilon\,\cos\vartheta \\
\gamma_1 &= \mathbf{k}\cdot\mathbf{i}' = \sin\epsilon\,\sin\psi \\
\gamma_2 &= \mathbf{k}\cdot\mathbf{j}' = \sin\epsilon\,\cos\psi \\
\gamma_3 &= \mathbf{k}\cdot\mathbf{k}' = \cos\epsilon
\end{aligned}
\right\} \quad (1)
$$

The matrix

$$
\mathscr{G} = \left\|
\begin{array}{ccc}
\alpha_1 & \alpha_2 & \alpha_3 \\
\beta_1 & \beta_2 & \beta_2 \\
\gamma_1 & \gamma_2 & \gamma_3
\end{array}
\right\|
$$

is called the *rotation dyadic*.

Motion of the x', y', z' system relative to the x, y, z axes can be specified by the instantaneous angular velocity $\boldsymbol{\omega}(t)$. Since the rate of change of the Eulerian angles also specifies the relative motion, it is clear that the two representations of the rotation are equivalent. The components of $\boldsymbol{\omega}$ in the two coordinate systems are given by

$$
\begin{aligned}
\omega_1 &= \dot\epsilon\,\cos\vartheta + \dot\psi\,\sin\epsilon\,\sin\vartheta & \omega'_1 &= \dot\epsilon\,\cos\psi + \dot\vartheta\,\sin\epsilon\,\sin\psi \\
\omega_2 &= \dot\epsilon\,\sin\vartheta - \dot\psi\,\sin\epsilon\,\cos\vartheta & \omega'_2 &= -\dot\epsilon\,\sin\psi + \dot\vartheta\,\sin\epsilon\,\cos\psi \quad (2) \\
\omega_3 &= \dot\vartheta + \dot\psi\,\cos\epsilon & \omega'_3 &= \dot\psi + \dot\vartheta\,\cos\epsilon
\end{aligned}
$$

in terms of the Eulerian angles. Here the primed and unprimed quantities are components in the x', y', z' and the x, y, z systems, respectively; thus $\omega_1 = \boldsymbol{\omega}\cdot\mathbf{i}$, $\omega_1' = \boldsymbol{\omega}\cdot\mathbf{i}'$, etc.

It is now necessary to relate the Moon's position to events on the Earth. If r is the Moon's distance from the centre of the Earth, β and λ the Moon's celestial latitude and longitude at any instant in the non-rotating system, then

$$x = r \cos \beta \cos \lambda$$
$$y = r \cos \beta \sin \lambda \qquad\qquad (3)$$
$$z = r \sin \beta$$

are the Moon's rectangular coordinates. The trouble is that β and λ are not the coordinates that are directly observed. The Moon's latitude is usually referred to the true ecliptic of date and its longitude to the true equinox of date. These reference points differ from the fixed ones owing to planetary perturbations of the Earth's orbit and to the precession and nutation. If not too much accuracy is required a great simplification is obtained by neglecting the movement of the ecliptic and the nutational terms. The obliquity ϵ' is then constant and the maximum error incurred over a short period of time (few thousands of years) will be about $10''$. If λ' is longitude reckoned from the mean equinox of date (by assumption there is now no distinction between mean and true), then

$$\lambda = \lambda' - \sigma \, (t - t_0), \ \ \sigma > 0,$$

where the period of precession is $2\pi/\sigma$ and t_0 is the time chosen for the epoch. Let α be the right ascension, measured eastward from the mean equinox of date along the celestial equator, and let δ be the declination. The relation between the two sets of coordinates is

$$\sin \beta = \sin \delta \sin \epsilon' - \cos \delta \sin \epsilon' \sin \alpha$$
$$\cos \beta \cos \lambda' = \cos \delta \cos \alpha \qquad\qquad (4a)$$
$$\cos \beta \sin \lambda' = \sin \delta \sin \epsilon' + \cos \delta \cos \epsilon' \sin \alpha$$

or

$$\sin \delta = \sin \beta \cos \epsilon' + \cos \beta \sin \epsilon' \sin \lambda'$$
$$\cos \delta \cos \alpha = \cos \beta \cos \lambda' \qquad\qquad (4b)$$
$$\cos \delta \sin \alpha = -\sin \beta \sin \epsilon' + \cos \beta \cos \epsilon' \sin \lambda'$$

(Smart, 1956, p. 40). Any point α, δ on the celestial sphere is over a definite point on the Earth at any given instant of time. Let θ, ϕ be the colatitude and east longitude, respectively, of that point on the Earth. The relationship is

$$\alpha = \phi + t + h - \pi, \ \ \theta + \delta = \frac{\pi}{2} \qquad\qquad (5)$$

provided that we neglect the oblateness of the Earth. Here t is Greenwich mean time expressed as angle, and h is the mean longitude

F

(λ') of the Sun. The foregoing relationships allow one to transform from coordinates β, λ to θ, ϕ as a function of time (see Clemence, 1958, for a description of the frames of reference used). If ω coincides with the z' axis and the meridian $\phi = 0$ is taken to coincide with the x' axis, then

$$\left.\begin{aligned}
\epsilon &= \epsilon' \\
\vartheta &= \lambda - \lambda' \\
\psi &= t + h - \pi
\end{aligned}\right\} \tag{6}$$

(Smart, 1956, p. 41–44).

The equations of motion of the Earth about its centre of mass are

$$\mathbf{L} = \dot{\mathbf{H}}, \tag{7}$$

where the angular momentum $\mathbf{H}(t)$ and the torque $\mathbf{L}(t)$ are as usually defined. It is convenient to consider the angular momentum as composed of two parts: that due to the motion of the x', y', z' axes relative to the x, y, z system, and that due to motion relative to the x', y', z' system. Thus

$$\mathbf{H} = \mathbf{\Phi} \cdot \mathbf{\omega} + \mathbf{h}, \tag{8}$$

where $\mathbf{\Phi}$ is the *tensor of inertia* of the Earth, equal to

$$\int (r^2 \mathbf{I} - \mathbf{r}\mathbf{r}) \rho \, dv; \tag{9}$$

the integral being taken over the volume we wish to consider as the Earth. $\mathbf{I}$ is the unit tensor and $\mathbf{r}$ the position vector from the origin. The tensor of inertia is properly called a *dyadic*, and its operation upon a vector, such as in (8), produces another vector (for example, see Morse and Feshbach, 1953, Vol. 1, Section 1.6). When the nine components of the dyadic, relative to some coordinate system, are written as a matrix, and the three components of the vector in the same system are written as a column matrix, the components of the resulting product are given by ordinary matrix multiplication. When the dyadic is written as the sum of pairs of vectors in juxtaposition, as in (9), its operation upon a vector is carried out according to the associative law in the following manner:

$$\mathbf{(ab + cd)e} = \mathbf{a(b \cdot e)} + \mathbf{c(d \cdot e)}.$$

The contribution of relative motion to the angular momentum is

$$\mathbf{h} = \int \mathbf{r} \times \mathbf{u} \rho \, dv, \tag{10}$$

where **u** is velocity relative to the x', y', z' axes

$$\mathbf{i}'\,\frac{dx'}{dt} + \mathbf{j}'\,\frac{dy'}{dt} + \mathbf{k}'\,\frac{dz'}{dt}$$

following the motion of a particle. We shall refer to the components of $\mathbf{\Phi}$ in the x', y', z' system as the *moments* and *products* of inertia. Thus the three moments of inertia are

$$A = \Phi'_{11} = \int (y'^2 + z'^2)\rho dv \qquad B = \Phi'_{22} = \int (z'^2 + x'^2)\rho dv \quad \Big\}$$
$$C = \Phi'_{33} = \int (x'^2 + y'^2)\rho dv, \qquad\qquad\qquad (11a)$$

and the products of inertia are

$$F = -\Phi'_{23} = -\Phi'_{32} = \int y'z'\rho dv \qquad G = -\Phi'_{13} = -\Phi'_{31} = \int z'x'\rho dv$$
$$H = -\Phi'_{12} = -\Phi'_{21} = \int x'y'\rho dv. \qquad\qquad (11b)$$

One can obtain the components of $\mathbf{\Phi}$ in the non-rotating system by premultiplying the rotating components by $\mathscr{G}$ and postmultiplying by $\mathscr{G}^*$ (the transpose): thus

$$\begin{Vmatrix} \Phi_{11} & \Phi_{12} & \Phi_{13} \\ \Phi_{21} & \Phi_{22} & \Phi_{23} \\ \Phi_{31} & \Phi_{32} & \Phi_{33} \end{Vmatrix} = \begin{Vmatrix} \alpha_1 & \alpha_2 & \alpha_3 \\ \beta_1 & \beta_2 & \beta_3 \\ \gamma_1 & \gamma_2 & \gamma_3 \end{Vmatrix} \cdot \begin{Vmatrix} A & -H & -G \\ -H & B & -F \\ -G & -F & C \end{Vmatrix} \cdot \begin{Vmatrix} \alpha_1 & \beta_1 & \gamma_1 \\ \alpha_2 & \beta_2 & \gamma_2 \\ \alpha_3 & \beta_3 & \gamma_3 \end{Vmatrix}. \qquad (12)$$

Equations (7), (8) and (10) can be used to study the effect of shifts of mass, winds and ocean currents on the Earth's rotation, as well as the Moon's effect. Here we shall consider only the latter, and therefore include the entire Earth, ocean and atmosphere in the integrals defining $\mathbf{\Phi}$ and $\mathbf{h}$.

Considering now the Moon as a point mass, its equations of motion can be written

$$\ddot{\mathbf{r}} + \frac{\mu \mathbf{r}}{r^3} = \nabla R, \qquad\qquad (13)$$

where $\mathbf{r}$ represents the position of the Moon's centre of mass, and

$$\mu = \gamma(m_0 + m);$$

m and m_0 being the masses of Moon and Earth, respectively, and γ the gravitational constant $(M^{-1}L^3T^{-2})$. The Sun, planets, and all mass in the universe contribute to the disturbing function $R(x, y, z, t)$, but here we shall consider only the effect of the mass distribution within the Earth. The potential of this mass distribution, for an exterior point **r**, is

$$\Psi = -\gamma \int \frac{\rho\, dv}{\Delta}$$

$$= -\frac{\gamma m_0}{r} + \frac{\gamma}{r^3}\left[\frac{3}{2r^2}\mathbf{r}\cdot\boldsymbol{\Phi}\cdot\mathbf{r} - \frac{1}{2}Tr\,\boldsymbol{\Phi}\right] + O\left(\frac{1}{r^4}\right),$$

(14)

Δ being the distance from the variable point inside the Earth to **r**. $Tr\,\boldsymbol{\Phi}$ designates the *trace* of the tensor of inertia, equal to

$$\Phi_{11} + \Phi_{22} + \Phi_{33} = A + B + C$$

owing to its invariance property under a rigid transformation of axes. For a point as distant as the Moon we neglect terms of order r^{-4}. The disturbing function is then

$$R = -\frac{m_0 + m}{m_0}\left(\Psi + \frac{\gamma m_0}{r}\right) = -\frac{\mu}{m_0}\frac{1}{r^3}\left[\frac{3}{2r^2}\mathbf{r}\cdot\boldsymbol{\Phi}\cdot\mathbf{r} - \frac{1}{2}Tr\,\boldsymbol{\Phi}\right]. \quad (15)$$

The gradient of R can be written as

$$\nabla R = \frac{\mu}{m_0}\left[r^{-7}\mathbf{r}\left(\frac{15}{2}\mathbf{r}\cdot\boldsymbol{\Phi}\cdot\mathbf{r} - \frac{3}{2}r^2 Tr\,\boldsymbol{\Phi}\right) - 3r^{-5}\boldsymbol{\Phi}\cdot\mathbf{r}\right]. \quad (16)$$

The reaction of this disturbing force on the Moon is a torque on the Earth about its centre of mass, equal to

$$\mathbf{L} = m\mathbf{r} \times \nabla\Psi = 3\gamma m r^{-5}\mathbf{r} \times \boldsymbol{\Phi}\cdot\mathbf{r}. \quad (17)$$

Equations (7), (8) and (17) express the Moon's disturbing effect on the Earth's rotation, and equations (13) and (15) express the Earth's disturbing effect on the Moon's motion. The components of these equations in either coordinate system can be written readily, but one should be careful when determining the components in the rotating system that the time derivatives take into account the rate of change of the variable unit vectors $\mathbf{i}'$, $\mathbf{j}'$, $\mathbf{k}'$. For example, the components of (7) relative to the rotating axes are

$$L_1' = \dot{H}_1' + \omega_2' H_3' - \omega_3' H_2',$$
$$L_2' = \dot{H}_2' + \omega_3' H_1' - \omega_1' H_3',$$
$$L_3' = \dot{H}_3' + \omega_1' H_2' - \omega_2' H_1'.$$

$$\left.\begin{array}{r}\\ \\ \\ \end{array}\right\} (18)$$

The instantaneous angular velocity $\boldsymbol{\omega}$ has not yet been related to the rotation of the Earth, and in fact relates only the motion of the x', y', z' to the x, y, z axes. This motion is completely arbitrary. The only restriction is that at every instant the x', y', z' axes must be obtainable from the x, y, z axes by a rigid rotation. For example, the x', y', z' system could oscillate with respect to the x, y, z system as a torsion pendulum with respect to its base.

After the x', y', z' axes are fixed in the Earth the Eulerian angles and angular velocity $\boldsymbol{\omega}$ will give the orientation of the Earth and its axis of rotation. Three representations are generally of interest: (1) the position of $\boldsymbol{\omega}$ relative to the Earth, (2) the position of $\boldsymbol{\omega}$ in space, and (3) the orientation of the Earth in space. The three representations are related by the kinematical relationships (2).

We can now treat some specific examples. Let us consider first a rigid Earth. In this case $\mathbf{h}$ is zero identically if the x', y', z' axes are fixed to the Earth's material. Also, the moments and products of inertia are constants. The Earth's motion can be expressed by combining (7), (8) and (17) to obtain

$$3\gamma mr^{-5}\mathbf{r}\times\boldsymbol{\Phi}\cdot\mathbf{r} = \boldsymbol{\Phi}\cdot\dot{\boldsymbol{\omega}}+\dot{\boldsymbol{\Phi}}\cdot\boldsymbol{\omega} \tag{19}$$

whose x' component, for example, is

$$3\gamma mr^{-5}[x'(z'H-y'G)+F(z'^2-y'^2)+y'z'(C-B)]$$
$$= \omega_1'(\omega_3'H-\omega_2'G)+F(\omega_3'^2-\omega_2'^2)+\omega_2'\omega_3'(C-B)+A\dot{\omega}_1'-H\dot{\omega}_2'-G\dot{\omega}_3'$$

The equations (2), (13), (15) and (19) could, in theory, be solved simultaneously yielding a complete specification of the positions of Earth and Moon for all time (neglecting other perturbations). But it is more practical to attack the problem by successive approximations. The Moon's position is first obtained by solving (13) using methods outlined in Chapter 1, neglecting the Earth's contribution (15) to the disturbing function. Then with $\mathbf{r}(t)$ known the equations (19) are solved for ω_1', ω_2', ω_3', and the differential relations (2) determine the components ω_1, ω_2, ω_3. Finally the disturbing function of the Earth's mass distribution can be evaluated as a function of the x, y, z coordinates by means of (15) to calculate the correction to the Moon's motion. Observations are used at each step to evaluate, or refine, the values of the fundamental quantities such as the Earth's moments of inertia, etc. Here, when discussing the Earth's motion we shall assume that the Moon's motion is adequately known, and vice versa.

This rigid-Earth idealization already contains the effects of precession and nutation. To take tidal deformation of the Earth into account, the way in which the x', y', z' axes are imbedded in the Earth must be specified. There are several possibilities, each offering its own peculiar simplifications. (1) The mean axes of the Earth are defined so that **h** is always zero. (2) The principal axes of the Earth are defined so that the products of inertia F, G, H are zero. In view of winds, ocean currents, fluid motion of the core, tidal deformation of the entire Earth, and possible convective motion of the mantle, polar wandering and continent drift, it is evident that, for both (1) and (2), the Earth's rotation as measured at the observatories fixed to the Earth's crust will not coincide with the rotation of the x', y', z' axes. We shall, therefore, follow Munk and MacDonald (1960) and use the "geographic axes" (3), fixed to the Earth's mean crust, the z' axis near the mean direction of the North Pole, the x' axis toward the present position of Greenwich and the y' axis 90° east of Greenwich.

The moments and products of inertia are then no longer constant, and **h** no longer vanishes. If the variation of $\boldsymbol{\Phi}$ can be postulated, obtained from tidal theory or observation, then the disturbing function (15) can be determined and the effect on the Moon's motion evaluated. Also, the torque on the Earth can be determined from (17) and the angular momentum from (7). In order to go from the angular momentum to the angular velocity, as determined by the observatories on the Earth's crust, **h** as well as $\boldsymbol{\Phi}$ must be known. The effect of **h** is not important in the case of a large change in the Earth's rotation related to a slow secular effect acting over a long period of time. But we need to evaluate the tidal effect on $\boldsymbol{\Phi}$ in order to solve any of these problems.

III. Tidal Deformation

The Moon's gravitational potential acting on the Earth is conveniently thought of as the sum of two terms: (1) a term

$$\Psi_c = -\gamma m r_m^{-3}\mathbf{r}\cdot\mathbf{r}_m,$$

whose gradient is constant at any given instant and equal to the (negative of the) Moon's actual gravitational acceleration at the Earth's centre of mass, and (2) the tide-generating potential. Here $\mathbf{r}_m$ designates the Moon's position. The constant Ψ_c exerts no stress on any part of the Earth; the deformation arises from the tide-generating potential

$$\Psi_T = -\frac{\gamma m}{r_m}\left\{\left[-\frac{1}{2}\left(\frac{r}{r_m}\right)^2 + \frac{3}{2}\frac{(\mathbf{r}\cdot\mathbf{r}_m)^2}{r_m^4}\right]\right.$$
$$\left. + \left[-\frac{3}{2}\frac{r^2(\mathbf{r}\cdot\mathbf{r}_m)}{r_m^4} + \frac{5}{2}\frac{(\mathbf{r}\cdot\mathbf{r}_m)^3}{r_m^6}\right] + O\left[\left(\frac{r}{r_m}\right)^4\right]\right\}. \tag{20}$$

Equation (20) is a series of spherical harmonics: the first bracket is a second-degree harmonic and is of order $(r/r_m)^2$ and the second bracket is a third-degree harmonic and is of order $(r/r_m)^3$. In all subsequent developments we shall neglect all but the second-degree term, since (r/r_m) is a small number in the vicinity of the Earth. However, this second-degree term exerts no net force on the Earth, regardless of the mass distribution, although it does exert a torque. To evaluate the tidal perturbation to the Moon's net force on the Earth it is necessary to consider the third-harmonic term.

For practical work on tides it is expedient to express the tide-generating potential as a series of harmonic terms. Each term is a solid spherical harmonic (of second degree) which rotates with constant speed about the Earth's axis. The fact that the tide-generating potential is expressible in this fashion has greatly simplified the study of tides—to compute the tide-generating potential for any point at any instant it is only necessary to have a table of the frequency, epoch and coefficient of each term. Evaluation of these constants is very laborious, owing to the complexity of the motion of Earth, Moon and Sun. For a full discussion of the harmonic development of the tide the reader is referred to Doodson (1921) or Schureman (1941). The resultant series can be expressed in the form

$$-\tfrac{1}{2}U\frac{gr^2}{a}[\tfrac{1}{2}(1-3\cos^2\theta)\sum_0 C_i \cos A_i + \sin2\theta\sum_1 C_i \cos(A_i+\phi)$$
$$+\sin^2\theta\sum_2 C_i \cos(A_i+2\phi)], \tag{21}$$

where θ and ϕ are the geographic coordinates, a is the Earth's mean radius, c^{-1} is the mean inverse distance of Moon,

$$U = \frac{3}{2}\frac{m}{m_0}\frac{a^3}{c^3}$$

is a dimensionless constant whose present value is 0.843×10^{-7}, C_i are *constituent coefficients* and the A_i are linear combinations of the six parameters,

$\tau_0 = t-s+h$: Greenwich mean lunar time reduced to angle

s: Moon's mean longitude

h: Sun's mean longitude

p: mean longitude of Moon's perigee,

N': negative of mean longitude of Moon's ascending node

p_1: mean longitude of Sun's perigee,

all increasing (almost exactly) linearly with time, where t is Greenwich mean solar time reduced to angle. The longitudes are reckoned from the mean equinox of date. The subscripts "0", "1" and "2" refer to summation over the long-period, the diurnal and the semidiurnal constituents, respectively. The values of the C_i depend on the Moon's motion. Their values corresponding to the Moon's present actual motion are given by Doodson (1921).[†]

Every term in (21) is a second-degree disturbing potential acting on the Earth, whose response may be considered as the linear sum of the individual responses to each term. If the Earth were composed of homogeneous spherical shells the problem of the Earth's response would be simpler. The presence of irregular ocean basins complicates the problem, and also makes it more interesting. Still the idealization of a stratified Earth is probably adequate for the Earth's body. In this case it can be proved that a disturbing potential of the nth degree will produce a response, at any height or depth within the Earth, of a surface spherical harmonic of the nth degree. Also, disturbing potentials of the same degree will cause responses proportional to their magnitudes. At points exterior to the Earth's mass, the potential of the deformed Earth will be a solid harmonic of the nth degree. For relatively high frequencies, such as the tides, the Earth's body behaves essentially as an elastic solid. The response is instantaneous and can be represented by the appropriate Love numbers. The numbers h_2 and k_2 are defined so that

$$- \frac{h_2 \Psi_T}{g}$$

represents the final amount by which the Earth's surface is lifted, and

$$k_2 \left(\frac{a}{r} \right)^5 \Psi_T \tag{22}$$

is the resulting increment in the potential for exterior points. These Love numbers take into account the effect of deformation of the Earth's body, only. The subscripts "2" refer to the second degree, being that of the tide-generating potential. The Love numbers can be determined, theoretically, from any model of the Earth in which the properties are postulated as a function of distance from centre.

The increment to the Earth's tensor of inertia arising from elastic deformation due to the tide-generating potential can be found. At any given distant point of space the expression (22) must be equal

---

[†]It should be kept in mind that if (21) expresses the tide-generating potential the arguments of Doodson's schedule 1 must be reduced by $\pi/2$, since his arguments of the first species are to be used with sines, not cosines.

to the increment of (14) arising from a change $\Delta\boldsymbol{\Phi}$. Also, $Tr\,\boldsymbol{\Phi}$ is invariant for a spherically symmetrical Earth suffering a small deformation due to a tidal potential of degree $n \neq 0$. Thus

$$\Delta\Phi_{11} + \Delta\Phi_{22} + \Delta\Phi_{33} = 0.$$

We thus obtain

$$\left.\begin{aligned}
\Delta\Phi_{11} &= -k_2 m(a/r)^5(x^2 - \tfrac{1}{3}r^2) \\
\Delta\Phi_{22} &= -k_2 m(a/r)^5(y^2 - \tfrac{1}{3}r^2) \\
\Delta\Phi_{33} &= -k_2 m(a/r)^5(z^2 - \tfrac{1}{3}r^2) \\
\Delta\Phi_{12} &= -k_2 m(a/r)^5 xy \\
\Delta\Phi_{13} &= -k_2 m(a/r)^5 xz \\
\Delta\Phi_{23} &= -k_2 m(a/r)^5 yz
\end{aligned}\right\} \qquad (23)$$

which actually defines the Love number k_2 in terms of $\Delta\boldsymbol{\Phi}$ directly instead of the resulting exterior potential. Here x, y, z, r refer to the position of the Moon. Either coordinate system could have been used, and so we may replace the coordinates and $\Delta\boldsymbol{\Phi}$ by their primed counterparts and obtain expressions for the increment in the moments and products of inertia in terms of the Moon's position relative to the geographic axes.

For prolonged stresses the Earth's body suffers plastic deformation and the principles of statics cannot be used. Indeed, even for frequencies as high as the tide the small departure from an elastic response may give rise to important effects, as concern the motion of the Earth-Moon system. Munk and MacDonald (1960) have introduced the concept of *Love operators* as a convenient way of summarizing the plastic properties of the Earth's body as a whole. The Earth's response is then properly characterized as depending on the frequency of the disturbing potential, and dissipation of energy is allowed.

In addition to the tide-generating potential, the varying thickness of water in the oceans contributes to the deformation and exterior potential. This ocean tide exerts direct pressure on the Earth's body, because of the varying weight of water, as well as a new disturbing potential arising from its own gravitational attraction. In the previous case, the tide-generating potential did not "load" the Earth. It is convenient to define another set of Love numbers for a disturbance which does load the Earth. For a gravitating load q_n (ML^{-2}) having the form of an nth degree surface harmonic its exterior potential would be

$$\Psi_n = -\frac{4\pi\gamma a}{2n+1}\left(\frac{a}{r}\right)^{n+1} q_n$$

on a rigid Earth. Let h_n' and k_n' be defined so that

$$-\frac{h_n'\Psi_n}{g} = \frac{h_n'}{g}\frac{4\pi\gamma a}{2n+1}\left(\frac{a}{r}\right)^{n+1}q_n$$

represents the final amount by which the surface of the Earth's body is lifted, and

$$(1+k_n')\Psi_n = -(1+k_n')\frac{4\pi\gamma a}{2n+1}\left(\frac{a}{r}\right)^{n+1}q_n$$

is the total resulting potential for exterior points. It is evident that a zero degree surface load would violate conservation of Earth's mass, while a first degree surface load would shift the Earth's centroid from the origin. Harmonics of higher degree die off rapidly and can be neglected at distances as great as the Moon. We shall therefore consider only the second degree harmonic. Let $\zeta(\theta, \phi, t)$ be the actual tidal height as observed in the ocean, defined as the departure from the mean (in time) of the distance from sea surface to sea bottom, and let ζ_2 be the contribution to the second degree surface harmonic of the function $\zeta\Theta$, where $\Theta(\theta, \phi)$ is Munk and MacDonald's *ocean function* defined to be unity over the oceans and zero over land. The total contribution to the potential at great distances, arising from tidal deformation of the Earth, is then

$$k_2\left(\frac{a}{r}\right)^5\Psi_T - \frac{4}{5}(1+k_2')\,\pi\gamma a\rho\left(\frac{a}{r}\right)^3\zeta_2 \tag{24}$$

where ρ is the density of sea water. Although Ψ_T is approximated by a 2nd degree harmonic near the vicinity of the Earth, only, the first term of (24) represents the reaction of the Earth's body, which is also a second degree harmonic. Therefore, the same asymptotic form for Ψ_T that is used near the Earth will enter the expression (24) for distant points.

The increment in the Earth's tensor of inertia associated with a load of sea water $\zeta(\theta, \phi, t)$ relative to the deformed sea bed, plus the deformation in the Earth's body caused exclusively by this load is

$$\left. \begin{aligned} \Delta A &= \frac{4\pi}{15}(1+k_2')a^4\rho(a_2{}^0 - 3a_2{}^2) \\[2ex] \Delta B &= \frac{4\pi}{15}(1+k_2')a^4\rho(a_2{}^0 + 3a_2{}^2) \end{aligned} \right\} \tag{25}$$

$$\Delta C = -\frac{8\pi}{15}(1+k_2')a^4\rho a_2{}^0$$

$$\Delta F = \frac{2\pi}{5}(1+k_2')a^4\rho b_2{}^1$$

$$\Delta G = \frac{2\pi}{5}(1+k_2')a^4\rho a_2{}^1$$

$$\Delta H = \frac{4\pi}{5}(1+k_2')a^4\rho b_2{}^2$$

(25)
(cont.)

relative to the geographic axes, where $a_i{}^j$ and $b_i{}^j$ are the five second-degree coefficients in the expansion of the function ζ over the sea and zero over land; i.e.

$$\zeta_2(\theta, \phi, t) = a_2{}^0(\tfrac{3}{2}\cos\theta - \tfrac{1}{2}) + \tfrac{3}{2}\cos\theta\sin\theta(a_2{}^1\cos\phi + b_2{}^1\sin\phi)$$

$$+ \tfrac{3}{2}\sin^2\theta(a_2{}^2\cos 2\phi + b_2{}^2\sin 2\phi)$$

(26)

Now it only remains to relate ζ in some way to the initial disturbing potential Ψ_T. Tidal theorists since Laplace have been trying to do this but have been successful only in certain cases of hypothetical oceans of simple geometric shapes. Doodson (1958) gives a good summary of these attempts. In the case of the long-period tide there is reason to believe that the equilibrium theory is adequate. But the entire potential must be considered in determining the equilibrium form. We might consider the following sequence of events: the tide-generating potential deforms the Earth's body and sea surface into the shape of a 2nd degree surface harmonic. But the ocean tidal load, being zero over the continents, is rich in the higher surface harmonics. Each of these higher harmonics causes an additional deformation of the Earth's body and an additional self-attraction on the ocean masses, etc. Munk and MacDonald (1960) have calculated the first several surface spherical harmonics of the "ocean function" $\Theta(\theta, \phi)$. These coefficients enter into relationships by which it is possible to calculate the equilibrium shape of the sea surface, ground, and exterior potential, given the initial disturbing potential.

Studies of bodily tides and Chandler wobble give the values $h_2 = 0\cdot59$, $k_2 = 0\cdot29$. Calculations by Takeuchi (1950), based on certain distributions of density and elastic properties of the Earth as deduced from seismic and other evidence, give (1) $h_2 = 0\cdot59$, $k_2 = 0\cdot29$, or (2) $h_2 = 0\cdot61$, $k_2 = 0\cdot28$ for two models proposed by Bullen (Jeffreys,

1959, p. 224). The observed and theoretical values are in close agreement, and are consistent with Munk and MacDonald's values based on an elastic, incompressible, homogeneous sphere modified to give the observed equatorial bulge in the case of zero rigidity. As for the load Love numbers an incompressible homogeneous sphere gives the relations

$$h_n' = -\tfrac{2}{3}(n-1)h_n \qquad k_n' = -\tfrac{2}{3}(n-1)k_n$$

(see Munk and MacDonald, 1960; Section 5.8). The above values of h_2 and k_2 give approximately $h_2' = -0.39$, $k_2' = -0.19$. The negative value of h_2' indicates that the sea bottom is depressed by a positive tide, as one would expect. There are as yet no determinations of the load Love numbers from observations.

IV. Rotation of the Earth

In studying the Earth's rotation one can consider variation of $\boldsymbol{\omega}$ with respect to the geographical axes or with respect to the non-rotating system. The first point of view concerns wobble, while the second concerns precession and nutation. However, sometimes the free oscillation of the Earth's axis of rotation relative to the geographic axes is also referred to as "free nutation". Let us first consider the wobble. The equations (18) and (8) can be simplified by a great deal by a perturbation scheme, which works as long as the poles of figure and rotation remain close enough to the geographic (z') pole. Let

$$A = A_0 + A' \qquad\qquad \omega_1' = \Omega m_1$$
$$B = A_0 + B' \qquad\qquad \omega_2' = \Omega m_2$$
$$C = C_0 + C' \qquad\qquad \omega_3' = \Omega(1 + m_3)$$

where A_0 is the mean value of $\tfrac{1}{2}(A+B)$, C_0 is the mean value of C, and Ω is the mean angular speed of the Earth. Consider the dimensionless parameters A'/C_0, B'/C_0, C'/C_0, F/C_0, G/C_0, H/C_0, m_i and $h_i/\Omega C_0$, and their derivatives as small quantities whose products and squares can be neglected. Equations (8) and (18) can then be written

$$\frac{\dot{m}_1}{\sigma_r} + m_2 = \phi_2, \qquad \frac{\dot{m}_2}{\sigma_r} - m_1 = -\phi_1, \qquad \dot{m}_3 = \dot{\phi}_3, \qquad (27)$$

where

$$\sigma_r = \frac{C_0 - A_0}{A_0}\Omega$$

corresponds to the free nutation of a rigid Earth, and is equal to about 2π radians in 10 months,† and

$$
\left.
\begin{aligned}
\phi_1 &= \frac{1}{A_0\Omega\sigma_r}[-\Omega^2 G - \Omega \mathrm{F} + \Omega h_1 + \dot{h}_2 - L_2{}'], \\[2mm]
\phi_2 &= \frac{1}{A_0\Omega\sigma_r}[-\Omega^2 F + \Omega \dot{\mathrm{G}} + \Omega h_2 - \dot{h}_1 + L_1{}'], \\[2mm]
\phi_3 &= \frac{1}{C_0\Omega}[-\Omega C' - h_3 + \textstyle\int_0^t L_3{}' dt].
\end{aligned}
\right\}
\qquad (28)
$$

These expressions (28) have been called the "excitation function" by Munk and MacDonald. The relations (27) and (28) show that wobble results from torque exerted by extra-terrestrial bodies, from variable motions of mass within the Earth or from variation in the moments and products of inertia. The latter is the predominant effect. If the torque terms of (28) arise solely from the Moon's gravitation then they can be expressed in terms of the moments and products of inertia according to (17). The torque components $L_1{}'$ and $L_2{}'$ are smaller than the corresponding terms, $\Omega^2 G$ and $\Omega^2 F$ by a factor of the order of $3\gamma m r^{-3}\Omega^{-2} \simeq 10^{-4}$, r being the Moon's distance. Therefore, the wobble components m_1 and m_2 are influenced more by the direct effect of the tidal bulge on the Earth's free rotation than by the Moon's torque on the same bulge. But, in any case, the tidal effect is small compared to that of geophysical events. However, the tides have an appreciable effect on variations in the length of day, as determined by variation of C' in the expression for ϕ_3. The lunar and solar tides slightly perturb the Earth's oblateness and moment of inertia, affecting the free rotation. Observations on the length of day show the accumulated time discrepancy, and so the long-period tides, especially Ssa, give the predominant effect. Mintz and Munk (1951 and 1954) calculate that the Ssa bodily tide makes the day 0·3 milliseconds longer in March and September than in June and December. There are annual and semi-annual geophysical effects of about the same magnitude. The lunar fortnightly and monthly tide produce a variation in the length of day which is free from meteorological or geophysical effects. This variation has been observed to agree nicely with theory (Markowitz, 1955). If the fluctuating torque components $L_1{}'$ and $L_2{}'$ have a non-vanishing mean value, a minute constant displacement of the Earth's

†The actual frequency of the free nutation, or Chandler wobble, on the actual (deformable) Earth is about one cycle in 14 months (see Munk and MacDonald, 1960, Section 6.2).

pole of rotation will result (Groves and Munk, 1958). A steady contribution to L_3', however, will lead to a secular change in the Earth's rate of rotation as will be taken up later.

Now let us consider precession and nutation. Equation (19) can be applied in the case of a rigid Earth, but the components of the tensor of inertia must be obtained relative to the non-rotating axes, according to (12). Assuming that the moments and products of inertia are A, A, C, O, O, O, relative to the rotating axes in the Earth, the components relative to the x, y, z axes are

$$
\left.
\begin{aligned}
\Phi_{11} &= A + (C-A)\sin^2\vartheta\,\sin^2\epsilon & \Phi_{12} &= -(C-A)\cos\vartheta\,\sin\vartheta\,\sin^2\epsilon \\
\Phi_{22} &= A + (C-A)\cos^2\vartheta\,\sin^2\epsilon & \Phi_{13} &= (C-A)\sin\vartheta\,\cos\epsilon\,\sin\epsilon \\
\Phi_{33} &= A + (C-A)\cos^2\epsilon & \Phi_{23} &= -(C-A)\cos\vartheta\,\cos\epsilon\,\sin\epsilon,
\end{aligned}
\right\} (29)
$$

and the torque becomes

$$
\begin{aligned}
\mathbf{L} = 3\gamma m r^{-5}(C-A)\{ &\mathbf{i}[xy\sin\vartheta\,\cos\epsilon\,\sin\epsilon + xz\cos\vartheta\,\sin\vartheta\,\sin^2\epsilon \\
&\quad - y^2\cos\vartheta\,\cos\epsilon\,\sin\epsilon + yz(\cos^2\epsilon - \cos^2\vartheta\,\sin^2\epsilon) \\
&\quad + z^2\cos\vartheta\,\cos\epsilon\,\sin\epsilon] \\
+ &\mathbf{j}[-x^2\sin\vartheta\,\cos\epsilon\,\sin\epsilon + xy\cos\vartheta\,\cos\epsilon\,\sin\epsilon + xz(\sin^2\vartheta\,\sin^2\epsilon - \cos^2\epsilon) \\
&\quad - yz\cos\vartheta\,\sin\vartheta\,\sin^2\epsilon + z^2\sin\vartheta\,\cos\epsilon\,\sin\epsilon] \\
+ &\mathbf{k}[-x^2\cos\vartheta\,\sin\vartheta\,\sin^2\epsilon + xy\sin^2\epsilon(\cos^2\vartheta - \sin^2\vartheta) - xz\cos\vartheta\,\cos\epsilon\,\sin\epsilon \\
&\quad + y^2\cos\vartheta\,\sin\vartheta\,\sin^2\epsilon - yz\sin\vartheta\,\cos\epsilon\,\sin\epsilon]\}.
\end{aligned}
\tag{30}
$$

As we should expect, the tensor of inertia does not depend upon the amount of rotation ψ about the $\mathbf{k}'$ axis, and the torque has no component in the direction of $\mathbf{k}'$ because of the assumed symmetry. Woolard (1953) gives a complete development of the Earth's precession and nutation, but here we shall consider one special case only: the Moon's orbit is taken to be circular and lying in the xy plane. Thus the Moon's position can be represented by

$$
x = r\cos\sigma't, \quad y = r\sin\sigma't, \quad z = 0, \quad r = \text{const.}
$$

The variation in ϵ and ϑ is much slower than in the Moon's position coordinates x and y, so we can replace the torque by its mean value over a one-month cycle assuming that ϵ and ϑ are constant during this period: thus

$$
\overline{x^2} = \overline{y^2} = \tfrac{1}{2}r^2, \quad \overline{xy} = \overline{xz} = \overline{yz} = \overline{z^2} = 0.
$$

Equation (19) then becomes

$$\overline{L_1} = -\tfrac{3}{2}\gamma mr^{-3}(C-A)\cos\vartheta\,\cos\epsilon\,\sin\epsilon$$

$$= \frac{d}{dt}[A\,\dot\epsilon\cos\vartheta + C\dot\psi\sin\vartheta\,\sin\epsilon + (C-A)\dot\vartheta\,\sin\vartheta\,\sin\epsilon\,\cos\epsilon\,]$$

$$\overline{L_2} = -\tfrac{3}{2}\gamma mr^{-3}(C-A)\sin\vartheta\,\cos\epsilon\,\sin\epsilon \qquad (31)$$

$$= \frac{d}{dt}[A\dot\epsilon\sin\vartheta - C\dot\psi\cos\vartheta\,\sin\epsilon - (C-A)\dot\vartheta\,\cos\vartheta\,\sin\epsilon\,\cos\epsilon]$$

$$\overline{L_3} = 0 = \frac{d}{dt}[C\dot\psi\cos\epsilon + (A\sin^2\epsilon + C\cos^2\epsilon)\dot\vartheta]$$

One set of values satisfying these equations is

$$\dot\epsilon = 0;\quad \vartheta = \sigma t,\quad \dot\psi = \Omega \text{ (const.)},$$

provided that σ is a root of the quadratic,

$$\sigma^2 + \frac{C\Omega}{C-A}\sigma\sec\epsilon + \tfrac{3}{2}\gamma mr^{-3} = 0 \ . \qquad (32)$$

One root of (32) corresponds to a motion in which the axis of rotation deviates considerably from the axis of figure (see Routh, 1905, p. 349) and is not of interest here. The other is approximately

$$\sigma = -\tfrac{3}{2}\gamma mr^{-3}\Omega^{-1}\left(\frac{C-A}{C}\right)\cos\epsilon \ . \qquad (33)$$

To account for the solar effect we can take for mr^{-3} the Sun's value plus the Moon's value. The solar to lunar ratio is $0\cdot460$, the same as for the tide-generating potential, and so it is only necessary to insert a factor of $1\cdot460$ in expression (33) and use lunar values to get the entire effect. Then if we take for Ω and ϵ the present speed of the Earth's rotation and obliquity and take $(C-A)/C = 0\cdot00327$, we come out with 25,400 years for the period of precession, $2\pi/\sigma$. The minus sign shows that ϑ continually decreases; i.e. the precession is a westward motion of the equinoxes. In practice the procedure is reversed; the observed precession has been used to evaluate $(C-A)/C$.

For a complete solution the actual coordinates of the Moon (or Sun) must be substituted into (30). Then it is found that both ϵ and ϑ contain a series of periodic terms representing the forced nutation in addition to the steady precession. The principal term ($18\cdot6$ yearly) corresponds to the regression of the nodes of the Moon's orbit and has an amplitude of $9''$ in the obliquity. The most complete development of these terms yet made is Woolard's (1953; see also Smart, 1953, Chapter 20).

Kelvin has shown that deviation from rigidity has a negligible effect on the precession and forced nutations. If there is any difference in the moments of inertia about the axes in the equator, A must represent the mean of the greatest and least of these moments. Anyway, no conclusive deviation from axial symmetry in the Earth has yet been found. Even if such assymmetry did exist, it would lead to no motions of astronomical interest. Thus there is some justification for the rigid axially-symmetric model used.

V. Secular Variation: the Evidence

In 1695 Halley examined ancient and recent eclipses, and was led to suspect that the Moon's mean motion had been increasing (relative to the Earth's rotation). Subsequent investigators confirmed this, and showed that the observations could be brought into agreement by adding a term of approximately $10'' \, T^2$ to the Moon's calculated longitude; T being expressed in Julian centuries of 36,525 mean solar days with the time origin at 1900·0. If the Moon's mean longitude is expressed as

$$a + bT + cT^2,$$

then the mean motion is $n = b + 2cT$ and the acceleration is $\dot{n} = 2c$. However, the coefficient c of T^2, and not $2c$, is usually referred to as the acceleration.

Laplace sought an explanation for this secular acceleration, and in 1787 announced that it was due to a secondary planetary perturbation. The effect is explained in the following way. The solar perturbation of the Moon's motion works against the Earth's gravity, on the average, and decreases the mean motion. The strength of the solar perturbation depends on the Sun's mean distance which, in turn, depends on the eccentricity of the Earth's orbit. The planetary perturbation is presently diminishing the eccentricity of the Earth's orbit and, consequently, also the mean strength of the Sun's perturbation. Laplace's value of the acceleration was $10''·18$, which agreed nicely with the observed one. However, Adams (1853) found the calculations of Laplace to be incomplete. Subsequent terms in a slowly converging series reduced Laplace's value to $5''·70$. It is a curious fact that Adams' result was not generally accepted until it was demonstrated that tidal friction could account for the discrepancy.

Let us disregard, for the moment, the obliquity, inclination of the Moon's orbit to the ecliptic, and the eccentricity. Then if E is the total kinetic and potential energy of the Earth-Moon system and $-N$ the mean lunar gravitational torque on the Earth's tidal bulge, about the axis, then

$$-\frac{dE}{dt} = N(\Omega - n)$$

represents the rate at which energy is being degraded into heat by tidal friction, assuming conservation of angular momentum. This must be positive, since heat is not transformed into kinetic or potential energy. Therefore, since $\Omega > n$, we must have $N > 0$ and the torque acts in such a sense as to diminish the Earth's rate of rotation and to accelerate the Moon's orbital speed. The net result is, however, that the angular momentum imparted to the Moon's motion by the slowing Earth's rotation goes entirely into increasing the Moon's potential energy. The kinetic energy, mean motion and linear speed all actually decrease as the Moon spirals away from the Earth. While the Moon's mean motion is seen to decrease if measured with an absolute clock, it actually increases with respect to time based on the Earth's rotation. Hence, astronomers have always referred to the secular tidal effect as an *acceleration* of the Moon's mean longitude.

Now, it must be remembered that the portion of the observed acceleration accountable for from the gravitational (point-mass) theory is not a true secular change (Brown, 1896, p. 268). After about 24,000 years the eccentricity of the Earth's orbit will have reached its minimum value and will have begun to increase, and its effect on the Moon's mean motion will be reversed. If we lived long enough, we could separate the secular and the long-term periodic effects by direct observation. For the present we are limited to estimates of the secular change by observing the combined effects and subtracting off that part which can be calculated by planetary theory. Of course, only the true secular change is pertinent to the problem of the initial configuration of the Earth-Moon system at its beginning or other cosmological problems. It should also be kept in mind that the planetary acceleration of the Moon's motion would be called an "acceleration" even if measured with an absolute clock, since there is no reaction on the Earth's rotation. The Moon is spiraling inward, for the time being, as associated with this effect. But over the relatively short span for which there are historical observations we are justified in treating the planetary as well as the tidal effect as secular.

Such phenomena are intimately related with the measurement and definition of time, and great confusion results if the kind of time referred to is not specifically stated. For most practical Earth-bound problems astronomical time (as either sidereal time or universal time)

G

has served well. It is determined by observation of transits of stars. But one obviously needs recourse to an independent time standard to study problems related to the Earth's variable rate of rotation. Ephemeris time is defined as the independent variable in the solar, lunar or planetary theories, and is supposed to "flow continuously and uniformly." Its scale is fixed so that the length of the day in ephemeris time is equal to the average length of the day in universal time over the last three centuries. Aside from the tidal effects under consideration, a unique ephemeris time could be determined by observation of the Sun, Moon or any planet. If all empirical terms are deleted from the ephemerides of the Sun, Moon and planets, then any discrepancy, in ephemeris time, between the observed celestial longitude of the Moon and that of the Sun or planets is presumably attributable to the tidal effect on the Moon's motion. There should be no discrepancy between longitudes of Sun and planets as the tidal effects on the motion of these bodies are negligible. In astronomical time, discrepancies in the observed longitude of the Moon can be attributed to anomalies in the Earth's rotation as well as to the tidal effect on the Moon's motion. If geophysical events alone are altering the Earth's rate of rotation (no tidal friction) then the discrepancies in the mean longitude of all bodies, observed minus theoretical, based on astronomical time, should be proportional to their mean motions.

The planetary and the tidal accelerations can be distinguished, one from another, by the fact that the former does not influence the Earth's rotation, while the latter does so in a predictable manner. The following analysis is based on Jeffreys (1959; see also Spencer Jones, 1956). Obliquity, eccentricities, inclinations, and the solar perturbation are neglected. If m', n', c', $-N'$ denote the Sun's mass, mean motion, distance and tidal couple on the Earth, respectively, then

$$n^2 c^3 = \gamma(m_0 + m), \qquad n'^2 c'^3 = \gamma(m_0 + m'),$$

from Kepler's laws. Let

$$c = c_0 \xi^2, \qquad n = n_0 \xi^{-3}, \qquad c' = c_0' \xi'^2, \qquad n' = n_0' \xi'^{-3},$$

the suffix 0 denoting the present value. The angular momentum of the orbital motion of the Earth and Moon about their centre of mass is

$$\frac{m_0 m c^2 n}{m_0 + m} = \frac{m_0 m c_0^2 n_0}{m_0 + m} \xi \ .$$

The couples $-N$ and $-N'$ acting on the Earth must be associated with couples N and N' tending to increase the orbital motions. The effects are almost independent of each other, as the principal periods of the solar and the lunar tides are distinct. The interaction through the "sidereal" tides K_1 and K_2 (Groves and Munk, 1958) does not alter the result. Thus

$$\left.\begin{array}{c} \dfrac{m_0 m c_0{}^2 n_0}{m_0+m}\dfrac{d\xi}{dt} = N \\[2ex] \dfrac{m_0 m' c_0'{}^2 n_0'}{m_0+m'}\dfrac{d\xi'}{dt} = N' \\[2ex] C\dfrac{d\Omega}{dt} = -N-N'-\delta \end{array}\right\} \qquad (34)$$

where

$$\delta = \Omega\,\frac{dC}{dt}$$

takes geophysical effects on the Earth's rotation into account. The differentiation is, of course, with respect to an absolute time, not astronomical time. Let us now consider the effect of the variable rotation and revolutions on the observation of a celestial body. The rate at which the Moon's motion is apparently accelerating, due exclusively to the change in the Earth's rotation is

$$-\frac{n}{\Omega}\frac{d\Omega}{dt}.$$

To this must be added the rate of acceleration due to variation $\dot{n}$ in its mean motion. If v designates the apparent acceleration in the Moon's position, defined as the coefficient of T^2, then

$$v = \tfrac{1}{2}\left(\frac{dn}{dt} - \frac{n}{\Omega}\frac{d\Omega}{dt}\right), \qquad (35)$$

where the factor $\tfrac{1}{2}$ is necessary because of this peculiar definition of acceleration. Similarly, the apparent acceleration of the Sun is

$$v' = \tfrac{1}{2}\left(\frac{dn'}{dt} - \frac{n'}{\Omega}\frac{d\Omega}{dt}\right). \qquad (36)$$

The accelerations in the mean motions can be written

$$\frac{dn}{dt} = -3n_0\xi^{-4}\frac{d\xi}{dt} + 2P, \qquad \frac{dn'}{dt} = -3n_0'\xi'^{-4}\frac{d\xi'}{dt}, \qquad (37)$$

where P denotes that part of the acceleration in the Moon's mean motion arising from planetary theory ($P = 5''\cdot70$ century^{-2}). Now for intervals of time as short as a few thousand years the mean motions, etc., deviate by an inappreciable fraction of themselves, so we can put $\xi = \xi' = 1$. Also, the first term of (36) is about 10^{-6} of the second term and can be neglected. Then combining (34), (35), (36) and (37) and dropping the subscripts 0 on c, c', n, n', we obtain

$$v = \frac{m_0 + m}{2m_0 mc^2}[\kappa'(N + N' + \delta) - 3N] + P$$

$$v' = \frac{m_0 + m}{2m_0 mc^2}\frac{n'}{n}\kappa'(N + N' + \delta)$$

$$(38)$$

where κ' is the present ratio of the orbital angular momentum to the angular momentum of the Earth's rotation

$$\kappa' = \frac{m_0 m}{m_0 + m}\frac{c^2 n}{C\Omega} = 4.82.$$

The quantities v and v' are commonly referred to as the secular accelerations, and are determined from observation. The torques N and N' can be estimated theoretically once a model of tidal deformation has been postulated. The quantity δ depends on geophysical events and is presently impossible to evaluate independently. It can be noted that N' and δ enter the expressions only as $(N' + \delta)$ and so astronomical observations alone can not distinguish between them. The acceleration v_m of any body not involved with tidal effects (Mercury, for example) is given by

$$v_m = \frac{m_0 + m}{2m_0 mc^2}\frac{n_m}{n}\kappa'(N + N' + \delta).$$

This is justified by observation: all celestial bodies except the Moon apparently follow the same ephemeris time (see Fig. 2).

Figure 1 shows the discrepancy of the Moon's longitude based on observation of occultations and the ephemerides reckoned in astronomical time, as taken from Munk and MacDonald (1960, Section 11.2). The observed minus theoretical values are based on Spencer Jones (1932, Table 5) for the period 1680 to 1908, and on Brouwer (1952a, Table VIIIa) for 1908 to 1950 (see also Spencer Jones, 1939, Table 1). All empirical terms have been removed from the Moon's theoretical longitude. The 2nd derivative of the plot at any instant therefore represents $2(v - P)$ according to our notation. It should be kept in mind that the values represent yearly mean longitudes and have been smoothed in various ways. Three features are apparent: (1) a general decrease in values, (2) a smooth hump between 1680 and 1850 representing Newcomb's "Great Empirical Term", and (3) a relatively high-frequency wiggle between 1900 and 1950. Figure 2 shows the

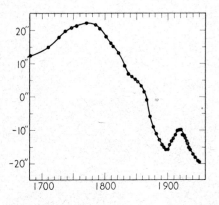

FIG. 1. Discrepancy of the Moon's longitude based on occultations. Reproduced from "The Rotation of the Earth", by W. H. Munk and G. J. F. MacDonald, by courtesy of the Cambridge University Press.

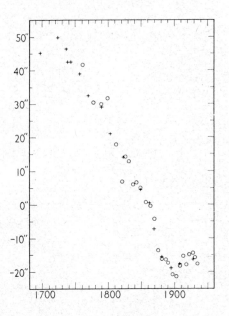

FIG. 2. Discrepancy in the Sun's (⊙) and Mercury's (+) longitude (November transits), weighted for their mean motion. There are no observations of solar longitudes for the period 1680 to 1740. The reduction of the observations of Mercury for this period depends on the extrapolated longitude of the Sun.

discrepancy for the Sun and Mercury, defined in the same way, but multiplied by the ratios

$$\frac{n}{n'} = 13\cdot37, \qquad \frac{n}{n_m} = 3\cdot32.$$

The 2nd derivative of either curve should represent

$$\frac{m_0+m}{m_0mc^2}\kappa'\,(N+N'+\delta) = \frac{n}{C\Omega}(N+N'+\delta).$$

Now if the discrepancies were due entirely to a variable rate of the Earth's rotation not affecting the positions of other celestial bodies, then the three plots should be identical. They are strikingly similar, but not identical. Apparently the Sun and Mercury do not differ by more than the scatter, as they should not according to the above considerations. The difference between the Moon curve of Fig. 1 and either of the curves of Fig. 2 is called the "weighted discrepancy difference", and is plotted in Fig. 3. The 2nd derivative of this curve should equal

$$-3N\frac{m_0+m}{m_0mc^2} = \frac{dn}{dt} - 2P, \tag{39}$$

which corresponds to that portion of the Moon's acceleration arising from the tidal couple, but referred to absolute time. The important thing to note is that the two curves of Fig. 3 fit reasonably well to

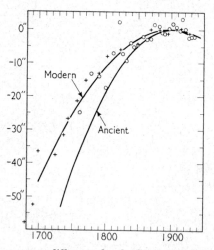

Fig. 3. Weighted discrepancy difference for the Sun ($\odot$) and for Mercury ($+$). Prior to 1740 the Mercury values depend on the extrapolated longitude of the Sun. The curve labelled Modern corresponds to $-11''\cdot2T^2$, Ancient to $-18''\cdot85T^2$. Reproduced from "The Rotation of the Earth", by W. H. Munk and G. J. F. MacDonald by courtesy of the Cambridge University Press.

$-11''\cdot2T^2$. Apparently lunar tidal friction in the Earth is retarding the Moon's mean motion by that amount. This value corresponds to $N = -3\cdot9 \times 10^{23}$ dyne cm. The data are not as yet adequate to discern any variation in the deceleration of the Moon's mean motion, so we might as well be content to consider $\dot{n}$ as a constant. The Great Empirical Term and the 20th century wiggle do not show up in the weighted discrepancy curves, and apparently reflect either variations in the solar tidal torque or geophysical irregularities in the Earth's rotation. The latter is more likely.

Evaluation of the acceleration depends principally on observations of occultations since 1680 and on records of ancient eclipses. Suppose that an eclipse should have occurred at time t_0 relative to a time origin close to the present, if based on the present ephemeris and present values of Ω, n and n'. At that time the Moon and the Sun (or antisun) would have each had the same celestial longitude λ_0 in the absence of the secular acceleration. But at time t_0 the actual longitudes were

$$\lambda = \lambda_0 + 2\int_0^{t_0}\!\!\int_0^t v\,\mathrm{d}t = \lambda_0 + vt_0^2 \,,$$

$$\lambda' = \lambda_0 + 2\int_0^{t_0}\!\!\int_0^t v'\,\mathrm{d}t = \lambda_0 + v't_0^2 \,,$$

provided that we take the accelerations to be constant. If the actual eclipse occurred at $t_0 + \Delta t$, when the Sun and Moon occupied the longitude $\lambda_0 + \Delta\lambda$, we have

$$\Delta\lambda = vt_0^2 + n\Delta t = v't_0^2 + n'\Delta t \tag{40}$$

and so the eclipse was actually retarded by the amount

$$-\Delta t = \frac{v - v'}{n - n'}t_0^2 \,,$$

during which time the Earth would have rotated through an additional angle $\Omega\Delta t$ had it not been for the secular accelerations. For $t = -20$ centuries, approximately, the eclipses would be displaced by a few hours of time and a few tens of degrees of geographic longitude. The observed quantities in (40) are $\Delta\lambda$ and Δt; n and n' are known. The longitude discrepancy $\Delta\lambda$ requires more refined observation and usually cannot be deduced from the ancient writings describing an eclipse. Thus any one eclipse gives a single relation between v and v', and so more than one eclipse is necessary for a unique determination. The trouble has been that the many eclipses studied do not give consistent results. Ancient eclipses have been the object of extensive study by Fotheringham, a classisist turned astronomer. De Sitter (1927) has evaluated Fotheringham's data and concludes that the average secular accelerations since ancient times are

$$v = 5''\!\cdot\!22 \pm 0''\!\cdot\!30$$
$$v' = 1''\!\cdot\!80 \pm 0''\!\cdot\!16$$

These values would correspond to a weighted discrepancy difference of $-18''\!\cdot\!85\ T^2$, which is indicated in Fig. 3 as "Ancient". This value depends critically on the secular acceleration of the Sun, and does not seem to fit the modern observations. For a complete discussion and bibliography of observations the reader is referred to Spencer Jones (1956) and Munk and MacDonald (1960).

VI. The Tidal Couple

The question arises as to whether the bodily tide or the ocean tide has the more important effect on the Earth's rotation. The present knowledge is insufficient to answer this question. In fact, both the bodily tide and ocean tide may contribute an appreciable share of the dissipation of energy and to the couple.

The effect of the bodily tide can be approximated as follows. The additional potential contributed by the tidally-deformed body of the Earth can be calculated from the first term of (20) and (22). We obtain for the additional exterior potential,

$$\Psi = -\frac{1}{2}\frac{k_2\gamma m r^2}{r_m{}^3}\left(\frac{a}{r}\right)^5 (3\cos^2\theta' - 1)$$

where θ' is the angle between the position vector $\mathbf{r}$ and the Moon's position $\mathbf{r}_m$. This formula, of course, assumes an elastic, instantaneous, response of the Earth's body. If the response is not elastic the Moon will be at $\theta' = -\kappa$ instead of at $\theta' = 0$, with respect to the additional potential, where 2κ is the phase lag of the Earth's response to the semi-diurnal tide. The torque exerted on the Moon is then

$$-\frac{m}{r_m}\frac{\partial\Psi}{\partial\theta'}\bigg|_{\substack{r\,=\,r_m \\ \theta'\,=\,\kappa}} = \frac{3}{2}\frac{k_2\gamma m^2 a^5}{r_m{}^7}\sin 2k$$
$$\simeq 5\!\cdot\!5 \times 10^{24}\sin 2\,\kappa\ \text{dyne cm}$$

taking $k_2 = 0\!\cdot\!29$. If this is equated to the value $(3\!\cdot\!9 \pm 1\!\cdot\!0) \times 10^{23}$ dyne cm, as deduced from the lunar discrepancy, we see that a phase lag of about two degrees would account for the entire lunar retardation of the Earth's rotation.

This value is very small to be detected with confidence by gravimeters

and other bodily tide observations. Parliskii (1960) has examined
Melchoir's (1959) gravimetry data from various stations in Europe and
Asia, and concludes that the average phase lag is positive and of
approximately the right value. However, Louis Slichter (personal
communication from Walter Munk) believes that the individual values
of phase from the various stations are so badly scattered as to make the
mean value doubtful. Melchoir (1958) gives a good discussion of the
problems involved in measuring Earth tides. Jeffreys (1954) believes
that tidal friction cannot be mainly bodily.

   Taylor (1919) made a detailed study of the dissipation of tidal
energy in the Irish Sea, and found that it could account for 2% of
the observed secular change. This is 30 times the total rate of tidal
dissipation for the entire deep oceans! If the friction of the tidal
current against the bottom obeys a square law, the rate of dissipation
goes like the cube of the current speed. The tides are higher and the
velocities greater in the shallow seas and shelves of the world, and
hence account for a disproportionate share of the tidal dissipation.
Jeffreys (1959, p. 234) took some observed values of tidal currents
in the Bering Sea and concluded that 80% of the necessary dissipation
occurs there. But Munk and MacDonald believe that the current
observations upon which this figure was based were not representative
of the whole Bering Sea, and reduce the effect by an order of magnitude.
They have looked at tidal current data from many seas and shelve
areas, and conclude that there is difficulty in getting the entire dissipation from the oceans. But the issue of ocean versus bodily tide dissipation is still unsettled, especially in view of the fact that the Moon's
torque on the ocean tide, discussed below, could give the entire effect.
Charles Cox (personal communication) has proposed an intriguing
possibility: energy from tidal motion in the ocean can be transferred
into internal oscillations at the coastlines or anywhere there is irregular
bottom topography. Internal oscillations of tidal period have been
frequently observed in the ocean as a varying temperature-versus-
depth profile. These internal waves can then radiate from their point
of origin, and ultimately dissipate all their energy in the open ocean.
Cox estimates that the total energy dissipated in this manner might
attain the value $1 \cdot 5 \times 10^{19}$ ergs sec^{-1} over the entire oceans. On the
other hand, it is noteworthy that the Moon and Mercury, without
oceans, apparently suffered enough tidal dissipation to end up per-
petually facing their primaries.

   Heiskanen (1921) calculated the lunar and solar torque on the known
ocean tide, based on Sterneck's (1920) cotidal charts of the world.
Within the uncertainties involved his result agreed with the torque

needed to explain the observed secular acceleration of the Moon. Groves and Munk (1958) recomputed the ocean tidal effect using Dietrich's more recent (1944) cotidal charts and came to the same conclusion that the ocean tide might account for the entire tidal dissipation and torque needed. But the uncertainties, especially in knowledge of the tide in the middle of the oceans far from tide gauges, could make either calculation too low by a factor of two or too high by an even larger amount. The method used is essentially as follows.

The tidal torque is given by

$$\mathbf{L} = -\int \mathbf{r} \times \nabla \Psi'_{T} \rho dv.$$

This can be written as the sum of harmonic terms by making use of the development (21) of the tide-generating potential. In view of (11b) and (25) we can write

$$
\mathbf{L} = \frac{\pi}{15} U \frac{g}{a} (1 + k_2') a^4 \rho \{ \mathbf{i}' [-9b_2 \, ^1\Sigma C_i \cos A_i + 12b_2{}^2 \Sigma_1 C_i \cos A_i
$$
$$
+ 12(a_2{}^0 + a_2{}^2) \Sigma_1 C_i \sin A_i + 6b_2{}^1 \Sigma_2 C_i \cos A_i
$$
$$
+ 6a_2{}^1 \Sigma_2 C_i \sin A_i]
$$

$$
+ \mathbf{j}' [9a_2{}^1 \Sigma_0 C_i \cos A_i + 12(a_2{}^0 - a_2{}^2) \Sigma_1 C_i \cos A_i + 12b_2{}^2 \Sigma_1 C_i \sin A_i \qquad (41)
$$
$$
+ 6a_2{}^1 \Sigma_2 C_i \cos A_i - 6b_2{}^1 \Sigma_2 C_i \sin A_i]
$$
$$
+ \mathbf{k}' [-6b_2{}^1 \Sigma_1 C_i \cos A_i - 6a_2{}^1 \Sigma_1 C_i \sin A_i - 24b_2{}^2 \Sigma_2 C_i \cos A_i
$$
$$
- 24a_2{}^2 \Sigma_2 C_i \sin A_i] \} .
$$

Now if the actual tide responds linearly to the tide-generating potential the tidal height at any place is composed of the same constituents as the potential (21) but with altered amplitudes and phases. Thus

$$\zeta = \Sigma H_i \cos (A_i - G_i) \qquad (42)$$

where the amplitudes $H_i(\theta, \phi)$ and the Greenwich epochs $G_i(\theta, \phi)$ are determined from tidal observations and are the functions read off the cotidal charts. The coefficients of (26) are determined by intergrating

$$a_2{}^0 = \frac{5}{8\pi} \int \zeta (3 \cos^2\theta - 1) \sin \theta d\theta d\phi$$

$$b_2{}^1 = \frac{5}{2\pi} \int \zeta \cos \theta \sin^2\theta \sin \phi d\theta d\phi$$

$$a_2{}^1 = \frac{5}{2\pi} \int \zeta \cos\theta \sin^2\theta \cos \phi d\theta d\phi$$

$$b_2{}^2 = \frac{5}{8\pi} \int \zeta \sin^3\theta \sin 2\phi d\theta d\phi \qquad (43)$$

$$a_2{}^2 = \frac{5}{8\pi} \int \zeta \sin^3\theta \cos 2\phi d\theta d\phi$$

over the oceans (see, for example, MacRobert, 1947). When the second-degree coefficients are determined from (43) and substituted into (41) the result contains products of series of sines and cosines of A_i. For the secular effect we are interested only in the average value and consequently retain only the constant term. The result for the average torque component along the Earth's axis is

$$\langle L_3' \rangle = -\tfrac{1}{2} U g a^3 \rho (1 + k_2') \{ \sum_1 C_i \!\! \int \!\! H_i \sin \kappa_i \cos \theta \sin^2 \theta \, d\theta d\phi$$
$$+ \sum_2 C_i \!\! \int \!\! H_i \sin \kappa_i \sin^3 \theta \, d\theta d\phi \}, \tag{44}$$

where

$$\kappa_i = G_i + \phi \quad \text{for diurnal constituents,}$$

$$\kappa_i = G_i + 2\phi \quad \text{for semidiurnal constituents.}$$

It would indeed be laborious if the integrals of (44) had to be evaluated for each important tidal constituent. If the oceans as a whole respond linearly and are not near resonance to the tide, then one can approximate the amplitude of any constituent by taking it proportional to that of the corresponding equilibrium constituent, and by taking the phases equal. This is the basis for the so-called "inference" method for determining the tidal constants of the smaller constituents (Schureman, 1941). This relationship can be used only among constituents belonging to the same species. Thus the number of numerical

TABLE I

	Heiskanen's Lunar Semidiurnal	Lunar			Solar			Total
		Semid.	Diurnal	Total	Semid.	Diurnal	Total	
Pacific								
+	3·8	2·8	0·6	3·4	0·7	0·2	0·9	4·3
−	−2·5	−1·9	−0·0	−1·9	−0·5	−0·0	−0·5	−2·4
total	1·3	0·9	0·6	1·5	0·2	0·2	0·4	1·9
Atlantic								
+	1·8	2·1	0·1	2·2	0·5	0·0	0·5	2·7
−	−1·2	−1·1	−0·1	−1·2	−0·2	−0·0	−0·2	−1·4
total	0·6	1·0	0·0	1·0	0·3	0·0	0·3	1·3
Indian								
+	1·8	1·5	0·2	1·7	0·4	0·1	0·5	2·2
−	−1·6	−0·9	−0·1	−1·0	−0·2	−0·0	−0·2	−1·2
total	0·2	0·6	0·1	0·7	0·2	0·1	0·3	1·0
Total	2·1	2·5	0·7	3·2	0·7	0·3	1·0	4·2

Work done by the tidal forces of Moon and Sun on the oceans, in units of 10^{19} ergs sec^{-1}. Positive and negative areas were summed independently to indicate degree of uncertainty.

integrations to be performed in (44) is reduced to two, one for each species. Groves and Munk did the computations for K_1 and M_2, these being the principal constituents. The results of Heiskanen and of Groves and Munk are summarized in Table I.

The ratio of the lunar to solar torque is of interest. On the assumption that the ocean's response and the frictional force of the tidal current are linear, Jeffreys (1959) obtains a value of 5·1 for the ratio. If the frictional force is proportional to the square of the current speed, the value is 3·4. With the "inference" assumption and the torque approach Groves and Munk obtained ratios of 4·00 and 2·94 for the semi-diurnal and diurnal tides, respectively, allowing for the interaction of lunar and solar effects through the sidereal constituents K_1 and K_2. (There are lunar and solar contributions of the same frequency to each of these constituents.) But there is no theoretical guide as to how these values are weighted. The semi-diurnal to diurnal ratio as indicated by Dietrich's cotidal charts leads to a lunar to solar ratio of about 3·2.

VII. Inclination and Eccentricity

Without tidal dissipation of energy within the Earth there are no interesting effects on the Moon's motion. Any effect on the movement of the nodes or line of apsides would be extremely small compared to the solar perturbations. The mean distance, eccentricity and inclination of a satellite's orbit, and the obliquity of the Earth's rotation would show no secular change. Darwin (1908) made an exhaustive theoretical study of the secular change in these elements, taking the Earth to be a rotating viscous fluid. Although his results are not immediately applicable to the actual Earth they are nevertheless worthy of note.

The Earth's speed of rotation, period and mean motion of the Moon, and mean distance or semi-major axis of the Moon's orbit are all interdependent, and we shall refer to the effect on the Moon's mean motion implying that there is also the appropriate change in the others. We have already seen one quite general result: that tidal dissipation, whatever the detailed mechanism, decreases the mean motion. Darwin found that this rate of decrease depends on the value of viscosity taken for the Earth's body. With the value that would give the greatest effect he found that as little as 50,000,000 years ago the Earth and Moon could have been very close together revolving with a period of four hours or less. The process will continue until a state is reached where both bodies keep a constant face to the other and revolve with a period of about 50 present days. However, it is difficult to interpret his results in view of the fact that the tidal dissipation is mainly not by viscous forces, and perhaps not even bodily, and Darwin clearly did not insist on his time scale.

With respect to the other elements—the eccentricity, inclination and obliquity—the calculations were very complicated and much more difficult to interpret. Unfortunately, Darwin found that he could not tell whether any of these elements were increasing or decreasing from purely general principles alone, as could be done in the case of the mean motion. The details of the dissipation mechanism are important. For example, Darwin found that ". . . if the obliquity of the ecliptic be zero, the ellipticity will either increase or diminish, according as 18 rotations of the planet take a shorter or a longer time than 11 revolutions of the satellite." This statement applies only for the limiting case of very small viscosity. Darwin concludes that the eccentricity (and ellipticity) of the Moon's orbit was originally small, rose to a maximum and ultimately diminished again, until the oceans were formed and began to contribute the major share of the dissipation. Darwin believed that ocean tidal friction would again increase the eccentricity. The obliquity and inclination are subject to other similarly detailed conditions. Kuiper (1949) shows that under certain simple conditions the obliquity will increase. Darwin believed that the obliquity was originally 12° or less with the inclination of the Moon's orbit having about the same value. Thereafter the obliquity continually increases while the inclination decreases (Gerstenkorn, 1955).

In an elliptic orbit it is natural to suppose that the accelerating force on the Moon will be greatest near perigee, since the tides raised on the Earth will then be greatest owing to the closer proximity of the Moon. If the accelerating force on the Moon occurred only at perigee, the Moon's distance at apogee would continually increase while the perigee distance would remain constant. Thus the eccentricity would increase. On the other hand, if the accelerating force on the Moon were constant throughout the entire orbit, the eccentricity would diminish. Whether the eccentricity is actually increasing or diminishing depends on how the average accelerating force on the Moon (or tidal torque on the Earth) varies with Moon's distance. Assuming a reasonable inverse variation of tidal torque with Moon's distance, it can be shown (Groves, 1960) that the eccentricity will increase. Urey et al. (1959) show how tidal dissipation within the Moon is presently tending to diminish the ellipticity.

Since the ocean tide has been shown capable of accounting for the entire secular decrease in the Moon's mean motion, it is not unreasonable to suspect that it may be working on the obliquity, inclination and eccentricity at an appreciable rate from a cosmological point of view. Let us follow the usual scheme in the study of perturbations of an elliptic orbit. Let α designate any osculating element such as the eccentricity, inclination, total energy, etc. An osculating element can be any constant of two-body motion. If all perturbations were suddenly to cease acting on a system composed of two point masses, the motion of either one with respect to the other would be an ellipse. Its shape and orientation in space would be invariable; all the α's would be truly constant in accordance with their definition. Furthermore, the resulting ellipse would be tangent and osculating to the actual trajectory at the time the perturbations were turned off. Where the elliptic motion is "perturbed" the concept of osculating element is still useful. The α's are considered to be slowly varying parameters. The method is generally known as variation of parameters.

If the position and velocity of the Moon are known at any given instant, any desired osculating element can be calculated: thus

$$\alpha = \alpha(x, y, z, \dot{x}, \dot{y}, \dot{z}). \tag{45}$$

The explicit form of the function (45) for any particular element can be found in any standard treatise on celestial mechanics (see, for example, Smart, 1953). Three elements are of particular interest to us; a, the semi-major axis, e, the eccentricity, and i, the inclination. It is convenient to represent these as functions of the components of angular momentum,

$$A_1 = y\dot{z} - \dot{y}z$$
$$B_1 = z\dot{x} - \dot{z}x$$
$$C_1 = x\dot{y} - \dot{x}y$$

the speed (relative to the Earth),

$$v = (\dot{x}^2 + \dot{y}^2 + \dot{z}^2)^{\frac{1}{2}}$$

and the magnitude of the angular momentum,

$$h = (A_1^2 + B_1^2 + C_1^2)^{\frac{1}{2}},$$

and to consider simple functions of the elements of interest. We have

$$a^{-1} = \frac{2}{r} - \frac{v^2}{\mu}, \quad \tan^2 i = \frac{A_1^2 + B_1^2}{C_1^2}, \quad e^2 = 1 - \frac{h^2}{\mu a}. \tag{46}$$

Each of the quantities, A_1, B_1, C_1, h, a^{-1}, $\tan^2 i$, and e^2 is an osculating element and could be designated by α.

Let us now consider how any osculating element α changes under the action of the disturbing function R. Differentiating (45) with respect to time gives

$$\dot{\alpha} = \frac{\partial \alpha}{\partial x}\dot{x} + \frac{\partial \alpha}{\partial y}\dot{y} + \frac{\partial \alpha}{\partial z}\dot{z} + \frac{\partial \alpha}{\partial \dot{x}}\ddot{x} + \frac{\partial \alpha}{\partial \dot{y}}\ddot{y} + \frac{\partial \alpha}{\partial \dot{z}}\ddot{z}$$

The acceleration components $\ddot{x}$, $\ddot{y}$, $\ddot{z}$, can be eliminated between this equation and (13). In accordance with the definition of α, we know that if $R = 0$, then $\dot{\alpha}$ must also equal zero. We finally obtain

$$\dot{\alpha} = \frac{\partial \alpha}{\partial \dot{x}}\frac{\partial R}{\partial x} + \frac{\partial \alpha}{\partial \dot{y}}\frac{\partial R}{\partial y} + \frac{\partial \alpha}{\partial \dot{z}}\frac{\partial R}{\partial z} \tag{47}$$

relating the rate of change of any osculating element with the disturbing force. It should be pointed out that (47) is not the form in which the perturbation equations are usually written. In planetary theory it is more convenient to relate the rate of change of any osculating element in terms of the others, so that the resulting system of different-ial equations can be solved to give the time history of each element. This is the method pursued by Darwin, and is particularly useful when a general relation between deformation and the tide-generating potential is known or postulated. If this relation is obtained only from observation during the present configuration of the Earth-Moon system, then (47) is simpler: there is no need to represent the disturbing function in terms of the osculating elements.

Care must be exercised in interpreting (47). It is apparently linear in the disturbing function—actually it is, but only for the purpose of calculating an instantaneous value for $\dot{\alpha}$. For example, suppose that the solar perturbation were omitted from R. The true path of the Moon would begin to deviate from the calculated path. Since all the functions on the right side of (47) depend on the position of the Moon an appre-ciable error would occur, after sufficient time had elapsed, because these functions would be evaluated at the wrong place.

As an example of the use of (47) to calculate the instantaneous mean secular change in an element let us consider $\alpha = a^{-1}$. The derivatives can be calculated from (46):

$$\frac{\partial a^{-1}}{\partial \dot{x}} = -\frac{2\dot{x}}{\mu}, \qquad \frac{\partial a^{-1}}{\partial \dot{y}} = -\frac{2\dot{y}}{\mu}, \qquad \frac{\partial a^{-1}}{\partial \dot{z}} = -\frac{2\dot{z}}{\mu} .$$

Then (16) and (47) give

$$\frac{da^{-1}}{dt} = -\frac{2}{m_0}r^{-7}\left[\left(\frac{15}{2}\mathbf{r}\cdot\mathbf{\Phi}\cdot\mathbf{r} - \frac{3}{2}r^2 Tr\mathbf{\Phi}\right)\dot{\mathbf{r}}\cdot\mathbf{r} - 3r^2\dot{\mathbf{r}}\cdot\mathbf{\Phi}\cdot\mathbf{r}\right] \tag{48}$$

There are similar, although somewhat more complicated, expressions for the change in the other elements. The tidal increment to Φ can be postulated in case of the bodily tide, or taken from tidal observations or cotidal charts for the ocean tide, according to (25). The position $\mathbf{r}$ and velocity $\dot{\mathbf{r}}$ of the Moon can be based on an idealized theory of the Moon's motion, or taken from Brown's tables (see Chapter 1) of the Moon's actual motion under present conditions. In either case the evaluation of (47) involves many multiplications of series of trigonometric terms. Finally only the non-periodic term is retained. If the Moon's motion under present conditions is used along with present tidal observations, only the present rate of secular change of the element is obtained. It is beyond our present ability to guess what the ocean tide was like during past or future geologic ages. There presently seems to be no prospect of tracing the ocean's effect on the changes of these elements through the ages after the manner that Darwin was able to do for a viscous Earth.

Acknowledgements

The author wishes to express his gratitude to Michael G. Rochester of the University of Toronto for his many valuable suggestions, and to apologize to those whose work pertinent to this subject has been inadvertently omitted from the discussion or references.

References

Adams, J. C. (1853). *Phil. Trans.* **A 143**, 397.

Brouwer, D. (1952*a*) *Astr. J.* **57**, 125.

Brouwer, D. (1952*b*). *Proc. Nat. Acad. Sci., Wash.* **38**, 1.

Brown, E. W. (1896). "An Introductory Treatise on Lunar Theory". Cambridge Univ. Press, 292 pp.

Clemence, G. M. (1958). In "Handbook of Physics", by E. U. Condon and Hugh Odishaw. Ch. 8, Pt. III. McGraw-Hill Book Co. Inc.

Condon, E. U. (1958). "Handbook of Physics", by E. U. Condon and Hugh Odishaw. Ch. 1, Pt. II. McGraw-Hill Book Co. Inc.

Darwin, G. H. (1911). "The Tides and Kindred Phenomena in the Solar System". 3rd ed. Houghton, Mifflin, New York.

Darwin, G. H. (1908). Scientific Papers. Vol. II, "Tidal Friction and Cosmogony". Cambridge Univ. Press. This series is a re-edition of Darwin's most important works. The papers pertinent to this subject contained in Vol. II are:

Phil. Trans. Pt. I, **170**, 1, (1879).

Phil. Trans. Pt. II, **170**, 447, (1879).

Phil. Trans. Pt. II, **170**, 539, (1879).

Phil. Trans. **171**, 713, (1880).

Proc. Roy. Soc. **30**, 255, (1880).

Phil. Trans. **172**, 491, (1881).

De Laplace, P. S. (1788). *Mém. Acad. Sci., Paris*, **235**, (1786). See also "Mécanique Céleste," Book 7, Chapter I, Section 16, and Chapters IV and XXIII.

De Sitter, W. (1927). *Bull. Astr. Insts Netherlds*, **4**, 21.

Dietrich, G. (1944). "Die Gezeiten des Weltmeeres als geographische Erscheinung". *Z. Ges. Erdk., Berlin*.

Doodson, A. T. (1921). *Proc. Roy. Soc.* **A 100**, 305.

Doodson, A. T. (1958). In "Advances in Geophysics" (H. E. Landsberg and J. Van Mieghem, eds.), Vol. 5, Chapter on "Oceanic Tides". Academic Press Inc., New York.

Gerstenkorn, H. (1955) *Z. Astrophys.* **36**, 245.

Groves, G. W. and Munk, W. H. (1958). *J. Mar. Res.* **17**, 119–214.

Groves, G. W. (1960). *Mon. Not. R. Astr. Soc.* **121**, No. 5, 497–502.

Halley, E. (1695). *Phil. Trans.* **19**, 174.

Heiskanen, W. (1921). *Ann. Acad. Sci. Fenn.* **A 18**, 1.

Jeffreys, Sir Harold (1954). "The Earth as a Planet" (Gerard P. Kuiper, ed.), Ch. II. Univ. Chicago Press, 749 pp.

Jeffreys, Sir Harold (1959). "The Earth", 4th ed. Cambridge Univ. Press, 420 pp.

Jones, Sir Harold Spencer (1932). *Ann. Cape Obs.* **13**, Pt. 3.

Jones, Sir Harold Spencer (1939). *Mon. Not. R. Astr. Soc.* **99**, 541.

Jones, Sir Harold Spencer (1954). "The Earth as a Planet" (Gerard P. Kuiper, ed.), Ch. I. Univ. Chicago Press, 749 pp.

Jones, Sir Harold Spencer (1956). The Rotation of the Earth. *Handb. Phys.* **47**, 1.

Kuiper, G. P. (1949). "On the Origin of the Solar System". Yerkes Observatory, Nov. 1949, mimeographed.

MacRobert, T. M. (1947). "Spherical Harmonics", 2nd revised ed. Dover Publications, New York, 371 pp.

Markowitz, W. (1955). *Astr. J.* **60**, 171.

Melchior, P. (1958). In "Advances in Geophysics" (H. E. Landsberg and J. Van Mieghem, eds.), Vol. 4, Chapter on "Earth Tides". Academic Press Inc., New York.

Melchior, P. (1959). *Marées Terrestres Bulletin d'Information* No. 16 (August 25th, 1959).

Mintz, Y., and Munk, W. H. (1951), *Tellus*, **3**, 117.

Mintz, Y., and Munk, W. H. (1954). *Mon. Not. R. Astr. Soc., Geophys. Suppl.* **6**, 566.

Morse, P. M., and Feshbach, H. (1953). "Methods of Theoretical Physics". McGraw-Hill Book Co., Inc. 2 Vols., 1978 pp.

Munk, W. H., and MacDonald, G. J. F. (1960). "The Rotation of the Earth; a Geophysical Discussion". Cambridge Univ. Press, 301 pp.

Parliskii, N. N. (1960). *Soviet Astr.* **4**, 515. Translated from *Astr. Zhur.* **37**, 543.

Routh, E. J. (1905). "Advanced Dynamics of a System of Rigid Bodies" 6th ed. reprinted in 1955 by Dover Publications Inc., New York.

Schureman, P. (1941), "Manual of Harmonic Analysis and Prediction of Tides". U.S. Dept. of Commerce, Coast and Geodetic Survey, Special Publication No. 98.

Smart, W. M. (1953). "Celestial Mechanics". Longmans, Green & Co. Ltd., London. 381 pp.

Smart, W. M. (1956). "Spherical Astronomy". Cambridge Univ. Press, 430 pp.

H

Sterneck, R. v. (1920). *S.B. Akad. Wiss. Wien, Abt. IIa,* **129,** 131.

Takeuchi, H. (1950). *Trans. Amer. Geophys. Un.* **31,** 651.

Taylor, G. I. (1919). *Phil. Trans.* **A 220,** 1.

Urey, H. C., Elsasser, W. M., and Rochester, M. G., (1959). *Astr. J.* **129,** 842.

Woolard, E. W. (1953). Theory of the Rotation of the Earth around its Center of Mass. *Astronomical Papers,* **XV,** Pt. 1, published by the Nautical Almanac Office, U.S. Naval Observatory.

CHAPTER 4

Photometry of the Moon

V. G. FESSENKOV

I. Introduction.. 99
II. Integral Brightness as a Function of the Phase-Angle............... 100
III. Absolute Magnitude and Albedo of the Moon........................ 106
IV. Brightness of Surface Details 111
V. Laws of Reflection... 113
VI. Colorimetric Characteristics..................................... 121
VII. Conclusions... 125
References... 128

I. Introduction

Over a considerable period of time it has been known that the Moon is characterized by certain remarkable photometric properties, depending evidently on the special structure of its surface. For instance, at full Moon the distribution of brightness over the disk is approximately the same at the centre as it is near the edges, although every diffusing sphere illuminated by a distant source of light and observed near zero phase-angle must necessarily be brighter in its centre. This particular property of the Moon was considered as early as 300 years ago by Galileo Galilei in his well-known "Dialogues on Two Systems of the World". Later, Bouguer in his "Traité d'Optique" attempted to explain it by postulating a certain degree of roughness of its surface. He considered the photometric effect produced by very steep mountains casting shadows which can be seen even at small angles between the incident and reflected rays.

Even 200 years ago, therefore, it was realized that there existed some close relation between the photometric properties of the Moon and the structure of its surface. At the present time this becomes of a certain practical value, owing to the possibility of cosmic voyagers landing on the Moon's surface. Nevertheless, for reliable deductions precise photometric measurements are necessary; and these did not become possible until quite recently. At the beginning, astrophotometric methods were represented by visual estimates which for point sources were developed by Argelander and Pickering. The analogous scale for visual estimates of different details on the Moon was proposed by Schröter towards the end of the 18th century and applied by various

99

authors until quite recently (Güssow, 1937; Markov). But the basic problems of the Moon's photometry require instrumental means which are sufficiently precise to permit objective measurements to be made. These problems can be formulated as follows:

(a) Determination of the variation of integral brightness of the Moon as a function of its phase-angle.

(b) Determination of the stellar magnitude of the full Moon and its colour index, as well as the corresponding absolute illumination.

The same problems also include the determination of the total reflecting power of the Moon—the so-called lunar albedo—which can be immediately obtained from (a) and (b) provided that the stellar magnitude of the Sun is sufficiently well known.

(c) Determination of the phase-angle function of the positive edge of the lunar crescent. Knowledge of this function is necessary in order to deduce the reflecting power of the Earth by measurement of the intensity of ash-light of the Moon, and also to characterize the reflecting properties of its surface.

(d) Determination of absolute and relative brightness of different lunar formations—mountain regions, dark areas (maria), bright rays around some craters, etc., also under different conditions of illumination. These data can be employed to deduce the reflection index of light for every detail on the Moon as a function of the angles of incidence, reflection and phase.

(e) Interpretation of such indices of reflection by their comparison with different terrestrial substances, with a view to obtaining some insight on the micro-structure of the lunar surface.

(f) Investigation of systematic variation of the lunar details at different positions of the Sun above the corresponding horizon and at different moments of time.

We are not concerned here with the problems of the Moon's illumination during eclipses (cf. Chapter 6), nor with the brightness of the ash-light of the Moon depending on the Earth as a source of light.

II. Integral Brightness as a Function of the Phase-Angle

The first problem of the photometry of the Moon is to determine the variation of its integral brightness as a function of the phase-angle. Many series of observations were made on this subject by different authors. Thus, Herschel (1847) during his stay at the Cape of Good Hope, studied the relative brightness of the Moon with his astrometer producing a reduced lunar image. Further, Bond (1861) in the U.S.A., compared with different stars of known stellar magnitude the reduced image of the Moon formed by reflection from a small silvered sphere. His observations were made during 13 nights. He was the first to realise that the theory then current could not represent truly the particular behaviour of the illumination from the Moon depending on its phase-angle. Zoellner (1865) also made very successful observations with his polarizing visual photometer. Pickering (1908) made a series of visual comparisons of the Moon's illumination, using a shadow photometer with a pentane lamp and blue water filter. King (1909) produced numerous comparisons of the colour of the Moon directly with extra-focal images of different stars without any artificial etalon. Stebbins and Brown using a selenium photo-element compared the direct illumination by the Moon with a standard amyl-acetate lamp, placed at the distance equalizing the intensity of illumination from both sources. They were the first to distinguish the inequality of illumination at the same phase-angles before and after full Moon. Wislicenus made a series of comparisons of a reduced image of the Moon with Polaris using a visual Zoellner photometer. Some years later these measurements were discussed and reduced by Wirtz (1915).

It is to be noted that very great deficiency in all these observations was lack of precision in the knowledge of the corresponding atmospheric extinction, without mentioning the insufficiently worked out observational methods. Therefore, great merit belongs to Russell (1916) who succeeded in reducing sufficiently good values from all these very different measurements.

Russell re-discussed all these observations, compared them and deduced a mean value with errors (according to him) no greater than $0\text{m}05$ for phase-angles up to $150°$. As a result he obtained the following variation of the integral brightness of the Moon taken equal to 100, and the corresponding stellar magnitude as $0·00$ at $\alpha = 0°$.

The next series of observations was made by Rougier (1933) with his photoelectric photometer at Strasbourg Observatory. This very careful investigation, made with precise instruments, marked a new epoch in the study of this problem. Rougier not only applied to it a more precise technique, but also paid attention to the necessity of thorough measurement of atmospheric extinction. As he pointed out, for instance, Wislicenus usually made only a single measurement in any one evening. But if there were two or more measurements referring to different moments of the same evening, allowing the approximated value of atmospheric extinction to be deduced, the corresponding results would fit the mean curve of the Moon's brightness in function of the phase-angle much better. But Rougier also did not fully realise the significance of precise measurement of the atmospheric extinction, because he restricted himself to the application of the well-known Bouguer method in drawing the straight line only up to 2·5–3·0 atmospheric masses, or down to 65°–70° in zenith distances.

Rougier's apparatus consisted of a tube, without any optics, but with diaphragms eliminating the diffusion of light inside. A photo-cell with an amplifier was employed as a receiver. The illumination from the Moon was compared with an analogous illumination from an etalon installed at different distances. As the etalon, an electric lamp was adopted, working under standardized conditions and previously

TABLE I

Phase-Angle	Before full Moon		After full Moon	
0°	100	0·00	100	0·00
10	81·7	0·22	81·7	0·22
20	66·7	0·44	64·3	0·48
30	54·0	0·67	50·6	0·74
40	43·6	0·90	38·7	1·03
50	35·3	1·13	29·9	1·31
60	28·3	1·37	23·3	1·58
70	21·9	1·65	18·0	1·86
80	16·1	1·98	13·6	2·17
90	11·5	2·35	10·0	2·50
100	7·73	2·78	7·18	2·88
110	5·15	3·22	4·92	3·27
120	3·10	3·77	3·19	3·74
130	1·75	4·39	1·90	4·30
140	0·88	5·14	1·02	4·98
150	0·37	6·09	0·44	5·89

tested for changes in voltage over some 20 hours. The photo-cell was placed at a branch of a Wheatstone bridge, variable resistances being placed at the three other branches. According to Rougier, the mean error determined from the deviations of individual measurements from the mean curve was nearly 0^m05. This error could have been made still smaller if atmospheric extinction had been determined more precisely (see Fig. 1). Rougier's results are given in the following Table II.

There is some difficulty in reducing the observed values of illumination at full Moon where the phase-angle becomes zero. At phases less than 1·5⁰ the Moon enters partially in the Earth's shadow, and direct observations become impossible. This difficulty of extra-polation arises from the very peculiar behaviour of the illumination curve —i.e. from its very steep slope at very small phase-angles. This is a characteristic property of the photometry of the Moon. Rougier's curve shows a somewhat more rapid decrease with phase-angles than

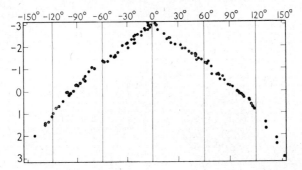

Fig. 1. The integral brightness, in stellar magnitudes, of the Moon before and after the full phase, as a function of the phase-angle (after Rougier, *L'Astronomie*, **48**, 224, 1934).

that of Russell (see Fig. 2). Besides, it is evident that there is no such marked discrepancy between the illumination curves before and after full Moon as reported previously by Stebbins and Brown.

The most immediate explanation of this peculiar behaviour of the curve of illumination may be sought in the extreme roughness of the Moon's surface: the influence of the shadows diminishing the apparent brightness most seriously, even at very small deviations from zero phase-angle. In order to verify this conjecture, Rougier carried out a series of observations in the laboratory, examining the reflection of light from a diffusing sphere of 35 mm in diameter covered by a layer of thin gravel, the size of grains being nearly 1·5 mm. In such a

TABLE II

Phase-Angle	Before full Moon Brightness in Stellar Magn		After full Moon Brightness in Stellar Magn	
0°	100	0·00	100	0·00
10	78·7	0·26	75·9	0·30
20	60·3	0·55	58·6	0·58
30	46·6	0·83	45·3	0·86
40	35·6	1·12	35·0	1·14
50	27·5	1·40	27·3	1·41
60	21·1	1·69	21·1	1·69
70	16·1	1·98	15·6	2·02
80	12·0	2·30	11·1	2·39
90	8·24	2·71	7·80	2·77
100	5·60	3·15	5·81	3·09
110	3·77	3·56	4·05	3·48
120	2·49	4·01	2·61	3·96
130	1·51	4·55	1·58	4·50
140			0·93	5·08
150			0·46	5·84

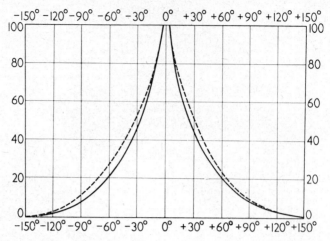

FIG. 2. The total brightness of the Moon as a function of the phase. After Rougier
(full line) and Russell (dotted line).

manner a model was prepared representing the lunar surface and
reproducing in certain respects the conditions on the Moon. But it
was found that even this model of a very rough surface could not
represent the observed phase-function of the Moon (see Fig. 3). Apparently, the complete explanation requires not only that the lunar
mountains should obliterate to a certain extent their own shadows, but

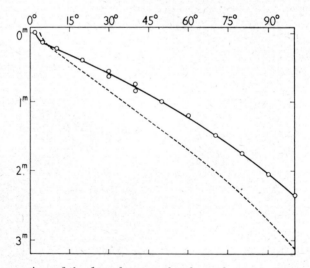

FIG. 3. A comparison of the dependence on the phase of a rough illuminated sphere
(full line), with that of the Moon (dotted line). After Rougier (*L'Astronomie*, **48**, 228,
1934).

calls also for specific structure of very small details of the lunar surface:
namely, of the substance of which the surface consists.

It is interesting also to measure the brightness of the positive limb
of the Moon as a function of the phase-angle, although this entails
some additional difficulties. Such results were given in a paper by
Schönberg, published in 1925, and were obtained with the aid of a
visual surface-photometer of original construction mounted on a small
Fraunhofer refractor of 80 mm aperture. As the absolute photometry of the Moon was not the aim of his investigation, the measurements were made in arbitrary units for points along the whole contour
of the positive limb of the Moon's crescent, as well as for those following
the equator of intensity; (i.e. the mean limb of the lunar disk as it is
viewed by the terrestrial observer). Only during some successive days
was it possible to rely on the constancy of the photometric lamp and
on the value of the atmospheric extinction. Besides, the area measured
by Schönberg's photometer was considerable and could not be centred
exactly on the limb of the Moon, but only at the distance of 0·03 from
it in units of its radii. As the mean for 7 points of the positive limb of
the Moon, the following relative brightnesses for different phase-angles
were obtained:

Phase-angle: $-4·6° - 30·8° \ -67·8° \ -69·4° \ -81·4° \ -85·2° \ -120·2°$
Brightness: $\quad 1·00 \quad 0·92 \quad 0·555 \quad 0·592 \quad 0·570 \quad 0·540 \quad 0·275$

According to Schönberg, these brightnesses are nearly constant over a
large range of the arc of the positive limb of the Moon (approximately
for ¾ of its circumference), but decrease rapidly with the phase-angle.

Another, and much more reliable, determination of this function
was made by Danjon (1933) at Strasbourg Observatory in connection
with his investigation of the albedo of the Earth. For this purpose,
Danjon constructed his so-called "cat's eye" photometer, which
couples two optical systems giving two somewhat displaced images of
the Moon arranged in such a manner as to be precisely tangent. One
image—namely, that of the positive limb—is then attenuated arti-
ficially by a known factor.

The great advantage of this instrument is the fact that it almost
eliminates the background illumination caused by the scattering of
light inside the instrument as well as by the atmospheric halo. Besides,
the comparison can be performed without any intermediate area of
reference and, consequently, at the some position of the Moon in the
sky. Only some small corrections for differential extinction are needed.
This instrument can also be used for the determination of the brightness of the positive limb of the Moon, with the purpose of reducing all

these observations to the full Moon as it is needed for the determination of the Earth's albedo.

In the course of these measurements Danjon established one very interesting fact: namely, that the lunar crescent fully disappears when the angular distance from the Sun becomes less than 7°. The following Table III gives an account of this phenomenon by listing the extent of the crescent 2ω under various phase-angles:

TABLE III

Phase-angle:	140°	145°	150°	155°	160°	165°	170°	171°	172°	173°
2ω:	180°·0	177°·6	173°	167°	158°	142°	104°	88°	66°	0°

It is seen that, at the phase of 173°, the crescent of the Moon disappears completely.

Nevertheless, Danjon's results concerning the brightness of the positive limb are not free from objections. As he points out, the size of the area of comparison is not constant, but steadily decreases as the lunar crescent becomes narrower. The results are represented in the following Table IV.

TABLE IV

		Brightness of the Positive Limb of the Moon			
Phase-angle	J	Magn	Phase-angle	J	Magn
0°	100	0·00	90°	25·6	1·48
10	73·8	0·38	100	23·3	1·58
20	57·5	0·60	110	20·7	1·71
30	46·6	0·83	120	17·7	1·88
40	40·2	0·99	130	14·3	2·11
50	36·0	1·11	140	11·0	2·40
60	32·8	1·21	150	7·66	2·79
70	30·5	1·29	160	4·32	3·41
80	28·0	1·38			

It should be noted that also in this case the brightness diminishes rapidly with increasing phase-angle up to about 30°. Thereafter the rate of decrease becomes slower; but for $\alpha > 150°$ the brightness diminishes again more rapidly and disappears completely for $\alpha < 180°$, as mentioned above.

III. Absolute Magnitude and Albedo of the Moon

The absolute stellar magnitude of full Moon is one of the important constants in astrophysics. The difference of stellar magnitude of the

Sun and the Moon is also of considerable value, because of its immediate connection with the lunar albedo.

The first summary of different determinations of stellar magnitude of the full Moon according to measurements of Herschel, Bond, Zoellner, and Pickering, with reference to the stars as well as to the Sun, was accomplished by Russell in 1916. On the Harvard system he obtained:

visual magnitude of the Moon : weighted mean $-12^{\mathrm{m}}55 \pm 0 \cdot 07$.

Subsequently, Kuiper reduced it to the system of international stellar magnitudes, taking into account also other determinations. His data are collected in the following Table V.

TABLE V

Observer	Method of Observation	Magnitude
Pickering	visual	$-12 \cdot 83$
Zoellner	visual	$-12 \cdot 29$
King	photographic	$-12 \cdot 40$
Pettit	radiometric	$-12 \cdot 75$
Calder	photoelectric	$-12 \cdot 69$
Nikonova	photoelectric	$-12 \cdot 67$

The photographic magnitude of the full Moon is $-11 \cdot 37$, according to King (photographic method); and $-11^{\mathrm{m}}74$, according to Calder (photoelectric method).

In order to determine the albedo of the Moon, it is necessary to compare its brightness directly with that of the Sun at different phase-angles—or with the stars—taking the stellar magnitude of the Sun as known. With this aim in view, Rougier designed a special photometer analogous to the one mentioned previously. In the tube of the photometer he placed two small objectives, with focal lengths of $16 \cdot 26$ and $9 \cdot 075$ mm respectively. This arrangement can considerably reduce the sunlight and allows comparison with that of the Moon. A determination of the focal length must, however, be accomplished with an error of the order of $0 \cdot 01$ mm, and is influenced by the thermal conditions.

The spherical albedo of the Moon, according to Bond's definition, can be represented by the well-known expression

$$ A = \frac{2\mathscr{I}_L}{\mathscr{I}_0 s} \int_0^{\pi} f(\alpha) \sin \alpha \, d\alpha, \tag{1} $$

where $\mathscr{I}_L$ is the integral brightness of the Moon at phase-angle $0°$ and $\mathscr{I}_O$ is that of the Sun: s being the angular radius of the Moon expressed in radians. If $f(\alpha)$ is standardized in such a manner that $f(0) = 1$, then, according to Rougier's data,

$$2 \int_0^\pi f(\alpha) \sin \alpha \, d\alpha = 0.5845. \qquad (2)$$

Therefore, the determination of albedo depends uniquely on the ratio which must be reduced to the mean distance of the Moon and the Sun. Rougier assumes that the phase-function $f(\alpha)$ is the same in visual as well as in photographic light, and generally does not depend on wavelength. Comparing determinations of the difference in stellar magnitudes of the Moon and the Sun according to previous authors, he deduced that, in the mean,

$$m_\odot - m_L = -23.93 \text{ magn}$$

for the same distance from the Earth, whence the visual albedo of the Moon results as

$$A = 0.073.$$

Moreover, he states that his photocell is characterized by the same sensitivity distribution in wavelength as the photographic plate. Consequently, his photoelectric magnitudes should be equivalent to the photographic ones. The difference in stellar magnitudes of the Sun and the Moon then results as

$$m_\odot - m_L = -27.24,$$

and corresponding albedo,

$$A = 0.055.$$

As is seen, the Moon appears to be definitely fainter in photographic light. Its colour-index resulting from these measurements is

$$C.I. = 1.10 \text{ magn}$$

More recently, Martynov (1959) re-discussed anew all values of the integral stellar magnitude of the Moon and the Sun, as well as of the international lux constant. This discussion became necessary because of the considerable number of new and exact determinations, and partly because of some uncertainty inherent in the so-called international photovisual system. As is known, the visual system of stellar magnitudes is based on Zinner's catalogue, published by Bamberg

Observatory in 1926, corresponding to an average human eye with a universally accepted spectral sensitivity. There is some difference between this system and the so-called international photovisual system which, according to Kuiper, is connected with Potsdamer Durchmusterung by the following expression

$$IPv - PD = -0.22 + 0.11 C.I.$$

More recently, this system began to be gradually abandoned in favour of that by Johnson-Morgan. As in the photometric systems the brightness of comparison stars is expressed somewhat differently; the reduced integral brightness of the Moon and the Sun being given by three separate numbers. Martynov has utilized the following observations: Zoellner (comparison star: α Aur), Fabry (comparison star: α Lyrae), Ceraski (comparison with Venus), W. H. Pickering (comparison stars: α Aur, α Boo, α CMa), photographic observations of King and Birk which are reduced to the visual system by application of a correction of 0.50 magn; also he took into account the very elaborate and numerous photoelectric observations made by Nikonova (1949) at the Crimean Astrophysical Observatory in 1949, and also the visual observations of Kariaguina (1955) at the Astrophysical Institute near Alma Ata in 1955. The photoelectric comparison of the Sun and the Moon with fourteen carefully chosen stars made by Stebbins and Kron (1957) in six regions of the spectrum, as well as direct determinations of the differences between the Sun and α CMa made by Woolley and Gascoine, were also taken into account, together with the radiometric measurements of Pettit and Nicholson (1930) (with Kuiper's reduction corrections).

As the mean value from all these determinations, Martynov gives the following values for the integral magnitude of the Sun in the three systems mentioned:

System of Zinner	Intern. Photovis. System	System of Johnson-Morgan
(1)	(2)	(3)
-26.0 ± 0.04	-26.78 ± 0.04	-26.80 ± 0.03

The integral magnitude of the full Moon was deduced by Martynov on the basis of a phase-curve previously obtained by Rougier which was fully confirmed by the latest photoelectric measurements. Accordingly, all earlier reductions by Russell were computed anew from Rougier's curve. In this work all determinations of Herschel, Zoellner, W. H. Pickering, Calder, King, Nikonova and Pettit were also taken into account; Kuiper's corrections being duly applied,

The mean stellar magnitude of full-Moon, expressed in the three systems, resulted as follows:

(1)	(2)	(3)
$-12 \cdot 52 \pm 0 \cdot 07$	$-12 \cdot 65 \pm 0 \cdot 06$	$-12 \cdot 24 \pm 0 \cdot 07$

Such are the most trustworthy visual integral brightnesses of full Moon, which have been deduced from all material available at present. Moreover, there exist some very precise direct determinations of the difference in brightness between the Sun and the Moon, which are nearly free from errors depending on colour: namely, the determinations of Rougier and Nikonova. In the mean, we have,

	(1)	(2)	(3)
Difference Moon–Sun	14·6	14·08	14·10 magn.

The uncertainty of these results is nearly $\pm 0 \cdot 035$ magnitude.

Lastly, the determinations of the luminous lunar constant can be utilized for the same purpose. This is the illumination, expressed in luxes, produced by the full Moon at the distance from the Earth equal to the mean radius of the lunar orbit and at the mean distance of the Earth from the Sun. The observations of the luminous lunar constant performed before 1934 by Scharonov gave 0·301 lux, and the new ones discussed by Sytinskaya (1932–1955) gave 0·342 lux. Moreover, from his very extended series of observations Graff obtained in 1914 the corresponding value equal to 0·303 lux. The mean of all these determinations comes out to be 0·322 lux within a small margin of error. On the other hand, the solar luminous constant, according to the latest summary prepared by Scharonov, may be taken as nearly 13·4 phot, within an error of about $\pm 0 \cdot 3$ phot. If so, the difference in illumination by the Moon and the Sun at standard conditions results as 14·04 $\pm 0 \cdot 05$ magn.

If we take account of these supplementary data, the following final results can be obtained:

TABLE VI

Stellar Magnitudes				
	(1)	(2)	(3)	
Sun	$-26 \cdot 59$	$-26 \cdot 76$	$-26 \cdot 80$	$(\pm 0 \cdot 03)$
Moon	$-12 \cdot 54$	$-12 \cdot 68$	$-12 \cdot 71$	$(\pm 0 \cdot 06)$

In conclusion, it is to be noted that the colour of the Moon does not differ greatly from that of the Sun. Indeed, according to the measurements by Rougier and Danjon made with different filters, the corresponding difference in colour indices is only 0·13 and 0·33. Taking, with

Rougier, the colour index for the Sun as 0·79, we obtain for the Moon 1·11. Very similar values are given also by Scharonov in his recent summary of the lunar colour according to different authors.

IV. Brightness of Surface Details

Let us consider now the results of measurements of the brightness of different lunar details. Originally, this brightness was estimated on the visual scale of Schröter, which in the hands of a trained observer can have a real scientific value. This scale is a purely conventional one, but it proved to be very uniform in representing corresponding brightnesses (see Table VII).

TABLE VII

Name of Representative Object	Scale Number	Albedo
Floor of Grimaldi and Riccioli	1	0·061
Floor of crater Boscovich	1·5	0·067
Floor of Julius Caesar and Endymion	2·0	0·074
Floor of Pitatus and Marius	2·5	0·081
Floor of Taruntius, Plinius, Flamsteed, Theophilus, Mercator	3·0	0·088
Floor of Hansen, Archimedes and Mersenius	3·5	0·095
Floor of Ptolemaeus, Manilius, Guericke	4·0	0·102
Environs of Aristillus	4·5	0·109
Wall of Arago, Landsberg, Bullialdus and the neighbourhood of Kepler	5·0	0·115
Wall of Picard, Timocharis, the rays of Copernicus	5·5	0·122
Wall of Macrobius, Kant, Bessel, Mösting and Flamsteed	6·0	0·129
Wall of Lagrange, La Hire, Theatetus	6·5	0·135
Wall of Feon Jun., Ariadaeus, Behaim and Bode B	7·0	0·142
Wall of Euclides, Ukert, Hortensius	7·5	0·149
Wall of Godin, Copernicus, Bode	8·0	0·156
Wall of Proclus, Bode A, Hipparchus C	8·5	0·163
Wall of Mersenius, Mösting A	9·0	0·169
Interior of Aristarchus	9·5	0·176
Central mountain of Aristarchus	10·0	0·183

This visual scale has not lost its value up to the present, although it is not sufficiently precise and remains somewhat subjective. Indeed, the lunar surface is distinguished by numerous heterogeneous details of different brightness and also of very different photometric behaviour. The ordinary visual or photoelectric photometer, intercepting a finite angular area, is not suitable for measurements of very fine details. It is sufficient to take a large-scale photograph at full Moon and at adjoining phases to be convinced of the photometric diversity and peculiarity of the lunar surface formations. Even such formations as the lunar "seas", which appear more or less smooth and flat, have in reality an abundance of spots of different brightness and colour. For instance, the floors of the craters and walled plains are generally dark, but their walls are seen at full Moon as bright thin rings. The bright rays are also very peculiar photometrically and exhibit very complicated structure. The cracks at full Moon appear as very thin bright streaks, but in other cases are dark enough. All these formations are of different nature and, as a matter of fact, must be studied individually, a task made difficult by the fine structure of their details.

The albedos of the same objects are given in the last column of the preceding table. As was shown by Sytinskaya, there exists some definite relation between the number N of the scale and the corresponding value of albedo, of the form

$$\rho = 0.047 - 0°136\,N.$$

It is seen that the brightness ratio between the darkest and the brightest details on the Moon does not exceed 3. The mountainous regions are, on the average, only 1·8 times brighter than the seas. This gradation is generally very small as compared with different terrestrial specimena. Besides, the scale under consideration can be applied only at full Moon. At other phase-angles the illumination of the Moon's surface becomes quite different, and this scale cannot be applied any more. Therefore, the real photometry of the Moon can be accomplished only by objective methods. But these methods have so far led to quite discordant results, owing to instrumental imperfections. For instance, according to photographic measurements by Goetz (1919) at Osterberg Observatory, the difference between the brightest and the darkest details was measured as 1·14 magn (2·9 times). Visual measurements of E. C. Pickering (1882) gave 5·5 magn (160 times); and Wislicenus, 2·3 magn (8·3 times).

Indeed, the primary photometric means are not very appropriate for measuring the lunar details. Thus Wislicenus observed simply the disappearance of the artificial point-source as formed in the Zoellner photometer on the bright lunar area. In fact, the first reliable photometric measurements on the Moon were accomplished by Goetz, who obtained six pictures of the Moon in 1913 and 1914 with a 5-inch refractor, and measured on the negatives of very good definition 55 separate points. In 1924, at Dorpat Observatory, Öpik also made a series of photographs of the Moon with a visual refractor, standardizing them with extra-focal images of different stars.

The measurements of Goetz were fully confirmed by Rosenberg (1921) at the same observatory of Osterberg, working with his well-known visual photometer. This photometer, manufactured by the

firm Askania Werke in Germany, was of very great value in the photometric and colorimetric researches of Scharonov, Sytinskaya and their
pupils. Schönberg, as was mentioned before, made his observations
with the aid of a visual photometer of his own construction, con-
centrating on several points close to the positive limb of the lunar
crescent and also along the equator. Fessenkov and his collaborators
measured photometrically seventeen pictures of the Moon, obtained at
different phases with the normal astrograph of Tashkent Observatory
in 1923–1924. The standardization was secured by the extra-focal
images of Polaris, with account being taken of its variability. Different
sources of possible errors, such as halo effect or variable brightness of
background were also taken into account. The measurements were
performed at regular intervals of 2 mm in a rectangular system of
coordinates, related with the selenographic ones by means of numerous
points of reference on the lunar surface. In such a manner the angles
of incidence, reflection, and phase could be derived for each set of
coordinates x and y.

But it was Barabashev who established first two basic photometric
laws for the Moon, amply verified by all subsequent work. Barabashev,
with his 10-inch reflector at Kharkov Astronomical Observatory,
obtained some thirty negatives of the Moon suitable for precise photometric analysis. He found that, at full Moon, the apparent brightness
of every detail attains a maximum, irrespective of its angular distance
from the centre of the lunar disk.

V. Laws of Reflection

The amount of light reflected from a given element of the lunar
surface depends, in general, on its albedo as well as on the angles of
incidence i, reflection ϵ and phase α. As the measurements are made
on the lunar disk at some definite phase-angle, it is reasonable to
suppose that the law of reflection can be represented by the product of
two different functions

$$\mathscr{I} = \Gamma f(i, \epsilon, \alpha)\phi(\alpha). \tag{3}$$

There are two laws of diffuse reflection. One is that of Lambert,
which is deduced simply by considering the emission of a solid incandescent body, appearing equally bright in all directions. Therefore,
the quantity of emitted light varies as the apparent size of emitting
area: namely, as $\cos \epsilon$. According to this law, the quantity of light
reflected at the angle ϵ from the area ds illuminated at the incidence
angle i is

$$\mathscr{I}\, ds = \Gamma \cos i \cos \epsilon \, ds. \tag{4}$$

1

Therefore, the apparent brightness of a given surface obeying this law is

$$j \sim \cos i.$$

For instance, a sphere illuminated by a distant source of light, when viewed at some small phase-angle, will appear bright at its centre, but completely dark at the edges. Something similar can be observed on the planet Mars, the surface of which is really covered by dust; but on the Moon the conditions are apparently quite different.

Lambert's law is completely devoid of any theoretical foundation, but satisfies fairly well the behaviour of smooth diffusing surfaces. For instance, according to the measurements of Barabashev, the reflection from a barium screen with a flat surface compares with Lambert's law at the same angles of incidence and reflection (see Table VIII) in the following manner:

TABLE VIII

Angle of Incidence: $i\pm$	80°	70°	60°	50°	40°	30°	20°	10°	0°
				$\epsilon = 0°$					
Lambert's Law:	0·17	0·34	0·50	0·64	0·77	0·87	0·94	0·99	1·00
Barium Screen:	0·17	0·35	0·48	0·63	0·74	0·84	0·92	0·98	1·00
				$\epsilon = 60°$					
Barium Screen:	0·07	0·27	0·42	0·55	0·67	0·74	0·79	0·98	1·00

It is seen that the agreement is very satisfactory at least for small angles of reflection.

Another law of diffuse reflection, that of Lommel-Seeliger, is based on some theoretical considerations; but its foundations are not wholly sound. It assumes that the incident light is not reflected at all by the surface of the body under consideration, but penetrates into its substance where it is diffused uniformly in all directions. Some fraction of light escapes to become observable. Under these assumptions, the resulting expression for the light emitted in the unity of solid angle in the direction of the observer, i.e. at reflection angle ϵ, is

$$\mathscr{I}\,ds = \frac{\Gamma \cos i \cos \epsilon \, ds}{\cos i + \lambda \cos \epsilon}. \tag{5}$$

The coefficient λ in the denominator of this expression enters by an artificial assumption that extinction of light penetrating into the substance is different from that of the outgoing one. As the difference between these rays grows with the phase angle, it is reasonable to suppose the coefficient λ to be a certain function of α. Besides this, the natural improvement of this expression rests in the introduction of some real scattering function, instead of spherical diffusion of light which never occurs in reality.

For the Rayleigh scattering by very small particles independent of each other, this function becomes

$$\phi(\alpha) = 1 + \cos^2 \alpha.$$

Generally, the quantity of light scattered by a diffusing surface according to Lommel-Seeliger law becomes

$$\mathscr{I}\,ds = \frac{\Gamma\phi(\alpha)\,\cos i\,\cos\epsilon\,ds}{\cos i + \lambda\cos\epsilon}, \qquad \Gamma = L\frac{\mu}{k}, \tag{6}$$

L being the incident illumination; μ and k, the coefficients of diffusion and extinction. The most appropriate value of λ is found to be

$$\lambda = 0.225(1 + \tan^2 \tfrac{1}{2}\alpha) \qquad \text{(Fessenkov).}$$

But even if we adopt this scheme, it is necessary to take into consideration the scattering of higher orders. The corresponding expression is not difficult to deduce (at least for the scattering of second order), but it assumes an extremely complicated and impracticable form which need not be given here. It may only be noted that the terms of second order are multiplied by the factor $(\mu/k)^2$; those of third order, by the factor $(\mu/k)^3$, etc. This factor depends not only on scattering but also on pure absorption, which may be very great for dark reflecting surfaces encountered on the Moon.

There exists a well-known relation

$$k = 2\pi\mu \int_0^\pi \phi(\alpha)\sin\alpha\,d\alpha + k_1, \tag{7}$$

between k and μ, where k_1 denotes the coefficient of pure absorption; and k, that of a resulting extinction. As is seen, the expression μ/k rapidly diminishes with increasing value of k_1. Therefore, for a smooth dark substance it can be assumed that its apparent brightness is represented by the expression

$$j \sim \frac{\phi(\alpha)\cos i}{\cos i + \lambda\cos\epsilon},$$

where the phase-function $\phi(\alpha)$ should be determined from the observations.

This was realized by Schönberg, who invoked two methods for estimating $\phi(\alpha)$: namely, by referring it to the positive limb of the lunar crescent, and to the whole Moon, at different phase-angles. Indeed, for the very limb of the Moon (where $\epsilon = 90°$), the observed brightness is represented as

$$j \sim \frac{\phi(\alpha) \cos i}{\cos i + \lambda \cos \epsilon} \sim \phi(\alpha). \tag{8}$$

For some area situated at a definite distance from the limb we have

$$\phi(\alpha) \sim \frac{j\alpha}{j_0} \frac{1 + \lambda \cos \epsilon_0 \sec i}{1 + \lambda},$$

where the angle ϵ_0 of reflection is referred to the area of reference at the distance from the centre r, so that $r = \sin \epsilon_0$.

Another method of determining $\phi(\alpha)$ is to compare the observed integral brightness of the Moon with its theoretical expression. Indeed, at a given phase-angle α we should have

$$Q = \phi(\alpha) \int \int f(i, \epsilon) \, ds, \tag{9}$$

where

$$ds = R^2 \cos b \, db \, dl$$

stands for the element of lunar surface in selenographical coordinates. Consequently,

$$Q = \Gamma \frac{\pi R^2}{2m} \phi(\alpha) \left\{ 2 \cos \frac{\alpha}{2} \cos \left(\mu - \frac{\alpha}{2} \right) \right.$$

$$\left. + \sin \alpha \sin(\mu - \alpha) \log \left(\cot \frac{\alpha - \mu}{2} \cot \frac{\mu}{2} \right) \right\} \tag{10}$$

and

$$\sin \alpha = m \sin \mu: \qquad \lambda + \cos \alpha = m \cos \mu.$$

If $\alpha = 0°$, then

$$Q_0 = \tfrac{3}{4} \Gamma \pi R^2 \phi(0); \qquad \phi(0) = 1.$$

A comparison of both expressions then furnishes $\phi(\alpha)$. As was pointed out by Schönberg, both methods lead (except for the coefficient of (proportionality) to the same results.

Another attempt to specify the law of reflection from the lunar surface was made by Bennett (1938) in his detailed photovisual investigation of fifty-nine points on the Moon at eleven different phase-angles. A filter with transmission in the region 4830–5900 Å was used, and the objective of the Clark refractor was stopped to 3 inches in order to prolong the exposure to several seconds for ease of timing. Standardization was ensured by a lamp etalon operated under controlled conditions, with a diffusing screen of known reflecting power. The necessary corrections for libration and lunar parallax were introduced in the coordinates of the corresponding points on the lunar disk.

The lunar points under investigation were chosen preferentially to lie near the equator of intensity: twenty points in the seas, twelve in the crater floors, eighteen in the mountain regions—with relatively smooth appearance, three in bright rays, and three in nimbes. Bennett was the first to show that the variation of brightness of the lunar details depended to a large extent on the angle of reflection ϵ as well as on the azimuth of the reflected ray referred to the plane of incidence. Bennett also tried to explain the photometric peculiarities of the lunar surface by its specific constitution, but applied rather arbitrarily the Lambert law to each element under consideration. A similar problem was considered previously also by Barabashev and Markov. These authors investigated the photometric behaviour of very steep ditches or cracks. Bennett considered not simple cracks, however, but ellipsoidal cavities the depth of which is considerably greater than width, and with a flat surface between them; but even in this manner he did not succeed in representing exactly the observed particularities of the Moon.

On the basis of Bennett's data, an attempt was made to deduce some general expression for reflection as a function of the angle of incidence by Tschunko (1949), who adopted some simplified expression of purely linear character representing the brightness of the lunar details. He stated that every point attained its maximum brightness just at full Moon; but beginning from $\alpha = 0°$ there was a very rapid decrease. Moreover, he deduced the approximate expressions for the integral brightness at different phase-angles which corresponded to reality.

At nearly the same time, in the summer of 1938, Scharonov and Sytinskaya organized the detailed investigation of the Moon with Rosenberg's visual photometer, attached to the normal astrograph of Tashkent Observatory. Their observing programme included numerous typical objects—such as seas, mountain regions, craters, bright rays— occurring in many parts of the lunar disk. The details near the equator

of intensity were measured with special care. Great attention was paid to the atmospheric extinction, determined by means of the same lunar details as observed at different zenith distances. Lastly, a careful standardization was undertaken with the aim of expressing all measured data on a uniform system of units.

The results obtained so far have been summarized in numerous Tables giving, for every object, the corresponding date of observations, the angles of incidence, reflection and phase, and the coefficient of brightness (i.e. the brightness of the object referred to an absolutely white screen under the same conditions of illumination). These results are illustrated by eighty-eight curves representing the brightness as the function of the angle ϵ (see Fig. 4). The general behaviour of all these graphs shows a very sharp maximum at $\alpha = 0°$, and a rapid fall with increasing α, nearly linear or with some curvature around $\alpha = 0°$. This linearity may be observed ordinarily in the case of symmetry around $\alpha = 0°$ for the point under consideration. But if this curve is unsymmetrical, i.e. if the observed point is situated at one side of the central meridian of the Moon and thus can be observed longer in one direction than in the other—then the photometric curve is clearly deformed in the direction of its greater extension. Such are the general photometric properties of all details on the Moon, which indicate the inapplicability of the far-reaching simplifications by Tschunko.

Very careful investigation on the photographic photometry of the Moon was carried out by Fedoretz (1952) with a luni-solar camera attached to the 160 cm refractor of the Kharkov Observatory. The size of the image was sufficiently large for the purpose: namely, 60 mm in diameter. In order to reduce all images to a common photometric system, each plate was provided with two images of the Moon taken at different phase-angles: in this manner all negatives were inter-connected. In addition, every plate was provided with extra-focal images of Polaris and other stars taken at different zenith distances in order to deduce the value of atmospheric extinction. The total number of lunar images at forty different phase-angles was nearly 160, and all were duly measured within the mean photometric error of the order of 0·01 magn. The halo effect, etc., was duly taken into account during the reductions.

The principal results of this work can be summarized as follows:

(1) At $\alpha = 0°$, the brightness of different details on the Moon is independent of their distances from the centre and attains their maximum values.

(2) Near $\alpha = 0$, the variation in brightness is very rapid.

(3) In some cases, the maximum is displaced from $\alpha = 0$ in the sense

of the Sun's culmination above a given detail (for the craters Tycho, Copernicus, etc.). It is interesting to note that the lunar seas have nearly the same photometric properties as the mountain regions, but the bright rays and also some bright craters are characterized by much more sharp maxima near $\alpha = 0°$. The highest contrast in relation to

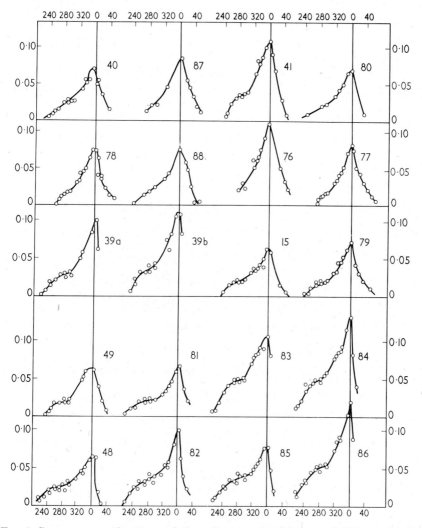

FIG. 4. Curves representing the variation of apparent brightness of different details on the lunar surface as function of the phase-angle α before and after full Moon ($\alpha > 0$ before full Moon; $\alpha < 0$ after full Moon). After Sytinskaya and Scharonov (*Utch. Zapisky Univ. Leningrad*, No. 153, 1952).

the neighbouring regions appears to be in the rays of Aristarchus (the corresponding difference being 0·58 magn).

N. S. Orlova (1956) discussed the lunar photometric catalogues of Scharonov and Fedoretz with the aim of deducing some conclusions about the structure of the lunar surface. She chose the same type of objects on the Moon and constructed for them the mean indices of reflection at every angle ϵ for constant angles of incidence and phase. These indices appear to possess some very remarkable properties. They are elongated in the direction of the incident ray wherever $i = \epsilon$ (i.e. $\alpha = 0°$). This elongation, very great in itself, seems to increase with the angle of incidence. The indices for the mountainous regions and for the seas are nearly the same; the latter being somewhat more elongated, as illustrated by Fig. 5.

Lastly, it should be mentioned that an extensive careful investigation concerning the photometric properties of several homogeneous objects was recently made by van Diggelen (1959) at the Utrecht Observatory.

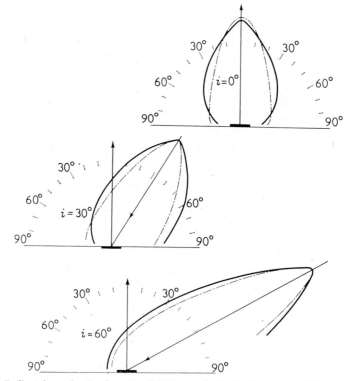

FIG. 5. Indicatrices of reflection: the full lines refer to the lunar mountainous regions; the dotted lines, to the maria. After Orlova, *Astr. J. U.S.S.R.*, **33**, 93, 1956.

The corresponding measurements were performed on photographs obtained by Minnaert at Yerkes Observatory in 1946, for five different phase-angles of the Moon. A total of thirty-eight crater floors was investigated. The corresponding wavelength was nearly 5500 Å. The photographs used for this purpose were not standardized at all, but only calibrated with a tube photometer. Nevertheless, they could be related to the same photometric system by use of the phase-function for integral brightness of the Moon as obtained by Rougier and mentioned previously. This procedure required a large amount of supplementary work; namely, the measurement of several thousand points distributed over the whole disk of the Moon, needed to deduce the corresponding integral brightness for every exposure for the sake of comparison with that of Rougier.

Generally, the results obtained so far by different authors are in fair agreement, which indicates that the photometric properties of the floor of lunar craters are nearly the same as those of other regions.

VI. Colorimetric Characteristics

Some supplementary data about the nature of the lunar surface can be obtained from colour measurements. However, the results in this respect differ somewhat, depending on the method of investigation. If, for instance, the colour is obtained by a colorimeter or deduced from a spectrogram, the differences between the colours of various details are found to be smaller than if we use the photographs taken with different filters and referring, in fact, not exactly to the same points.

For instance, Wilsing and Scheiner at Potsdam Observatory, working in 1907–1910 with a spectrograph standardized by reference to a black body, showed that the differences in the apparent colour temperature of different lunar regions were not very great—ranging somewhere about 4000°–4300° for bright objects and 4700° for dark ones (seas). The lowest colour temperature, equal to 4200°, was obtained for the mountainous region near Proclus and the highest for Mare Crisium, as well as for the floor of Grimaldi. But the colour temperatures for the terrestrial rocks investigated with the same spectrograph—forty-seven in number—showed a much greater range: namely, from 3500° to 5900°.

Similarly, Vigroux (1956) at the Haute Provence Observatory, investigating the Moon by means of a spectrograph in the range 3500–6300Å, did not find any noticeable difference in colour, with very few exceptions (for instance, in Mare Tranquilitatis). Their

general conclusion was that all details of the lunar surface were nearly
of the same colour.

Fessenkov, working with blue-wedge colorimeter, likewise also
obtained but very small differences; exceeding scarcely 400° in colour
temperature. Analogous results were obtained also by Radlova at
Tashkent Observatory with a similar instrument: namely, colour
temperatures ranging from 5220° to 5550°, and corresponding to
spectral classes G1–G3, or to colour indices of 0·95–1·16. This very
small dispersion in colour was also confirmed by some additional
experiments of Sharonov, but the filter observations of Barabashev
and Tchekirda show much greater differences in colour. The reason
for these divergencies is not yet clear. Nevertheless, some differences
in colour of the lunar details are evidenced by direct colour photography. In some exceptional cases, these differences may become very
large—as, for instance, in the case of the Wood object discovered
near the crater Aristarchus by comparison of pictures taken in the
ultra-violet and infra-red light.

According to the latest work of Barabashev, the most reddish details
are mountainous regions—Tycho, its ramparts, the Wood spot; the
most greenish-dark region near Kepler—the region to the West of
Plato; the most bluish—Mare Frigoris and the floor of Grimaldi; but
the absolute differences are very small. In fact, the lunar surface is
nearly of the same colour (see Fig. 6).

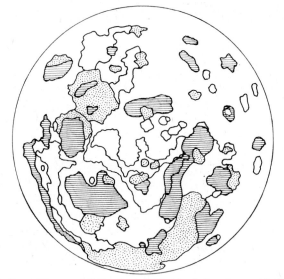

FIG. 6. Distribution of the most distinctly reddish (shaded) and greenish (dotted) regions
on the Moon (after Barabashev and Tchekirda, *Trud. Kharkov. Astr. Obs.* **3**, 13, 1954).

Sytinskaya pointed out that it is preferable to work simultaneously with both the brightness and colour characteristics, as may be seen from the diagram which she constructed (see Fig. 7 on which the

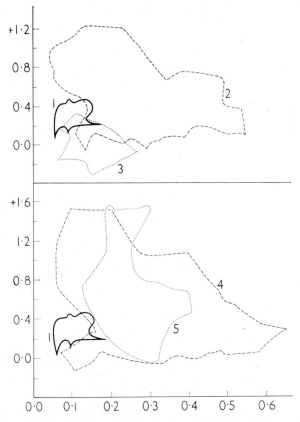

Fig. 7. A colour-brightness diagram for lunar details (solid line "1") and for different terrestrial specimena (dotted lines, 2, 3, 4, 5). After Shcaranov, "The Nature of the Planets", Moscow 1958, p. 380.

abscissae represent the brightness; and the ordinates, the colours). The curve (1) related to the objects on the Moon's surface, those (2, 3, 4, 5) to the terrestrial specimena—acid magmatic rocks (granite); basic and ultra-basic rocks (basalts, etc.); limestone and conglomerates, respectively. As it is seen, the details on the Moon are characterized by very small dispersion in colours and brightnesses—in striking contrast with one on the Earth.

This fact cannot be understood by only considering the differences in petrographic structure of the lunar surface. It is more probable that the lunar rocks, exposed to interplanetary space and subjected continuously to the impact of primary cosmic rays and meteoritic bombardment, must eventually become of very porous and spongy structure. A meteorite falling on the lunar surface can destroy and vaporize a quantity of matter several thousand times greater than its own weight. The matter of the lunar rocks then mixes with that of the meteorites after solidification. This process must necessarily tend to diminish the differences in colour between the various details on the Moon without obliterating them completely.

In order to characterize the spectral distribution of the brightness of different objects on the Moon, let us summarize Barabashev's results obtained with five different colour filters:

TABLE IX

Object	Effective wavelength				
	λ8400	6800	5020	4150	3650
Craters with rays	−0·778	−0·606	0·000	0·329	0·419
Mountain regions	−0·859	−0·540	0·000	0·296	0·448
Seas	−0·852	−0·579	0·000	0·241	0·409
Crater floors	−0·853	−0·530	0·000	0·153	0·268
Bright rays	−0·778	−0·491	0·000	0·371	0·479

These data are expressed in stellar magnitudes, relatively to a white screen illuminated by the Sun and related to the green part of the spectrum.

The photometric behaviour of minor lunar details, in exceptional cases, can vary with the time. For instance, the bright halo around Linné, a well-known crater in Mare Serenitatis, is subject to small variations in size and brightness. Near 1930, Lohrmann evaluated its brightness on the scale of Schröter, as 7°; in 1866, Schmidt gave 5°.5; W. H. Pickering in 1897 gave also 5°.5; and Markov, in 1915, 7°.0. These variations, referred to the full Moon, correspond to 0·2 magn, i.e. a rather small quantity. Nevertheless, Markov is convinced of its reality. Furthermore, the size of its halo always varies during the lunar eclipses—from 5 km at the entrance in the shadow, to 9 km at the middle of eclipse, and to 5·5 km at its end.

The white spot in Plato likewise appears to be subject to some variations. Its general photometric behaviour is very similar to that of the bright rays, attaining maximum relative brightness at full Moon, but merging with other details at low position of the sun. According to Wirtz (1869–1871), Stanley Williams (1881–1884), and W. H. Pickering (1899), the brightness of this sector somewhat varies in connection with some alteration of the spots inside it. Between 1870 and 1890, the contrast of this detail apparently became greater; later it diminished and afterwards remained constant. In addition, some observers—especially W. H. Pickering—repeatedly reported other considerable variations—such as the appearances of bright and dark spots, etc. Some of these variations were confirmed by Christie at the Jamaica station of Harvard Observatory in 1921.

VII. Conclusions

The photometric properties of the Moon are of the greatest importance for any conclusions about the nature and structure of its surface. It is evident that the lunar surface has nothing in common with ordinary diffusing surfaces, obeying, in some degree, Lambert's law; and, consequently, it cannot be covered by some uniform layer of dust as some authors—for instance, Wesselink—have supposed, on the basis of thermal radiation of the Moon (cf. Chapter 11).

The conclusions concerning the structure of the Moon's surface were drawn originally on the basis of purely theoretical considerations, but lately by way of direct comparison with different terrestrial models. A most extensive work of this kind was made by Orlova in the laboratory of Leningrad University with a specially constructed indicator. This instrument permits the comparison of every sample with a standard plate normally illuminated, at different angles of incidence and reflection. As can be seen from the survey of the indices for numerous samples investigated in this way, the following are the principal types of reflection for terrestrial minerals: (1) orthotropic ones, which satisfy Lambert's law—at least for the angles of incidence between 0°–40°; (2) reflecting ones, with maximum of intensity in the direction of the regularly reflected ray; (3) completely rough ones with a maximum of reflexion in the direction of incident ray; and (4) mixed ones, with two maxima in the directions of regularly reflected and incident rays.

Each of these types also has several sub-divisions. It was stated that each specimen of terrestrial mountainous rocks can be referred to some definite type of this classification (Fig. 8). Magmatic rocks, such as granites and basalts, with sufficiently flat surfaces, are conspiciously of type 2. Generally speaking, the minerals which split naturally belong to this type, with a maximum in the direction of regularly reflected ray (selenite, apatite, gematite, nepheline, diabase, gneiss, sandstone, etc.) (Fig. 9). The flat layers of sand are of the first type; on the other hand, the volcanic slugs and slugged lava, as well as

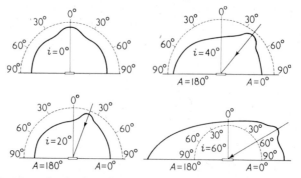

Fig. 8. Indicatrices of reflection of quartz sand (grain size 0·07–0·11 mm) for 0°, 20°, 40° and 60° angles of incidence (after Orlova, *Utch. Zap. Univ. Leningrad*, No. 153, 1952).

different kinds of tufts, are related to the third type, with some analogy with the Moon (see Figs. 8 and 9). In fact, it is found that the surface of the Moon must be classified into the third type; but it is characterized by very much greater elongation of the corresponding index in the direction of incident beam, greatly surpassing every terrestrial sample. Consequently, according to these results, the lunar surface exhibits the greatest similarity with models covered by deep holes with vertical walls and sharp edges.

The analogous laboratory experiments on different substances were also performed by van Diggelen (1959) in his interpretation of the properties of the crater floors. He found that a layer of agglomerated stones or volcanic ashes does not conform to the observations. On the contrary, the photometric properties of the Moon can be partly explained by models, the surface of which consists of porous wells for two-thirds, and the depth of which is much greater than the width. Other experiments were carried out by him, based on the assumption that the lunar surface can be compared with some very porous substance, replete with torn or broken details as, for instance, the layer

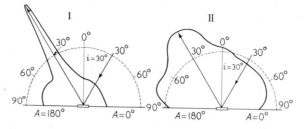

Fig. 9. Indicatrices of reflection for reddish (I) and white (II) selenites (after Orlova, *Utch. Zap. Univ. Leningrad*, No. 153, 1952).

of lichens. The bright rays diverging radially from some craters cannot represent any deposit of tektites (glassy meteorites), the lunar origin of which is strongly advocated by some writers, but they can be approximated by a surface covered by holes or indentations over three-quarters of the total area.

Another insight into the nature of the lunar surface can be obtained by an inspection of equation (6), where $\phi(\alpha)$ is an empirical function of phase-angle for the brightness of the positive limb of the Moon. Indeed, this simple formula satisfies all basic properties of the photometry of the Moon, i.e. the independence on reflection angle and maximum brightness of every detail at full Moon, true representation of the integral brightness at every phase-angle, as well as the indices of reflection at every angle of incidence. For instance, adopting the curve of Danjon for the positive limb of the Moon, we can calculate, according to expression (10), the following value for its integral brightness (see Table X).

TABLE X

Representation of the integral brightness of the Moon

Angle of phase:	$\alpha = 0°$	90°	120°
Calculated according to equation (10)	1·00	0·0956	0·0313
Observed (Russell)	1·00	0·107	0·0315
Observed (Rougier)	1·00	0·0824	0·0249

Moreover, Fig. 10 gives the calculated indices of reflection represented, as usual, in polar co-ordinates for every ϵ and for the angles of incidence between 0° and 60°. As can be seen, the representation of observations is sufficiently good. Curiously enough, the photometric behaviour of every detail on the Moon, as well as its integral brightness

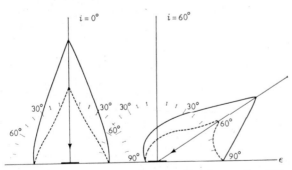

Fig. 10. Theoretical indicatrices of reflection according to equation (10). The dotted lines correspond to the case of $\lambda = 1$.

at each phase-angle, can be represented by single function referring to the positive limb of the lunar crescent; this indicates that all lunar details have apparently the same structural properties. This microstructure is such as to give a very strong maximum of reflection in the backward direction; therefore, the effective indices of scattering cannot be that of small unhomogeneities, but of grains considerably greater than the wavelength of visible light.

It appears that the lunar surface is covered by a layer composed of an extremely porous substance, containing separate grains which are capable of reflecting light backwards and to cast shadows in their neighbourhood. A more complete understanding of the nature of the lunar surface can emerge only from a renewed thorough discussion of all observational data available up to this time.

References

Barabashev, N. P. (1924). *Astr. Nachr.* **221**, 289.
Barabashev, N. P. (1925). *Astr. J. U.S.S.R.* **1**.
Barabashev, N. P. (1929). *Publ. Kharkov. Astr. Obs.* **1**, 35.
Barabashev, N. P. (1952) *Astr. Circ. Acad. Sci. U.S.S.R.* No. 127.
Barabashev, N. P. and Tchekirda, A. T. (1945). *Astr. J. U.S.S.R.* **22**, 11.
Barabashev, N. P. and Tchekirda, A. T. (1954). *Trav. Kharkov Univ.* **3**, 13.
Barabashev, N. P. and Tchekirda, A. T. (1956). *Astr. J., U.S.S.R.* **33**, 549.
Bennett, A. L. (1938). *Astrophys. J.* **88**, 1.
Bond, W. C. (1861). *Mem. Amer. Acad. Arts Sci.*, NS. 8.
Bullrich, K. (1948). *Ber. deutsch. Wetterdienstes U.S. Zone*, No. 4.
Calder, W. A. (1936). *Bull. Astr. Obs. Harv.* No. 904.
Calder, W. A. (1938). *Ann. Harv. Coll. Obs.* **105**, 445.
Christie, W. H. M. (1921). *Mon. Not. R. Astr. Soc.* **81**, 451.
Danjon, A. (1933). *Ann. Obs. Strasbourg*, **3**, 139.
Danjon, A. (1949). *Bull Astr.* **14**, 315.
Diggelen, J. van (1959). *Rech. Astr. Obs. Utrecht*, **14**, No. 2.
Ensley, E. (1937). *J. Brit. Astr. Ass.* **48**, 76.
Fabry, Ch. (1903). *C.R. Acad. Sci. Paris*, **137**, 973, 1242.
Fedoretz (1952). *Utch. Zap. Kharkow Univ.* **42**, 49.
Fessenkov, V. G., Staude, N., Vinogradova, E. and Barantseva, M. (1926). *Astr. J. U.S.S.R.* **3**, 75.
Fessenkov, V. G., Staude, N. and Parenago, P. (1928). *Publ. Astro. Inst. Russ.* **4**, 1.
Fessenkov, V. G. (1928). *Astr. J., U.S.S.R.* **5**, 219.
Fessenkov, V. G. (1928). *Astr. Nachr.* **236**, 7.
Fessenkov, V. G. and Parenago, P. P. (1929). *Astr. J., U.S.S.R.* **6**.
Goetz, W. (1919). *Veröff. Astr. Sternw. Oesterberg-Tübingen*, No. 1.
Graff, K. (1914). *Astr. Nachr.* **198**, 14, 483.
Graff, K. (1949). *Mitt. Sternw. Wien*, **4**, No. 6.
Güssow, K. (1937). *Die Sterne*, **17**, 91.

Herschel, F. J. W. (1847). "Results of Astronomical Observations made at the Cape of Good Hope". London.

Johnson, H. (1955). *Ann. Astrophys.* **18**, 202.

Kaiser, H. (1937). *Himmelswelt*, **47**, 110.

Kariaguina, Z. (1955). *Izv. Astrophys. Inst. Alma-Ata*, **1**, Nos. 1–2.

Keenan, P. C. (1931). *Publ. Astr. Soc. Pacif.* **43**, 203.

King, E. S. (1909). *Ann. Harv. Coll. Obs.* **59**, Part 3, 63.

King, E. S. (1912). *Ann. Harv. Coll. Obs.* **59**, 248.

King, E. S. (1922). *Pop. Astr.* **30**, 617.

Markov, A. (1923). *Bull. Soc. Astr. Russe*, 165.

Markov, A. (1924). *Astr. Nachr.* **221**, 65.

Markov, A. (1927) *Astr. Nachr.* **231**, 57.

Markov, A. (1927). *Astr. J., U.S.S.R.* **4**, 60.

Markov, A. (1950). *Byull. Abastuman Astro-fiz. Obs.* No. 11, 107.

Markov, A. (1952). *Izv. Astr. Obs., Pulkovo*, **19**, No. 149.

Markov, A. and Barabashev, N. (1925) *Astr. Nachr.* **226**, 129.

Markov, A. and Barabashev, N. (1926). *Astr. J., U.S.S.R.* **3**, 55.

Martynov, D. Y. (1959), *Astr. J., U.S.S.R.* **36**.

Nikonova, E. (1949). *Izv. Crimean Astrophys. Obs.* **4**, 114.

Öpik, E. (1924). *Publ. Obs. Tartu*, **16**, No. 1.

Orlova, N. S. (1941). *Utch. Zap. Univ. Leningrad*, No. 82.

Orlova, N. S. (1952). *Utch. Zap. Univ. Leningrad*, No. 153.

Orlova, N. S. (1955). *Astr. Circ. Acad. Sci. U.S.S.R.* No. 156.

Orlova, N. S. (1956). *Astr. J., U.S.S.R.* **33**, 93.

Orlova, N. S. (1957). *Vestn. Univ. Leningrad*, No. 152–157.

Pettit, E. (1935). *Astrophys. J.* **81**, 17.

Pettit, E. (1940). *Astrophys. J.* **91**, 408.

Pettit, E. and Nicholson, S. B. (1930). *Astrophys. J.* **71**, 102.

Pickering, E. C. (1882). *Selenographical J.*

Pickering, W. H. (1908). *Ann. Harv. Coll. Obs.* **61**, 56.

Pickering, W. H. (1917). *Pop. Astr.* **25**, 149.

Pickering, W. H. (1924). *Pop. Astr.* **39**, 302.

Pickering, W. H. (1926). *J. Brit. Astr. Ass.* **37**, 65, 98.

Puiseux, P. (1908). "La Terre et la Lune", Paris.

Puiseux, P. (1917). *Bull. Astr. Soc. France*, **30**, 113.

Radlova, L. N. (1941). *Utch. Zap. Univ. Leningrad*, **32**, 99.

Radlova, L. N. (1943). *Astr. J., U.S.S.R.* **20**, 1.

Rosenberg, H. (1921). *Astr. Nachr.* **214**, 137.

Rougier, G. (1933). *Ann. Obs. Strasbourg*, **2**, 205.

Rougier, G. (1934). *J. Phys. Radium*, **5**, 25.

Rougier, G. (1934). *Astronomie*, **48**, 224, 228.

Russell, H. N. (1916). *Astrophys. J.* **43**, 103.

Scharonov, V. V. (1934). *Astr. J., U.S.S.R.* **11**, 225.

Scharonov, V. V. (1954). *Astr. J., U.S.S.R.* **31**, 442.

Scharonov, V. V. (1956). *Astr. Circ. Acad. Sci. U.S.S.R.* No. 166.

Scharonov, V. V. (1958). "The Nature of Planets", Moscow (in Russian).

Schönberg, E. (1925). *Acta. Soc. Sci. Fenn.* **50**, No. 9.

Schönberg, E. (1929). *Handb. Astrophys.* II, **1**, 68.

Stebbins, J. and Kron, G. E. (1957), *Astrophys. J.* **126**, 266.

Sytinskaya, N. (1953). *Astr. J., U.S.S.R.* **30**, 295.

Sytinskaya, N. (1956). "The Moon and its Observations", Moscow (in Russian).
Sytinskaya, N. (1957). *Astr. J.*, *U.S.S.R.* **34**, 899.
Sytinskaya, N. (1957). *Vop. Kosmogonii, Akad. Nauk. S.S.S.R.*, **5**, 13.
Sytinskaya, N. and Scharonov, V. V. (1952). *Utch. Zap. Univ. Leningrad*, No. 153.
Tschunko, H. F. A. (1949). *Z. Astrophys.* **26**, 279.
Vigroux, E. (1956). *J. Observateurs*, **39**, 134.
Wesselink, A. J. (1948). *Bull. Astr. Insts Netherlds*, **10**, 351.
Wesselink, A. J. (1954). *Observatory*, **74**, 215.
Wirtz, C. (1915). *Astr. Nachr.* **201**, 289.
Wood, R. W. (1910). *Mon. Not. R. Astr. Soc.* **70**, 226.
Wood, R. W. (1912). *Astrophys. J.* **36**, 75.
Woolley, R. v. d. R., and Gascoine, S. C. B. (1948). *Mon. Not. R. Astr. Soc.* **108**, 491.
Wright, F. E. (1929). *Publ. Astr. Soc. Pacif.* **41**, 125.
Zinner, E. (1926). *Bamberg Veröff.* No. 2.
Zoellner, F. (1865). "Photometrische Untersuchungen". Leipzig.

CHAPTER 5

The Polarization of Moonlight

AUDOUIN DOLLFUS

I. Introduction... 131
II. Polarization of Light from the Whole Disk..................... 132
III. Polarization by Different Regions of the Disk................. 133
IV. Polarization of Light by Mineral Substances................... 134
V. Substances with Vitreous Surfaces............................. 134
VI. Slightly Absorbing Powdered Substances........................ 137
VII. Substances with Rough or Diffusing Surfaces................... 141
VIII. Powdered Opaque Substances.................................... 143
IX. The Interpretation of the Polarization of the Light from the Moon.. 144
X. Origin of the Powdery Nature of Lunar Ground................. 146
XI. Polarization of the Ashen Light of the Moon.................. 148
XII. The Study of the Polarization of Ashen Light................. 150
XIII. Origin of the Polarization of the Ashen Light............... 151
XIV. Polarization Curve of the Earth.............................. 151
XV. The Nature of the Lunar Ground............................... 153
XVI. The Investigation of an Atmosphere Surrounding the Moon......... 154
References... 159

I. Introduction

As is well known, the light which illuminates the Moon comes from the Sun. The transverse vibrations of which it is composed are of equal intensity in different directions. When falling on the surface of the Moon, solar light is reflected, refracted, scattered and absorbed; and a part of it is sent off again in all directions. The intensities of the vibrations for the different planes are, however, no longer equal and the light becomes partially polarized.

The difference I_1-I_2 between the maximum intensity and that in a direction perpendicular to this is a measure of the quantity of polarized light. The ratio of the polarized light to the total light—i.e. the proportion of polarized light is then usually expressed as

$$P = \frac{I_1-I_2}{I_1+I_2}.$$

This proportion of polarized light should depend essentially on the nature of the surface of the Moon. By examining the polarized light from different parts of the lunar disk at different phases we should, therefore, be able to determine the polarizing properties of the material which covers the lunar surface. In the laboratory we may look for

131

samples offering the same properties; we shall proceed to identify them and to attempt, in some measure, to reconstitute the nature of the surface of the Moon.

The polarization of the light is caused by the structure of the Moon's surface at a microscopic level, and is not much affected by undulation, rills and depressions, which have a greater effect on the total intensity of the light. Polarization can, however, reveal the fine texture of the surface, as it would appear if we were able to examine it under a microscope.

II. Polarization of Light from the Whole Disk

The first research into lunar polarization was carried out by Arago as far back as 1811. Around 1860 Secchi obtained more reliable results, despite the still fairly crude apparatus which he had at his disposal (Secchi, 1859, 1860, 1860a). He discovered that, towards quadrature, the direction of the vibration with maximum intensity is perpendicular to the "plane of vision" containing the directions of illumination and of observation, as in the simple case of reflection. The proportion of polarized light was found to be the same in regions of different brightness; towards quadrature it was stronger on the dark regions and maria. About 1878 Lord Rosse and Parsons obtained some similar results when studying the dark patch of Mare Crisium. Landerer (1889, 1890) produced some measurements with a different instrument and in 1927 Barabashev obtained other results, more numerous but still fairly conflicting.

The first detailed and precise analysis of the polarization of the light from the Moon dates from 1924 and is due to Lyot (1924). Its success was due to the high sensitivity of the polarimeter invented by this brilliant astro-physicist (cf. Lyot, 1929). He showed that the direction of polarization was always exactly perpendicular or exactly parallel to the plane of vision. By alloting the proportion of polarized light with the positive sign (+) for the first case and the negative sign (−) for the second, Lyot was able to describe completely the properties of the polarization of the light from the whole disk by means of a single "curve of polarization". The latter is obtained by plotting the phase angle along the abscissa and the proportion of polarized light, together with its sign, along the ordinate.

This curve is reproduced in Fig. 1, and Lyot described it as follows: "The maximum is 0·066 when the Moon waxes, and 0·088 when it wanes. This difference arises because the maria occupy twice as large an extent in the last quarter as in the first. About two days before full Moon, when the angle of vision has a value 23° 30', the polarization goes to zero and reappears, a few hours later, in a perpendicular plane. It then passes through a negative minimum of 0·012 at an angle of 11°, then bends rapidly enough towards zero as to disappear at the same time as the angle of vision."

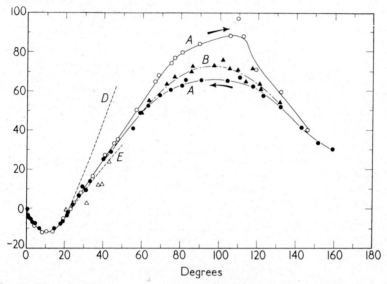

Fig. 1. The polarization curve of the Moon (after Lyot, 1929). Abscissae: proportion of polarized light of the Moon and Mercury (in units of 0·001). Ordinates: phase-angle (in degrees).

III. Polarization by Different Regions of the Disk

A detailed study of the polarization of the light on the different patches and regions on the surface of the Moon has also been undertaken by Lyot (1929). The direction of the maximum vibration was found to be exactly the same, at each point on the disk, with a precision better than half a degree, even at the edge of the limb where the lunar surface is greatly foreshortened.

Nevertheless, at the time of the full Moon, when the phase angle is very small and the observations are carried out from nearly the same direction as that of the illuminating source, Lyot observed at the extreme limb of the disk, under very oblique illumination, a faint polarization of 1 to 2 thousandths having the maximum vibration normal to the lunar edge. Only linear polarization has been encountered; no elliptical polarization was detected. Towards the time of quadrature the proportion of polarized light varies greatly from one point to another over the disk; it is maximum on the dark regions and minimum on the bright regions; it varies approximately in an inverse proportion according to the brightness of the measured region. On the bright regions it remains reasonably constant from one point on the disk to another; it is more variable in the different regions of the maria.

From first quarter to full Moon, the polarization of all the regions diminishes and approaches that which is shown by the general light of our satellite, and the differences between the land and the maria, so conspicuous around the times of quadrature, become nearly undetectable. Figure 1 shows this phenomenon clearly: the continuous curve A gives the general polarization of the Moon, the dotted curves D and E correspond to two regions where the polarization is the strongest (Oceanus Procellarum, east of Kepler—Mare Serenitatis, west of Linné) and where the polarization is the weakest (Hipparchus). The polarization was also found to depend, to a small extent, on the angle of incidence of the illuminating rays, but to increase somewhat along the terminator where the illumination becomes very oblique.

Lyot's results were completed by Wright (1935) who directed the Carnegie Institution Moon Committee until 1938. The complete polarization curves of 24 lunar regions were determined (cf. Wright, 1927, 1935, 1936). In 1949, Öhman obtained the polarization curve of Mare Serenitatis using a photographic polarimeter, and secured plates of the Moon showing polarization in certain regions. The results obtained by the author (Dollfus, 1955) on some smaller regions of the surface of the Moon will be found below.

IV. Polarization of Light by Mineral Substances

In order to interpret the nature of the lunar ground, some polarimetric research was carried out in the laboratory—first by Lyot, then by Wright and more recently in a synthetic fashion by the author (cf. Dollfus, 1955, 1956). The general study which follows will allow substances to be classified first into several groups. By selection into convenient groups, numerous substances will be eliminated and an initial picture be obtained. A more detailed study of these groups will thereby provide more precise information.

The principal polarimetric characters of groups investigated by the author are as follows.

V. Substances with Vitreous Surfaces

A part I_s of the incident light is reflected by the surface and acquires a proportion P_s of polarized light. The remainder of the light I_i

penetrates to the interior of the substance where it is partially absorbed and diffused; a small proportion K of the light is sent out and undergoes a refraction, which polarizes the light in the proportion P_i and in a perpendicular direction to that P_s given by the reflection on the surface. The resulting polarization is then the resultant of the two fluxes I_s and KI_i as given by

$$P = \frac{P_s I_s + P_i K I_i}{I_s + K I_i}.$$

When the surface is vitreous, P_s, P_i, I_s and I_i are entirely determined by Fresnel's laws of reflection and refraction, as a function of refractive index and of the geometry of the surface for all angles of illumination and of observation. The value of K depends on the absorption, on the diffusion and on the internal structure of the material.

If the surface is a plane, the flux I_s is concentrated in direction in accordance with the normal laws of reflection, where it gives a very strong polarization under the Brewster angle of illumination. In other directions the re-emitted light emanates mainly from the interior of the body; the polarization is then due to refraction, the vibrations being maximized in the plane containing the normal to the surface and the direction of observation and their proportion increasing with the inclination to the surface.

Figure 2 shows a result of measurements carried out on a specimen of milky quartz with a nearly plane vitreous surface. The top left-hand curve gives the variation in the proportion of polarized light as a function of the angle v between the directions of illumination and of observation, for a line of sight normal to the surface.

The curves to the right give the variations of polarization under different angles v when the surface is inclined from both sides of the direction of the observer, the normal being in the plane of sight. The direction of exact reflection gives pronounced maximum of polarization, under an inclination exactly equal to half the angle of sight v.

The curves on the left give the polarization for an inclination of the normal in the plane perpendicular to the plane of sight; if we ignore the accidental reflections under small angles of sight which can be attributed to the minor irregularities of the surface, the polarization is entirely due to the refracted light emanating from the substance. A molten vitreous flow, the surface of a calm water or ice, polarizes light in this manner. A less smooth surface reflects light in different directions; the maximum of polarization is spread out and becomes less pronounced. This phenomenon, as observed on a piece of sugar, is illustrated on Fig. 3.

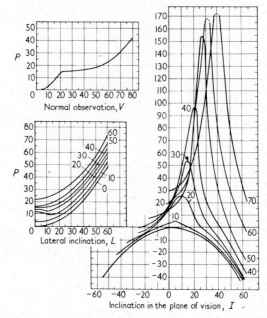

FIG. 2. Polarization by a scattering homogeneous substance with a plane vitreous surface (quartz sandstone); (after Dollfus, 1956).

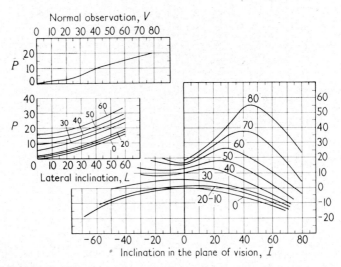

FIG. 3. Polarization by a granular transparent substance with an irregular vitreous surface (a piece of sugar); (after Dollfus, 1956).

If the material is not transparent, light having penetrated into its interior is partly absorbed and re-emitted with reduced intensity. The polarization is then produced practically solely by the surface and becomes much more pronounced. Figure 4 has been obtained from quartz substance; under normal observation the polarization increases very rapidly with the angle of sight and the curves under different inclinations are more separated.

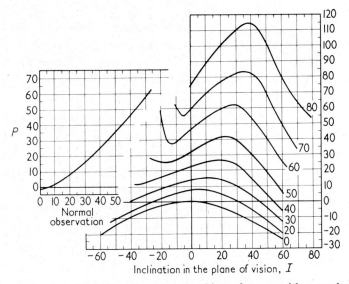

Fig. 4. Polarization of light by a granular absorbing substance with a rough vitreous surface (quartz sandstone); (after Dollfus, 1956).

These different characteristics allow one to reconstruct at a distance the smoothness and transparency of the matter by a simple examination of the polarization. In particular, if substances with vitreous surfaces occur in appreciable amounts on the surface of the Moon, they would show a bright patch in the direction of regular reflection; even if this patch were too weak or too widespread to be detected by the eye, polarimetry would still reveal a concentration of very strongly polarized light. From an absence of such observed phenomena, one must exclude all vitreous substances from the surface of the Moon even in very small amounts.

VI. Slightly Absorbing Powdered Substances

The properties of these substances appear in Fig. 5 corresponding to powdered glass. The transparent particles are crowded together;

the facets, orientated at random, give specular reflection in all directions. The polarization is largely unified by the different inclinations; the maxima of the polarized light are flattened.

For large angles of sight, the polarization curves under lateral inclination are concave; in fact, under small inclinations, some facets send out again towards the observer a reflected light favouring the vibration perpendicular to the plane of sight; for large inclinations the light coming from inside the grains is refracted very obliquely and gives rise again to polarization. Some pulverized substances, deposits of transparent crystals, powders of chlorides, nitrates or non-tinted carbonates, fresh snow and hoar frost exhibit these criteria of polarization.

When the material is less transparent, the light coming from inside the powder is absorbed. The polarization increases and the curves spread out as shown in Fig. 6 corresponding to mildly tinted sand. The quartz sedimentary formations, such as sands, are of such importance on the Earth that they have been made the object of a detailed

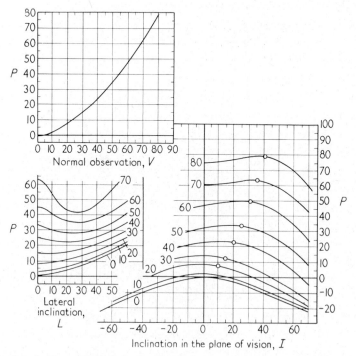

Fig. 5. Polarization of light by a powdery substance, consisting of transparent grains of powdered glass (after Dollfus, 1956).

study by A. Cailleux and the author of this article (cf. Dollfus and Cailleux, 1950).

On silica sands, made transparent by dissolving their ferruginous coatings by hydrochloric acid, the main contribution is due to the light from the interior; consequently, the shape of the polarization curve scarcely depends on the state of the surface of the grains. In Fig. 7, grains rounded and polished under the action of water (EL_1 and EL_2) and a non-worn out specimen (NU) give similar curves with a relatively flat maximum of polarization.

The ordinary sands, more or less tinted by iron oxides are partially absorbing. The polarization then depends mainly on the nature of the surface. Figure 8 gives the curves for the same specimens as previously, with their original colour; the rounded polished sands show a maximum as high as 0·280, the rough specimens of sand give 0·180 and the wind-worn specimens between 0·120 and 0·090 only.

For the sands composed of the smallest particles, the general polarization diminishes and the maximum is displaced towards larger angles of

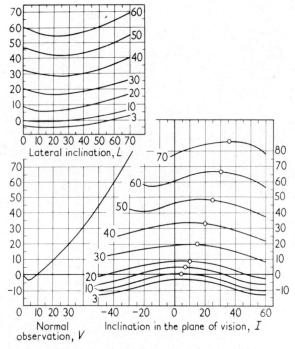

Fig. 6. Polarization of light by a powdery substance which consists of absorbing grains (yellow sand); (after Dollfus, 1956).

vision. The clays (*LI*), composed of a fine quartz powder give a maximum of 0·055 only, under the angle of sight of 135°. All these sediments exhibit a very weak polarization under angle of sight less than 25°.

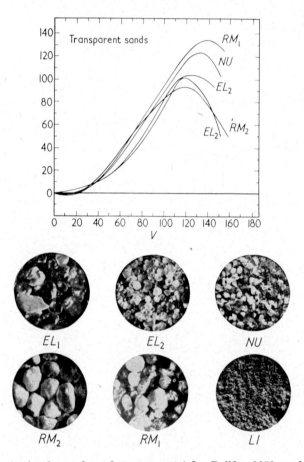

FIG. 7. Polarization by sands made transparent (after Dollfus, 1956; and Dollfus and Cailleux, 1950). *EL* = polished shining grains, eroded by water. *RM* = round unpolished grains, eroded by wind. *NU* = unworn grains. *LI* = quartzy clay.

All preceding curves are, however, very different from those obtained from observation of the surface of the Moon. Therefore, we must conclude that there is an absence of all appreciable quantities of quartz in the top layers of the ground of our satellite. In a like manner, we must eliminate chalky sediments, because of the too large quantity of light coming from the interior of the substance.

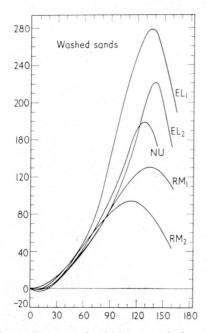

FIG. 8. Polarization of light by sands which are washed out, but not de-coloured. The letters of the diagram refer to the same samples as on Fig. 7.

VII. Substances with Rough or Diffusing Surfaces

Let us examine now a partially transparent homogeneous body, the surface of which is rough or unpolished. This would be the case, for example, with a thick plate of frosted glass (Gouy, 1884; Lafay, 1894; Wright, 1927). The proportion of light I_s re-emitted by the surface is spread out in all directions by diffraction and diffusion. A proportion KI_i of light re-emitted from the interior of the body is spread out similarly. The light mixed like this as a whole remains weakly polarized; the polarization varies but little with the inclination of the surface; it depends mainly on the angle v between the direction of illumination and of observation.

With very absorbing materials only the light diffused by the surface is apparent, and the polarization no longer depends on the inclination of the observed rays. This category of materials includes all igneous rocks with a freshly broken rough surface. Lyot (1929) has given polarization curves as a function of angle of sight for the specimens of porphyry, granites, sandstone, basalts and 11 volcanic lavas (cf.

Fig. 9); Wright (1927) has studied the specimens of diabases, peridotites, magnetites, lephrites, etc. The maximum of polarization is
always observed to occur between the sight angles of 110° and 138°.

When the albedo decreases, the material becomes more absorbing
and allows a diminishing amount of refracted light to be re-emitted;
the polarization maximum tends to increase and, for very dark bodies,
it can exceed 0·350. Towards small angles of sight, the curve often
starts off in a negative direction; at angles of less than a few degrees
it generally passes through a minimum, having the value between
0·005 and 0·010 before increasing again to zero between 13° and 18°.

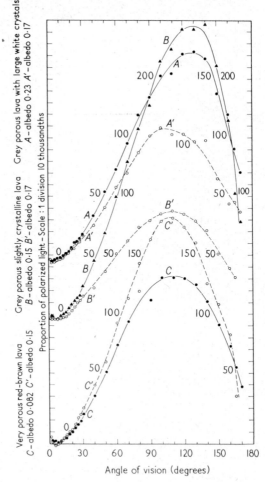

FIG. 9. Polarization of light by different types of volcanic lava (after Lyot, 1929).

This very curious property was discovered by Lyot, who attributed it to diffraction of the granules of which the surface of the body is composed.

The polarization produced by this type of material resembles that of the Moon more than any other previously examined. We find, in particular, the nearly total independence of polarization on the inclination of the surface; and also that the magnitude of the maximum of polarization varies inversely with the albedo. The Moon shows, however, this maximum polarization at a smaller angle (around 110°). The initial negative trend is much more pronounced than on the igneous rocks previously considered; the minimum attains 0·012 at an angle of sight of 12° and the inversion is produced at an angle as large as 23·5°. We shall see later that it is indeed possible to reproduce these characteristics faithfully.

VIII. Powdered Opaque Substances

The polarization of the light by completely opaque granular substances is almost completely independent of the inclination of the surface, as in the case of the broken pieces of igneous rocks. The polarization curve commences with a much more pronounced negative trend. It passes through a minimum which may attain 0·016, and thereafter it passes through zero to change sign under angles of sight between 18° and 28°. This well-developed trend is a perfectly specific criterion for powders with opaque grains.

The negative polarization results from multiple diffraction and diffusion of light, from one grain to another, in the plane of the surface. It becomes all the more pronounced when the material is more finely divided and when the surface of the deposit is more irregular. According to the experiences of the author (Dollfus, 1955, 1956) this negative trend takes its maximum development on perfectly opaque substances

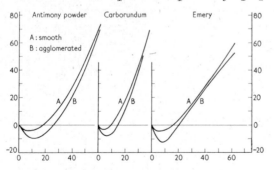

FIG. 10. Polarization of light by powders consisting of small, very absorbing, grains (after Dollfus, 1956).

divided into fine grains, collected together themselves into larger particles and deposited as a rough surface. For antimony powder and the finely crushed iron oxides, the angles of inversion are as large as 25° even 28° (Fig. 10). A large number of volcanic ashes, which present all these properties, was studied by Lyot.

IX. The Interpretation of the Polarization of the Light from the Moon

The polarization of the light from the Moon is exactly that of granular opaque substances previously studied. We must conclude, therefore, that the lunar surface is covered with a very absorbing powder, having a constitution similar to that of volcanic ash. This powder could be spread out in a very thin layer but it must apparently cover all the surface. Lyot had indicated this result as early as 1929. He had prepared a mixture of volcanic ash in the laboratory matching the optical properties of lunar ground. The continuous line on Fig. 11 shows the polarization of the Moon, and the dotted curve which is raised slightly shows that of Lyot's mixture.

The researches that followed since have completely confirmed this result (Dollfus, 1955). Figure 12 shows a microscopic view of volcanic ash, selected by the author, having exactly the optical characteristics of the bright regions of the lunar ground.

The observed polarization of moonlight does not exclude the possibility that the surface is even more irregular. Photometric measurements have shown that the lunar surface is riddled at every point by very numerous cavities. The powder must stick even to the walls of these cavities. The author has measured, in particular, the cliff of the "Straight Wall" presenting a steep slope, and also the sloping rim of "Schröter's Valley". Under a phase angle of 28·5°, near the zero of polarization, no difference of polarization was detectable between the sloping region and neighbouring flat regions. At the phase angle 94° giving maximum polarization, the polarization remained identical with that of surrounding regions of the same brightness. A column of bare igneous rock would have given the zero of polarization at a much smaller angle, and a much better defined maximum of polarization. We must conclude, therefore, that the powder covers even the steepest slopes.

Certain craters—like Messier or Linné—show curious changes of appearance in the course of a lunation, and have often been interpreted as indications of structural changes of the surface. The polarization measurements reveal that the ground in these regions is composed of powder of different diffusion indices. The ratio of the brightness of two neighbouring patches can be inverted when the angle of

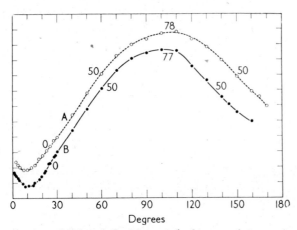

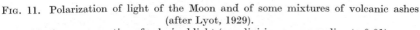

Degrees

Fig. 11. Polarization of light of the Moon and of some mixtures of volcanic ashes
(after Lyot, 1929).
Abscissae: proportion of polarized light (one division corresponding to 0·01).
Ordinates: angle of sight (in degrees).

A = mixture of ashes with an albedo of 0·13.
B = mean curve for the Moon.

illumination changes. Figure 13 shows a deposit of volcanic ash having
the polarization properties of the Moon, marked by two lines made
by sprinkling an ash of different nature on the deposit; when the
illumination is oblique the surface appears uniform; at normal illumination the lines form a clearly defined cross.

At the time of the impacts which may have formed many of the lunar

Fig. 12. An example of ash with very dark grains, reproducing the observed polarization
properties of the lunar ground. Dimensions of the field: 3 × 3 mm.

L

craters, the release of heat may have been sufficient to locally change the nature of the material; at least certain craters appear to have their floors or ramparts covered by a different type of powder. In certain cases the powder may have been projected to a great distance to form huge halos or rays. The polarization of the light can reveal some particular properties of this deposit of powder. The ramparts of the large crater Archimedes, for example, polarize light less than its floor; the internal slope is as bright as the external, but light scattered from it is distinctly less polarized.

FIG. 13. Changes in appearance of a surface formed by two kinds of powders having the polarization properties of the lunar surface.
Right: illumination perpendicular to the surface;
Left: illumination by grazing light.

X. Origin of the Powdery Nature of Lunar Ground

According to Buettner (1952) and Gold (1955) a superficial weathering of the lunar surface could be accounted for by the effect of ultraviolet rays and solar X-rays on the crystalline lattice of surface minerals. But so far neither the existence, nor even the possibility, of such a mechanism has been proved. We could consider, in this connection, the cracking of the rocks under the rapid variations of temperature. Let us calculate the tensions set up in rapidly cooling rock. The simplest and most favourable case is that of a small thin slab placed horizontally on the powdery ground. The slab does not receive any heat by conduction through the lower surface which is thermally insulated; the upper face is heated by the solar rays, and the equilibrium temperature is that given by thermocouple measurements on the Moon. When the plate ceases to be irradiated, its surface cools and the temperature variations propagate through the slab according to the equation:

$$\frac{\partial T}{\partial z} = \left(\frac{C\rho}{2Kt}\right)^{\frac{1}{2}} \Delta T.$$

For igneous rocks, the thermal conductivity K has a value of 0·005 cal cm^{-1} sec^{-1}. The specific heat C is 0·3 cal/gm and the density ρ about 3·3 gm cm^{-3}. The change in temperature induces an expansion which is provisionally supposed to be linear and to obey the equation

$$\frac{\mathrm{d}l}{\mathrm{d}t} = lD,$$

where the coefficient of expansion D is approximately 7×10^{-6} in c.g.s. units for igneous rocks. The expansion induces a tension F such that

$$\frac{\delta l}{l} = M \times F \;;$$

Young's modulus M being $0·5 \times 10^{-12}$ when the tension is expressed in dynes/cm^2. By identifying $Ddt = M \times F$ and

$$F = \frac{D}{M} \sqrt{\frac{C\rho}{2Kt}} \Delta T \mathrm{d}z,$$

we find numerically that $F = 1·4 \times 10^8 \ \Delta T/\sqrt{t} \ \mathrm{d}z$ dynes/cm^2. In fact, this tension acts in both directions and its value may be nearly doubled; so that

$$F = \frac{3\Delta T}{\sqrt{t}} \mathrm{d}z \ \text{kg/mm}^2.$$

During an eclipse of the Moon, the temperature as measured by the thermocouple changes by $\Delta T = 100°$ during $t = 30$ minutes. The tension in the slab placed on the insulating powder varies then approximately according to the gradient

$$F = 7 \, \mathrm{d}z \ \text{kg/mm}^2.$$

At the time of the cooling, this slab is going to become concave, which will notably reduce the calculated tension. But the breaking load by tension of igneous rocks is at least equal to 7 kg/mm^2, and it is not certain that even in this very favourable case the slab would be able to break into pieces. During the diurnal changes the cooling is less rapid; a broken ground is first covered by the penumbra and then by the full shadow of neighbouring obstacles in something like 45 minutes.

In spite of the uncertainties of the calculation, it does not seem possible that the rapid cooling of the ground could, except for occasional fractures, lead to a systematic pulverization of the surface. The polarization measurements confirm this conclusion in the following manner. During each lunation, the cooling is bound to be slower near the poles where the pulverization should, therefore, be less severe; but the polarimeter reveals no difference in structure between the centre, limb and the poles. The planet Mercury gives the same polarization curve as the Moon, and appears then to be covered by a similar pulverized substance; however, it has turned the same face to the Sun probably for a long time, and is not subject to thermal variations. It rather seems that the pulverized structure of the surface is due to the dust ejected at the time of the explosion of the meteorites which formed the craters.

Certain large craters are surrounded by vast rings of powdery matter, brighter than the maria, ejected horizontally to several diameters of the crater. These rings prove that the impacts of the meteorites are accompanied by the formation of dust. An examination of the surface of the Moon shows that approximately 5×10^{20} cm^3 of matter has been removed from the ground by the formation of larger craters over the whole visible face. This hemisphere covers 2×10^{17} cm^2. If only one-thousandth of the displaced material was ejected to a sufficient distance to settle uniformly over the whole of the Moon, the thickness of this layer would be 25 mm.

Such an effect must have been appreciable before the appearance of the maria, at the time of the formation of the majority of very large craters. But this process does not explain the colour difference of the powder covering the maria. The principal reason may be the bombardment by much smaller and more numerous meteorites.

According to the statistics by Wylie, the Earth intercepts about 6 meteorites heavier than 5 kg each year per 10^6 km^2. In a 1000 million years the total fall should score an impact every 12 metres. If the velocity of impact were 20 km/sec, the mean diameter of the craters should, according to Öpik, or Gilvarry and Hill, be at least 4 metres. The greatest part of the ground would be covered with pits. Meteorites ten times smaller appear, according to Wylie, to be more than ten times as numerous; their pitholes should be several centimetres in diameter and the ground would be covered at every point by the craters resulting from their explosions. Each such explosion should eject a small amount of powder. Finally, very fine cosmic dust swept up by the Moon on its journey through interplanetary space should settle over the ground.

XI. Polarization of the Ashen Light of the Moon

The light diffused by the Earth feebly illuminates the whole of the lunar surface in such a manner that the part of the disk, not illuminated by the Sun, shines faintly against the background of the sky. This "ashen light" is quite noticeable shortly after the new Moon when the Earth is illuminated in the direction of the Moon and diffuses light over all its surface. As the phase angle decreases, the Earth is illuminated more obliquely and the ashen light decreases in brightness. The light from the waxing Moon increases, however, in intensity; and observation of the ashen light becomes difficult, with ordinary instruments, under phase angles less than a quadrature.

FIG. 14. A photograph of the ashen light of the Moon, extending from behind the obscurator in the coronograph.
The obscurator is perforated on the left, revealing a part of the opposite lunar limb greatly weakened in intensity by two absorbing filters. Behind the right edge of the obscurator we can see the last lunar mountains along the terminator.

However, the use of Lyot's coronograph allows a considerable reduction in the intensity of light from the lunar crescent. Observations of the ashen light then became possible up to one day before or after the full Moon.

The accompanying photograph (Fig. 14) was taken with the coronograph at the Pic-du-Midi on the 1st of January, 1950, at a phase angle of 28° 42′. We observe, at the right, the thin crescent of the ashen light emerging from behind the screen, and revealing the glimpse of the last lunar mountains along the terminator. In order to calibrate the image photometrically, the screen was perforated at the left admitting two adjacent portions of the lunar surface near the limb reduced in intensity by the ratios 0.7×10^4 and 58×10^4 respectively. Making use of the advantages offered by such observations, the author of this article has measured the polarization of the ashen light of the Moon under all phase angles greater than 35° (Lyot and Dollfus, 1949; Dollfus, 1952a, 1955). The majority of the measurements were carried out visually, using a polarimeter with a grid, except near the full Moon when the feeble illumination made photographic techniques necessary.

XII. The Study of the Polarization of Ashen Light

The directions of the maximum vibration of the ashen light were always found exactly perpendicular to a plane passing through the Sun. The polarization does not depend on the gradient of the surface; and for similar regions it has the same value at the centre and at the edge of the lunar disk. It depends only on the phase angle and on the brightness of the surface. In the dark regions, where the scattering power is approximately 0.12, the proportion of polarized light varies with the phase angle of the Moon according to the curve given on Fig. 15. The points relative to phase angles 0° and 180° were measured

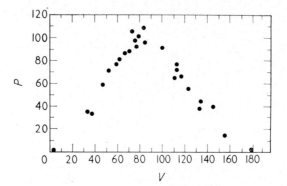

Fig. 15. The polarization curve of the ashen light of the Moon, observed in the dark regions (after Dollfus, 1956).

during eclipses. The polarization, zero at full Moon, increases regularly with phase to attain a maximum of approximately 0.100 in yellow-green light at 83°. It then decreases regularly.

The brighter regions of the lunar ground polarize light a little less than the dark regions, by an always constant ratio. Their polarization curves are deduced from that given on Fig. 15 by a simple proportionality. The maximum of polarization varies inversely with the brightness of the surface. Figure 16 gives the maximum of polarization as a function of the scattering on nine small regions of the lunar surface.

The measurements were obtained photographically. Figure 17 shows a photograph obtained for this purpose on October 5th, 1950, at a phase angle of 78°. The ashen light projects from the straight edge of the screen of the coronograph; the image is traversed by the bands produced by the polariscope and their intensities give the polarization of each region of the surface.

The very selective polarization of the ashen light decreases by a large amount in the red. An exposure made through a filter passing wave lengths centred on 6300 Å gave the proportion of polarized light as 0·035; it was 0·054 in yellow-green light at about 5500 Å.

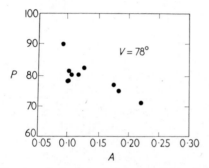

FIG. 16. The variation in polarization of the ashen light of the Moon as a function of the scattering power of lunar ground at a phase angle of 78° (after Dollfus, 1956).

XIII. Origin of the Polarization of the Ashen Light

The diffused light from the Earth is fairly strongly polarized because of the terrestrial atmosphere. The lunar surface re-emits this light towards the Earth after having partially depolarized it. Polarization of the ashen light reproduces, therefore, that of the light of the Earth, as seen from space, to a diminished degree. Polarization of the ashen light gives, therefore, the polarization curve of the Earth as seen from space. It also allows us to investigate the nature of the lunar ground, from the way in which the light becomes depolarized.

XIV. Polarization Curve of the Earth

The phase angle of the Earth, as seen from the Moon, is the complement of that of the Moon. The polarization curve of the Earth as seen from space can, therefore, be deduced from Fig. 15 by altering the phase angle by 90° and moving the curve vertically to compensate for the depolarization by the lunar ground.

In order to determine this relationship, the author has studied the polarization of the Earth by ascending into the atmosphere by free balloon. A small polarimeter allowed the ground to be observed from the gondola under different angles of illumination. The angle of sight was controlled by observing through a sight the image of the Sun reflected by a small turnable convex mirror (Dollfus, 1955). Ascents were carried out between 1948 and 1952, first in balloons of 600, 350 and 250 cubic metres, mainly over the polders of Holland, the Flemish planes and the Paris Basin. The measurements were generally carried out at altitudes between 200 and 1200 m above the ground and under various conditions of atmospheric transparency. These observations were complemented by numerous measurements taken on the ground on various types of terrain and in the mountains on different types of clouds (Dollfus, 1955, 1956).

Fig. 17. A photograph of the ashen light of the Moon, extending from behind the obscurator of the coronograph, and striated by bands of the polariscope.

These measurements have shown us that, at a height of about 1000 metres, the polarization due to the atmospheric scattering is already dominant over that coming from the ground, from low-lying mists and from the clouds. At 90° from the Sun, the ground, sea, dust and clouds behave all in the same way as a bright background, very slightly polarized, above which there extends the atmosphere strongly polarized by molecular scattering.

The brightness of pure atmosphere is, under normal conditions, for 1 cm thickness at a wavelength of 5500Å, about $2 \cdot 25 \times 10^{-8}$ times as bright as that of a perfectly white scattering screen. The assumed thickness of the terrestrial atmosphere in normal conditions of pressure is 8×10^5 cm; at the edge of the disc the oblique length is greater, nearly doubling the thickness of the intervening atmosphere. The brightness of the terrestrial atmosphere at $90°$ from the Sun is $2 \times 8 \times 10^5 \times 10^{-8} \times 2 \cdot 25 = 36 \times 10^{-3}$ times that of a similar screen, and its light is totally polarized.

The brightness of the Earth as seen from space is that of the ground, sea and of the clouds over the whole of the Earth. According to Danjon, the brightness of the Earth in the direction of the Sun is $0 \cdot 38$ times that of a perfect diffuser; at $90°$ from the Sun, the brightness is diminished $5 \cdot 5$ times and the illuminated surface is a half. The mean brightness related to the screen is, therefore, $2(0 \cdot 38/5 \cdot 5) = 0 \cdot 14$ for the whole illuminated crescent. The brightness from the background made up by the ground, sea and clouds without the atmosphere must be about $0 \cdot 10$ times that of the screen, and the proportion P_s of polarized light about $0 \cdot 10$.

The polarization of the Earth in yellow-green light at $90°$ from the Sun is of the order of magnitude of

$$P(90°) = \frac{P_s I_s + P_a I_a}{I_s + I_a} = \frac{0 \cdot 10 \times 0 \cdot 10 + 0 \cdot 036 \times 1}{0 \cdot 14} = 0 \cdot 33.$$

We must multiply the ordinates of Fig. 15 by such a factor that the polarization under $90°$ phase will be $0 \cdot 33$. The maximum does not appear at a phase angle $90°$ but at $100°$; the thickness of the air traversed is, in effect, greater at the limb of the terrestrial disk than at its centre and the atmospheric polarization is increased when the Earth appears as a crescent. At longer wavelengths, the brightness of the atmosphere as well as the resulting polarization decreases.

XV. The Nature of the Lunar Ground

The preceding results will allow us to specify at least some properties of the lunar ground. At a phase angle of $90°$ the light from the Earth is polarized to one-third. The scattering at the surface of the Moon partially depolarizes this light which is then reflected again. Figure 18 gives the residual polarization as a function of the brightness of the lunar ground. If the incident light had been totally polarized, the residual polarization would have been $1/0 \cdot 33$ times as great. Their values are represented by circles on Fig. 18.

The author has compared these polarizations with those given by samples illuminated by totally polarized light. Homogeneous substances with a granular surface depolarize the light nearly completely. Powders formed by slightly absorbing or transparent grains produce a weak polarization, rarely greater than $0 \cdot 10$. The broken igneous rocks give variable and dispersed values, without close relationship with the brightness of the surface. Only agglomerated powders made up of opaque grains have given residual polarizations, varying inversely with the reflecting power, of sufficiently high values.

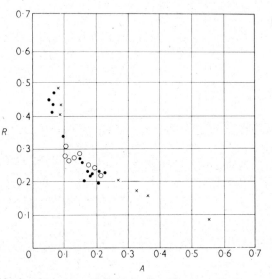

FIG. 18. Residual polarization of light in the direction of the source for a totally polarized incident light, as a function of the scattering power of the surface.
Circles: measurements on the Moon.
Crosses and points: measurements on volcanic ashes.

In Fig. 18, the measurements carried out on 22 volcanic ashes with very different brightnesses are represented by crosses and points: they fall on a smooth curve. The measurements corresponding to the Moon, marked by circles, fit exactly on this curve. One of these specimens having a diffusion power of 0·13 is reproduced in Fig. 12; it polarizes and depolarizes the light exactly as the lunar ground and possesses the same colour and same brightness as the maria.

The polarization measurements of the ashen light give further confirmation of the absorbing and pulverized nature of the surface of the lunar ground as being made up, on top, of a powdery layer formed by small agglomerated opaque grains, very similar to an irregular deposit of small volcanic ashes.

XVI. The Investigation of an Atmosphere Surrounding the Moon

The polarization of light should enable us also to search for traces of a very thin atmosphere which may be surrounding the Moon, and to establish that any such atmosphere must be more than 1000 million times less dense than that of the Earth (Lyot and Dollfus, 1949; Dollfus, 1952a, 1956).

When the Moon is observed at the time of first or last quarter, the thin gaseous atmosphere would be illuminated by diffusion of sunlight along the whole limb. A glimmer would extend beyond the horns of the crescent, where it could be observed against the background of a dark sky.

The form and brightness of this glimmer can be calculated (Dollfus, 1956). Figure 19 shows the contours of equal brightness at the phase of

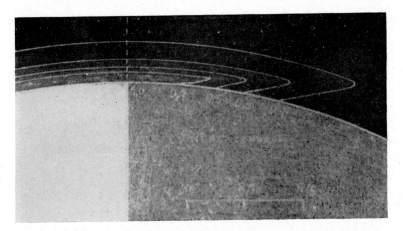

FIG. 19. Theoretical isophotae of the light that would be scattered in a hypothetical lunar atmosphere above the horns of the lunar crescent at a phase of 90°. The relative brightnesses are referred to the brightnesses just above the ground at different distances from the horn of the crescent.

90°. The vertical line of the terminator divides the sunlit part to the left, and that illuminated only by ashen light, to the right. Above the limb of the disk the lines of equal intensity of the twilight glimmer are traced for a hypothetical atmosphere, calibrated with respect to the intensity which would be observed on ground level at the tip of the crescent.

Figure 20 gives the actual photometric analysis of the distribution of light. The altitude above the edge of the Moon is plotted on the abscissae, and brightness on the ordinates. The different sections correspond to radial sections at distances from the limb of the crescent in the direction of the ashen light. The brightness at ground level has been calculated on the assumption that the lunar atmosphere consists of carbon dioxide.

If the density at ground level was 10^{-6} times that of the Earth's
atmosphere, the twilight glimmer along the extension of the horns of
the crescent could be estimated according to Fig. 19 and its brightness
above the ground would attain 10^{-5} stilb. The brightness should be
comparable with that of ashen light, and observable easily with an
ordinary telescope.

Far less intense traces of atmospheric glimmer could be detected
by use of a coronograph. The instrument reduces considerably the light

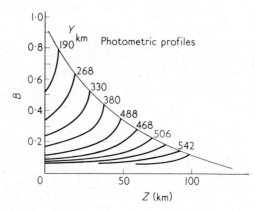

FIG. 20. Radial sections giving the brightness as a function of the distance from the
lunar limb on Fig. 19, at increasing distance from the horn of the crescent.

diffused by the illuminated crescent of the Moon, so that the background
sky around the lunar limb becomes very dark. Lyot and the author
(1949) have used the 20 cm coronograph at the Pic-du-Midi Observatory for this purpose. Figure 21 is the reproduction of a plate exposed
for 30 minutes on May 7th, 1949, at a phase angle of 119°. The black
disc of the coronograph can be seen at the bottom. To the right the
ashen light surrounds the disk and forms a very strongly over-exposed
crescent. The exact position of the horn of the crescent is defined by
the last mountains at the lunar limb that give bright patches at the
centre of the picture.

The scattered light is seen to be much fainter than the ashen light.
It decreases regularly outwards. The distribution of brightness as
indicated on Fig. 19 appears to be conspicuous by its absence. The
scattering of moonlight, the illumination by the ashen light, the effect
of the exhaustion of the developer along the limb at the time of development are sufficient to explain the observed blackening; but of any
lunar atmosphere there appears to be no trace. The brightness of

the sky against the lunar limb amounted to 10^{-6} stilb, and a photometric analysis of the negative shows that a lunar atmosphere giving rise, on ground, to an illumination of the order of $5 \cdot 5 \times 10^{-8}$ stilb would have been detectable. The density at the base of the lunar atmosphere is, therefore, certainly lower than one hundred millionth part of that of the Earth.

FIG. 21. A photograph of the scattered light around the obscurator of the coronograph along the extension of the horn of the lunar crescent. To the right, a greatly overexposed ashen light emerges from behind the obscurator. At the centre, the last lunar mountains illuminated by the Sun can be seen at the tip of the crescent.

An analysis of polarized light would allow us to detect an even much fainter atmospheric glimmer (cf., Dollfus, 1952a, 1956). At quadrature, the light scattered at 90° should be completely polarized. It is observed through a faintly polarized luminous background resulting from the diffusion of the moonlight and ashen light; for a phase angle of 100° these two sources exhibit the same polarization; while that of the background is uniform and exactly compensated at each point in the field. The light scattered on a hypothetical lunar atmosphere would be polarized, and scarcely weakened by that of the background.

The image given by the coronograph was focussed on infinity by a collimator, followed by a Savart polariscope and then projected on a photographic plate by a second objective. The lunar crescent is striated by many close fringes produced by the polariscope. The fringes are perpendicular to the lunar limb and to the plane of sight. Their contrast at each point is proportional to the proportion of polarized light.

A thin glass plate was interposed in front of the lens; its inclination about an axis parallel to the direction of the fringes allowed the background polarized light to be compensated. This plate is followed, as in Lyot's polarimeter (Lyot, 1929), by a second plate which can be either parallel or perpendicular to that of the first plate; it produced an auxiliary polarization which made the weak fringes to appear over all the field; against the background of diffused light the contrast of these fringes was the same for the two positions of the plate. In the region of the field where any lunar atmosphere should make itself felt, the equality of the contrast of the fringes would be disturbed.

This method should allow us to attain a very high sensitivity. Series of photographic plates exposed alternately for one hour for the two positions of the auxiliary plate were compared. On April 25th, 1950, under a phase angle of 95°, the good transparency of the air gave a background of scattered light of only $1 \cdot 6 \times 10^{-7}$ stilb. A lunar atmosphere of density at ground level of $0 \cdot 5 \times 10^{-9}$ times that of the Earth would have caused a difference in contrast of the fringes of $0 \cdot 01$, which was not observed. The permanent atmosphere of the Moon— if any—must, therefore, contain less than 10^{10} molecules per cubic cm and is extraordinarily rarefied.

This very low upper limit for the possible density of a hypothetical lunar atmosphere, gives rise to certain comments. Thus one may object that the fall of meteorites on the surface of the Moon should liberate some gas, immediately spreading out round the globe to produce a temporary atmosphere before its eventual escape into space. However, the equivalent height of the atmosphere should be $4\pi r^2 z$ or $1 \cdot 74 \times 10^{21}$ litres. The terrestrial air weighs $1 \cdot 29$ gm/litre and the total mass of the atmosphere detectable on the Moon would correspond then to $1 \cdot 74 \times 10^{21} \times 1 \cdot 29 \times 10^{-9} = 2 \cdot 25 \times 10^{12}$ or $2 \cdot 25 \times 10^6$ tons. Only a small proportion of the mass of a meteor is volatilized and only a part of this gas could be retained in the lunar gravitational field. It would, therefore, need the impact of a meteorite more than 10 million tons in weight to create a detectable temporary atmosphere. The crater formed by such an explosion would be several kilometres in size, and should be easily observable.

A permanent atmosphere could subsist round the Moon as the result of the continuing escape of gas from the interior. The equilibrium between the speed of release and that of the loss by evaporation into space is difficult to determine. According to the calculations of Spitzer (1952) the rate of evaporation of the heavy molecules depends critically on the temperature (i.e. the kinetic energy) of the gas, determined by very complex dissociation processes. Be that as it may, the very small value for the upper limit of the pressure of hypothetical lunar atmosphere, as indicated by the polarimetric measurements, demonstrates that the rate of a continuous escape of gases from the lunar interior is likely to be extremely low.

References

Arago, F. (1811). "Oeuvres Complètes", Paris.

Barabashev, N. (1927). *Astr. Nachr.* **229**, 7.

Buettner, K. (1952). *Publ. Astr. Soc. Pacif.* **64**, 11.

Dollfus, A., and Cailleux, A. (1950). *C.R. Acad. Sci., Paris,* **230**, 1411.

Dollfus, A. (1950). *C.R. Acad. Sci., Paris,* **234**, 2046.

Dollfus, A. (1952a). *C.R. Acad. Sci., Paris,* **235**, 1013.

Dollfus, A. (1955). *Ann. Astrophys.,* **18**, (Supplement).

Dollfus, A. (1956). *Ann. Astrophys.,* **19**, 71.

Gold, T. (1955). *Mon. Not. R. Astr. Soc.* **115**, 585.

Gouy, (1884). *C.R. Acad. Sci., Paris,* **98**, 978.

Lafay, A. (1894). *C.R. Acad. Sci., Paris,* **119**, 154.

Landerer, J. J. (1889, 1890, 1910). *C.R. Acad. Sci., Paris,* **109**, 360; **111**, 210; **150**, 1164.

Lyot, B. (1924). *C.R. Acad. Sci., Paris,* **179**, 1796.

Lyot, B. (1929). *Ann. Obs. Paris,* **8**, Fasc. 1.

Lyot, B., and Dollfus, A. (1949). *C.R. Acad. Sci., Paris,* **228**, 1773.

Lyot, B., and Dollfus, A. (1949a). *C.R. Acad. Sci., Paris,* **229**, 1277.

Öhman, Y. (1949). *Ann. Stockholm Obs.* **15**, 30.

Rosse, Lord, and Parsons, W. (1878). *Proc. Roy. Soc., Dublin,* **1**, 19.

Secchi, A. (1859, 1860). *Mon. Not. R. Astr. Soc.* **19**, 289; **20**, 70.

Secchi, A. (1860a). *Astr. Nachr.* **52**, 91.

Spitzer, L. (1952). In "The Atmospheres of the Earth and Planets" (G. P. Kuiper, ed.), Univ. Chicago Press, pp. 211–247.

Wright, F. E. (1927). *Proc. U.S. Nat. Acad. Sci.* **13**, 535.

Wright, F. E. (1935). *Ann. Rep. Smithson. Inst.* p. 169 (cf. also the *Carnegie Yearb.*, **26**, 383; **29**, 407, **33**, 332; **34**, 348; **35**, 353; **36**, 366; and **37**, 381).

Wright, F. E. (1936). *J. Opt. Soc. Amer.* **26**, 230.

CHAPTER 6

Lunar Eclipses

FRANTIŠEK LINK

I.	Introduction	161
II.	The History of Lunar Eclipses	162
III.	The Basic Characteristics of the Eclipses	164
IV.	Future Eclipses	166
V.	Increase of the Earth's Shadow	167
VI.	The Photometric Model of the Eclipses	170
VII.	General Transmission Coefficient	172
VIII.	Computation of the Refraction and of the Air-mass	175
IX.	Brightness of the Solar Elementary Ring	177
X.	Structure of the Auxiliary Shadow	179
XI.	Normal Densities of the Shadow	180
XII.	The Eclipse on the Moon	184
XIII.	Geographic Circumstances of Eclipses	186
XIV.	Effects of Light Scattering	188
XV.	Photometry of Lunar Eclipses	190
XVI.	Comparison between Theory and Observations	193
XVII.	Atmospheric Ozone	194
XVIII.	High Absorbing Layer	198
XIX.	Meteorological Analysis of the Eclipse	206
XX.	Lunar Luminescence	209
XXI.	Possible Manifestations of Lunar Luminescence Outside the Eclipses	213
XXII.	The Variation in Brightness of the Eclipse	217
XXIII.	Further Phenomena during Lunar Eclipses	222
	A. Temperature of the Lunar Surface	222
	B. Changes of Brightness	223
	C. Dust-Shadow	223
	D. Changes in the Terrestrial Ionosphere	223
	E. Observations of Faint Bodies	224
XXIV.	Allied Phenomena	224
	A. Optical Occultations of Stars by the Moon and Planets	224
	B. Radio Occultations by the Moon and Planets	224
	C. Radio Occultations by the Solar Corona	224
	D. Transits of Venus over the Sun	225
	E. Eclipses of Jupiter's Satellites	225
	F. Einstein's Light Deflection	225
XXV.	Conclusions	225
	References	226

I. Introduction

From the earliest beginnings of civilization, the picturesque phenomenon of lunar eclipses, unrivalled but for those of the Sun, has kept

on challenging man's speculative spirit. We speak of a lunar eclipse when
the Earth's shadow is cast over the lightless Moon, which causes its temporary obscuration observable all over the terrestrial hemisphere facing it.

An analysis of this definition showed, however, essential *deviations*
from the purely geometrical conditions, and revealed numerous new
facts concerning the Earth's atmosphere and the Moon itself. It is for
this reason that this monograph on the Moon contains a chapter dealing with the lunar eclipses. This chapter is introduced by a short
historical review featuring the part played by lunar eclipses in the
evolution of astronomy; the classical theory of lunar eclipses will then
be outlined, dealing with the geometrical aspects of the eclipse, together
with the determination of the radius of the Earth's shadow and of its
enlargement. It will be in this section that the first deviations from
geometrical theory will make their appearance. These deviations will
take us to the photometric theory of lunar eclipses, the origin of which
may be found in the 1930's: in this theory a prominent role is played
by the Earth's atmosphere. Further on, an account will be given of
the methods of photometric observations of eclipses, and the results
of these observations will be compared with the theory. From the
discrepancies between theory and observations, new notions concerning the terrestrial atmosphere will arise. Lunar eclipses, moreover,
aided the discovery of the phenomenon of lunar luminescence, particularly prominent in the penumbra. Special attention will be given to
some of these results, and to further potentialities of these phenomena.

Several sections of this present chapter will also deal with the
problems of other phenomena related in one way or another to lunar
eclipses. This analysis has significantly contributed to a better understanding of the Moon and other celestial bodies.

II. The History of Lunar Eclipses

Reports on lunar eclipses are available from the most remote past.
Schoch in 1931 published records on eclipses observed in Mesopotamia
as early as 2202 and 2282 B.C. From China we have another such
record dating back to 1135 B.C. (Gaubil, 1740). Later on, the number
of reports on lunar eclipses increased. From the beginning of the
8th century B.C., we have further records from Mesopotamia, Greece,
and from other parts of the Mediterranean region supplemented also
by reports from the rest of Europe. Lists of eclipses observed in ancient
times, together with some circumstances concerning the phenomenon
itself, were assembled by Calvisius (1650), Riccioli (1651), Struyck (1740)
and, from the Chinese region, by Gaubil (1740). All these reports are

excerpts from chronicles or similar historical documents. From the 'fifties of the 17th century onwards, reports of observations of lunar eclipses began to be published in transactions of various scientific societies arising at that time. Bibliographically, until the end of the 18th century, these works were registered by Reuss (1804). An extensive source of records on observations from the 17th century is also the compilation by Pingré-Bigourdan (1901).

In the 19th century, we find observations of lunar eclipses scattered all over various astronomical and general scientific magazines. Various bibliographical expedients are available from this period. A good guide in looking up eclipses is Oppolzer's detailed catalogue (1887) of computed eclipses from 1200 B.C. until A.D. 2163. The history of eclipses is briefly dealt with by Chambers (1899).

Lunar eclipses constitute also an important chronological expedient, since various historical events may be localized in time according to them. The author is not familiar with the first instance of the application of this method; it is certain, however, that it has been frequently used from ancient times on, and that the lists of observed eclipses in the above-mentioned works served this purpose.

Lunar eclipses played an important part in the evolution of astronomy. As early as in the 4th century B.C., Aristotle (Prantl, 1881) mentions the circular edge of the terrestrial shadow projected on the Moon as proof of the spherical shape of the Earth. Aristarchos of Samos (Heath, 1913), in the 3rd century B.C., and after him Hipparchos in the 2nd century B.C. (Wolf, 1877a), suggested the use of eclipses for the determination of the system Earth-Moon-Sun. Hipparchos (Wolf, 1877b) also reports on simultaneous observations of lunar eclipses from two localities as a means of establishing the difference of the geographical longitudes of these places. Ptolemaios, in the 2nd century A.D., resorted to ancient and contemporaneous observations of lunar eclipses for a more exact formulation of the theory of lunar motion. This method was also used later on, as mentioned in Chapter 1.

In the 17th and 18th centuries, lunar eclipses were beginning to be used for the determination of the differences of geographical longitudes, particularly when—as suggested by Langrenus (1644)—the contacts of craters with the shadow were observed, which fact palpably increased the accuracy of the method.†

The first to deal with the photometric aspect of eclipses was Kepler

---

† Later on this method, attaining an accuracy of 0.1 of a minute at the utmost, was replaced by other more exact methods. Nevertheless, it rendered good service during its time. Peiresc (Doublet, 1922), for instance, established in 1634 from observations of eclipses in Cairo, Aleppo and in Europe, that the Mediterranean Sea was some 1000 kilometres shorter than assumed at that time.

(Frisch, 1858) who explained the Moon's illumination in the shadow by a refraction of solar rays in the terrestrial atmosphere. After him, this problem was rather thoroughly studied by Du Séjour (1786) whose work, published under a too general title, long escaped the attention of astronomers dealing with the eclipses.

If we disregard some minor studies by various authors writing during the 19th century, the interest in lunar eclipses became more enlivened in connection with the problem of the enlargement of the Earth's shadow. This problem was investigated particularly by Brosinsky (1888) and Hartmann (1891) and in continuation of their works in Hepperger (1895) and Seeliger's (1896) theory from the end of the 19th century. In the 'twenties of this century, it was Danjon's results concerning the effects of solar activity on the brightness of the eclipse that aroused attention. In their wake, and also stimulated by the interest in the upper atmosphere, came Fessenkov's, M. de Saussure's and Link's photometrical theories of eclipses, as will be shown in more detail.

III. The Basic Characteristics of the Eclipses

Tangent to the Earth illuminated by the Sun are two conic shadows, one of which, the full shadow or umbra, is convergent, the other, penumbra, divergent. The surfaces of both these shadow cones are tangent to the Sun as well as to the Earth (Fig. 1). Both shadows are projected on a plane perpendicular to the Moon's radius-vector as concentric circles, the angular dimensions of which, as observed from the Earth, are

$$\sigma = \pi_{\mathbb{C}} + \pi_{\odot} - R_{\odot}, \quad \text{for the umbra,}$$
$$\sigma' = \pi_{\mathbb{C}} + \pi_{\odot} + R_{\odot}, \quad \text{for the penumbra.} \qquad \left.\right\} \ (1)$$

If the Moon in its orbit around the Earth passes through this shadow, an eclipse occurs. Thus, eclipses may take place only when the Moon is full, and only when this full Moon stands in close proximity to the node between the lunar orbit and the ecliptic of the Sun. This is the reason why not all full moons are accompanied by eclipses. There are some years ahead of us which will be without any eclipses at all (1962, 1966, 1969); other years, on the other hand, will bring one or two; and exceptionally even three eclipses (1982, 2028). The visibility of the eclipse, due to the nature of this phenomenon, is determined solely by the position of the Moon above the horizon of the observer; in all the other respects, its course is entirely independent of the observer's position. Therefore, even total lunar eclipses are less scarce than the eclipses of the Sun.

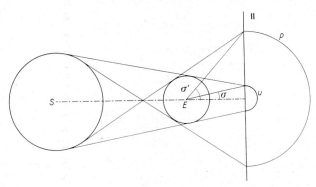

FIG. 1. Umbra and penumbra during lunar eclipses. Half of plane II is rotated into the plane of the picture.

The determination of the occurrence of lunar eclipses constitutes one of the elementary problems of spherical astronomy; frequently, a mere graphical solution of this problem will fully satisfy our purpose. Thus, in this respect, it will suffice to refer the reader to some of the standard compendia (Buchanan, 1907; Chauvenet, 1908) on spherical astronomy.

The following brief description of the course of a lunar eclipse will prove useful for later chapters. The beginning of the ingress of the Moon into the penumbra is wholly imperceptible (Fig. 2). Only after the Moon's entrance to about one-half of its diameter into the penumbra, may a faint obscuration be observed on its limb. This obscuration then rapidly grows up to the first contact of the limb of the Moon with that of the shadow; this marks the commencement of the partial eclipse.

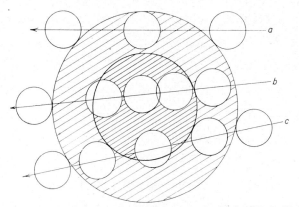

FIG. 2. Diagram of various types of eclipses: (a) penumbral eclipse, (b) total eclipse, (c) partial eclipse.

At first, the part of the Moon which has entered the shadow is not at all, or only partially, discernible; mainly because of the contrast with the still bright part of the Moon in the penumbra. Only after the greater part of the Moon has entered into the shadow, does its obscured part also begin to become visible again. Sometimes, even, major details on its surface are detectable. The total phase of the eclipse commences with the internal contact of the Moon with the limit of the shadow. At this stage, the Moon, together with the contours of its seas and some of its craters, begins to be discernible, and its colour is mostly of a distinct red hue. In the full shadow, the Moon presents a very picturesque spectacle; and its brightness and colour, varying from one limb to the other, create the impression of a sphere. After the maximum eclipse, the course of the events is reversed, even if—in contrast to the first phase—the deviations in colour and brightness sometimes appear more marked.

IV. Future Eclipses

The following Table I presents a list of future lunar eclipses according to Oppolzer (1887) together with their basic ephemeris. The Table contains: (1) The number of the eclipse according to Oppolzer; (2) the Gregorian and (3) the Julian date; (4) the middle of the eclipse in G.M.T.; (5) the magnitude of the eclipse in inches (12 inches equal the Moon's diameter); (6) the semi-duration of the partial phase; (7) the semi-duration of the total phase; (8) the geographical longitude; and (9) the geographical latitude of the locality, where, at the conjunction, the centre of the shadow is in the zenith. Columns (2) and (4) are in accordance with the civilian custom of dating with zero hour at midnight.

TABLE I

List of Future Eclipses

(1)	(2)		(3)	(4)		(5)	(6)	(7)	(8)	(9)
No.	Date		J.D.*	h	m		m	m	°	°
4903	1961 III	2	7 361	13	32	9·8	92	—	+160	+7
4904	VIII	26	538	3	8	12·1	99	7	− 46	−11
4905	1963 VII	6	8 217	22	00	8·6	88	—	+ 31	−22
4906	XII	30	8 394	11	07	16·2	107	42	−166	+23
4907	1964 VI	25	8 572	1	7	18·8	110	49	− 16	−33
4908	XII	19	8 749	2	35	14·2	104	32	− 40	+23
4909	1965 VI	14	8 926	1	51	2·4	50	—	− 28	−23
4910	1967 IV	24	9 605	12	07	16·0	107	41	+178	−13

TABLE I. *continued*

(1)	(2)		(3)	(4)		(5)	(6)	(7)	(8)	(9)
No.	Date		24*	h	m		m	m	°	°
4911	1967 X	18	9 782	10	16	13·7	103	28	− 158	+ 10
4912	1968 IV	13	9 960	4	49	13·6	103	28	− 72	− 8
4913	X	6	0 136	11	41	14·1	104	31	− 178	+ 5
4914	1970 II	21	0 639	8	31	0·6	26	—	− 124	+ 11
4915	VIII	17	0 816	3	25	5·0	71	—	− 50	− 14
4916	1971 II	10	0 993	7	42	15·6	107	39	− 112	+ 14
4917	VIII	6	1 170	19	44	20·7	112	51	+ 65	− 17
4918	1972 I	30	1 347	10	53	12·9	102	21	− 160	+ 18
4919	VII	26	1 525	7	18	6·9	80	—	− 108	− 20
4920	1973 XII	10	2 027	1	48	1·2	36	—	− 29	+ 23

* Add to 2,430,000 for J. D.

V. Increase of the Earth's Shadow

As early as at the beginning of the 18th century, astronomers were well aware of the fact that the Earth's shadow projected on the Moon during eclipses, somewhat exceeded the value given by the theoretical formula (1). This phenomenon is called the shadow-increase, and the first to mention its size was Lahire (1707). He gave the value of 60″ at the observed times of contacts which corresponded to about 1/41 of the shadow's radius. Later mention of the shadow-increase may be found in the works of J. D. Cassini (1740), who attributed it to the influence of the Earth's atmosphere, and also in those of Lemonnier (1746), Lalande (1783), and Lambert (1782). However, a method, for the determination of this quantity was not discovered by any of these authors. Legentil (1755) even found a certain flattening of the shadow which, however, was opposed to its actual direction—a similar and as erroneous opinion as that prevailing at the same time concerning the geoid.

The first one to develop a mathematical method for the determination of the shadow increase was Maedler (Beer, 1834). His method was based on the length of the chord circumscribed by a certain crater within the shadow, as derived from the duration of the eclipse. Related to his work was that of Schmidt (1856) who used numerous observations of his own. The first attempt at a complete solution of this problem was made by Brosinsky (1888) who, by the application of Maedler's method, treated twenty-three eclipses observed from 1776 to 1888. This method is advantageous, since it does not require an accurate knowledge of the moments of ingress and emergence of the craters to and from the shadow, but only of the duration of their obscuration. Neither is it necessary to know accurately the longitude of the Moon —i.e. an element that has always been the weak spot of all theories of lunar motions, while the latitude and parallax are usually known with an accuracy amply sufficient for this purpose. This method is, of course, confined to cases in which the whole course of the phenomenon has been observed.

After Brosinsky, Hartmann (1891) analysed twenty-eight eclipses between 1802 and 1889. He did not, however, take into account the duration of the eclipse for the individual craters, but for each contact of the crater with the border of the shadow he computed its distance from the centre of the shadow, and thus, simultaneously, its enlargement. This method requires, of course, a good knowledge of the moments of contact, and assumes, moreover, a reliable ephemeris of the Moon. Its advantage consists in the possibility of treating even incomplete observational series, when either the ingress or egress of some of the craters are missing.

All these works used the ecliptical co-ordinates current during earlier times. Today, for modern investigations of eclipses, the equatorial system in which detailed hourly ephemerids of the Moon are given, is more appropriate. It was by Kosik (1940) that our problem was treated in this system. His method, very neat from the mathematical point of view and very clear for the computer, is as follows:

Let us locate the origin of a rectangular system of co-ordinates at the centre of the Earth, so that the axis Oz will be directed along the axis of the shadow, taken positively in the direction of the solar rays. The Oy-axis will be in the direction of the celestial north pole, and Ox lies in the equatorial plane in the direction of the lunar motion round the Earth. In this geocentric system the co-ordinates of the Moon will be

$$
\left.
\begin{aligned}
x_{\mathbb{C}} &= \frac{\cos\delta_{\mathbb{C}}\sin(\alpha_{\mathbb{C}}-\alpha_1)}{\sin\pi_{\mathbb{C}}}, \\[2mm]
y_{\mathbb{C}} &= \frac{\sin(\delta_{\mathbb{C}}-\delta_1)}{\sin\pi_{\mathbb{C}}}+0{\cdot}008726(\alpha_{\mathbb{C}}-\alpha_1)x_{\mathbb{C}}\sin\delta_1, \\[2mm]
z_{\mathbb{C}} &= \frac{\cos(\delta_{\mathbb{C}}-\delta_1)}{\sin\pi_{\mathbb{C}}}-0{\cdot}008726(\alpha_{\mathbb{C}}-\alpha_1)x_{\mathbb{C}}\cos\delta_1,
\end{aligned}
\right\} \qquad (2)
$$

where $\alpha_{\mathbb{C}}, \delta_{\mathbb{C}}$ are the apparent equatorial co-ordinates of the Moon, α_1, δ_1 analogous co-ordinates of the antisun, and $\pi_{\mathbb{C}}$ the lunar parallax.

Moreover, we shall introduce the selenographic system of co-ordinates, in which each crater is characterized by the spherical co-ordinates β, λ and the distance $R_{\mathbb{C}}$ from the centre of the Moon, or the rectangular co-ordinates

$$
\left.
\begin{aligned}
x_0 &= R_{\mathbb{C}} \cos\beta \sin\lambda, \\
y_0 &= R_{\mathbb{C}} \sin\beta, \\
z_0 &= R_{\mathbb{C}} \cos\beta \cos\lambda.
\end{aligned}
\right\} \tag{3}
$$

These selenographic co-ordinates will be transformed into the geocentric system previously mentioned by means of the respective translation of origin and the rotation of the axes of co-ordinates according to the equations

$$
\left.
\begin{aligned}
x &= x_{\mathbb{C}} + a_x x_0 + b_x y_0 + c_x z_0, \\
y &= y_{\mathbb{C}} + a_y x_0 + b_y y_0 + c_y z_0,
\end{aligned}
\right\} \tag{4}
$$

where the direction cosines of the axes Ox, Oy and Oz of the first system in the second system are given by relations

$$
\left.
\begin{aligned}
a_x &= -\cos\lambda_\odot \cos P + \sin\lambda_\odot \sin P \sin\beta_\odot, \\
b_x &= \sin P \cos\beta_\odot, \\
c_x &= \sin\lambda_\odot \cos P - \cos\lambda_\odot \sin P \sin\beta_\odot, \\
a_y &= \cos\lambda_\odot \sin P - \sin\lambda_\odot \cos P \sin\beta_\odot, \\
b_y &= \cos P \cos\beta_\odot, \\
c_y &= -\sin\lambda_\odot \sin P - \cos\lambda_\odot \cos P \sin\beta_\odot,
\end{aligned}
\right\} \tag{5}
$$

in which $\lambda_\odot$, $\beta_\odot$ are the selenographic co-ordinates of the Sun, and P the angle of position of the lunar rotation axis projected into the plane perpendicular to the axis Oz and passing through the centre of the Moon. These quantities as well as α, δ, π may be found in the current ephemerides.

It is sufficient to compute all the above-mentioned quantities for hourly intervals and to interpolate them, in addition, for the observed moment of contact of the crater with the edge of the shadow. The distance of the crater from the centre of the shadow will, then, be found from the equation

$$
r = \sqrt{x^2 + y^2}, \tag{6}
$$

and the position angle computed from the equator

$$
\log\psi = \frac{y}{|x|}. \tag{7}
$$

Owing to the fact that the crater lies always nearer to the Earth than the centre of the Moon, the following slight correction

$$\Delta r = 0.0046(z - z_{\mathbb{C}}) \tag{8}$$

must be introduced for r, while the angle ψ does not change appreciably.†

At the end of the 19th century, when Hartmann's (1891) results concerning the enlargement of the Earth's shadow had been published, attempts were made to explain this phenomenon by the course of the illumination in the vicinity of the shadow's edge, where it very abruptly changes with the distance from the centre of the shadow. This was the stimulus from which the photometric theory of lunar eclipses developed. Today, this theory has become an integral part of astronomy. In what follows, its outlines, together with a comparison with other theories, will be given.

VI. The Photometric Model of the Eclipses

We shall consider the illumination of a certain element N of the lunar plane II (Fig. 3) by the Sun which we shall imagine as projected into plane I. A certain element M of it gives in N the illumination

$$de = kTbdq, \tag{9}$$

where b is the surface brightness of the Sun at the point M, dq the size of its area, T the general transmission coefficient of the rays on the trajectory between M and N, and k the constant of proportion which, during one and the same eclipse, practically does not change. The total illumination at the point N will be obtained by integration

$$e = k \int Tbdq \tag{10}$$

over the whole solar disk.

In order to be able to carry out the integration, a so-called auxiliary shadow will be introduced. At the point N, where the illumination by the Sun is unknown, we assume a luminous point projecting the Earth's shadow—the auxiliary shadow—into the solar plane. Let the Sun be substituted by a diffusing disk, the albedo of which varies just as the brightness of the solar disk decreases towards its limb. The total light scattered by this disk towards A is, then, proportional to the source for illumination at the point N, provided that the value of the transmission coefficient T is independent of the direction of the ray, as will be proved later (Section VII).

In this way, the illumination integral (10) may be expressed more explicitly. As integration element, by which the whole solar surface

† The value of $z - z_{\mathbb{C}}$ can be estimated.

will be exhausted, we shall choose a ring of the radius of $E'M$ corresponding to the geocentrical angle r (Fig. 3). This ring subtends a mantle of a cone from the rays MN rotated round the axis NEE'. On a certain mantle, the transmission coefficient T is, then, constant, being only a function of the minimum altitude of the rays h_0, or of the angle r.

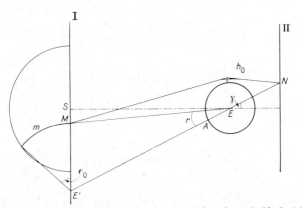

FIG. 3. Photometric diagram of lunar eclipse. I = Solar plane, half of which is rotated into the plane of the picture, II = lunar plane, E = centre of the Earth.

The light flux from the ring of the radius r and thickness dr will be (Fig. 3)

$$di = 2 \int_0^{\epsilon_0} br \, dr \, d\epsilon. \tag{11}$$

The attenuation of this flux owing to its passage through the atmosphere will be $T(r)$, so that the illumination integral will be transformed into the expression

$$e = k \int_{\gamma-R\odot}^{\gamma+R\odot} T(r) \, di, \tag{12}$$

where $\gamma = \measuredangle\, NEC$ is the geocentric distance of the point N from the centre of the shadow.

Beyond the eclipse $T(r) = 1$, so that the illumination is reduced to

$$E = k \int_{\gamma-R\odot}^{\gamma+R\odot} di. \tag{13}$$

The shadow density at the point N is, then, given by the expression

$$D = \log_{10}\frac{E}{e}. \tag{14}$$

This clear-cut procedure of treating the complex problem of the eclipse has not always been applied. Hepperger (1895), for instance, and after him Seeliger (1896), in integrating the illumination, proceeded from the view at the eclipse as it appears to the lunar observer. This picturesque—but from our point of view very involved procedure—will be described further down (Section XII). The same path has, later on, been entered by Saussure (1931). Fessenkov (1937) integrates already in the solar plane; as integration element, however, he chooses rather inopportunely a ring concentric with the Sun, as against our ring, concentric about the centre of the auxiliary shadow E'.

VII. General Transmission Coefficient

For the numerical evaluation of the integral of illumination (12), the general transmission coefficient $T(r)$ and the angle r must be expressed by means of the minimum altitude of the ray h_0 above the Earth's surface. In other words, the path of the rays in the terrestrial atmosphere requires a closer examination.

For the angle r it will be easy to derive from the geometrical configuration of the rays (Fig. 3) the equation

$$r = (\pi_\odot + \pi_\mathbb{C})\left(1 + \frac{h_0'}{a}\right) - \omega, \tag{15}$$

where $\pi_\odot$, $\pi_\mathbb{C}$ are the parallaxes of the Sun and Moon, h_0' the elevation of the rays' asymptote, and ω its total deviation due to the refraction in the atmosphere of the Earth.

In an ideal atmosphere (Rayleigh's atmosphere) the general transmission coefficient $T(r)$ consists of two components. The first component is the extinction

$$10^{-AM}, \tag{16}$$

where M is the air-mass or equivalent path of the ray, and A the extinction-coefficient for the given wavelength, so as it results from the theory for the molecular scattering of light (Section XVIII).

The second component is the attenuation of light by refraction which causes the normal divergence of the rays to be altered. A thin pencil of rays (Fig. 4) contained between the cones of the angles of vertex

τ and $\tau + d\tau$ would—if there were no refraction—subtend a ring of the area of dS in the lunar plane II. The pencil deflected by refraction subtends, however, a ring of dS'. Since the light flux is equal in both cases, in the lunar plane an attenuation of the illumination in the

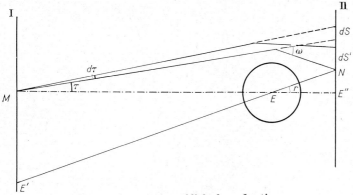

FIG. 4. Attenuation of light by refraction.

ratio $dS : dS'$ is produced. From the geometry of the rays the following expression for this ratio may be derived:

$$\phi = \frac{dS'}{dS} = \left[1 - \frac{\omega}{\pi_\odot + \pi_\mathbb{C}}\left(1 - \frac{h_0{}'}{a}\right)\right]\left[1 - a\frac{d\omega}{dh_0{}'}\frac{1}{\pi_\mathbb{C} + \pi_\odot}\right]$$

$$= \frac{r}{(\pi_\mathbb{C} + \pi_\odot)\left(1 + \dfrac{h_0{}'}{a}\right)}\left(1 - a\frac{d\omega}{dh_0{}'}\frac{1}{\pi_\mathbb{C} + \pi_\odot}\right). \tag{17}$$

Thus, the general transmission coefficient in Rayleigh's atmosphere will become

$$T(r) = 10^{-AM\Phi-1}, \tag{18}$$

which apparently does not depend on the rays' direction, as assumed in Section VI.

The expression for the attenuation of refractions consists of two parts: namely,

$$1 - \frac{\omega}{\pi_\mathbb{C} + \pi_\odot}\left(1 - \frac{h_0{}'}{a}\right) \tag{19}$$

and

$$1 - a\frac{d\omega}{dh_0{}'}\frac{1}{\pi_\odot + \pi_\mathbb{C}}, \tag{20}$$

which act in the opposite sense.

The first part represents the increase of illumination, the second its attenuation. These circumstances may also be presented geometrically. Let a thin cylindrical pencil of rays (Fig. 5) penetrate into the terrestrial atmosphere. If it were refracted uniformly and independently of the height of the ray, the pencil—after having touched the lunar plane —would produce a ring ds, and an increase of illumination would ensue, which is the effect of the above-mentioned term (19). Actually, the refraction does change with the altitude and, in the plane II, a ring dS' is produced which corresponds to the attenuation of the illumination, as expressed by the second term (20).

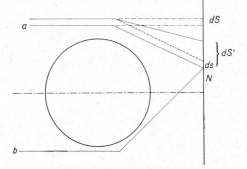

FIG. 5. Two components of light-attenuation by refraction. Double illumination at point N by the higher ray a as well as the lower ray b.

For various rays (i.e. for various h_0's) the value of both terms changes, and so will the resulting effect. For very high rays (i.e. for small refractions) we may write (29)

$$\frac{d\omega}{dh_0'} = -\beta\omega, \tag{21}$$

and the effect of refraction is then reduced to the simple expression

$$\Phi = 1 + \frac{a\beta\omega}{\pi_{\mathbb{C}} + \pi_{\odot}}. \tag{22}$$

This expression was already known to Pannekoek (1903) and Fabry (1929) who studied occultations of stars by planets. Elsewhere (Chapter 5) we have already seen the application of a similar phenomenon for a research of the lunar atmosphere.

Now, if we descend deeper into the atmosphere, the second term retains its predominance, and the resulting effect is a continuously growing attenuation with a maximum for rays round $h_0 = 13$ km (Table III). Lower down, the attenuation decreases; at an altitude of 2 km it equals unity, and for rays in which condition

$$\omega = (\pi_{\mathbb{C}} + \pi_{\odot})\left(1 + \frac{h_0{}'}{a}\right) \tag{23}$$

is fulfilled, in other words, where $r = 0$ (i.e. in the centre of the auxiliary shadow) the focusing of the rays takes place. This fact was known already to Laplace (1860). In this case, the altitude of the rays is a little lower than 2 km.

For still lower rays, r as well as Φ become negative. This is, however, only of geometrical significance. Into point N of the auxiliary shadow (Fig. 5), the rays now arrive along path b—i.e. from the antipodes of the point of the higher rays a which previously were incident on the point N. The inner parts of the auxiliary shadow are thus illuminated twice as far as to the distance $r = -17'$ (for the mean lunar parallax $57'$). The effect of the second illumination is, of course, practically negligible; since atmospheric layers below 2 km of altitude are very little transparent and, moreover, their transparence may be impaired by clouds.

VIII. Computation of the Refraction and of the Air-mass

For practical applications of the foregoing equations, the knowledge of the refraction ω of the air-mass M is necessary for horizontal rays as functions of their minimum altitude h_0. A similar problem has already been dealt with by classical astronomy in numerous variants of the refraction theory. There is, however, one basic difference. Classical astronomy computes the refraction and, eventually, the air-mass, as a function of the zenith distance for the vertex of the ray in a low altitude above sea-level; while in our case, the argument is precisely the elevation of the vertex of the horizontal rays extending to considerable altitudes. The classical refraction theories mostly fail, or attain only a limited accuracy at the horizon—i.e. just where a knowledge of the refraction is required for our purposes.

The principal cause of this deficiency of classical theories rests in the approximations of the function which represents the variation of the air-density ρ with the altitude h. This generally complicated function was represented by such analytical approximations as to enable us to evaluate the refraction integral by a development into a series. In classical astronomy, this method was adequate as, according to the well-known Oriani-Laplace theorem, the refraction is practically independent of the structure of the atmosphere to considerable zenith distances.

In the problem of lunar eclipses, if the results are to be compared
with those of observations, we must approximate the reality more
closely. Therefore, we shall use only the numerical form of function
$\rho = f(h)$ as given, for instance, by the average results of aerological or
rocket soundings of the atmosphere. With this air-density the refraction index is then associated through the well-known relation

$$\mu = 1 + c\rho, \tag{24}$$

where $c = 293 \times 10^{-6}$ for the centre of the visible spectrum.

If we designate the angle subtended in a general point by its radius-
vector with the ray by i we obtain, according to the invariant theorem,

$$\mu(a+h)\sin i = \mu_0(a+h_0)\sin z. \tag{25}$$

The total deviation of the ray, that is, the angle ω is given by the
integral (Link, 1933)

$$\omega = 2 \int_0^1 K \, dZ, \tag{26}$$

where the independent variable is given by the equation

$$Z = \cos i, \tag{27}$$

and

$$K = \frac{c\rho\beta}{1 - c\rho\beta} \tag{28}$$

where

$$\beta = \frac{d\rho/dh}{\rho} \tag{29}$$

denotes the gradient of density with the altitude.

Similarly, for the air-mass M we obtain (Link, 1933)

$$M = 2 \int_0^1 \frac{K}{c\beta} \, dZ. \tag{30}$$

In this form, ω and M may be computed by numerical integration.
Let us depart from the numerical form of function $\rho = f(h)$ given, for
instance, in the form of a table of values for the equidistant values
h (for instance, by 1 km). From this function we derive quantity β.
Then, by means of equations (27)–(29), the functions behind the sign of
integration of the integrals (26) and (30) may be computed, and, finally,
also the values of these integrals. Their form is generally given by the

curve in Fig. 6, from which it is evident that the greatest influence on the magnitude of the integral is exerted by the structure of the atmosphere in the vicinity of the vertex of the ray's path (i.e. at the altitude h_0 and some 10 km above). Higher altitudes enter the integral only with relatively small weight. Should we stop the integration at an altitude of $h_0 + 12$ km, this would entail an error of only about 5% of

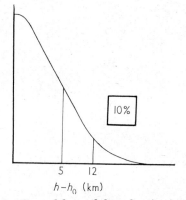

$h - h_0$ (km)

FIG. 6. General form of the refraction integral.

the total value of the integral. If, on the other hand, the values from the altitude $h_0 + 12$ km on are subject to an error up to 20%, the error of the whole integral will be less than 1%. As will be shown in the following section, our knowledge of the atmosphere is sufficient for a computation of ω and M within the whole range of the shadow and penumbra. Here, the structure of higher atmospheric strata appears only as correction term.

IX. Brightness of the Solar Elementary Ring

The first photometric theories of lunar eclipses neglected the limb darkening of the solar disk. The brightness of this latter disk is, however, known to decrease from the centre towards its limb about twice as fast in the violet as in the red region of the spectrum. If we neglect it, the resulting densities of the shadow will be somewhat lower—particularly at the edge of the shadow, where the effective part of the solar disk is reduced to a narrow crescent.

Later, beginning with Seeliger (1896), this important factor has been taken into account by the photometric theories. In our theory there appears the light intensity of a ring of the width of dr subtended on the Sun by the radius r from the centre, at a fractional distance

N

γ from the centre of the Sun. In accordance with equation (11), the general expression for it becomes

$$di = 2 \int_0^{\epsilon_0} b(R)r \, dr \, d\epsilon,$$ (11)

where the function $b(R)$ defines the distribution of brightness over the solar apparent disk. If we approximate it by the usual expression

$$b(R) = 1 - u + (u/R_\odot)\sqrt{R_\odot^2 - R^2}$$ (31)

well satisfied up to the distance of 97% of the solar radius (Fig. 7)

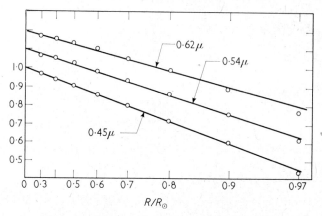

Fig. 7.   Change of brightness on the solar disk.

with the coefficient u of limb-darkening appropriate for the respective wavelength, the general expression (11) will be transformed into the expression

$$di = (P - uQ) \, dr,$$ (32)

where P and Q are functions dependent on r, γ. They may be expressed for $\gamma \geqq R$.

$$P = \epsilon_0 r \qquad Q = P - \frac{r}{R_\odot}\sqrt{2r\gamma} \, I_m$$

and for

$$I_m = \frac{\pi m \sqrt{2}}{8}\left(1 + \frac{m}{32} + \frac{3m^2}{1024} + \ldots\right),$$ (33)

$$m = 4\sin^2\frac{\epsilon_0}{2} = \frac{(R_\odot + \gamma - r)(R_\odot + r - \gamma)}{r\gamma}.$$

Their values have been tabulated in detail (Link, 1956a). Here, we shall present only a brief extract from the Tables. From the ratio of both terms P and Q, given in this extract, the effect of the limb darkening becomes evident.

TABLE II

$r-\gamma$	$\gamma=0'$		$10'$		$20'$		$30'$		$36'$		$40'$		$50'$	
	P/2	Q/2	P/2	Q/2	P/2	Q/2	P/2	Q/2	P/2	Q/2	P/2	Q/2	P/2	Q/2
+16	50·3	50·3	0·0	0·0	0·0	0·0	0·0	0·0	0·0	0·0	0·0	0·0	0·0	0·0
14	44·0	22·7	12·1	7·5	10·1	6·3	9·4	5·8	9·1	5·7	9·0	5·6	8·8	5·4
12	37·7	12·8	16·0	7·7	13·5	6·5	12·6	6·0	12·2	5·9	12·1	5·8	11·8	5·7
10	31·4	6·9	18·3	7·2	15·5	6·0	14·5	5·6	14·2	5·5	14·0	5·4	13·7	5·3
8	25·1	3·4	19·5	6·4	16·6	5·3	15·7	5·0	15·4	4·9	15·2	4·9	14·9	4·8
6	18·8	1·4	20·0	5·6	17·2	4·8	16·4	4·3	16·1	4·4	16·0	4·4	15·7	4·3
4	12·6	0·4	20·0	5·2	17·3	4·2	16·7	4·0	16·5	4·0	16·3	3·9	16·1	3·8
+ 2	6·3	0·0	19·5	4·8	17·0	3·8	16·6	3·7	16·4	3·6	16·4	3·6	16·2	3·6
0	0·0	0·0	18·5	4·6	16·5	3·6	16·2	3·5	16·1	3·5	16·1	3·5	16·0	3·4
− 2			17·5	5·0	15·5	3·5	15·5	3·5	15·6	3·5	15·6	3·5	15·6	3·5
4			16·8	5·2	14·3	3·5	14·6	3·5	14·7	3·6	14·8	3·6	14·8	3·6
6			12·6	3·5	12·9	3·6	13·4	3·7	13·7	3·7	13·8	3·8	13·9	3·8
8			6·3	1·5	11·1	3·6	12·0	3·9	12·3	3·9	12·5	4·0	12·7	4·1
10			0·0	0·0	9·1	3·6	10·3	4·0	10·7	4·2	10·9	4·2	11·2	4·3
12					6·9	3·3	8·3	4·2	8·7	4·2	8·9	4·3	9·2	4·4
14					4·3	2·7	5·7	3·5	6·0	3·7	6·3	3·9	6·6	4·1
−16					0·0	0·0	0·0	0·0	0·0	0·0	0·0	0·0	0·0	0·0

X. Structure of the Auxiliary Shadow

The computation of the structure of the auxiliary shadow presumes the knowledge of function $\rho = f(h)$. This computation was carried out (Link, 1933, 1958) for the atmosphere and lower stratosphere to an altitude of 26 km from Humphreys' (1929) data, and higher up to 120 km according to data from Rocket Panel (1952). These data made it possible satisfactorily to compute the structure of the auxiliary shadow for mean latitudes and for the mean season of the year as far as to its limit of 58'. An excerpt from the results for the mean parallax $\pi_{\mathbb{C}} = 57'$ is presented in Table III.

This Table is instructive from several points of view. If we observe the way in which the component d_1 arising from the attenuation by refraction, and the component of extinction d_2 are represented in the total density of the auxiliary shadow, we see that in the borderline regions it is attenuation by refraction that plays the predominant part. This is independent of the frequency of light, so that the borderline regions, too, will be neutral in colour. In the internal regions, the component of extinction—strongly selective—begins to prevail; and this accounts for the reddish colouring of the auxiliary shadow. At the very centre of the shadow, there is an apparent decrease of the component d_1 due to focusing of the rays, also reflected in the total density.

TABLE III

Auxiliary Shadow

h km	ω ′	M †	r ′	d_1	d_2	d_3	d_4	D_2	D_3	D_4
2	55·7	60·6	1·4	1·30	2·79	0·32	0·12	4·09	4·41	4·53
5	40·5	41·9	16·6	2·18	1·92	0·33	0·12	4·11	4·44	4·56
10	25·2	21·4	32·0	2·24	0·98	0·33	0·12	3·22	3·55	3·67
15	12·2	9·8	45·0	2·24	0·45	0·33	0·12	2·69	3·02	3·14
20	5·6	4·4	51·6	1·95	0·20	0·32	0·12	2·15	2·47	2·59
25	2·6	2·0	54·7	1·64	0·09	0·29	0·12	1·73	2·02	2·14
30	1·4	0·9	56·2	1·31	0·04	0·17	0·12	1·35	1·52	1·64
35	0·5	0·5	56·8	1·00	0·02	0·07	0·11	1·02	1·10	1·21
40	0·2	0·2	57·3	0·70	0·01	0·01	0·10	0·70	0·71	0·81
50	0·1	0·1	57·5	0·26	0·00	0·00	0·10	0·26	0·26	0·36
60	0·0	0·0	57·7	0·09	0·00	0·00	0·08	0·09	0·09	0·17
70	0·0	0·0	57·8	0·02	0·00	0·00	0·08	0·02	0·02	0·10
80	0·0	0·0	57·9	0·00	0·00	0·00	0·06	0·00	0·00	0·06
90	0·0	0·0	57·9	0·00	0·00	0·00	0·04	0·00	0·00	0·04
100	0·0	0·0	58·0	0·00	0·00	0·00	0·00	0·00	0·00	0·00

†In 8 km normal atmosphere units.

Computed for $\pi_{(\!(} = 57'$ and $\lambda = 5400$ Å.
d_1 the attenuation by refraction.
d_2 the extinction in the Rayleigh's atmosphere.
d_3 the absorption by ozone.
d_4 the absorption by high absorbing layer.
$D_2 = d_1 + d_2$ $D_3 = D_2 + d_3$ $D_4 = D_3 + d_4$.

The density of the actual shadow is computed by integration (equation (12)) from the extended region ($2R_{\odot}$) of the auxiliary shadow. The above-mentioned characteristics of the auxiliary shadow are also transferred into the actual shadow, even if with a lesser contrast—a fact which is fully confirmed by the observations.

XI. Normal Densities of the Shadow

The normal densities of the shadow have been computed (Link, 1933, 1948a) for Rayleigh's atmosphere in three spectral regions—the red, green and blue—under application of the following constants, for

TABLE IV

Colour		c	A	u
Red	6200 Å	$292 \cdot 0.10^{-6}$	0·0263	0·54
Green	5400 Å	$293 \cdot 2.10^{-6}$	0·0460	0·62
Blue	4600 Å	$295 \cdot 5.10^{-6}$	0·0889	0·73

that of three values 54′, 57′, 61′ of the lunar parallax. The results are presented in the following Table V.

TABLE V

Normal Densities in the Shadow

$\pi_{\mathbb{C}}$ \ γ		D						M_0					
		0′	5′	10′	20′	30′	35′	0′	5′	10′	20′	30′	35′
Red	54	3·10	3·09	3·06	2·97	2·76	2·58	49·5	48·4	43·5	27·8	17·5	11·8
6200 Å	57	3·21	3·20	3·17	3·09	2·83	2·70	52·2	51·7	46·3	31·1	21·2	15·5
	61	3·36	3·35	3·31	3·20	2·92	2·80	56·7	54·9	51·8	36·8	24·1	19·3
Green	54	4·10	4·04	3·91	3·49	3·09	2·79	44·9	43·3	37·8	24·7	15·3	9·9
5400 Å	57	4·30	4·24	4·09	3·63	3·21	2·97	48·0	46·1	40·8	27·7	18·1	13·2
	61	4·55	4·49	4·35	3·87	3·37	3·16	53·3	52·7	47·3	32·9	21·7	17·0
Blue	54	5·86	5·69	5·30	4·46	3·68	3·18	42·0	37·6	32·1	20·9	12·5	7·7
4600 Å	57	6·23	5·98	5·60	4·72	3·93	3·48	46·3	42·4	35·2	23·7	15·1	10·5
	61	6·76	6·56	6·11	5·16	4·24	3·84	52·3	48·4	41·1	28·3	20·3	14·1

The numerical results indicate one useful characteristic of the shadow: namely, that the structure of its limb is practically independent of the Moon's parallax when, instead of the angular distance from the centre of the shadow γ, we introduce as argument the distance from the edge of the shadow, defined by relation

$$\gamma'' = \pi_{\mathbb{C}} - R_{\odot} - \gamma. \qquad (34)$$

This property of the shadow is associated with the fact that, in the auxiliary shadow, the solar radius is rather small when compared with the curvature of the isophotes—particularly in the outer parts. Nearer towards the centre, the influence of the parallax becomes greater, so that with a decreasing parallax (increasing distance) the brightness of the eclipse increases which—besides—also follows from the geometrical conditions.

TABLE VI

Normal Densities on the Periphery of the Shadow DM₀

γ''	0'	1'	2'	3'	4'	5'	6'	7'	8'	9'	10'
Red 2·35	2·46	2·52	2·58	2·63	2·67	2·70	2·73	2·75	2·78	2·81
6200 Å 7·3	8·8	10·2	11·7	13·0	14·5	15·5	16·7	17·8	19·0	20·1
Green 2·48	2·61	2·70	2·78	2·85	2·92	2·97	3·02	3·07	3·13	3·17
5400 Å 5·7	7·1	8·4	9·7	11·0	12·1	13·2	14·3	15·3	16·3	17·2
Blue 2·71	2·89	3·04	3·16	3·28	3·38	3·48	3·58	3·67	3·76	3·84
4600 Å 4·1	5·4	6·4	7·5	8·5	9·5	10·5	11·4	12·4	13·3	14·1

For further discussion it will be useful to investigate the form of the integral of illumination as defined by equation (12). This form is present on Fig. 8 for several points of the shadow. These curves clearly indicate the effect of various atmospherical layers, or of clouds, on the brightness of the shadow in its individual parts. Thus, for instance, at the edge of the shadow the cloudiness of the troposphere (up to 11 km) has a negligible effect. From the distance of 30' on (that is 11' from the edge of the shadow), lower layers, too, begin to assert themselves. Local cloudiness has, however, only a slight effect, since the angular amplitude of the effective part of the terminator increases towards the centre of the shadow. At a distance of 30', this amplitude exceeds the quadrant (10,000 km), so that only the average cloudiness along this long track is relevant in this connection. Thus, it may be expected that the outer parts of the shadow will reflect the structure of rather limited parts of the high atmosphere,

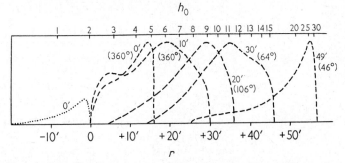

FIG. 8. Forms of the illumination integrals for $\pi\mathbb{C} = 57'$. The maxima are normalized to 100. The upper scale indicates the altitudes of the ray h_0, the lower scale the distances r from the centre of the auxiliary shadow. The figures at the curves indicate the distance γ from the centre of the shadow in minutes of arc and the angular amplitude of the terminator of the shadow in degrees.

while the intermediate and central parts of the shadow will be influenced by the global transparency of the low atmospheric layers.

The form of the curves in the outer regions of the shadow is also of importance. It is apparent from them that even a comparatively thin pencil of the highest rays exerts a decisive effect on the illumination in these parts of the shadow. Such a pencil has, then, the character of tangential sounding rays, which is useful for the understanding of the structure of the upper atmosphere.

In the preceding tables, moreover, the so-called mean air-mass M_0 is presented. The integral of illumination (equation (12)) may be written

$$e = k \int 10^{-AM} \frac{dS}{dS'} di. \tag{35}$$

The slight change of the extinction-coefficient of the atmosphere A causes a change of the illumination

$$\frac{de}{dA} = -2 \cdot 30 \ldots k \int 10^{-AM} \frac{dS}{dS'} di \, dM \tag{36}$$

or a change of the shadow-density

$$\frac{dD}{dA} = \frac{\int 10^{-AM} \frac{dS}{dS'} di \, dM}{\int 10^{-AM} \frac{dS}{dS'} di} = M_0. \tag{37}$$

This expression has the dimension of the air-mass and is called the mean air-mass. It is very useful in the analysis of the differences observation–computation, as will be shown later.

For illustration, the following table presents a comparison with the results of other theories, all computed for the green light and for Rayleigh's atmosphere at $\pi_{\mathbb{C}} = 57'$.

TABLE VII

Comparison of Different Theories

	Hepperger (1895)	Seeliger (1896)	Saussure (1931)	Fessenkov (1937)	Link (1933)
0	5·33	5·79			4·30
20	4·35				3·63
30	3·58				3·21
35	3·15			3·13	2·97
40	2·60		2·70	2·82	2·61
41	2·42	2·82	2·58	2·61	2·48

XII. The Eclipse on the Moon

To a lunar observer, the eclipse of the Moon is, in fact, an eclipse of the Sun by the Earth. In contrast with the terrestrial eclipses of the Sun, the occulting body—the Earth—is surrounded by an atmospheric layer that substantially modifies the entire geometry of the phenomenon.

At a certain point N of the shadow on the Moon, at an angular distance γ from the centre of the shadow, we see the centre of the Sun projected into the distance

$$\gamma' = \frac{\pi_{\mathbb{C}}}{\pi_{\mathbb{C}} + \pi_{\odot}} \gamma \tag{38}$$

from the centre of the Earth. The angle γ' is consequently slightly, about for 0·25%, smaller than γ. The apparent solar radius, observed from the Moon, is also reduced in the same ratio; and the radius of the Earth will be visible under the angle

$$\psi_0 = \pi_{\mathbb{C}}(1 + c\rho^*), \tag{39}$$

where ρ^* is the air-density on the Earth's surface at the level of the cloud layer which restricts the passage of the solar ray.

A thin pencil of rays emanating from point N under the angle ψ subtends at the Sun an elementary ring AB visible from the Earth under the angle (Fig. 9)

$$r = (\pi_{\mathbb{C}} + \pi_{\odot})\left(1 + \frac{h_0'}{a}\right) - \omega; \tag{40}$$

from the Moon, it will be visible as $A'B'$ under the angle

$$\psi = \frac{a + h_0'}{l} = \pi_{\mathbb{C}}\left(1 + \frac{h_0'}{a}\right). \tag{41}$$

The central angle ϵ does not change. Equations (40) and (41), in fact, define the optical imaging of the solar disk by the terrestrial atmosphere. The refraction image of the whole Sun will be obtained by a superposition of a great number of the elementary images $A'B'$.

The course of the whole eclipse on the Moon in a few characteristic phases is given on Fig. 10, and may be described as follows: From the first contact between the Sun and the Earth, which corresponds to the position of the observer N at the edge of the penumbra, the solar disk becomes gradually occulted by the opaque Earth. At the same time, the refraction image of the Sun begins to appear on both cusps of the solar crescent as well as at places symmetrically conjugate about the centre E' on the opposite side of the terrestrial limb. This

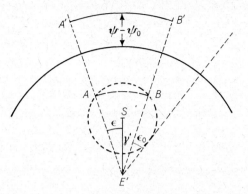

FIG. 9. Refraction image of the Sun. S is the centre of the Sun, the geometrical position of which is dashed.

second refraction image originates from the lower pencil of rays incident into point N, as has been explained in more detail in Section VII.

Following the second (i.e. the internal) contact of the eclipse, on the edge and within the shadow, only both refraction images of the Sun remain visible, and continuously creep along the limb of the Earth until they blend together into a closed ring. These refraction images are, of course, only very narrow—at most only a fraction of one minute of arc. Their brightness rapidly decreases towards the internal edge (i.e. towards the Earth) and their red colouring simultaneously intensifies. The first image on the internal side, and the whole of the second image may be locally interrupted by clouds or mountain ranges. The structure of the Earth's atmosphere, varying with the geographical latitude, generally produces an increase in width of the refraction

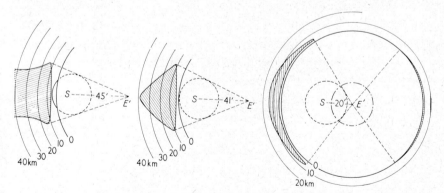

FIG. 10. Example of changes of the refraction image of the Sun. The distances from the limb of the Earth are amplified a hundred times.

image in the direction towards the poles (as the refraction there is greater), and the altitude of the cloudy layer, restricting the internal edge of the image, lower.

The description of these phenomena is no longer in the domain of idle theory, as it was at the end of the last century, when Proctor and Raynard (1892) dealt with these picturesque phenomena in some detail. The development of astronautics should enable us to observe these phenomena in the near future either by television or directly, and their analysis will provide us with a very expressive overall picture of the structure of the terrestrial atmosphere along the 40,000 km of the Earth's circumference.

Incidentally, similar phenomena, though on a different scale (and, unfortunately, only very rarely) may be observed during the transits of Venus across the Sun. Such transits may be used with advantage in the research of the physical conditions prevailing on Venus. The results of the observations from the latest four transits (1761, 1769, 1874, 1882) permitted an estimate of the air-pressure on the level of the cloud-layer and the determination of the temperature-variations along the limb of Venus. They simultaneously helped to refute the long-standing opinion concerning the equality of the period of rotation and revolution round the Sun (Link, 1959).

XIII. Geographic Circumstances of Eclipses

For the purpose of a more detailed discussion of lunar eclipses, the position of the terminator of the Earth's shadow must be established (Link, 1947a). The terminator of the shadow is defined as the locus of points on the Earth's surface at which—with regard to refraction—the upper limb of the Sun rises or sets at the same time. Its position may be easily determined from astronomical ephemerides, where such moments are given for various days of the year and for various geographical latitudes. These times indicate simultaneously the geographical longitude of the terminator for 0 hr GMT positive eastward of Greenwich. At the time H of GMT, the terminator will be shifted for H westward. In this way the terminator position may be plotted for arbitrary phases of the eclipse.

In general, of the entire terminator 40,000 km long, only a certain part participates in the projection of the shadow, which becomes apparent from the solar eclipse as seen from the Moon (Fig. 11). This part is a section of the central angle ϵ_0, where

$$\sin \epsilon_0 = \frac{R_\odot}{\gamma}. \tag{42}$$

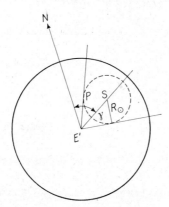

FIG. 11.   Central angle of the shadow terminator.

If P is the angle of position of the point in question of the lunar plane measured from the north, the point half-way between in the arc of the terminator will have the geographical latitude

$$\sin\phi = \cos\delta_\odot \cos P, \tag{43}$$

and the end points of the arc will be characterized by the latitudes

$$\sin\phi_{1,2} = \cos\delta_\odot \cos(P \pm \epsilon_0). \tag{44}$$

The refraction image of the Sun observed from the Moon is doubled. The second, lower and consequently fainter, image of the Sun corresponds to the arc of the terminator symmetrically conjugate with respect to the Earth's centre with the first arc. Its half-way point

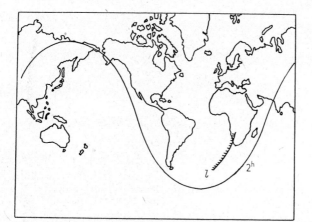

FIG. 12.   Shadow terminator at the eclipse 1954.I.19 at 2^h G.M.T. Position l corresponds to the end of the eclipse.

possesses the latitude $-\phi$ and its end points the latitudes $-\phi_1$ and $-\phi_2$. From the moment when the refraction image passes into a continuous ring surrounding the dark Earth (i.e. when $\gamma' = R_{\odot}'$) the terminator coincides with the full great circle of the length of 40,000 km. In Fig. 12, the position is represented of the terminator for the eclipse of 1954. I.19.

XIV. Effects of Light Scattering

Scattering of light in the terrestrial atmosphere brings about a reduction of the intensity of the ray passing through it as well as a restitution of part of the lost radiation in the illumination of the shadow. In other words, the illuminated atmosphere becomes a secondary source of light which is added to the direct illumination of the shadow, as was first pointed out by Rougier and Dubois (1944). While the direct illumination decreases in the direction towards the centre of the shadow, the parasitic light arising from diffusion changes only slightly, and might have an appreciable effect in the central parts of the shadow.

The brightness of the elementary volume db of the diffusing medium is given by the expression (Link, 1950a),

$$db = CE\,dD, \tag{45}$$

where E is the illumination, and dD the optical density in the direction of the ray. Let A (Fig. 13) be the entrance and B the exit points

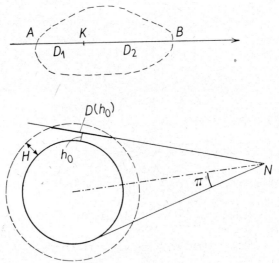

FIG. 13.   Light scattering in the atmosphere.

in the ray passing through the scattering medium, and K an arbitrary point between A and B. The brightness of a volume element in point K will be

$$db = CE_0\exp(-D_1-D_2)\,dD = CE_0\exp(-D_0)\,dD, \left.\vphantom{\begin{array}{c}1\\1\end{array}}\right\} \quad (46)$$
$$D_0 = D_1+D_2,$$

where D_1 and D_2 are the optical densities between BK and AK.

Let us apply this formula to the ring of terrestrial atmosphere of a radius of $a+h_0$ and of width dh_0. Its brightness will be

$$b(h_0) = \int db = CE_0 D(h_0)\exp[-D(h_0)] \quad (47)$$

and, viewed from the Moon, it will appear under the solid angle

$$d\Omega = \frac{2\pi[1+(h_0/a)^2]\pi\mathbb{C}^2}{a}dh_0; \quad (48)$$

so that the illumination on the Moon will be

$$d\eta = b(h_0)\,d\Omega \quad (49)$$

and the illumination by the whole atmosphere

$$\eta = \frac{2\pi CE_0\pi\mathbb{C}^2}{a}\int_0^H \left(1+\frac{h_0}{a}\right)D(h_0)\exp[-D(h_0)]dh_0, \quad (50)$$

where we have integrated over the whole height H of the atmosphere.
The upper limit of this illumination will be

$$\eta < \frac{2\pi CE_0\pi\mathbb{C}^2}{a}0{\cdot}368\left(H+\frac{H^2}{a}\right) \quad (51)$$

or at a mean parallax of the Moon $\pi^{\mathbb{C}} = 57'$ and $C = 1/4\pi$

$$\frac{\eta}{E_0} < 7{\cdot}9 10^{-9}H + 1{\cdot}2 10^{-12}H^2, \quad (52)$$

where we have assumed an orthotropic diffusion of light. For $H = 100$ km, we obtain $\eta/E_0 = 8\times 10^{-7}$. Švestka (1948) computed the case of diffusion for the actual atmosphere by numerical integration, and obtained

$$\frac{\eta}{E_0} = 1{\cdot}9\times 10^{-7}\ (7000\text{Å}) \quad \text{or} \quad 2{\cdot}1\times 10^{-7}\,(4500\text{Å}). \quad (53)$$

These estimates of the upper limit of parasitic light will be used further on in Section XX.

XV. Photometry of Lunar Eclipses

The aim of the photometry of lunar eclipses is to determinate the shadow-density defined by the expression

$$D = \log_{10} E/e. \tag{14}$$

Up to the present, this determination has been attempted, with varying success, by the visual, photographic, and photoelectric methods.

All measurements of the shadow-density have to recognize several difficulties inherent in the nature of the measured object. During the partial phase, there is a great light contrast (1 : 100) between the part of the Moon in the penumbra and the part in full shadow. Parasitic light from the bright crescent of the Moon diffused within the atmosphere and on the optics of the instrument penetrates into the pencil of light from the full shadow, and reduces its apparent density. Moreover, further trouble arises from the variation of extinction during the eclipse, since in its course we relate the initial measurement within the penumbra to the subsequent measurement within the shadow. Finally, certain difficulties may result from the great amplitude of the intensities in the ratio $1 : 10^4$ and more, and the associated faint intensity in the full shadow. Therefore, in addition to the required spectral selectivity of the radiation receivers, also a high sensitivity becomes indispensable. The efficiency of the photographic method is further limited by the rapid changes during the eclipse which do not permit longer exposures.

The most reliable and at the same time most numerous results have been obtained up to now by Danjon's visual method (Danjon, 1928) utilizing his cat's-eye photometer. In principle, this is a double-image photometer comparing the brightest and faintest parts of the lunar disk in the course of the eclipse. In front of the objective O (Fig. 14), there is a system of two prisms P_1 and P_2, which only partially covers its free aperture. In the focal plane of the objective two images of the Moon may be observed—namely, a direct image produced by the free aperture of the objective, and an indirect image produced by reflection on the system of prisms. By means of their variable orientation we easily obtain an external contact of the brightest and faintest parts of both images (Fig. 14) during the eclipse. It is, therefore, necessary to tilt the system of prisms also tiltable round the optical axis of the objective into the position angle of the line connecting of the centres of the Moon and shadow. A square diaphragm D is inserted in the optical path of the rays passing through the prisms, the aperture of which is continuously varied (cat's-eye). By means of this diaphragm the observer equalizes the brightnesses of both images where they come in contact.

During the eclipse, the measurements commence when the Moon enters the penumbra, and give the density curve in the penumbra. The same procedure is adopted when the Moon begins to enter into the

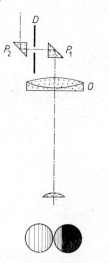

FIG. 14. Danjon's photometer with cat's eye. Below, view of the Moon during measurement.

shadow, whereby the density-curve in the edge part of the shadow is obtained—related of course to the penumbra, the profile of which has already been ascertained at the beginning and in the same manner we proceed during the total eclipse, and its second partial phase. These results are, of course, affected by the differences of the albedo along the Moon's limb, which must be determined by additional measurements before, or after the eclipse. The parasitic light in the field of view of the photometer is relatively harmless, as it disturbs practically in the same way both adjacent places. The extinction is usually also harmless, since it appears only differentially as a difference of the extinctions between both limbs of the Moon. The sensitivity of the eye is sufficient to permit the use of three-colour filters as far as to the centre of the shadow.

For a successful performance, Danjon's method requires of course a longer series of measurements which would enable a continuous intercomparison of the individual parts of the penumbra with the full shadow. Furthermore, it is tacitly assumed that the density depends only on the distance γ, and not on the position angle P. Whenever the

Moon does not pass through the shadow radially—which is a very
frequent case—this may cause a certain heterogeneity of the results.

Of the photographical methods specially adapted to the purposes of
lunar eclipses, let us mention that of Link and Guth (1936a) which, to a
certain extent, eliminates the above-mentioned disturbing influences.
Immediately in front of the photographic plate on which the image of the
Moon is projected, we place a neutral gelatine filter F (Fig. 15) of the
density of about 2, cut to the radius of the shadow. The filter is inserted

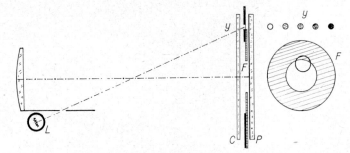

Fig. 15. Link's photographic photometer. C = colour filter, F = neutral filter
I = intensity scale, P = photographic plate.

so as to cover precisely the part of the Moon in the penumbra which,
to a certain degree, compensates for the great light contrast between
the shadow and the penumbra. The scattered parasitic light will be
determined from the intensity of the fog in the vicinity of the Moon's
image. Moreover, by means of an incandescent lamp L, an intensity
scale will be impressed on the plate. Otherwise the procedure of the
measurement—that is, a continuous intercomparison of the individual
parts of the penumbra and shadow—is similar to that of Danjon's
method, whereby also the influence of the extinction is eliminated. An
advantage of this method consists in the possibility of determining the
isophotes of the shadow in those parts which the Moon's disk has
traversed. The selectivity of the filters and, consequently, also the
sensitivity of the method are limited by the rate of the movement of
the shadow which does not permit longer exposures.

The photoelectric method also has been adapted to the purposes of
lunar eclipse. Walker and Reaves (1957), in order to reduce the effect
of parasitic light, measured only that part of the Moon which lies
farthest from the centre of the shadow. This part is always the brightest
and, consequently, the influence of the parasitic light is relatively smallest. Cimino and Fresa (1958) photoelectrically compared two opposite
points of the Moon, and by this practically eliminated the influence of
extinction.

In numerous cases one or the other of the three photometric methods were used (sometimes, without due regard to their respective merits) for the observations of the eclipsed Moon. For reasons mentioned above, such heterogeneous results cannot be wholly reliable. Of an equally limited usefulness are measurements of the global brightness of the Moon during the eclipse. In this way we may obtain interesting curves reminiscent of the light curves of eclipsing variables, but their interpretation is very difficult, as they depend on the course of the shadow-density within the interval $2R_{\mathbb{C}}(= 31')$ and on the diversity of the albedo of the Moon's disk.

XVI. Comparison between Theory and Observations

This comparison will be based on the differences $\Delta = O - C$ between the measured and computed density of the shadow or penumbra, at various angular distances γ from their centre. Under application of his theory and on the basis of observational material which, as time went on, became more abundant, Link (1956b, f) carried out detailed comparisons of this kind. In his material the prevalent measurements were those made by Danjon and his followers, Rougier and Dubois.

The final results may be summarized as follows. In the penumbra, near to the edge of the shadow (Fig. 16), the observed shadow-density is usually lower than that obtained by computation. Furthermore, the results—both measured and computed—are practically independent of the colour of the light. Thus, in this part, the penumbra is brighter than suggested by the theory, in all colours. Close to the edge and within the shadow, the densities obtained by measurements are mostly greater than the computed ones. These differences are greatest in the

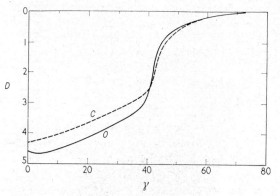

FIG. 16. Schematic course of the density of the shadow and penumbra. O = observed, C = computed density curve.

o

red colour and diminish towards the violet end of the spectrum. In the blue, they frequently happen to be negative (i.e. the measured density comes out lower than the computed). The magnitude of the positive values of Δ (in the green and red colours) does not vary too much across the disk; and in the blue colour the amount of these differences even decreases towards the centre of the shadow.

In addition to this variation of the differences Δ with the angular distance γ from the centre, attention must be given also to their dependence on the angle of position at a constant distance from the centre of the shadow. In the equatorial plane we have, approximately, $P' = \phi$, i.e. P' is equal to the geographic latitude of the effective part of the terminator (Section XIII). This dependence of Δ on P' or ϕ, changes its sense on both sides of the shadow's edge. In the penumbra, Δ increases in the direction towards the equator, while in the shadow it usually decreases in this direction. All these peculiarities and some others should now be the object of our analysis.

XVII. Atmospheric Ozone

First, we shall attempt to explain the behaviour of the differences Δ in the central and outer parts of the shadow. In Fig. 17 a typical case observed during the eclipse of 16th October, 1921, is shown, which has been measured by Danjon in the green and red regions of the spectrum. In Fig. 17, the differences Δ are plotted as functions of the mean air-mass. Moreover, to certain points of the curve the minimum elevations h_0 of the rays are added, corresponding to the upper limit of the integral of illumination (12)—i.e. of the highest rays from the whole pencil illuminating the measured spot within the shadow.

The trend of the differences Δ may be explained by the absorption of light in the terrestrial ozone layer. Let us assume, in the first approximation, that the ozone is concentrated in a thin layer between the altitudes h_1 and h_2 (Fig. 18). The trajectory of a horizontal ray of altitude h_0 in the layer will, if the refraction is neglected, be

$$\frac{G(h_0)}{G(0)} = \frac{\sqrt{h_2 - h_0} - \sqrt{h_1 - h_0}}{\sqrt{h_2} - \sqrt{h_1}}, \tag{54}$$

where $G(0)$ is the trajectory of the ray of the zero altitude $h_0 = 0$.

The ratio (54) rises at first only very slowly, but later more rapidly, to the maximum attained at the lower edge of the layer, only to drop steeply almost to zero at the upper edge of the layer. A similar behaviour may also be observed in the differences which begin rapidly to diminish below the altitude of about 21 km. This is the level at which

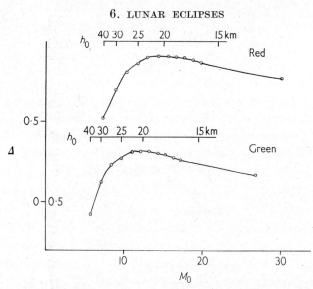

FIG. 17. Curve of the differences $\Delta = O - C$ depending on the mean air-mass M_0 for the eclipse of 16th October, 1921. Scale of the altitude of the ray h_0 corresponds to the upper limit of the illumination integral.

the lower limit of the ozone layer must be located. Earlier, in fact, the ozone layer was placed much higher, at about 50 km (Cabannes, Dufay, 1927), and only the first results from lunar eclipses (Link, 1933) directly indicated its lower position which also had been indirectly derived by means of the Umkehreffekt (Götz, 1931).

Similar curves of the differences were derived also for other eclipses (i.e. for other positions of the terminator on the Earth). Here, essential differences depending on the geographical latitude of the terminator became apparent. In Fig. 19 some such curves (Link, 1946a) have been plotted. The curves from lower latitudes (10°) give lower

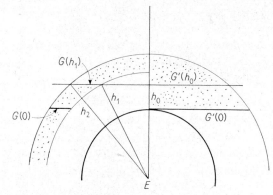

FIG. 18. Diagram of the ozone layer (left) and the absorbing layer (right).

differences than those from higher latitudes (50°). Accordingly, the
amount of ozone in the atmosphere seems to decrease towards the
equator, a fact which has been confirmed by direct measurements
(Dobson, 1930). In the curves from higher latitudes, the steep drop of
the differences is well noticeable, while in the curves from lower latitudes this drop is not apparent within the limits of our diagram. This
would seem to indicate that the altitude of the ozone layer increases
towards the equator, and Dobson's measurements in Arosa and Tromso
confirm this phenomenon. In other words, the isophotes of the central

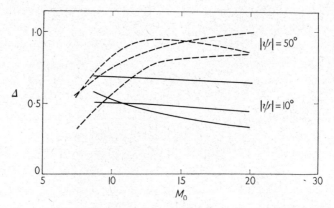

FIG. 19. Curves of the differences Δ for several eclipses from lower and higher latitudes
as functions of the mean air mass M_0.

parts of the shadow are flattened on the equator and elongated on the
poles, owing to the varying amount of terrestrial ozone in various
geographic latitudes.

A more accurate determination of the distribution of ozone with the
altitude during lunar eclipses was attempted by Paetzold (1950, 1951,
1952). When the refraction is neglected, the total amount of ozone
along the ray passing through at the minimum elevation of h_0 may be
expressed (cf. Fig. 18) as

$$O(h_0) = \sqrt{2a} \int_{h_0}^{\infty} \frac{o(h)\, dh}{\sqrt{h - h_0}}, \tag{55}$$

where $o(h)$, the concentration of ozone at the altitude h, is known
from spectro-photometric measurements carried out by the author.
From this equation, the function $o(h)$ must be determined. This can
be done by recognizing in (55) an integral equation of Abel's type,

whose inversion yields

$$o(h) = -\frac{1}{\pi\sqrt{2a}} \int_h^\infty \frac{[d\,O(h_0)]/(dh_0)}{\sqrt{h_0 - h}}\, dh_0. \qquad (56)$$

The observations do not, of course, give the amount of ozone for a specific ray of the altitude h_0, but for the whole pencil of rays illuminating the given point in the shadow—i.e. they provide us with some kind of the mean value $O^*(h_0)$. This difficulty may be obviated by substituting for the whole pencil a mean ray passing through the air-mass

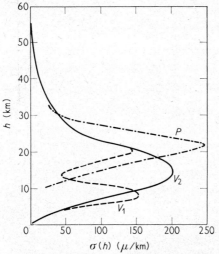

FIG. 20. Curves of ozone distribution, according to results of eclipses V_1 (equatorial), V_2 (polar) Vigroux, 29th January, 1953, Paetzold, 16th October, 1921 (measured by Danjon, Fig. 17).

equal to that of M_0 (Section XI). From spectro-photometric measurements of several eclipses, Paetzold (1952) obtained rather good curves of the function $o(h)$ of the distribution of ozone with the altitude (Fig. 20). Similar results were reported by Vigroux (1954) from the eclipse of 29th January, 1953 (Fig. 20), when on the equator the possibility of a double maximum was indicated. On the north pole, the concentration of ozone is higher, and the maximum of the curve lies lower than on the equator. This agrees well with what has been known of the ozone layer so far.

Today, however, when the distribution of the atmospheric ozone is relatively well known from balloon and rocket ascents, the whole procedure may be reversed. From the known distribution of $o(h)$, and from the absorption-coefficients of ozone obtained by laboratory experiments, we can compute its absorbing power for various altitudes of the rays. We proceed either according to equation (55), or we also may take into account the refraction effect by means of formulas analogous to those for the computation of the air mass (30).

TABLE VIII

Mean Ozone Layer

h_0	0	5	10	15	20	25	30	35	40 km
$o(h_0)$	3·3	4·1	5·5	7·2	9·1	10·3	9·1	4·6	$1·5 \times 10^{-3}$ cm
$O(h_0)$	8·7	8·9	9·1	9·0	8·7	7·8	4·7	1·9	0·3 cm

Table VIII summarizes the results of such computations based on the mean values of function $o(h)$. As can be seen, the total amount of ozone $O(h_0)$ is somewhat variable at altitudes ranging from 0 to 20 km, equals approximately thirty-three times the amount of ozone in the zenith. This means that in the auxiliary shadow (Table III) as far as to $52'$, and in the actual shadow as far as to $52' - 16' = 36'$, the absorption by ozone is constant. Its value for various wavelengths obtained from the known laboratory values of the absorption coefficient have been computed in Table IX. Under actual field conditions, the annual and geographic variations of ozone should be taken into consideration. Their amplitude, however, will not surpass 100% of the value given in the table (Mitra, 1952).

TABLE IX

Constant Ozone Absorption

λ	4600	5400	5800	6200	6800	7000	7600 Å
Δ	0·03	0·33	0·53	0·43	0·15	0·09	0·02

XVIII. High Absorbing Layer

A comparison of the absorption by ozone with the differences $\Delta = O - C$ found by measurements indicates that, in most cases, the ozone alone cannot explain them adequately. We still encounter remainders attaining 0·2 to 0·7 in densities which are also constant in a wide range of the air-masses, and which cannot be explained by ozone absorption. We associate it with a high absorbing layer. Unlike the case of the ozone layer, its upper limit seems to lie much higher—around 100 km—and, for lack of more detailed information, we shall consider it tentatively as homogeneous. The ratio of the trajectory of rays is given, analogously with equation (54), by the formula

$$\frac{G'(h_0)}{G'(0)} = \sqrt{1 - \frac{h_0}{h_2}}. \tag{57}$$

Its course may be best seen from the numerical values of the density of the layer in Table III, computed for a density of 0·006, and with an upper limit of the layer $h = 100$ km. It is constant for a considerable range of altitudes, and drops steeply only in close vicinity of the upper limit, as can be seen in Fig. 21.

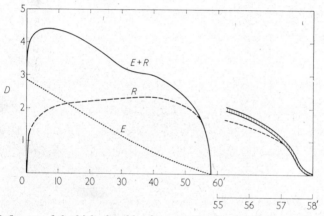

FIG. 21. Influence of the high absorbing layer on the density of the auxiliary shadow. E = extinction, R = attenuation by refraction; right-hand, in detail; influence of the absorbing layer (dashed).

The high-absorbing layer reveals itself in the phenomena of eclipses, particularly by an enlargement of the Earth's shadow. A treatment of all previous determinations (Link and Linková, 1954a) indicates an average value of 2·3%. The enlargement of the shadow is a physiological phenomenon. At the edge of the shadow, where illumination e changes very rapidly with the distance γ, the eye locates the edge of the shadow by estimating the point of the fastest change—i.e. the inflection point of the curve $e = f(\gamma)$ (Kühl, 1928). This situation was analysed experimentally by Paetzold (1953), who repeated Seeliger's experiment (1896) with a rotating sector (Fig. 22), the central angle of which changes with the radius so as to be in every point proportional to the illumination in the corresponding point of the shadow. If rotating rapidly, the sector appears as a disk with a black central portion and a hazy border. The observer's task consists in determining, by means of a simple measuring instrument, the apparent radius of the disk. Experiments with various forms of sectors computed for various shadow structures revealed that only the high-absorbing layer may bring about an enlargement of the shadow; neither ozone nor a low-lying layer (like, for instance, fog) are effective to this end. This circumstance is also evident from the course of the density of the auxiliary shadow. The most rapid change in illumination will apparently occur at the moment when the Sun emerges from the comparatively sharp border of the auxiliary shadow (Fig. 21) which is apparently enlarged by the high-absorbing layer.

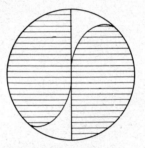

FIG. 22.   Seeliger's sector.

As has been shown by Kosik (1940), the enlargement of the shadow depends on the angle of position P'. The limit of the shadow may be considered as an ellipse which, however, is more flattened than may be computed from the oblateness of the geoid. For the eclipse, for instance, of the 3rd May, 1939, Kosik found

$$42 \cdot 90' - 0 \cdot 456' \sin^2 P' \qquad \text{Observation}$$
$$\underline{42 \cdot 12' - 0 \cdot 183' \sin^2 P'} \qquad \text{Computation} \qquad (58)$$
$$0 \cdot 78' - 0 \cdot 273' \sin^2 P' \qquad \text{Enlargement}$$

His results were also confirmed by later researches (Bouška, 1948; Koebke, 1951), the most important of which is the extensive treatment of the results from the years 1889 to 1938 (Link and Linková, 1954). A similar phenomenon may be observed on the border of the shadow, where it appears in the form of the curve $D = f(\gamma)$. Curves from lower latitudes (Fig. 23) exhibit a prominent bending, while curves from higher latitudes are more rounded.

The flattening of the shadow is also supported by photometric measurements of the density of the penumbra in the vicinity of the edge of the shadow. From a treatment of the measurements secured by means of the cat's-eye photometer, Link (1959) found that, whenever the measurements had been made in the first and second parts of the eclipse greater densities were registered in the equatorial parts of the penumbra than in higher latitudes; since the geographic latitude of the effective part of the terminator of the shadow was different in each part of the eclipse. This fact is even more apparent in the results of photographic photometry of the eclipse of the 19th December, 1945, where the isophotes of the interior penumbra (Link, 1948) show a flattening towards the poles.

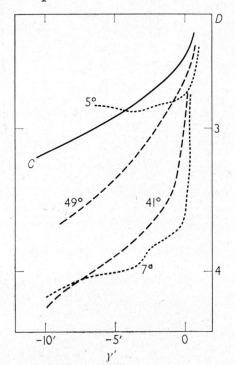

Fig. 23. Curves of density of the shadow in the vicinity of its geometrical limit. Figures indicate the mean geographic latitude of the terminator; C denotes the computed curve.

The explanation of the flattening of the shadow must be sought in the variable structure of the terrestrial atmosphere around the altitude of 100 km, varying with geographical latitude. At these altitudes, it is absolutely impossible to take into account the extinction by ozone, or an attenuation of the refraction (Table III); so that the only factor known up till now might be the high absorbing layer—composed, in all probability, of dust particles—which would be more elevated and dense in the equatorial regions than on the poles.

If, as has been mentioned above, the value of absorption for horizontal rays amounts to 0·2–0·7 in density of the shadow, it certainly should be much lower in the radial direction, in which it may be determined from terrestrial observations. The ratio of both absorptions depends on the structure of the layer. If it is homogeneous—an assumption which may be rather far from the actual reality—it should be approximately 1 : 20. Actually, it will be higher, if we admit an increase in the density of the layer with decreasing altitude.

In the measurements of the brightness of celestial bodies, the well-known formula

$$\log I = \log I_0 - (A + B + C)\sec z \qquad (59)$$

can be applied for zenith distances z not exceeding some 75°, where I is the brightness found by measurement at z; I_0, the extraterrestrial brightness; and A, B, C are the optical densities of Rayleigh's atmosphere, of the ozonosphere and of the high-absorbing layer in the zenith. Equation (59) defines the so-called Bouguer's straight-line which may be determined from measurements; and from its slope we may, in turn, determine also the sum $A + B + C$, which represents the total optical density at the zenith.

It is the theory of molecular light diffusion (Cabannes, 1929) that provides us with the expression for the absorption coefficient

$$A = 4·57 \times 10^{-12} \frac{c^2}{\lambda^4} \qquad (60)$$

occurring in the sum $A + B + C$. If we represent now the dependence of $A + B + C$ on the expression c^2/λ^4 in a logarithmic scale, we obtain a curve that differs from the line inclined by 45°, as should be true for the coefficient A alone (Fig. 24). In the region of 6000 Å, the deviation from it is caused by ozone absorption. Otherwise, the differences between the observed and theoretical curves (Fig. 24) are practically independent of the wave-length and of the altitude of the observation station—particularly if we confine ourselves to the series of measurements secured at the times of greatest atmospheric transparency. This difference ranges round 0·006 in density, and we attribute it to the high absorbing layer.

In some cases, when this layer appeared to be abnormally dense, its effect revealed itself also in the form of Bouguer's straight lines (Bauer and Danjon 1923; Link, 1929) by the fact that their inclination decreased in the direction towards the horizon. This phenomenon could be traced also in some earlier series of measurements (Link, 1929).

A few words remain to be said on the probable origin of this high-absorbing layer. The theory of its meteoric origin seems very plausible.

According to various phenomena reported in other branches of our science, it appears probable that a certain amount of interplanetary matter penetrates into the high atmosphere. Larger particles evaporate at altitudes of about 100 km; and smaller particles—micrometeorites— are only slowed down by the resistance of the gaseous medium. All such particles then fall freely through the molecular medium of the Earth's atmosphere. A simplified theory of this phenomenon (Link, 1950c)

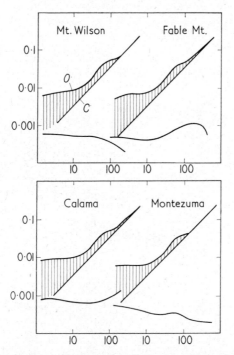

FIG. 24. Link's diagram. Dependence of the logarithm of optical density in the zenith on log c^2/λ^4. The inclined line gives the theoretical relation (60) for Rayleigh's atmosphere. Below: dependence of logarithms $O-C$, corresponding to the dashed region above with correction for ozone absorption in the orange region of the spectrum.
    The curves are valid for days of perfect transparency at the mentioned stations.

considered particles of equal radius as well as of equal density. If the total meteoritic accretion is m grams per cm^2 per second, and the duration of the fall of the particle is T, the optical density of the layer in the vertical direction should be

$$C = f(a)mT, \tag{61}$$

where $f(a)$ is the coefficient, computed by Greenstein (1937), depending on the semidiameter a and on the composition of the respective particles. The time of fall may be computed from the air density at various altitudes by means of the known formula for analogous cases occurring in the kinetic theory of gases.

The observational results show that the optical density of the layer in a vertical direction is about 0·006 and that it is practically independent of wavelength. According to Greenstein's computations, this requires that $a > 3 \times 10^{-5}$ cm. The time of fall is, of course, not known directly, but certain phenomena indicate its order of magnitude. Thus Švestka (1950) found that the average brightness of the eclipse on Danjon's scale abruptly decreased following the maximum of meteor swarms (Fig. 25), attaining a minimum after 30 to 40 days, while its normal

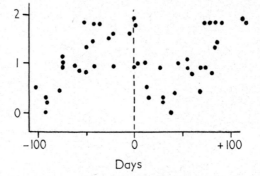

FIG. 25. Luminosity of lunar eclipses following the maximum of meteor swarms according to Švestka (1950).

value is not regained till 80 to 100 days after the maximum. The period of 30 to 40 days would, therefore, seem to correspond to the time of fall of most of the micrometeoritic material. Bowen (1953, 1954, 1957) showed in several papers that, on the average, a sudden increase of precipitations may be observed 30 days following the maximum of meteoritic swarms; and he interprets this phenomenon by the penetration of meteoritic particles into the troposphere, where they become active as catalysers of rain. Zacharov (1952) found that the transmission coefficients registered on Mt. Wilson are systematically lower for 24 days following the maximum of Perseids. Hansa and Zacharov (1958) found, moreover, in their dust collections lasting 14 days an increase of the ratio nickel : iron for intervals of time equal to the 2 and 3 multiples of the period of collection. All these phenomena taken together indicate an average time of fall in the neighbourhood of 30 days; and the smallest micrometeorites which are also optically the most effective ones may need as long as 200 days to descend to the ground.

If we take for the upper limit the time of fall to be $T = 10^7$ sec, a

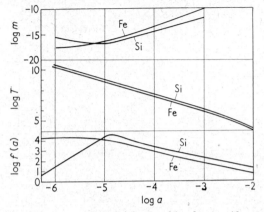

FIG. 26. Curve of the regime of the high absorbing layer. Above: meteoric accretion required for a density $\Delta = 0.004$ in the zenith; centre: duration of the time of fall T of meteoritic particles; below: Greenstein's absorption coefficient $f(a)$, all as functions of the radius a of the particle and of its composition; Fe = iron, Si = silicates.

diameter of the particles results as $a = 10^{-4}$ cm (Fig. 26) and the respective absorption-coefficient $f(a) = 10^3$. From equation (61), we obtain, for a known amount of mass accretion m_0, the optical density in the zenith C and vice versa. The amount of meteoritic accretion,

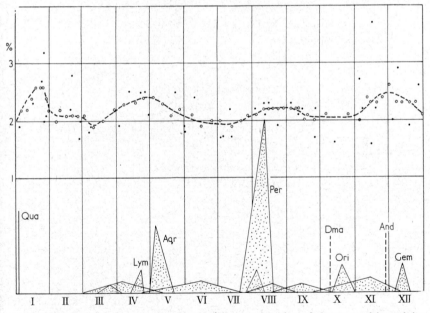

FIG. 27. Enlargement of the Earth's shadow as a function of the meteoritic activity
(Link and Linková, 1954b).

estimated from various phenomena, ranges between 10^{-12} to 10^{-14} gr/cm^2 . sec, which leads to an optical density at $0\cdot01$–$0\cdot0001$ at the zenith; while the rates of accretions estimated from observations of visual meteors to 10^{-17}–10^{-19} are found by far inadequate to produce a measurable absorbing layer.

Very substantial is also the correlation between the enlargement of the shadow and the meteoritic activity as found by Bouška and Švestka (1950) in Hartmann's material, and as confirmed, later, from much more abundant material on 57 eclipses (Fig. 27).

In conclusion it may be said that the meteoritic origin of the high-absorbing layer agrees well with other observed phenomena; although from the quantitative point of view this hypothesis requires more accurate data; for various parameters are concerned which are difficult to determine.

XIX. Meteorological Analysis of the Eclipse

As early as in the last century, many observers pointed out various peculiarities in the structure of the internal parts of the shadow visible in mere telescopes without any further measuring instruments. It was, for instance, Kirch (1727) who, on the occasion of the eclipse of the 21st October, 1725, made an observation rather remarkable for that time. He observed in the internal part of the shadow a darker elliptical spot, flattened on the poles, and explained it (quite correctly) as due to a greater air density in the polar regions of our Earth. In many eclipses, a marked asymmetry in the density and colour of the shadow was noted between the first and second part of the eclipse, in addition to considerable differences from one eclipse to another.

These phenomena in the internal parts of the shadow may, moreover, be explained by meteorological factors—such as the detailed structure of the atmosphere varying with seasons of the year, or the geographical latitude. As for the seasonal and geographical factors, the auxiliary shadows were computed for various conditions (Link and Guth, 1940, Bouška and Link, 1947); by means of the well-known aerological data (Ramanathan, 1929; Palmén, 1934); and from them the corresponding densities of the shadows were derived. The results indicate, as a matter of fact, certain systematic differences; but their values in most cases do not attain $\pm 0\cdot1$ in density. These computations were carried out for a cloudless Rayleigh's atmosphere.

Cloudiness may reveal itself either by the fact that the mean level of the family of cirrus clouds changes with the geographical latitude, or that in certain synoptical situations some parts of the effective terminator of the Earth's shadow may be more or less disturbed by clouds. Figure 28 represents schematically the isophotes of the auxiliary shadow in the month of November. The dashed line stands for the completely opaque isophote corresponding to the upper limit of cloudiness. The position of the solar disk S is chosen for the computation of the density of the shadow at the distance of 30′ and in the angle of position of 60°. The influence of the cloudy layer is rather evident. It will be greatest on the equator and smallest on the pole.

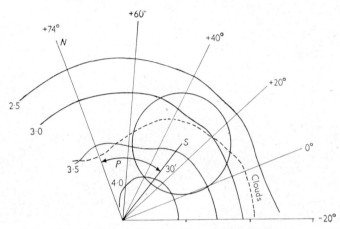

FIG. 28. Isophotes of the auxiliary shadow in November.

The computation for the angles of position of 0° (pole), 40° S (intermediate latitudes) and 80° (tropics) gives an increase of density due to cloudiness for $+0.07$, $+0.16$ and $+1.05$ at the distance of 25′ from the centre of the shadow. A further analysis shows that, on the poles, cloudiness is ineffective as far as to the distance of 35′ from the centre of the shadow; and that to a distance of 20′, the interference of cloudiness is only weakly apparent. On the equator, however, cloudiness begins considerably to make itself felt from 35′ downwards.

This is a picture of the effect of average cloudiness. This is, of course, a maximum; since we have assumed an uninterrupted belt of clouds along the whole length of the effective terminator. In certain synoptic situations, essential deviations may occur—as becomes evident from the meterological analysis of the eclipse of the 7th November, 1938. During this eclipse, a considerable flattening of the isophotes was found; and also density-changes with time occurred in certain parts of the shadow (Guth and Link, 1939). These circumstances are well shown on Fig. 29.

For three epochs of Greenwich Mean Time, when the isophotes of
the shadow were determined, Sekera used the Hamburg meteorological
maps to establish the schematical profile of the three corresponding
terminators of the Earth's shadow on the Earth (Fig. 30). It is evident
from them that the parts of the terminator in lower latitudes were
considerably disturbed by cloudiness; the effect being enhanced by a
higher altitude of the clouds at these latitudes. On the other hand, in
the polar regions of the terminator, the sky was almost cloudless. A
further reduction of the shadow-brightness was related to the fact that

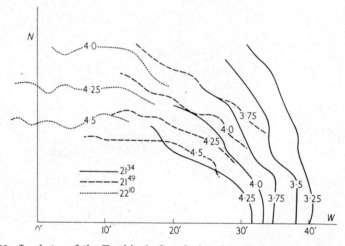

FIG. 29. Isophotes of the Earth's shadow during the eclipse on 7th November, 1938.

the terminator swept into localities with increased cloudiness. This
detailed meteorological analysis of the lunar eclipse—the only one
carried out so far—shows the way in which numerous anomalies in
the central parts of the shadow might be explained. Such an analysis
would frequently have to respect also various geographic factors—
such as the screening caused by powerful mountain ranges projected
in a sufficient length into the terminator—like, for instance, the
Cordilleras (Dufour, 1899).

In connection with the meteorological influences on the eclipse a few
additional words need to be said about the brightening up of the shadow
at its centre which may be observed in numerous curves (Fig. 16). One
of its causes may be the focusing of solar rays into the centre of the auxiliary shadow which, though blurred, passes over into the actual shadow.
Its effect is, of course, apparent only when the atmosphere is transparent up to 2 km (Section VII), and this is not always the case. A

more appropriate explanation may be the fact that, in polar regions, refraction is always much greater than at lower latitudes; while the average altitude of the cloudy layer is also smaller. Thus, as soon as the polar parts of the terminator begin to exert an effect in the vicinity of the centre of the shadow, more light than previously begins to penetrate into the centre of the shadow and brings about its brightening. These polar "windows" offer a good explanation of the central brightening of the shadow (Link, 1948a; Švestka, 1949).

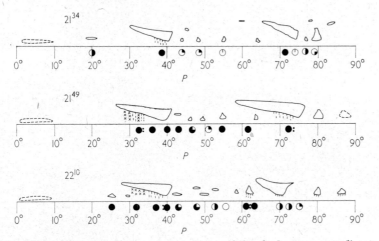

FIG. 30. Meteorological conditions on terminator of the shadow corresponding to the three moments in time as recorded on Fig. 29.

XX. Lunar Luminescence

A great majority of terrestrial minerals, if irradiated by short-wave or corpuscular radiation, give off visible light by the process of luminescence. On the Moon, the conditions for luminescence—i.e. the presence of suitable minerals and of exciting radiation—are amply fulfilled. For this reason, it is only logical to look for the phenomena by which lunar luminescence might reveal its presence. The first way—even if to a certain degree indirect—offered itself in the lunar eclipses; and this was followed by the study of other phenomena explainable also by lunar luminescence.

In lunar eclipses the possibility of luminescence revealed itself, first of all, in the penumbra (Link, 1946a, 1947b), when—in numerous cases —the computed density was found to be higher than the measured density. Let us compute the density of the penumbra from the viewpoint of the lunar observer who, in the penumbra, sees a partial solar

P

eclipse caused by the Earth (Section XII). For the purposes of compu-
tating the illumination we shall apply, in the first approximation, some
results of the theory of eclipsing variable stars. If the ratio of the
angular dimensions of the Sun and Earth observed from the Moon is

$$k = \frac{R_\odot{}'}{\pi_\mathbb{C}}, \tag{62}$$

and γ' denotes the angular distance of their centres, it follows that

$$\gamma' = \pi_\mathbb{C}\{1 + kp(k,\alpha;u)\}, \tag{63}$$

where the "geometrical depth of the eclipse" $p(k,\alpha; u)$ has been extensively tabulated by Tsesevich (1940) in series of k and α for several values
of the coefficient of limb-darkening u. The fractional loss of light α is,
in turn, associated with the density of the penumbra by the relation

$$D = \log_{10}(1-\alpha). \tag{64}$$

In the case of lunar eclipses, the value of k may range between 0·25
and 0·30, with a mean of 0·28. Furthermore, instead of the distance
from the centre γ', we find it advantageous to introduce the distance
γ'' from the edge of the shadow to obtain the formula

$$\gamma'' = \pi_\odot\{109\cdot05[1+p(\alpha,0\cdot28;u)]-1\}. \tag{65}$$

which is practically independent of the lunar parallax.

From this formula, the following table has been computed:

TABLE X

Densities of the Penumbra

γ''	D_1 Simplified theory	D_2 Complete theory	D_3 Preceding with ozone	D_4 Preceding with abs. layer	Observed	Observed $-D_3$
0′		2·48	2·74	2·88	2·87	+0·13
1		2·18	2·31	2·40	2·10	−0·21
2		1·80	1·85	1·92	1·60	−0·25
3	1·35	1·41	1·44	1·47	1·34	−0·10
4	1·16	1·20	1·21	1·24	1·10	−0·11
5	1·02	1·04	1·05	1·08	0·96	−0·09

In these results, the effect of the ozone layer as well as that of the
high-absorbing layer—both of which increase the density of the
penumbra—have been neglected. Furthermore, the effect of the
refraction image which decreases the density of the penumbra has also

been neglected. Accurate computations have been carried out (Link, 1958) with new data concerning the upper atmosphere, obtained by rocket soundings (Rocket Panel 1952), and with new data on the brightness of the solar disk in close vicinity of the edge (Heyden, 1954). The computations performed for the green light are to be found in the preceding table.

The influence of the neglected factors, influencing the density of the penumbra, becomes quite noticeable.

A total of 18 eclipses between 1921–1957 were investigated by Danjon's method (Section XV): 12 cases were found to exhibit an excess of light in the penumbra, 4 cases showed the reverse; and in two cases no adequate measurements in the penumbra were available (Link, 1958). In Table X, the median observed density of the penumbra is given. At a distance of 1' 40'' from the edge of the shadow, for instance, the density of the shadow is by 0·27 less than the computed density—i.e. the illumination there is about twice as large as that given by the theory. In some individual eclipses these differences were even greater. Other measurements, even if less suitable, carried out in Italy by photographic photometry (Cimino and Fortini, 1953; Cimino and Gianuzzi, 1955; Fortini, 1954, 1955) indicated a similar excess of light, so that its reality cannot be doubted.

In trying to explain this light-excess we shall proceed first by eliminating all known causes that might increase the illumination in the penumbra. One of them might be the scattering of light in the terrestrial atmosphere. Its value has already been computed (Section XIV); but now we wish to estimate it under very drastic conditions in order to estimate its upper limit. In order to obtain such a limit let us assume that the terrestrial atmosphere up to an altitude of 120 km radiates along the entire limb of the Earth with an intensity corresponding to a brightness $10^4 cd/m^2$—which, on the Earth, would correspond to a very clear veiled sky in full sunshine. The parasitic illumination of the penumbra by such a ring should then be given by

$$e = brightness \times solid\ angle = 10^4 \times 3 \times 10^{-5} = 0\cdot3\,\text{lux}, \tag{66}$$

while the direct illumination at the edge of the shadow is at least 100 lux. Hence, it follows that the scattering of light in the terrestrial atmosphere—even under the most favourable conditions—cannot increase appreciably the illumination in the penumbra.

In order fully to explain the light excess in the penumbra, we must, moreover, meet the objection (Barbier, 1959) that this phenomenon may be due to the special nature of the Moon's surface. As indicated by photometric measurements of the Moon (cf. Chapter 4), each point of its disk attains the maximum brightness at the moment of opposition, and the brightness at each point in close vicinity to the maximum varies rapidly, rendering the maximum quite sharp. Thus, it might occur that an increase of brightness of the penumbra over the theoretical curve is caused precisely by the fact that our measurements are carried out at a time immediately preceding the opposition. Although such an explanation, similarly as in the case of light-scattering in the atmosphere, is logically permissible, it is not quantitatively satisfying. The increase of the differences $O - C$ in the interval of the distances 5′ to 3′ from the limb of the shadow amounts, in densities to around 0·05/1′—i.e. 3·0 per degree. According to the photometric measurements in Mare Crisium (Wirtz, 1915), where the light excess in the penumbra was reliably established by photoelectric photometry (Cimino and Fresa, 1958), the increase in brightness was found to be about 0·02 per degree—a value which might, perhaps, have increased somewhat nearer the opposition, but manifestly not 150 times, as would be required by the light-excess measured in the penumbra.

Thus when all known possibilities of an increase of the illumination in the penumbra have failed to account for the observed facts, let us resort to luminescence as a working hypothesis for the explanation of the observed excess. Its influence on the density of the penumbra becomes evident from the following consideration. Let us assume that 90% of the light of the full Moon out of eclipse consists of Sun light scattered by the lunar surface, and that the residual 10% arises from luminescence due to excitation of lunar minerals by short-wave or corpuscular radiation from the Sun. If the Moon in the penumbra were in such a position that at a certain point, 90% of the photosphere becomes eclipsed, the first component decreases to one-tenth of its original value. The second component should, however, drop much less, since the source of exciting radiation—the corona—is less completely occulted by the Earth than the photosphere (Fig. 31). If, say, it will diminish to one-half of its original value, the relative contribution of luminescence should rise to 5 : 14 = 35% while, outside the penumbra, it amounted to 10%. Towards the border of the shadow, these differences will only increase the relative importance of the luminescence. A similar consideration also holds good for corpuscular radition; though in order to précis this argument it would be necessary to investigate the form of the corpuscular shadow of the Earth with due regard to the Earth's magnetic field.

The assumption that at least part of the exciting radiation comes from the solar corona agrees with modern concepts of its structure, particularly its high temperature; in the light of which the exciting

radiation would be of the nature of soft X-rays. Their emission, probably, would not be distributed uniformly over the solar disk, but a
maximum may be expected at its edge, so that the source of radiation would be the outer ring surrounding the solar edge. A closer
computation (cf. Fig. 31) shows that from the edge of the shadow, as
far as to a distance of about 16′ from its edge, the coronal ring is
comparatively less eclipsed than the photosphere. At greater distances,
this ratio is reversed. Therefore, it may be expected that in the internal
part of the penumbra up to $\gamma' = 16'$, an excess of light will be found;
and in the external parts for $\gamma' > 16'$ a light defect against the theory.
The course of the mean values of the differences $O - C$ in Fig. 31 fulfils
this expectation.

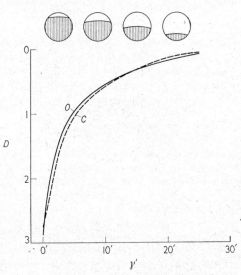

Fig. 31. Curves of the density of the penumbra: O = median values from 18 eclipses,
C = computed curve taking account of the ozone. Above: corresponding views of the
Sun from the Moon.

XXI. Possible Manifestations of Lunar Luminescence Outside the Eclipses

The fact of an excess of light in the penumbra lends support to an
assumption that luminescence participates in the total radiation of the
lunar disk at full-moon. Since the cause of luminescence—the solar
exciting radiation—seems to fluctuate in intensity with the solar
activity, a corresponding fluctuation should be reflected also in
luminescence, either in the penumbra, or also in the integrated light of
the Moon. The number of photometrically-measured eclipses being

rather small, the fluctuations of the Moon's total light were investigated in the unobscured lunar disk (Link, 1947c).

Rougier's (1933) excellent series of photoelectric measurements was used as observational material. Rougier himself endeavoured to establish the dependence of the global brightness of the Moon on its phase. Each of his determinations of the Moon's brightness was based on an extrapolation beyond the terrestrial atmosphere by means of Bouguer's straight line, so that the effects of the fluctuation of the transparency of the terrestrial atmosphere were eliminated from the results. From all results Rougier drew the mean curve of dependences of the stellar magnitude of the Moon on the phase-angle. We used the deviations Δm of the individual measurements from this mean curve as an indicator of the luminescence, and searched for a correlation with the fluctuation of the solar constant Δc as determined by Abbot (1942a).

In the question of the fluctuations of the solar constant found by Abbot, much paper has been spent in discussion. The method used by Abbot for the determination of the solar constant was, in fact, theoretically quite correct. It is, however, rather tedious and indirect, which exposed it to the danger of many systematic errors. The fluctuations of the order of 1% reported by Abbot are comparatively small, and could not be traced in the reflected light of the planets where they also ought to appear. It must be pointed out, however, that the required accuracy lies at the limit of observational errors of planetary photometry affected as it is, by the intrinsic fluctuations caused, for instance, by variable cloudiness. The statistical criteria applied to Abbot's results render them at the limit of significance, but cannot exclude their reality.

However, when the correlation of the fluctuations of the solar constant with the fluctuations of the lunar light was investigated (Link, 1947c), positive results were arrived at. The correlation coefficient (cf. Fig. 32) resulted as

$$r = -0 \cdot 438 \pm 0 \cdot 082 \ (m.e.); \qquad n = 94, \tag{67}$$

indicating that the correlation is real. The negative sign of the correlation arises from the definition of the stellar magnitude and, from the physical point of view, must be taken as positive. Furthermore, from the mean inclination of the regression curves, it may be deduced that the fluctuation of one per cent in the solar constant results in a fluctuation in the light of the Moon (i.e. of its luminescence component) of about 26%. The method is, in fact, much more sensitive than it was in the case of planets surrounded by atmospheres where one cannot expect to encounter any luminescence.

That small fluctuations of solar radiation in the visible part of the spectrum are accompanied by greater fluctuations in shorter wavelengths is, after all, a well-known fact. Thus Abbot (1942*b*) found that the ratio of the spectral variation to the solar constant increased towards shorter wave-lengths. At the limit of its accessible spectrum (around 3500 Å) it attained the value 6 and apparently keeps on increasing, as indicated by Pettit's (1933*a*, 1938) measurements and by rather numerous ionospheric results.

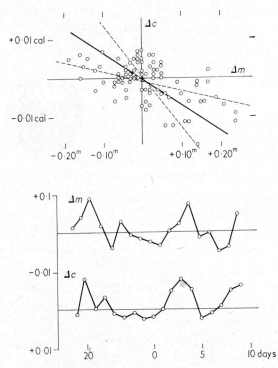

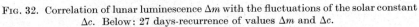

FIG. 32. Correlation of lunar luminescence Δm with the fluctuations of the solar constant Δc. Below: 27 days-recurrence of values Δm and Δc.

These results were, furthermore, treated so that the 27-day recurrence in the medians of the fluctuations of the solar constant Δc and of the brightness of the Moon Δm were investigated. The results reveal very neatly the mutual relation (Fig. 32)—with one peculiarity, however: namely, that three maxima in the curve Δm lag one day behind the corresponding maxima of Δc. This seems to indicate that the excitation of the lunar luminescence is caused by corpuscular solar radiation, reaching the Earth from the Sun with a time lapse of the order of 1 to 2 days (Link 1951).

A further possibility for the study of luminescence offers itself in the method of the depth of Fraunhofer's lines which was proposed by Link (1950b) at the Congress of I.A.U. in Zürich, 1948. If i stands for the central intensity of the line and I for the intensity of the continuous background, then (cf. Fig. 33) the ratio

$$R = \frac{i}{I} \qquad (68)$$

defines the so-called depth of the line, for instance, in the spectrum of

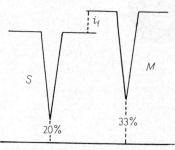

FIG. 33. Central intensity of a line in the solar (S) and lunar (L) spectrum in the presence of luminescence.

the Sun. The same line in the spectrum of the Moon will, however, possess the depth

$$R' = \frac{pi + i_f}{pI + i_f}, \qquad (69)$$

where p is the reflection coefficient of the lunar region at the particular wave-length, and i_f the intensity of the luminescence component which we express by ratio

$$\rho = \frac{i_f}{pI}, \qquad (70)$$

or also

$$\rho = \frac{R' - R}{1 - R'}. \qquad (71)$$

The depth of one and the same line can be measured with the same instrument in the spectra of the Sun and Moon; and with the help of the equation (71) we can compute the relative participation ρ of the luminescence component in the light of the Moon.

These kinds of measurements were carried out by Dubois (1956, 1957, 1959) and Kozyrev (1956). They revealed a distinct luminescence in some parts of the Moon, confined to certain emission bands of the spectrum. Out of 86 spots investigated by Dubois, luminescence was reported in 47 cases. It is interesting to note that Kozyrev (1956) found by the same method a comparatively intense luminescence in the region of the K and H lines in the light of the rays surrounding the crater Aristarchus; a fuller description of his observations will be given in Chapter 9.

XXII. The Variation in Brightness of the Eclipse

The observed historical eclipses of the Moon have indicated that the brightness of such phenomena on record varied within very wide limits. Thus there are reports of eclipses during which the Moon disappeared entirely from sight, or was only seen with great difficulty. This, for instance, appeared to be the case for the eclipse on 5th May, 1110, observed in England. The eclipse on 15th June, 1620, was, according to Kepler, very dark and the visibility of the Moon was greatly reduced. In the course of the eclipse of 14th April, 1642, the Moon disappeared completely from Hevelius's view; just as it did from Wargentin's during the eclipse on 18th May, 1761; and from Lee's on 10th June, 1816. On the other hand, there are also records of very bright eclipses characterized by rather lively colours. This was apparently true of the eclipse of 9th September, 1718, as observed by Cassini; and of that of 18th March, 1848, observed at a great number of observatories.

Similar reports on the fluctuations of the brightness of the eclipses prompted Danjon (1920a) to a treatment of the dependence of the brightness and colour of eclipses on the solar activity. In order to be able numerically to express verbal descriptions of eclipses, he introduced a luminosity-scale of eclipses ranging from $L = 0$, when the Moon is almost or wholly invisible, to $L = 2$, when the eclipsed Moon is exceptionally bright. Together with the brightening of the Moon, its colour varied from a neutral black $L = 0$, to brown, brick-red, red up to orange at $L = 2$. Danjon applied his procedure first to seventy eclipses from the period of 1823-1920. The results showed an interesting dependence of Danjon's degree of brightness L on the phase ϕ of the solar activity, computed in fractions of the eleven-year cycle from the minimum (Fig. 34). This dependence was supplemented and confirmed by de Vaucouleurs (1944) on the basis of the results obtained from observations of forty-seven eclipses between 1893-1943. At the minimum of solar activity, the dependence exhibits a distinct discontinuity. The eclipses preceding this minimum are brightest, and those following it rapidly become fainter. From one minimum to another, the

brightness of the eclipse increases and diminishes quite linearly, giving
rise to a saw-toothed curve.

Later, Danjon (1920b) extended these investigations back to 1583,
and reversed the whole procedure: namely, he took the dependence
given by the curve in Fig. 34 as proved, and used its jump at the
minimum for the determination of the epochs of the minima of solar

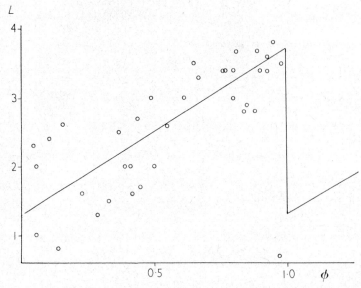

FIG. 34. Danjon's relation of the dependence of the luminosity of lunar eclipses L on
the phase ϕ within the 11 year-solar cycle.

activity in the past. The minima thus determined may be expressed
by the equation

$$\text{Min} = 1584 \cdot 8 + 10 \cdot 87E + 1 \cdot 7 \sin 2\pi \frac{t - 1608}{136}, \qquad (72)$$

which agrees well with the lunar minima of light and equally well with
the actual minima of solar activity according to Wolf, as long as we
confine ourselves to periods following 1800. At earlier periods, Danjon-
Wolf's deviations are much greater, which also might be due to an
error in the solar observations which in early days used to be very
incomplete.

The first to raise objections against Danjon's work was Maunder
(1921). His objections, as far as they were aimed at the essence of the
method were unsubstantiated, as has been shown by Danjon himself
(1925). Maunder also objected, however, to the length of the solar

cycle 10·87 years, as derived from lunar eclipses, in distinction to the currently used value of 11·2 years. It must be added, however, that the results of other investigations, based on the effect of the solar activity on the weather, lead to lower values approaching that of Danjon (Brooks, 1928; Link, 1955).

Fisher (1924) too raised objections against Danjon's results. He treated all eclipses observed within the period 1860-1922 on a different scale of brightness which was based on the simple visibility of lunar details by telescopes of increasing aperture. This criterion allows, however, of alternative interpretations; since the visibility of a diffuse object depends, among others, also on the magnification of the telescope. Nevertheless, some of Fisher's results must be regarded as a positive contribution—like, for instance, his proof of the dependence of the brightness of the eclipse on the season of the year (the hibernal eclipses being the brightest)—as also confirmed by Smith's findings (1885)—or the effect of volcanic eruptions (1883, 1902, 1912) on the brightness of the eclipse. Fisher confirmed neither Danjon's relation, nor did he find the dependence of total eclipses on the parallax, which is in direct conflict with both theories (see, e.g. Table V) and observation (Švestka, 1950). On the whole, an analysis of this controversy (Link, 1956c) allows us to state that Danjon's results are of a great value in the field of the study of lunar eclipses, and should become the starting point of many new investigations.

It would, however, be very desirable to verify Danjon's results both by a new treatment of the historical material, extended if possible to further sources, as well as by its comparison with the results of the measurement of the shadow densities.

For the time being, only the second part of this programme, namely, the comparison with measurements of the optical density, has been carried out (Link, 1960). This has been performed for eighteen eclipses measured by Danjon's method from 1921 on. The results are given in Fig. 35 for three spectral regions, the blue (B), green (G) and red (R). The results confirm, on the whole, Danjon's law—particularly as far as the colouring of the shadow is concerned—characterized numerically by the difference $B - R$. In the limb regions ($\gamma' = -10'$) as well as closer to the centre ($\gamma = 20'$) in 1944 and 1954, an abrupt decrease of the differences $B - R$ could be noted in the vicinity of the solar minima, when, in fact, the predominance of the red colour in the shadow steeply diminished. Both curves run, on the whole, synchronously with the curve of the brightness of the eclipse L on Danjon's scale. As for the density of the shadow, a similar fluctuation appears in the limb regions ($\gamma = -10'$), with the phase shifted with regard to the colour curve

B-R. The bright eclipses in 1950 do not stand out on the colour curve and the again marked maximum of colour around 1953 coincides with low brightnesses of the shadow.

A part of the density curves lies above the theoretical limit of density for Rayleigh's atmosphere with ozone D_c' (Fig. 35) and sometimes

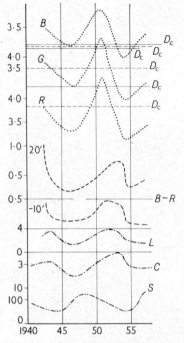

FIG. 35. Changes in brightness of lunar eclipse according to measurements of the shadow density. Above: changes of the shadow density at the distance $\gamma' = -10'$ for the blue (B), green (G) and red (R) colour. D_c density computed for Rayleigh's atmosphere, D_c' same but with ozone. Centre: differences $B-R$ for $\gamma = 20'$ and for $\gamma' = -10'$. Below: luminosity curve L, curve of the brightness of the earthlight on the Moon C, and curve S of sunspots.

even above the density D_c only in Rayleigh's atmosphere. Such a phenomenon may be ascribed only to the additive light in the shadow. The value of this additive light in the case of a very bright eclipse on the 26th September, 1950, is shown in the following Table XI.

As long as we wish to explain this excess by atmospheric light diffusion alone, it becomes apparent that this diffusion may yield only a very small part—a maximum of 10×10^{-6}. In this case, we encounter again a similar phenomenon, as in the case of the penumbra, which likewise finds a logical explanation in the luminescence either directly

TABLE XI

Eclipse of 26.9.1950 at $\gamma = 20'$

	Blue	Green	Red
Density in Rayleigh's atmosphere	4·60	3·56	3·02
Density due to the ozone	0·03	0·33	0·43
Computed density	4·63	3·89	3·45
Observed density	3·68	3·40	3·09
Obs. — Comp.	− 0·95	− 0·49	− 0·36
Observed illumination . 10^6	209	398	813
Computed illumination . 10^6	23	129	355
Obs. — Comp. . 10^6	+ 186	+ 269	+ 458

excited in the shadow (most probably by corpuscular radiation) or in the form of an afterglow of the luminescence from the period preceding the eclipse.

Very dark eclipses like, for instance, that of 19th January, 1954, also deserve our attention. In the green light, at a distance of $\gamma = 20'$, this eclipse is about ten times fainter than in Rayleigh's atmosphere. The difference of densities $O - C = 1$, may be only partially, to about 0·3, explained by ozone absorption, the remainder, 0·7, is of a different origin. It is not caused by absorption in the low atmosphere (dust, cloudiness) since the values $O - C$ do not reveal any apparent increase with the mean air-mass from $M_0 = 10$ to $M_0 = 30$, which is a characteristic property of the high-absorbing layer (Fig. 36).

Finally, let us mention an interesting relation between the changes in brightness of the earth-light with the solar activity, and also with

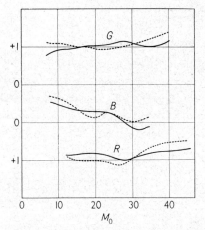

FIG. 36. Curves of differences $\Delta = O - C$ as functions of the mean air-mass M_0 for the very dark eclipse on 19th January, 1954.

the brightness of the eclipse, as pointed out by Dubois (1958). The curve of the brightness of the earth-light is in our Fig. 35 designated by *C*. It reveals, on the whole, a change similar to that of the brightness curve of eclipses on Danjon's scale. This led Vassy (1958) to the hypothesis that the cause must be looked for in aerosols, the percentage of which in the atmosphere changes with the solar activity. Before the solar minimum, when the centres of solar activity and simultaneously the sources of corpuscular radiation are in lower heliographic latitudes, this radiation may reach the Earth and support the production of aerosols. After the minimum has been attained, the centres suddenly pass into higher heliographic latitudes, and the corpuscular flux weakens abruptly. The presence of aerosols in the atmosphere then causes the terrestrial albedo to increase; and hence also the intensity of the earth-light. Vassy, moreover, allows for the effect of the aerosols to reach also into the Earth's shadow and thereby to scatter the solar light and to increase the brightness of the eclipse.

This is in itself a tempting explanation, but it cannot be confirmed quantitatively. The amplitude of earth-light is 1 : 2·6, while that of illumination in the shadow is 1 : 10, which, as such, does not support the causal connection between both phenomena. It becomes, moreover, apparent that the scattering of light in the atmosphere, even under very favourable conditions, far from attains an intensity of one-tenth of that of the direct solar illumination (Section XIV). A variation of such a small fraction of the total illumination would, therefore, be quite inconspicuous (of amplitude decidedly less than 0·1). It is not excluded that it is precisely the luminescence which constitutes the connecting link between both phenomena.

XXIII. Further Phenomena during Lunar Eclipses

Lunar eclipses cause an abrupt discontinuity in the comparatively calm state of the lunar body, not too disturbed by the slow alternation of the days of fourteen terrestrial days in length, and of the equally long nights. By the grace and accident of the phenomena of eclipses other observations can be made which would otherwise be impossible. In what follows we shall briefly mention some of these possibilities in turn.

A. TEMPERATURE OF THE LUNAR SURFACE

The temperature undergoes large changes during eclipses, since its source—the solar radiation—is suddenly cut off for several hours. Measurements of the long-wave radiation may provide us with certain information on the temperature-drop and simultaneously also on the thermal characteristics of the surface layers. All these phenomena will be dealt with more exhaustively in Chapter 11 by Sinton.

Let us point out Urey's (1952) interesting observation concerning a possible difference between the near and far side of the Moon. It is, in fact, on the near side alone that all eclipse changes occur, and with them the sudden temperature changes which may result in more marked disintegrations of the rocks than on the other side (where this factor is absent). It may be expected with confidence that this circumstance will be verified in the near future from the results provided by the astronautical flights.

B. CHANGES OF BRIGHTNESS

Changes of brightness of some of the details of the lunar surface have been reported already from time to time, but their reality could so far not be confirmed. Relatively greatest attention attached to the crater Linné, by its changes both during eclipses as well as when the lunar disk was not obscured. During eclipses, its diameter seems to increase, but it cannot be decided whether this is an actual or only apparent change caused by physiological factors. Link (1947) pointed out possible relevance of luminescence in this connection.

C. DUST-SHADOW

During the eclipse of the 16th November, 1910, a dust-shadow was observed by a group of students under the guidance of Babitchev at the Odessa Observatory. From the obscured Moon standing some 40° above the horizon, a shadowy cone issued which could be traced almost to the horizon. Witkowski, also present among the observers, later explained this phenomenon (Witkowski, 1949) as caused by a cloud of cosmic dust in which the lunar body created a dust-free space—something resembling a shadow. This explanation appears to be very probable, if we recall that it is around the 16th November that the maximum of Leonids takes place, and that during the eclipse of that date (Link, 1956d), an extraordinary great shadow-enlargement was found attaining 3·7% (Section XVIII). In many cases, some extension of the terrestrial shadow beyond the lunar disk could be observed.

D. CHANGES IN THE TERRESTRIAL IONOSPHERE

Changes may occur, theoretically, at least, owing to the fact that lunar radiation—insignificant as it is in comparison with solar radiation, yet capable of asserting itself more markedly at night—is absent for a short interval. Some suggestions of such phenomena were pointed out (Link, 1956d); but this question requires further attention.

E. Observations of Faint Bodies

Observations can be made in the vicinity of the eclipsed Moon—as, for instance, the occultations of stars too faint to be seen under normal circumstances. The search for natural or artificial satellites of the Moon would obviously be facilitated at such times.

XXIV. Allied Phenomena

An analysis of the contemporary problems in astronomy shows (Barbier, 1959) that their classification necessarily must be two-dimensional, partly depending on the subject (for instance, in rows), and partly in the working method (in columns)—be this method experimental or theoretical. These circumstances may be illustrated also in our case of lunar eclipses, when our methods embrace other subjects also. Thus, if we proceed in the columns of the method we arrive at the following applications:

A. Optical Occultations of Stars by the Moon and Planets

We proceed from the simplified equation for the attenuation of the light by refraction (equation (22)), as has been shown previously (Section VII).

B. Radio Occultations by the Moon and Planets

In the radiowave region, again equation (17) and the equation for the refraction (26)—after due conversions to the required form—may be used, provided that the Moon has an ionosphere. According to a theory formulated by Link (1955, 1956), minute traces of a lunar atmosphere are discernible. The method is about a thousand times more sensitive than the optical method used by Lyot and Dollfus. This method was used by Elsmore (1955), and he found the upper limit 10^{-12} of the density of terrestrial atmosphere (see also Chapter 12 by Evans).

C. Radio Occultations by the Solar Corona

Machin and Smith (1951) suggested using the occultation of the radio-source in Taurus by the solar corona for the determination of the coronal structure. Link (1952) developed a theory of occultation, based on lunar eclipses, that later served for the interpretation of the observed phenomenon (Hewish, 1955).

D. Transits of Venus over the Sun

These phenomena are an analogy of the lunar and solar eclipses. Their observations, based on our theory, are capable of throwing a new interesting light on some problems concerning the atmosphere of Venus (Section XII).

E. Eclipses of Jupiter's Satellites

To these phenomena our method may be very conveniently applied (Link, 1946). Its application to photometric measurements (Eropkin, 1931) suggests the presence of a very high-absorbing layer that lies beyond Jupiter's atmosphere and is reminiscent of some rudimentary remnant of a ring.

F. Einstein's Light Deflection

The deflection of light in the gravitational field of a sufficiently large mass entails consequences similar to those of the refraction of light in the atmosphere. A more detailed theory (Link, 1936b, 1937; Zwicky, 1937) leads again to the prediction of certain observable phenomena. It seems that the peculiar object in Serpens—observed by Hoag (1949) as a perfect halo 17″ radius which surrounds a diffuse central image—may possibly belong to this category.

XXV. Conclusions

At the end of our survey of the phenomena associated with lunar eclipses, let us summarize the most important scientific notions, arrived at with the aid of these phenomena, or independently confirmed by them:

1. Spherical shape of the Earth (4th century B.C.).
2. Relative dimensions of the system Earth-Moon-Sun (3rd to 2nd centuries B.C.).
3. Theory of the lunar motion (chiefly from the 2nd century A.D. onwards up to the present).
4. Determination of the geographical longitudes (16th to 18th centuries).
5. Chronology.
6. Enlargement of the Earth's shadow (beginning with the 17th century; particularly, however, at the end of the 19th century and at present).
7. Distribution of ozone in the atmosphere.
8. Existence of a high-absorbing layer and its relation to interplanetary matter.

9. Light excess in the shadow suggesting an existence of lunar luminescence.

10. Thermal characteristics of the lunar surface crust.

11. Variations of the brightness of lunar eclipses with the solar activity.

12. Application of the theory of lunar eclipses to optical and radio phenomena in the solar system (atmospheres of the planets and of the Moon, solar corona).

Points 7 to 12 represent achievements of the last four decades.

The perspectives of the further development of our scientific discipline lie apparently in a continuation of the tactics hitherto followed, and expressed by the motto: "To proceed from the known to the unknown." Today, when we may study the upper atmosphere directly, thanks to the rocket technique, it will be possible to compute on the basis of the data thus obtained the average structure of the Earth's shadow with a comparatively great accuracy. A comparison of these data with the results of detailed measurements will provide us with a deeper knowledge of the atmosphere. An advantage of this procedure consists in the fact that lunar eclipses give us a simultaneous, geographically extended picture of the terrestrial atmosphere, while rocket soundings are, and always will be, restricted to specific localities.

It would be erroneous to conclude that the development of the technique of artificial satellites will lead to a complete and direct understanding of all problems of the whole terrestrial atmosphere. There remains, in fact, a zone between 40 and 200 km of altitude, where the atmosphere is too dense to allow a protracted stay of these space laboratories flying at high velocities in accordance with the laws of celestial mechanics; but where the atmosphere is again too tenuous to support floating balloons. This zone (40–200 km) is, however, of a great importance from scientific as well as technical points of view, and its research remains, for the time being, almost exclusively the domain of high-altitude rockets together with the classical indirect methods used so far (including that of the lunar eclipses) which have the best opportunity to supplement and to support each other.

References

Abbot, C. G. (1942a). *Ann. Astrophys. Obs. Smithson. Instn.* **6**, 164.
Abbot, C. G. (1942b). *Ann. Astrophys. Obs. Smithson. Instn.* **6**, 85.
Barbier, D. (1959). Private communication, November 1959.
Bauer, E., and Danjon, A. (1923). *Bull. Soc. Astr. Fr.* **37**, 241.
Beer, W., and Maedler, J. H. (1834). *Astr. Nachr.* **11**, 290.
Bouška, J. (1948). *Bull. Astr. Insts. Csl.* **1**, 37, 75.
Bouška, J., and Link, F. (1947). *C.R. Acad. Sci., Paris*, **224**. 1483.

Bouška, J., and Švestka, Z. (1950). *Bull. Astr. Insts Csl.* **2**, 6.

Bowen, E. G. (1953). *Aust. J. Phys.* **6**, 490.

Bowen, E. G. (1956). *J. Metals N.Y.* **13**, 142.

Bowen, E. G. (1957). *Aust. J. Phys.* **10**, 412.

Brooks, C. E. P. (1928). *Mem. R. Met. Soc.* **2**, No. 12.

Brosinsky, A. (1888). "Über die Vergrösserung", etc. Göttingen.

Buchanan, R. (1907). "The Mathematical Theory of Eclipses", p. 202. Philadelphia.

Cabannes, J. (1929). "Sur la diffusion de la lumière", p. 167. Paris.

Cabannes, J., and Dufay, J. (1927). *J. Phys. Théor. Appl., Paris*, **8**, 125.

Calvisius, S. (1650). "Opus Chronologicum". Francoforti ad Moe.

Cassini, J. D. (1740). "Tables astronomiques", p. 34. Paris.

Chambers, G. F. (1899). "The Story of Eclipses". London.

Chauvenet, W. (1908). "Manual of Spherical and Practical Astronomy", p. 542. Philadelphia.

Cimino, M., and Fortini, T. (1953). *R.C. Accad. Lincei*, **14**, 619.

Cimino, M., and Gianuzzi, M. A. (1955). *R.C. Accad. Lincei*, **18**, 173.

Cimino, M., and Fresa, A. (1958). *R.C. Accad. Lincei*, **25**, 58.

Danjon, A. (1920a). *C.R. Acad. Sci., Paris*, **171**, 127.

Danjon, A. (1920b). *C.R. Acad. Sci., Paris*, **171**, 1207.

Danjon, A. (1921). *Astronomie*, **39**, 272.

Danjon, A. (1925). *Bull. Soc. Astr. Fr.* **39**, 272.

Danjon, A. (1928). *Ann. Obs. Strasbourg*, **2**, 1.

Dobson, G. M. B. (1930). *Proc. Roy. Soc.* A **129**, 411.

Doublet, E. (1922). "Histoire de l'Astronomie", p. 279. Paris.

Dubois, J. (1956). *Astronomie*, **70**, 225.

Dubois, J. (1957). *J. Phys. Théor. Appl., Paris*, **18**, 13, Suppl.

Dubois, J. (1959). *Rozpr. Ceskosl. Akad. Věd.* **69**, No. 6.

Dubois, J. (1958). *P.V. Soc. Sci. Phys. Nat. Bordeaux*, **24**, IV.

Dufour, C. (1899). *Astronomie*, **13**, 115.

Du Séjour, (1786). "Traité Analytique des Mouvements Apparents des Corps Célestes". Paris.

Elsmore, B. (1955). "I.A.U. Symposium on Radioastronomy", No. 4, p. 403.

Eropkin, D. J. (1931). *Z. Astrophys.* **3**, 163.

Fabry, C. (1929). *J. Observateurs*, **12**, 1.

Fessenkov, V. (1937). *Astr. J., Moscow*, **14**, No. 5.

Fisher, W. (1924). *Smithson. Misc. Coll.* **76**, No. 9.

Fortini, T. (1954). *R.C. Accad. Lincei*, **17**, 209.

Fortini, T. (1955). *R.C. Accad. Lincei*, **18**, 65.

Frisch, Cr. (1858). "J. Kepleri Opera Omnia", Vol. 2, p. 297. Francoforti.

Gaubil, A. (1740). "Observations Astronomiques", Tome 3. Paris.

Götz, P. (1931). *Gerland's Beitr. Geophys.* **31**, 119.

Greenstein, J. L. (1937). *Harv. Circ.* No. 422.

Guth, V., and Link, F. (1939). *Z. Astrophys.* **18**, 207.

Hansa, M., and Zacharov, I. (1958). *Bull. Astr. Insts Csl.* **9**, 236.

Hartmann, J. (1891). *Abh. Sachs. Ges. (Akad.)Wiss.* (Math.-Phys. Kl.). **17**, 365.

Heath, T. (1913). "Aristarchos of Samos". Oxford Univ. Press.

Hepperger, J. (1895). *S.B. Akad. Wiss. Wien* (Math.-Phys. Kl.). **54**/II.

Hewish, A. (1955). *Proc. Roy. Soc.* A **228**, 238.

Heyden, F. J. (1954). *Astrophys. J.* **118**, 412.

Hoag, A. (1949). *Astr. J.* **55**, 170.

Humphreys, G. W. (1929). "Physics of the Air". New York.

Kirch, A. (1727). *Misc. Berol.* p. 228.

Koebke, F. (1951). *Bull. Soc. Amis. Sci. Poznan,* 11.

Kosik, S. M. (1940). *Bull. Tashkent Astr. Obs.* 2, 79.

Kozyrev, N. A. (1956). *Izv. Crim. Astrophys. Obs.* 16, 148.

Kuhl, A. (1928). *Phys. Z.* 29, 1.

Lahire, P. (1707). "Tabulae astronomicae". Paris.

Lalande, J. F. (1783). *Astronomie,* 2, 337.

Lambert, F. (1782). "Briefwechsel." Berlin.

Langrenus, M. F. (1644). "Tractatus de vera longitudine", etc. Antverpiae.

Laplace, S. P. (1860). "Oeuvres Complètes", Vol. 6, Pt. I, p. 16. Paris.

Legentil, G. J. H. (1755). *Mém. Acad. Sci., Paris,* p. 36.

Lemonnier, P. C. (1746). "Institutions astronomiques", p. 251. Paris.

Link, F. (1929). *Bull. Obs. Lyon,* 11, 229.

Link, F. (1933). *Bull. Astr., Paris,* 8, 77.

Link, F., and Guth, V. (1936a). *J. Observateurs,* 19, 129.

Link, F. (1936b). *Bull. Astr., Paris,* 9, 227.

Link, F. (1936c). *C.R. Acad. Sci., Paris,* 202, 917.

Link, F. (1937). *Bull. Astr., Paris,* 10, 75.

Link, F., and Guth, V. (1940). *Z. Astrophys.* 20, 1.

Link, F. (1946). *Ann. Astrophys.* 9, 227.

Link, F. (1949b). *C.R. Acad. Sci., Paris,* 223, 976.

Link, F. (1947a). *Bull. Astr., Paris,* 13, 1.

Link, F. (1947b). *J. Soc. Math. Phys. Tchèque,* 72, 65.

Link, F. (1947c). *Coll. Lyon, C.N.R.S. Paris,* 1, 308.

Link, F. (1948a). *Ann. Geophys.,* 4, 47, 211.

Link, F. (1948b). *Bull. Astr. Insts. Csl.* 1, 13.

Link, F. (1950a). *Bull. Astr., Paris,* 15, 143.

Link, F. (1950b). *Trans. I.A.U.* 7, 135.

Link, F. (1950c). *Bull. Astr. Insts Csl.* 2, 1.

Link, F. (1951). *Bull. Astr. Insts. Csl.* 2, 131.

Link, F. (1952). *Bull. Astr. Insts. Csl.* 3, 6.

Link, F., and Linkova, Z. (1954a). *Publ. Obs. Nat., Prague,* No. 25.

Link, F., and Linková, Z. (1954b). *Bull. Astr. Insts. Csl.* 5, 82.

Link, F. (1955a). *Météorologie,* 12, 257.

Link, F. (1955b). "I.A.U. Symposium on Radioastronomy", No. 4, p. 400.

Link, F. (1956a). "Die Mondfinisternisse", p. 53. Leipzig.

Link, F. (1956b). "Die Mondfinsternisse", p. 71. Leipzig.

Link, F. (1956c). "Die Mondfinsternisse", p. 100. Leipzig.

Link, F. (1956d). "Die Mondfinsternisse", pp. 116–117. Leipzig.

Link, F. (1956e). *Bull. Astr. Insts Csl.* 7, 1.

Link, F. (1956f). *Publ. Obs. Nat., Prague,* No. 29.

Link, F. (1958). *Bull. Astr. Insts Csl.* 9, 169.

Link, F. (1959). *Bull. Astr. Insts Csl.* 10, 105.

Link, F. (1960). *Bull. Astr. Insts Csl.* 11, 13.

Machin, K. E., and Smith, F. G. (1951). *Nature, Lond.* 168, 589.

Maedler, J. H. (1800). *Astr. Nachr.* 15, 1.

Maunder, E. W. (1921). *J. Brit. Astr. Ass.* 31, 346.

Mitra, S. K. (1952). "The Upper Atmosphere", p. 152. Calcutta.

Oppolzer, Th. (1887). *Denkschr. Akad. Wiss. Wien,* 22.

Paetzold, H. K. (1950). *Z. Naturf.* **5a**, 661.

Paetzold, H. K. (1951). *Z. Naturf.* **6a**, 639.

Paetzold, H. K. (1952). *Z. Naturf.* **7a**, 325.

Paetzold, H. K. (1953). *Z. Astrophys.* **32**, 303.

Palmén, E. (1934). *Met. Z.* **51**.

Pannekoek, A. (1903). *Astr. Nachr.* **164**, No. 3913.

Pettit, E. (1933*a*). *Bull. Sol. Phenom. Zürich*, **24**.

Pettit, E. (1938). *Bull. Sol. Phenom. Zürich*, **44**.

Pingré, P. (1901). "Annales célestes", ed. Bigourdan, Paris.

Prantl, E. (1881). "Aristotelis de Coelo", Libri IV p. 21. Lipsiae.

Proctor, R. A., and Raynard, A. G. (1892). "Old and New Astronomy". pp. 503–509. London.

Ramanathan, R. R. (1929). *Nature, Lond.* **123**, 834.

Reuss, J. D. (1804). "Repertorium Comentationum", 5. Goetingae.

Riccioli, J. B. (1651). "Almagestum Novum". Bononiae.

Rocket Panel (1952). *Phys. Rev.* **88**, 1027.

Rougier, G. (1933). *Ann. Obs. Strasbourg*, **2**, 3.

Rougier, G., and Dubois, J. (1944). *Ciel et Terre*, **55**, No. 5.

Saussure, M. (1931). *Verh. Naturf. Ges. Basel*, **42**.

Schmidt, J. (1856). "Der Mond", p. 141. Leipzig.

Seeliger, H. (1896). *Abh. Bayer. Akad. Wiss.* II Kl, **19**/2.

Smith, M. (1885). *Phil. Mag.* (I), **66**, 169.

Struyck, N. (1740). "Inleiding to Algemeene Geographie." Amsterdam.

Švestka, Z. (1948). *Bull. Astr. Insts Csl.* **1**, 48.

Švestka, Z. (1949). *Bull. Astr. Insts Csl.* **1**, 109.

Švestka, Z. (1950). *Bull. Astr. Insts Csl.* **2**, 41.

Tsesevich, V. P. (1940). *Publ. Astr. Inst. Univ. Leningrad*, No. 50.

Urey, H. C. (1952). "The Planets", p. 20. New Haven.

Vassy, E. (1958). *J. Sci. Mét.* **8**, 1.

Vaucouleurs, G. de (1944). *C.R. Acad. Sci., Paris*, **218**, 655, 805.

Vigroux, E. (1954). *Ann. Astrophys.* **17**, 399.

Walker, M. F., and Reaves G. (1957) *Publ. Astr. Soc. Pacif.* **69**, 153.

Wirtz, C. (1915). *Astr. Nachr.* **201**, 22.

Witkowski, J. (1949). *Bull. Soc. Amis. Sci. Poznan*, p. 147.

Wolf, R. (1877*a*). "Geschichte der Astronomie", p. 174. München.

Wolf, R. (1877*b*). "Geschichte der Astronomie", p. 154. München.

Zacharov, I. (1952). *Bull. Astr. Insts Csl.* **3**, 82.

Zwicky, F. (1937). *Phys. Rev.* **51**, 290, 679.

Chapter 7

Topography of the Moon

Zdeněk Kopal

I. Lunar Topography: a Survey...................................... 231
II. Lunar Coordinates... 246
III. Determination of Altitudes on the Moon......................... 251
IV. Formations on the Lunar Surface................................ 265
    References.. 281

I. Lunar Topography : a Survey

The lunar topography constitutes a subject whose emergence and subsequent evolution as a scientific discipline can be traced with relative precision: for its sources go back to the very first days of telescopic astronomy inaugurated by Galileo Galilei in 1609. Although Galileo was not the real inventor of the telescope, he was indubitably the first one to use it for the observation of celestial bodies; and as he recorded a year later in his "Nuncius Sidereus", " Sed missis terrenis ad coelestium speculationes me contuli: ac Lunam prius tam ex propinquo sum intuitus, ac si vix per duas Telluris diametros abesset";† and further on (p.13) he continues that . . . "De facie autem Lunae, quae ad aspectum nostrum vergit primo loco dicamus; quam facillionis intelligentiae gratias in duas partes distinguo, alteram nempe clariorem, obscuriorem alteram . . . ut certo intelligamus, Lunae superficiem non perpolitam, aequabilem, exactissimeque sphaericitatis exsistere, ut magna Philosophorum cohors de ipsa deque reliquis corporibus co-elestibus opinata est, sed contra inaequalem, asperam, cavitatibus tumoribus confertam, non secus ac ipsiusmet Telluris faciem, quae montium ingis vallumque profunditatibus hic inde distinguitur."‡

Galileo's "Nuncius Sidereus" contains altogether five drawings of the Moon (the originals of which are 8 cm in diameter), one of which

---

†"When I gave up observation of the terrestrial objects, I turned my attention to the celestial bodies: first I saw the Moon from such proximity as if it were barely two terrestrial diameters distant."

‡"Further, with regard to the side of the Moon facing us, let it be said first that one part of it is noticeably brighter, the other darker . . . so that we could perceive that the surface of the Moon is neither smooth nor uniform, nor very accurately spherical, as is assumed by a great many philosophers about the Moon and other celestial bodies, but that it is uneven, rough, replete with cavities and packed with protruding eminences, in no other wise than the Earth which is also characterized by mountains and valleys."

is reproduced on the accompanying Fig. 1. A mere glance at it will convince us that Galileo was not a great observer; or else the excitement of so many telescopic discoveries had temporarily blurred his skill or critical sense; for none of the features recorded on this (and other) drawings of the Moon can be safely identified with any known markings of the lunar landscape.† In spite of the obvious shortcomings of these first telescopic observations of the Moon, their impact on the contemporary scientific thought was, however, profound, and promptly inaugurated the era of specifically selenographic literature.

The first book written in the wake of the telescopic observations and dealing predominantly with our satellite was Iulio Caesare La Galla's "De phenomenis in orbe Lunae" (Venetiis 1612). Its author's critical sense left much to be desired; and as it contained no map or drawing of the Moon‡ his book represented no real contribution to lunar topography. The first map which did constitute such a contribution was prepared by P. Ch. Scheiner, S. J.—the historic adversary of Galileo Galilei in their dispute over the sunspots— and can be found on p. 58 of his "Disquisitiones mathematicae de controversiis et novitatibus astronomicis" (Ingolstadtii, 1619). This drawing (reproduced on the accompanying Fig. 2) had a diameter of 92 mm in original, and depicts for the first time several features which can be safely identified.§

Further maps of the Moon, based on observations with the aid of the telescopes of increased resolving power and bearing progressively greater resemblance to the actual face of the Moon, were prepared by:

C. Malapert (1581–1630), in his "Oratio" (Duaci 1620);

Cl. Mellan (1598–1688), "Carte de la Lune" (1634–35);

A. Argoli (1570–1657), in his "Pandosion Sphaericum" (Patavii 1644);

M. F. van Langren (1600-1675), in his "Selenographia Langreniana" (Antverpiae 1645); for its reproduction cf. the accompanying Fig. 3.

A. M. Schyrlaeus de Rheita (1597–1660), in his "Opus Theologiae,

† The ring-like configuration near the centre of the apparent disk of Fig. 1 (which Galileo compared with the central European land of Bohemia), may represent the well-known crater Ptolemy (cf. Fig. 10).

‡ Contrary to an assertion in R. J. Wolf's "Handbuch der Astronomie, ihrer Geschichte und Literatur", none of the copies of La Galla's book preserved in the Bibliothèque Nationale in Paris contain any lunar maps.

§ Thus, in terms of the established nomenclature, A = Mare Crisium, B = Mare Smythii, C = Lacus Somnium, D = Mare Serenitatis, E = Mare Tranquilitatis, F = Mare Foecunditatis, G = Mare Nectaris; and of the craters, I = Maurolycus, K = Walter, L = Eudoxus, N = Theophilus, O = Petavius, R = Posidonius, etc.

Philosophiae et Verbi Dei Praeconibus utile et incundum (Antverpiae 1645);

F. Fontana (1585–1656), in his "Novae Coelestium Terrestriumque Rerum Observationes " (Neapoli 1646)†;

J. Hevelius (1611–1687), in his "Selenographia sive Lunae Descriptio" (Gedani 1648); see Fig. 4;

G. B. Riccioli (1598–1671), in "Almagestum Novum" (Bononiae 1651), containing a map prepared by his Jesuit confrère Fr. M. Grimaldi (Fig. 5).

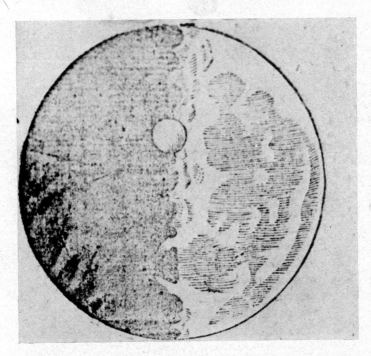

FIG. 1. One of the first drawings of the Moon made by Galileo Galilei, and published by him in his "Nuncius Sidereus". (Padua 1610).

The original drawing of Langren's map had a diameter of 35 cm; Rheita's map, 18 cm; that of Fontana, 24 cm, and of Hevelius, 29 cm. Langren and, following him, Hevelius, together with Riccioli should be regarded as progenitors of the nomenclature of lunar craters and maria which has survived up to the present time.

† Fontana's map was apparently reproduced also by M. Hirzgartner in his "Detectio dioptrica corporum planetarum verorum", Frankfurt 1643.

58   DISQVISITIONES

ficut & aliæ innumeræ vmbræ lunulis obiectæ, & ipfæ Luniformes,
ex obiectu partium eminentiorum creatæ. *Tertio*, Lux Lunæ ab
antiquis maculis diftincta & ipfa inæqualis, nam quædam quafi
gemmæ ex ea elucent intenfiffimi candoris, qualis eft N & O; Lu-

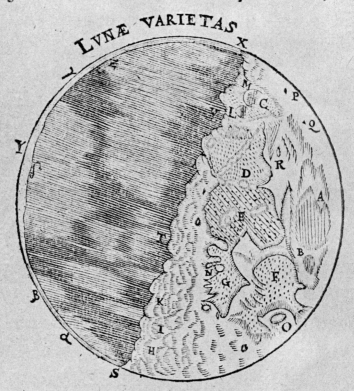

nula item apud H, apud I, ad K, iuxta L, M & D, aliæq; gemmæ innumeræ. *Quarto*, Maculæ nigræ, vt P, Q. R & aliæ hinc inde, exq;
fatis ftabiles. *Quinto*, confinium lucis & vmbrarum, quale nunc
eft, S T V X, femper anfractuofum afperum & inæquale, quod cauf-
fant partes eminentes lucem folarem inæqualiter impedientes.
Sexto vmbrofa Lunæ pars X Y S, tota lucida eft, luce fecundaria, &
fplendori Saturnio par. de qua mox difquifitione fequente. *Septimo*,
huius ipfius partis vmbrofæ triplex inuenitur lucis differentia; nam
ordinaria

FIG. 2. A map of the Moon, prepared by P. Chr. Scheiner and published on p. 58
of his book "Disquisitiones mathematicae de controversiis et novitabus astronomicis".
(Ingolstadt 1619).

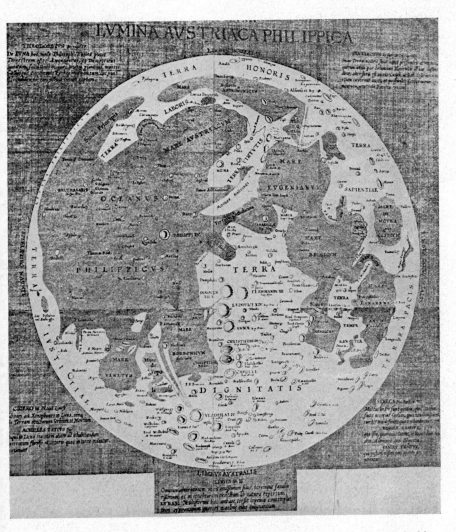

FIG. 3. A map of the Moon, prepared by M. F. van Langren, as it appeared in his "Selenographia Langreniana, sive Lumina Austriaca Philippica". (Antwerp 1645).

The foregoing brief list constitutes a survey of the principal contributions to lunar topography which we owe to our predecessors in the first half of the 17th century; and to continue with it in the same detail throughout subsequent ages would widely transcend the scope

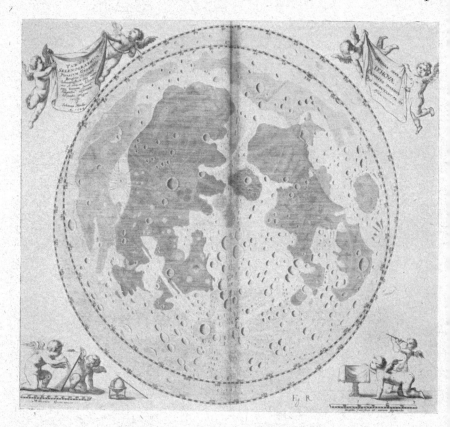

Fig. 4. The third lunar map prepared by Johannes Hevelius, as it appeared in his "Selenographia, sive Lunae Description". (Danzig 1648).

of the present chapter. The principal contributions of the second half of the 17th century (Borel, 1655; Muller, 1655; Cherubin, 1671; Francisci, 1676; Eimmart, 1696) were all overshadowed by a magnificent map by J. D. Cassini (1625–1712), founder and first director of the Paris Observatory. This map (reproduced on the accompanying Fig. 6) was prepared under Cassini's direction by Leclerc de Patigny, and engraved in copper by the aged Claude Mellan (who made his own quite accurate drawings of the Moon in the period 1634–1638 under the direction of Pierre Gassendi). The original copper plate is lost now

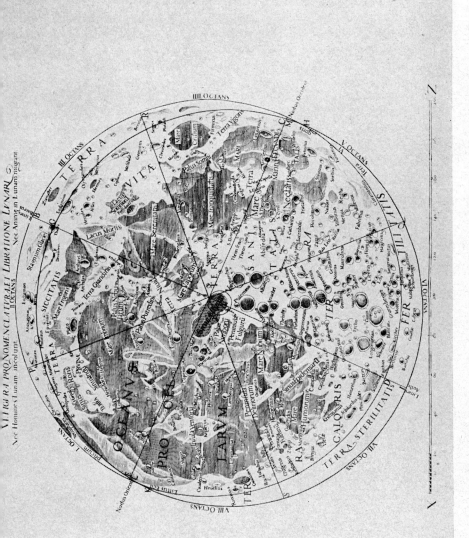

FIG. 5. The second lunar map by Fr. M. Grimaldi, as it appeared in Riccioli's "Almagestum novum". (Bologna. 1651).

and only two copies of its prints now exist—one at the Paris Observatory, and the other in the library of the Royal Astronomical Society in London; Fig. 6 is the reproduction of the latter.

The achievements of Cassini and his contemporaries in the field of lunar topography become all the more impressive when we stop to consider the telescopic means at their disposal for the observations of our satellite. Throughout this period we are still in the first geological age of optical Dinosauri, characterized by small heads on huge bodies. The apertures of their simple objectives seldom exceeded 6–8 inches; but their focal ratios were extremely large (to offset chromatic aberration), leading to focal lengths in excess of those of most telescopes existing at the present time. Thus the instrument with which Hevelius carried out most of his observations of the lunar surface at Danzig had a focal length of 49 metres! Needless to say, such telescopes could be but very crudely mounted. They had no tubes, and their objectives were mostly mounted at the end of a long pole, directed to different parts of the sky by pulling ropes. Sometimes, in desperation, the astronomer dispensed with the mounting altogether, and fixed his objective to the roof of a building, waiting for a transit of his celestial object on the ground, with an eyepiece in his hand! This was, indeed, the accepted practice of telescopic work at the Paris Observatory in the days of J. D. Cassini†; and most part of the details on lunar surface as shown on his map (Fig. 6) was apparently obtained in this way.

By the first half of the 18th century, the age of the long-necked telescopic Dinosauri of the earlier epoch was gradually closing to its end; and this fact was also fully reflected in the contemporary selenographical literature—or rather in the lack of it. For since about the turn of the century the production of new lunar maps came gradually to a standstill—as though astronomers were becoming satisfied with the efforts of their predecessors—deficient as they were in many respects. To be sure, Cassini's three laws (cf. Chapters 1 and 2) of motion of our satellite were already established by no more elaborate means; but no one could trace as yet, on any map, the position of the lunar equator. In fact, the concept of the lunar coordinates did not, and could not, emerge from contemporary records until mere drawings of the Moon gave way to micrometric measurements of its surface features.

This came to pass in the middle of the 18th century, and the pioneer of the new technique was Tobias Mayer (1723–1762). His "Bericht von den Mondskugeln" (Nürenberg 1750) contained an account

† According to A. Danjon and A. Couder, "Lunettes et Télescopes", Paris, 1935; p. 651.

of his method, and the first quantitative measurements of the coordinates of 23 reference points on the surface of the Moon—together with an invitation to subscribe (30 Gulden or $7\frac{1}{2}$ Ducats) for the construction of a lunar globus, constructed on the basis of such measurements. The response of the public to this offer is not known; and the short

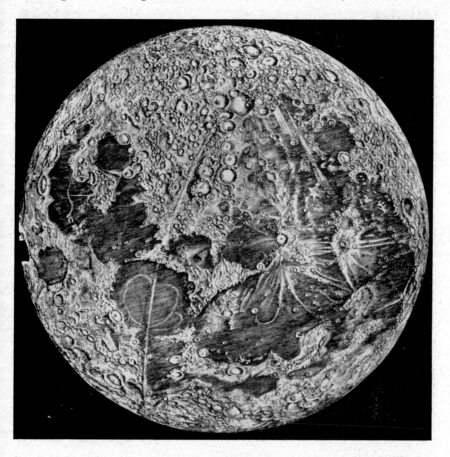

FIG. 6. A map of the Moon, engraved by Claude Mellan on the basis of observations by Jean Dominique Cassini, and published at Paris in 1680.

lifetime vouchsafed to Tobias Mayer on this Earth (he died before attaining the age of 40) did not permit him, at any rate, to complete his globus before his premature end; but maps based on his observations were eventually published by Lichtenberg in his "Tobiae Mayeri Opera Inedita" (Gottingae 1775) and, more than a century later, by Klinker-fuess in 1881. A reproduction of this latter map—35 cm in diameter on the original—is shown on the accompanying Fig. 7. Its principal innovation is, of course, the net of equatorial coordinates, rendering his work a real chart. Mayer's critical sense is also shown by the selection of the details measured by him and recorded on his maps. A glance at Fig. 7 and its comparison with a modern photograph

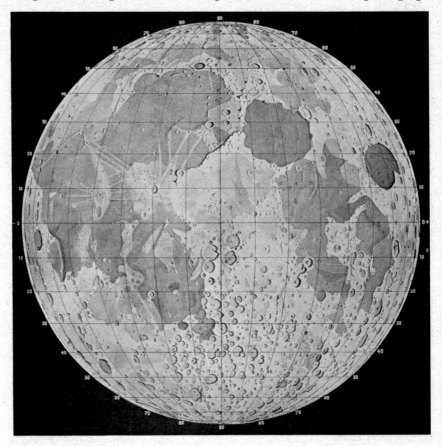

FIG. 7. A map of the Moon, based on the observations by Tobias Mayer around 1750, and published by Klinkerfuess in 1881. (North on top).

reveals that no important features are missing; but all small details, which could not be measured accurately with his telescope, were resolutely omitted.

Mayer's work centring around 1750 represents a veritable landmark in the selenographic literature, and inaugurated the era in which selenography has become an exact scientific discipline. Its principal contributors in the generations to come were:

J. H. Lambert (1728–1777), whose new lunar map based on micrometric measurements in stereographic projection, was published in the years 1780–83.

J. H. Schröter (1745–1816), whose "Selenotopographische Fragmente" (Lilienthal, 1791 and Göttingen, 1802) contained not only positional measurements of numerous lunar mountains, but also determinations of their heights;

W. G. Lohrmann (1796–1840), who produced two original maps of the Moon, the largest of which, published in the year of 1835 in Leipzig, was 385 mm in diameter; and left much additional material for a large map which was not published till in 1878 by J. F. J. Schmidt;

W. Beer (1797–1850) and J. H. Mädler (1794–1874) who prepared a new large map of the Moon—the first one to be divided in four quadrants—corresponding to a diameter of 97·5 cm for the apparent lunar disk, and containing practically all details that can be seen with the aid of a 4-inch refractor. The map by Beer and Mädler (a sample of which is reproduced on the accompanying Fig. 8) represents a veritable landmark in selenographic literature; and was not superseded till 1878 by the work of

J. F. J. Schmidt (1825–1884), whose "Charte der Gebirge des Mondes" based on observations extending between 1840–1874 and published in Berlin in 1878, represents by far the greatest selenographic work of its kind produced up to his time, and one which has scarcely been superseded ever since. Schmidt's map (a sample of which is reproduced on Fig. 9) consists of 25 sections printed on separate sheets, and corresponding in scale to a diameter of the apparent lunar disk of 194·9 cm. It records almost 33,000 individual features, and introduced the lunar nomenclature essentially as we know it to-day. Schmidt did not undertake many new positional measurements (these he took mostly from Mädler and Lohrmann), but carried out height determinations of more than 3000 lunar mountains (mostly while he served as director of the capitular observatory at Olomouc in Moravia). Maps comparable or larger in size than Schmidt's were, in more recent times, made only twice: namely, by

W. Goodacre (1856–1938), who in 1910 published in London a map of the Moon, based on (photographic) positional measurements by S. A. Saunder, and contained on 25 separate sheets. The original drawing of his map corresponded to an apparent diameter of the Moon of 192·5 cm. The largest existing map of the Moon was prepared by

R

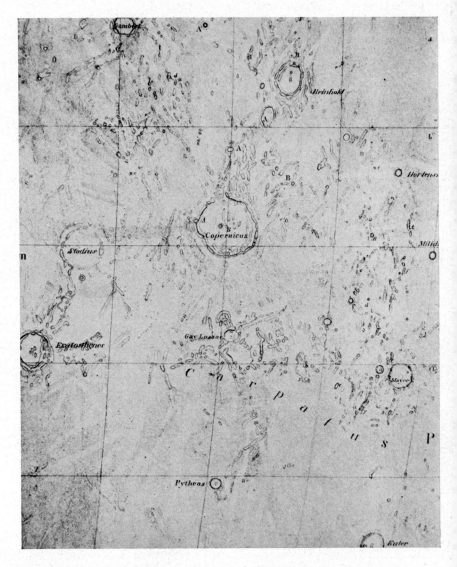

FIG. 8. A segment of the lunar map by Beer and Mädler, Berlin 1837, in the region of
Copernicus and Oceanus Procellarum.

H. P. Wilkins (1896–1960), whose own "200-inch Map of the Moon", divided in 16 separate sheets, contains many details copied from large-scale photographs. The material plotted on this map is, however, rather heterogeneous, and the accuracy of its coordinates system as well as workmanship in detail leave something to be

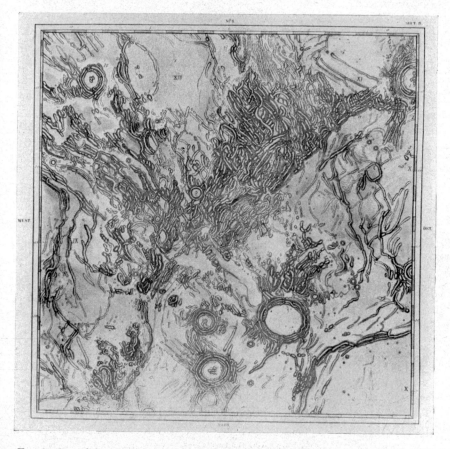

FIG. 9. One of the 25 sections of the lunar map by J. F. J. Schmidt, published in 1878 (the Appenines and Mare Imbrium region).

desired. Under these conditions, the large scale of this map did not prove an unmixed blessing; but as long as the work of Wilkins's predecessor Ph. Fauth (1867–1942) remains unpublished, Wilkins's map represents the latest—and possibly will also remain the last— effort of visual selenography expressed in cartographic form.

The reason why Wilkins will probably remain the last author of a lunar map of this kind is the fact that—as it already happened in so many other branches of astronomical science—visual selenographic work is, at the present time, about to be completely taken over by photography.

In 1839, a few years after the world was astounded by the notorious Moon hoax in the *New York Sun* on alleged discoveries of the lunarites by Sir John Herschel in South Africa, while the public chose to follow the speculations by F. P. Gruithuisen about the inhabitability of the Moon, a discovery was made which became primarily responsible for establishing that the surface of our satellite is dead and immutable; namely, that of the photographic process. When L. J. M. Daguerre, one of the originators of this process, devised in 1839 the way of copying photographic negatives on paper, he was encouraged by D. T. J. Arago, then Director of the Paris Observatory, to attempt a photograph of the Moon†, in order to discover whether or not the light of our satellite was chemically actinic. This proved indeed to be the case; though otherwise the experiment was a failure in so far as Daguerre's plate showed no distinguishable detail.

This failure did not, however, deter J. W. Draper (1811–1882) from repeating promptly Daguerre's experiment with improved means. He realized the main cause of it was the fact that Daguerre underexposed his plates; and in order to avoid that he exposed, in 1840, the 25 mm image of the Moon in the focus of his 12-inch mirror for 20 minutes. The outcome proved to be a success; and was further improved by W. C. Bond (1789–1859), first Director of the Harvard College Observatory, who, working together with J. A. Whipple, used the newly installed 15-inch Merz refractor. By 1850, these investigators were able to obtain lunar photographs exposed less than one minute, which were capable of enlargement and showed details of all principal features of the surface of our satellite.

The next forward step in lunar photography was taken by Warren de la Rue (1815–1889), who was the first to use the collodium plates exposed in the focus of a 12-inch reflector of 305 cm focal length. His negatives, taken in the years of 1852–1857, were sufficiently sharp to stand considerable enlargement, and can be regarded as true forerunners of the splendid series of photographs secured later by various large telescopes of the world.

Draper, Bond and de la Rue, together with L. M. Rutherfurd (1816–1892), can be regarded as the fathers of lunar photography near the

† It may be of interest to note, in this connection, that the term "photography" was first applied to the contemporary daguerrotypes by the well-known selenographer, J. H. Mädler.

middle of the 19th century. All four worked with telescopes (both refractors and reflectors) of 12 to 15-inch aperture; and the entire subsequent development of the subject was inseparably connected with the design and construction of the telescopes of larger apertures and focal length. The end of the 19th century witnessed the publication of two great photographic atlases of the Moon: one by the Lick Observatory, in 1896–97, based on photographs taken with the Observatory's 36-inch refractor of 1722 cm focal length; the other by the Observatoire National de Paris ("Atlas Photographique de la Lune", by M. Loewy and P. Puiseux, Paris 1896–1909), based on plates taken with the equatorial coudé of 24-inch aperture and 1806 cm focal length.†

These two great atlases have subsequently given rise to many other works based upon them. Thus a part of the Lick (and some Paris) negatives were subsequently selected and enlarged by L. Weinek (1848–1913) in Prague for the preparation of his "Photographischer Mond-Atlas" (Prag 1897–1900) consisting of 100 separate sheets covering most parts of the visible lunar surface; the degree of enlargement corresponding to an apparent diameter of the Moon of 396 cm (i.e. approximately twice the scale of Schmidt's map). Needless to say, the 23-fold enlargement adopted by Weinek did not increase proportionally the amount of information discernible on the individual prints; but such enlargements of these and other photographs were used by other able selenographers—such as J. N. Kreiger (1865–1901)— as a general layout for detailed visual topography of individual lunar regions. His work "J. N. Krieger's Mond-Atlas" (Wien, 1912) was published posthumously by R. König (1865–1927).

Enlargements of photographs taken fifty or seventy years ago could well be improved in detail by visual observation. More recent photographs secured in the past twenty or thirty years with some of the world's largest telescopes (Lick, Mt. Wilson, Pic-du-Midi, Yerkes) on modern emulsions are, however, fully on par with the best in the field of visual observation, and exceed it in objectivity as well as precision. A critical selection of the best available photographs from these sources has recently been assembled by G. P. Kuiper in his "Atlas of the Moon" (Univ. of Chicago Press, 1960); and all large-scale lunar mapping programmes now under way in the United States, in response to the anticipated need of such maps in the near future, will be based on the measurement of such photographs, by methods which will be outlined in the sequel.

† The objective of this telescope was removed in 1943 to the Observatoire du Pic-du-Midi, where it has of late resumed its distinguished service to the cause of lunar topography.

II. Lunar Coordinates

In order to describe or determine uniquely the position of any point on the surface of the Moon, it is necessary to define a suitable system of angular lunar coordinates β, λ analogous to the terrestrial latitudes and longitudes. The two great circles on the lunar surface from which such coordinates are conventionally measured are, respectively, the lunar equator (i.e. the circle in which the equatorial plane intersects the surface of the Moon) and the principal meridian, perpendicular to the equator, defined as a plane in which the radius-vector joining the centres of the Earth and the Moon is situated at the time of nodal passage (i.e. when the Moon's mean longitude is equal to that of the ascending node of its orbit). The north and south poles are taken to lie in the same directions as they do on the Earth; and the westward direction has traditionally been oriented towards the limb of Mare Crisium (which is, in fact, opposite to the direction in which an observer would see the stars to set on the surface of the Moon).

The actual positions of the equator and the principal meridian from which the lunar latitudes β and longitudes λ are reckoned cannot, however, be measured directly on the Moon; and their localization is inextricably connected with the determination of the orbital elements of the Moon, its shape, as well as libration (cf. Chapter 2 of this volume). On the basis of extensive measurements of the position of the Moon's axis of rotation in space, Hayn (1914) determined the mean value of the inclination I of the lunar equator to the ecliptic to be $1°32'20''$— a value adopted by Koziel in Chapter 2 of this volume. Of more modern determinations of this quantity published in the past decade, Koziel's own analysis of Hartwig's heliometric measurements led him (on slightly different grounds) to the alternative values of $I = 1°31'36'' \pm 23''$ and $1°31'10'' \pm 22''$, respectively (Koziel, 1948–49); the latter being considered as slightly more probable. Belkovich (1949) gave $I = 1°32'0'' \pm 14''$; Nefedjev (1950), $I = 1°32'4'' \pm 15''$; while according to Yakovkin (1950), $I = 1°33'48'' \pm 17''$—a value agreeing more closely with $I = 1°33'50'' \pm 19''$ as given by Watts (1955). In assessing the degree of internal consistency of these results, it should be borne in mind that an error of $1'$ in the determination of the position of the lunar equator entails effects of the order of $1'/60 \times 4 = 0''{\cdot}25$ as observable from the Earth. As this is close to the actual resolving power of any terrestrial telescopes (limited as they are by seeing conditions), it should be sufficient, for topographic purposes, to adopt the value of $I = 1°32' \pm 1'$ consistent with all existing determinations of this quantity, and to round off the determination of all lunar latitudes to $\pm 1'$ (corresponding, on the lunar surface, to a distance of ± 506 metres at the centre of the apparent lunar disk).

The determination of the position of the principal meridian on the Moon, from which the longitudes λ can be reckoned, cannot likewise be attempted directly, but only as a by-product of a grand solution for all the libration constants, from careful measurements of selected reference points on the lunar surface with respect to the limb of the Moon (by heliometer) or to the neighbouring stars (by photographic methods). Tobias Mayer—the father of selenographic positional measurements—chose the central mountain of the crater Manilius as his fundamental reference point (a choice in which he was followed by Bouvard and Nicollet); but all more modern observers have adopted for this purpose a small crater Mösting A (on the slopes of Flammarion —cf. Fig. 10), not quite on the principal meridian, but situated sufficiently near the centre of the apparent lunar disk. Its longitude λ and latitude β were found to be:

λ	β	Authority
$-5°10'26'' \pm 25''$	$-3°10'32'' \pm 2''$	Hartwig (1880)
$-5°10'19'' \pm 8''$	$-3°11'24'' \pm 5''$	Franz (1889, 1901)
$-5°10'10'' \pm 20''$	$-3°11'15'' \pm 14''$	Hayn (1902–14).

On the basis of an ensemble of these measurements Hayn (1914) adopted $\lambda = -5°10'7'' \pm 9''$ and $\beta = -3°11'2'' \pm 7''$ for the mean position of Mösting A; while the efforts of the subsequent investigators led to:

λ	β	h	Authority
$-5°11'50'' \pm 12''$	$-3°10'27'' \pm 17''$	$15'32''\cdot88 \pm 0''\cdot56$	Koziel (1948-49)
$-5°11'16'' \pm 13''$	$-3°\ 9'56'' \pm 18''$	$15'33''\cdot81 \pm 0''\cdot58$	
$-5°\ 9'20'' \pm\ 9''$	$-3°10'41'' \pm\ 7''$	$15'32''\cdot80 \pm 0''\cdot32$	Belkovich(1949)
$-5°10'13'' \pm 14''$	$-3°11'46'' \pm\ 9''$	$15'33''\cdot90 \pm 0''\cdot45$	Nefedjev (1950)
$-5°11'13'' \pm 14''$	$-3°13'11'' \pm 11''$	$15'34''\cdot52 \pm 0''\cdot60$	Yakovkin(1950)

where h denotes the radius-vector to Mösting A in angular units (i.e. the angular distance of its floor from the centre of the Moon, as seen at its mean distance from the Earth). Franz used, besides Mösting A, the positions of the craters Aristarchus, Byrgius A, Fabricius K, Gassendi, Macrobius A, Nicollet A, Proclus, and Sharp A as a system of nine fundamental reference points on the surface of the Moon; while Hayn used only five (i.e. Egede A, Kepler A, Messier A, Mösting A, and Tycho). Some of the positions of these reference points were subsequently re-measured by Schrutka-Rechtenstamm (1956, 1958).

Fig. 10. A photograph of the central portion of the apparent disk of the Moon, taken with the 24-inch refractor from Pic-du-Midi.

The two large formations in the upper part of the field are the craters Ptolemy and Alphonsus—144 and 120 kms in diameter—characterized by distinctly hexagonal forms of their ramparts.

The position of the crater Mösting A (on the eastern slopes of Flammarion) is marked on the photograph with white arrows.

The close constancy of the selenographic longitude of Mösting A, as deduced from the heliometric observations of the past hundred years, reveals, incidentally, that the axial rotation of the Moon is synchronized with the period of its revolution around the Earth within ± 0.1 second of time (i.e. about one part in 20–30 millions; cf. Banachiewicz, 1955).

With the aid of the system of lunar coordinates as determined by the measured positions of the crater Mösting A or other fundamental points, it should be possible to localize a greater number of reference points on the lunar surface for detailed topographic work. This has been done, partly visually (Franz, 1901), but mainly photographically (Saunder, 1905, 1911; König) and others. Franz's list contains the positions of a total of 1446 secondary reference points on the surface of the Moon; Saunder measured 2885 of them on the basis of the negatives secured by Loewy and Puiseux with the equatorial coudé at Paris (Saunder, 1905), and by Ritchey with the 40-inch Yerkes refractor (Saunder, 1911); while König's results, based on measurements of plates taken with much smaller instrument (8-inch refractor of 343 cm focal length) were only partly reduced after his premature death by others (Müller, Fischer), and partly remain still unpublished.

The task of using photographs for positional measurements on the Moon is quite involved, and entails many intermediate steps. In order to outline them briefly, let x_0, y_0 denote the rectangular coordinates of any point of the Moon's photographs, as measured at the measuring engine, with positive directions westwards and northwards, respectively. After correcting such measurements for (a) the optical distortion of the image in the focal plane (depending, in general, on the angular distance of the measured point from the optical axis of the telescope), (b) the differential refraction, and (c) the effects of the finite distance of the Moon (entailing a conversion from conical to orthographic projection; cf. Saunder, 1905, 1911), we obtain the reduced x, y-coordinates, to which z can be adjoined from the equation $x^2 + y^2 + z^2 = r^2$, where r denotes the actual distance (in suitable units) of the measured point from the Moon's centre. This distance, it should be stressed, cannot be obtained from any kind of relative measurements of objects on the apparent lunar disk, but requires measurements taken with respect to the limb of the Moon, or to the neighbouring stars.

Suppose, however, that such measurements are available and the local values of r as functions of x and y are known (cf. e.g. Franz, 1901; or Schrutka-Rechtenstamm, 1958). In order to relate x, y and z as measured from photographs taken in an arbitrary position of the Moon with the corresponding selenographic latitude β and longitude λ

as defined earlier in this section, account must next be taken of libration. Let b, l denote the total (optical as well as physical) libration of the Moon in latitude and longitude, respectively. If so, it follows that

$$
\left.
\begin{aligned}
x &= \quad \xi \cos l \qquad\qquad\qquad - \zeta \sin l, \\
y &= -\xi \sin l \sin b + \eta \cos b - \zeta \cos l \sin b, \\
z &= \quad \xi \sin l \cos b + \eta \sin b + \zeta \cos l \cos b,
\end{aligned}
\right\}
\tag{1}
$$

where ξ, η, ζ denote the rectangular coordinates of the point in question, identical with x, y, z if, at the time when the photograph was taken, the mean longitude of the Moon happened to be equal to that of the ascending node of its orbit. An inversion of the foregoing equations yields

$$
\left.
\begin{aligned}
\xi &= \quad x \cos l - y \sin b \sin l + z \cos b \sin l = \cos \beta \sin \lambda, \\
\eta &= \qquad\qquad + y \cos b \qquad + z \sin b \qquad = \sin \beta, \\
\zeta &= -x \sin l - y \sin b \cos l + z \cos b \cos l = \cos \beta \cos \lambda,
\end{aligned}
\right\}
\tag{2}
$$

from which (with x, y, z known from the measurements and b, l taken from the ephemeris) the angles β, λ can at last be evaluated.

Are the reference points, of known coordinates, on the surface of the Moon—available to us through the efforts of Franz, Saunder, or König—sufficient for detailed local topographic measurements of long-focus plates? The density of such points per unit area would indeed be sufficient if it were not for the difficulties in identification. Most points measured by these investigators referred to hills or mountains having no well-defined summits, and their exact locations are too vaguely defined to be identifiable without ambiguity on photographs taken at different angles of illumination with the requisite precision. The same is all the more true of several of the fundamental points (Tycho, for example) measured by Franz or Hayn.

In order to remove these difficulties and to meet the current needs of lunar topography, Kopal (1960) suggested recently that a new homogeneous set of control points (harmonized as far as possible with the existing systems of Franz and Saunder) be set up based on the positions, not of any mountains (because of their ill-defined nature), but rather of small craters, 1–3 km in diameter, the adoption of which should have the following advantages:

1. Because of their ubiquitous nature, a sufficient number of them could be located in any small segment of the lunar surface.

2. Their shallow depths would make their positions largely independent of the direction of incident sunlight.

The deficiences inherent in the present systems of selenographic coordinates (as reflected, e.g. in the Wesley-Blagg I.A.U. "Atlas" 1935) are probably displacing whole lunar regions by several kilometres relative to others; and their uncertainty constitutes also the principal source of error in the determination of the heights of the lunar mountains from the measured lengths of their shadows, by the methods to be expounded in the following section.

III. Determination of Altitudes on the Moon

The discussion of the preceding section has made it explicit that a determination of the *absolute* height of any point of the lunar surface, i.e. its distance from the centre of mass of the lunar globe—necessitates extensive and accurate measurements of the positions of that point at different librations with respect to the neighbouring stars (or the lunar limb). As a result, such determinations are available—largely through the efforts of Franz (1899, 1906), Yakovkin and Belkovich (1935), Weimer (1948, 1954), Schrutka–Rechtenstamm and Hopmann (1958) and others—for only a relatively limited number of fundamental points. Their discussion reveals that:

1. The deviations of any part of the actual lunar surface from a sphere scarcely exceeds 2000 metres (i.e. 0·1% of the mean radius of the Moon); and

2. A sphere offers as good an approximation to the actual form of the Moon as a three-axial ellipsoid of any orientation.

Since the deviations of the lunar surface from a sphere do not, therefore, exceed 0·1%, it should be legitimate to approach the problem of the altitude determinations on the Moon by measuring the *relative* heights of any eminences on the lunar surface with respect to the surrounding landscape, and to convert them into absolute heights by correcting them subsequently for the elevation of that particular landscape above the mean selenoid. This method is particularly applicable to the study of mountains or any ground irregularities in flat regions of the maria: and as it has been extensively applied for studies of diverse regions of the lunar surface, the aim of the present section will be to give a comprehensive account of its geometrical foundations as well as of some of their more practical aspects.

We mentioned already in the first section of this chapter that the detection of distinct irregularities on the surface of our satellite belongs among the first telescopic discoveries of Galileo Galilei (1610), who was also the first to attempt estimating the heights of lunar mountains from the distances beyond the terminator which appeared to receive the first (or last) rays of sunlight. Needless to stress, Galileo was in no position to perform any actual measurements with the aid of his rudimentary telescope; and the altitudes assigned by him to some (unidentified) peaks—rendering them as high as our terrestrial Mount Everest—represent gross overestimates of the actual situation, as was pointed out only a little later by Hevelius (1647).

The first investigator actually to measure the extent of the visibility of individual lunar peaks beyond the terminator was William Herschel (1780), using a home-made micrometer attached to his 6-foot telescope magnifying 222 times. Although Herschel exaggerated (as was his custom) the precision of his micrometric measurements—listing them to $0''\cdot 001$, while their actual errors must have been several hundred times as large—he was correct in his realization that the lunar peaks are, in general, much lower than was thought by Galileo or even Hevelius; the majority of them being between $\frac{1}{2}$ and $1\frac{1}{2}$ miles in height.

Herschel's work was soon followed by Schröter (1791, 1802) and, in the 19th century, by Beer and Mädler (1837) and Schmidt (1878), who set out to determine systematically the heights of the lunar mountains from the observed lengths of the shadows cast by the individual peaks on the surrounding landscape at the time of the sunrise and sunset. In more recent times, their method was adapted to photographic ciné-technique—first by McMath, Petrie and Sawyer (1937) at the McMath-Hulbert Observatory of the University of Michigan, and later by the Manchester astronomers working at Pic-du-Midi under the direction of the author of this chapter. The ciné-technique—consisting as it does of filming the sunrise or sunset over specific lunar regions—possesses not only all the customary advantages of photographic over visual work, but allows the use of the tip of the advancing or receding shadows as an indicator of any unevenness of the ground over which the shadows are cast. The geometrical basis of this method has first been outlined by Olbers; Beer and Mädler, together with Schmidt, have provided the bulk of the data we still possess on the dimensions and altitudes of various mountains on the Moon—a fact which is bound to give rise to some uneasiness when we recall the very modest optical means at the disposal of these observers.†

"It may, perhaps, be esteemed to be a mere matter of curiosity to search after the height of the lunar mountains", opined William Herschel (1912) in the early days of selenographic studies. Whatever may have been the views of his contemporaries on this matter, it can no longer be entertained at the present time, when a bodily contact

† Beer and Mädler used a refractor of only 4-inch aperture in all their work; while Schmidt used in Olomouc a somewhat larger refractor of 6 inches.

with our satellite—likely to be established by means of manned rockets in the relatively near future—will raise completely new requirements on our knowledge of lunar topography which astronomers will be called upon to provide; and perhaps the most important of them will be the construction of sufficiently detailed contour maps of the surface of the Moon, giving accurate positions of its landmarks as well as their elevations.

In order to ascertain such elevations from the measured lengths of their shadows, let us depart from the geometry as shown on the accompanying Fig. 11, with the aim of determining the height h of a sunlit

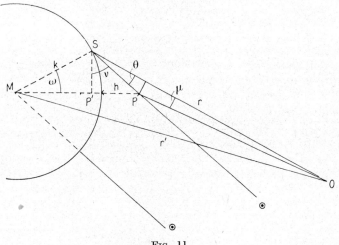

FIG. 11.

lunar eminence P, casting a shadow of which the tip, situated at the point S on the lunar surface, can be seen from the Earth. Let the points P and S be separated from each other by a length hereafter denoted as s. Let, moreover, the distance from S to the observing site O on the Earth be r. If so, the angle θ at S between the elevation of the peak and of the Earth can be solved for from the triangle OPS, leading to the equation

$$s \sin \theta = (r - s \cos \theta) \tan \mu, \qquad (1)$$

in which s denotes the linear distance between P and S, and μ the angular length of the shadow. As $s \ll r$ for all mountains on a target as distant as the Moon, the second term in parentheses on the right-hand side of (1) can be ignored in comparison with the first (giving a proportional error which is generally less than 10^{-4}), and the equation reduces to

$$\sin\theta = (r/s)\tan\mu \simeq \frac{r}{s}\left(\frac{\mu''}{206265}\right),\qquad(2)$$

if the (small) angle μ'' has been expressed in seconds of arc.

Furthermore, if ω denotes the angle PMS (cf. again Fig. 11) and $MS = k$ denotes the radius of the Moon, it follows that

$$k\sin\omega = s\cos\nu\qquad(3)$$

and also that

$$(h+k)\cos\nu = k\cos(\nu-\omega),\qquad(4)$$

where ν is the angle PSP. Our aim is to solve this latter equation for h. Dividing the latter by $\cos\nu$ and using (3) we find that

$$h+k = s\sin\nu + (k^2 - s^2\cos^2\nu)^{\frac{1}{2}}.\qquad(5)$$

Eliminating, moreover, the shadow length s in terms of the observable angle μ by means of equation (2) and expanding the radical on the right-hand side of (5) in a binomial series, we eventually establish that the altitude h/k of any particular peak on the Moon, expressed in terms of the radius k as our known unit of length, follows as

$$\left.\begin{aligned}h/k &= \Omega\tan\nu + \sqrt{1-\Omega^2}-1 \\ &= \Omega\tan\nu - \tfrac{1}{2}\Omega^2 - \tfrac{1}{8}\Omega^4 - \dots,\end{aligned}\right\}\qquad(6)$$

where we have abbreviated

$$\Omega = (r/k)\operatorname{cosec}\theta\tan\mu\cos\nu.\qquad(7)$$

How rapid is the convergence of the foregoing expansion? In order to determine the maximum value which the quantity Ω can assume, consider the maximum shadow length obtaining when the incident sunrays at S are tangent to the lunar surface. If so, then

$$s_{max} = (h+k)\sin\omega$$

and, from (3) and (4),

$$\omega = \nu\,;$$

whilst from (4) it also transpires that, under these conditions,

$$\cos\nu = k/(h+k).$$

In consequence,

$$\Omega_{max} = \sin\nu = \{1 - k^2/(h+k)^2\}^{\frac{1}{2}} \simeq (2h/k)^{\frac{1}{2}}.$$

Now no lunar mountains are known to possess altitudes in excess of 8 km. As, moreover, $k = 1738$ km, it follows that

$$\tfrac{1}{8}\Omega^4{}_{max} = \tfrac{1}{2}\left(\frac{8}{1738}\right)^2 = 0{\cdot}00001059.$$

A neglect of the quartic term in the expansion on the right-hand side of (6) would, therefore, entail a maximum error of $0{\cdot}00001059k$ or 18 metres in the computed altitude of a lunar eight-thousander; and this error would diminish to 10 or 5 metres if the altitude were six or four thousand metres, respectively. Moreover, with the rising Sun the error would, in any case, dwindle quite rapidly to insignificance. In what follows we shall, therefore, be able to limit ourselves, in most parts of our work, to the simplified version of (6) of the form

$$(h/k) = \Omega\tan\nu - \tfrac{1}{2}\Omega^2, \tag{6.1}$$

truncated with the quadratic term; while the use of the full-dress equation (6) should answer the requirements for the highest accuracy attainable today in lunar hypsometric work.

Returning to equation (7) defining Ω we note that, in the latter expression, the angle μ is a measurable quantity which depends upon the length of the shadow cast by any particular lunar peak. The angles μ and ν depend on the relative positions of the Moon, the Earth, and the Sun at the time of observation; and r signifies the instantaneous distance between the tip of each shadow and the observer on the Earth. This distance can be solved for from the triangle OMS (cf. Fig. 12) as

$$r^2 = r'^2 + k^2 - 2kr'\cos\eta, \tag{8}$$

where η denotes the angles between the vectors OM and MS, and (from the triangle EMO) it follows that

$$r'^2 = R^2 + l^2 - 2lR\cos\gamma, \tag{9}$$

where $R \equiv EM$ is the distance between the centres of the Earth and the Moon; $l \equiv OE$, the distance between the Earth's centre and the observing site; and the angle γ between the vectors $\overrightarrow{EO}$ and $\overrightarrow{EM}$ is given by the equation

$$\cos\gamma = \sin\delta\sin\phi + \cos\delta\cos\phi\cos H; \tag{10}$$

α and δ denoting the right ascension and declination of the Moon's centre, as given in any standard ephemeris; ϕ, the geocentric latitude of the observing site O on Earth; and H, the lunar geocentric hour angle.

Eliminating r' between (8) and (9) we find next that

$$r^2 = R^2 + k^2 + l^2 - 2lR\cos\gamma - 2k(R^2 + l^2 - 2lR\cos\gamma)^{\frac{1}{2}}\cos\eta$$
$$= R^2\{1 + p^2 + q^2 - 2p\cos\gamma - 2q(1 - p\cos\gamma + \tfrac{1}{2}p^2 + \ldots)\cos\eta\}, \quad (11)$$

where we have abbreviated

$$l/R = p \quad \text{and} \quad k/R = q. \quad (12)$$

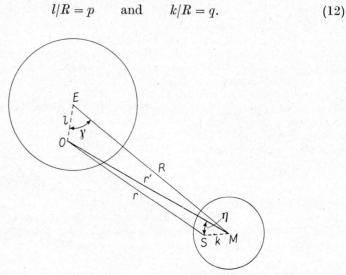

FIG. 12.

The quantities p and q just defined will, in general, be both quite small. At a mean distance of the Moon, $R = 384405$ km and $l = 6371$ km; in addition, $k = 1738$ km. Under these conditions, $p = 0\cdot016574$ and $q = 0\cdot004521$. If we regard these quantities small enough for their squares and cross-products to be negligible, the square root of equation (11) may then be expressed as

$$r = R(1 - p\cos\gamma - q\cos\eta + \ldots); \quad (13)$$

the magnitude of the largest term ignored—i.e. $pq\cos\gamma\cos\eta$—being of the order of 10^{-5}.

Moreover, by definition

$$p = \sin\pi \simeq \frac{\pi''}{206265}, \quad (14)$$

where π stands for the Moon's equatorial horizontal parallax. Inserting (13) and (14) in (7) we find that, more explicitly,

$$\Omega = \{X(\operatorname{cosec}\pi - \cos\gamma) - \cos\eta - \ldots\}\operatorname{cosec}\theta\tan\mu\cos\nu, \quad (15)$$

where

$$X = (l/k) = 3 \cdot 6699(1 - 0 \cdot 00235 \sin^2\phi + \ldots). \qquad (16)$$

Of the quantities involved on the right-hand side of equation (15), X for a given observing site reduces to a constant. The horizontal parallax π depends on the position of the observer on Earth and that of the centre of the Moon (though not on the location of any particular point on its surface); but the angles η, θ, and ν depend on the selenographic coordinates of the lunar point in question, as well as on the relative positions of the Earth and the Sun at the time of measurement.

The equatorial horizontal parallax π of the Moon at any time can be readily found, by interpolation, from an appropriate volume of the *Nautical Almanac* or any other standard ephemeris. In order to evaluate the remaining angles η, θ, and ν, let

$$\beta_P, \lambda_P$$

$$\beta_O, \lambda_O$$

$$\beta_\odot, \lambda_\odot$$

denote the selenographic latitude (β) and longitude (λ) of the point P on the surface of the Moon, of the observing place (O) on the Earth, and of the Sun ($\odot$), respectively. If so, it follows from the requisite spherical triangles that

$$\cos\eta = \sin\beta_O \sin\beta_P + \cos\beta_O \cos\beta_P \cos(\lambda_O - \lambda_P), \qquad (17)$$

$$\cos\theta = \sin\beta_\odot \sin\beta_O + \cos\beta_\odot \cos\beta_O \cos(\lambda_\odot - \lambda_O), \qquad (18)$$

and

$$\sin\nu = \sin\beta_\odot \sin\beta_P + \cos\beta_\odot \cos\beta_P \cos(\lambda_\odot - \lambda_P). \qquad (19)$$

As was already explained, the selenographic coordinates are defined with respect to a system of axes fixed in the body of the Moon; the latitudes being measured from the lunar equator positively towards the north (i.e. towards Mare Crisium) from the principal meridian. The axes, therefore, rotate with the Moon and are not fixed in space, but librate—a fact introducing some complications in computation of selenographic coordinates of the Earth and the Sun. The selenographic coordinates of the point P which casts the shadow may be determined by methods expounded in the preceding section, or read off directly from appropriate lunar maps or catalogues; but a determination of the values of (β_O, λ_O) or (β_O, λ_O) requires some care.

The selenographic co-ordinates β_E, λ_E of the Earth's centre (being the sums of the respective optical as well as physical librations of the

s

Moon) are tabulated, for each year, in the *Nautical Almanac:* and so are the values $\beta_\odot$ and $\lambda_\odot$—except for the fact that the *Almanac* actually lists the solar co-longitudes $\lambda_T = 90° - \lambda_\odot$, corresponding to the selenographic longitude of sunrise terminator reckoned eastward from the principal meridian. The tabular values of $\beta_\odot$ and λ_T refer, moreover, to the position of the Sun as seen from the Moon's centre M rather than from P; but as the radius of the Moon amounts to only 10^{-5} of its distance from the Sun, the solar coordinates at M and P should be indistinguishable within the scheme of our approximation.

In order to obtain the last remaining pair of selenographic coordinates β_O, λ_O of the point of observation on the Earth, it is necessary to take account of the fact that the directions of the vectors $R \equiv \overrightarrow{ME}$ and $r' \equiv \overrightarrow{MO}$ differ (on account of the Earth's finite angular size) by amounts depending on the horizontal lunar parallax; and this can be done in the following manner.

Let, as before, α, δ denote the geocentric right ascension and declination of the Moon at any time; and β, λ (without subscripts) be the corresponding (geocentric) lunar latitude and longitude. As is well known, the angles α, δ are related with β, λ by means of the equations

$$\left.\begin{aligned}
\cos\alpha\cos\delta &= \cos\beta\cos\lambda, \\
\sin\alpha\cos\delta &= \cos\beta(\sin\lambda\cos\epsilon - \tan\beta\sin\epsilon), \\
\sin\delta &= \cos\beta(\sin\lambda\sin\epsilon + \tan\beta\cos\epsilon),
\end{aligned}\right\} \quad (20)$$

where ϵ denotes the obliquity of the ecliptic. If we introduce a new auxiliary variable N, as defined by the equation

$$\tan N = \operatorname{cosec}\alpha \tan\delta, \qquad (21)$$

the foregoing equations (20) can be solved to yield

$$\tan\lambda = \cos(N - \epsilon)\sec N \tan\alpha, \qquad (22)$$
$$\tan\beta = \tan(N - \epsilon)\sin\lambda. \qquad (23)$$

The values of β and λ thus corresponding to any pair of the lunar coordinates α and δ are duly listed in all standard ephemerides.

Now, at the point O of terrestrial observation, the apparent topocentric coordinates α', δ' of the Moon are, not the geocentric values of α and δ as given in the almanacs, but rather

$$\alpha' = \alpha - \rho\sin\pi\cos\phi\sec\delta\sin H, \qquad (24)$$
$$\delta' = \delta + \rho\sin\pi(\sin\phi\cos\delta - \cos\phi\sin\delta\cos H), \qquad (25)$$

where, as before,

π = lunar horizontal parallax;

ρ = geocentric radius at O;

ϕ = geocentric latitude of O;

H = lunar geocentric hour angle.

Suppose now that the topocentric values of α' and δ' following from (24) and (25) correspond to a topocentric latitude and longitude λ' and β', obtainable from equations (22) and (23) by insertion of α', δ' for α, δ, respectively. If so, however, the desired selenographic coordinates β_O, λ_O of the observing point on the Earth can then be expressed as

$$\left. \begin{aligned} \beta_O &= \beta_E - \beta' + \beta, \\ \lambda_O &= \lambda_E + \lambda' - \lambda, \end{aligned} \right\} \quad (26)$$

which take into account most of the difference between geocentric and topocentric libration of the Moon. The use of equations (26) should be adequate for any but the most precise lunar hypsometric work; but should still higher accuracy be required, the complete effects of differential librations (both physical and optical) can be conveniently taken into account by a method worked out by Atkinson (1951), to whose paper the reader is referred for fuller details.

This concludes a brief account of the determination of the auxiliary angles γ, η, θ and ν occuring in our fundamental equation (6). All angles depending on the position of the Moon vary but slowly in the course of a single night; and if we evaluate them (say) for the times of the beginning and the end of a film run, all intermediate values can be deduced by linear interpolation. The only angle varying relatively fast is γ, due to the presence of the lunar hour angle H on the right-hand side of equation (10). A direct computation of γ may, therefore, become necessary at (say) hourly intervals; and its determination for intermediate exposures may require non-linear interpolation.

What is the accuracy with which the auxiliary angles η, θ, and ν can be evaluated ? Their values depend—in accordance with equations (17)–(19)—on the relative positions of the centres of the Sun, the Moon, and the Earth in space, as well as the position of the observer O on the Earth and the measured point P on the Moon. All these but the last are known, in general, to such a degree of accuracy that, for practical purposes, their values as given in the appropriate ephemerides can be treated as exact. This is, however, not yet the case with the selenographic co-ordinates β_P, λ_P of an arbitrary point P of the lunar surface, for reasons already explained in the foregoing Section II; and the errors inherent in them may indeed affect the computed heights

h of lunar mountains above the mean selenoid in a manner which we shall proceed to investigate.†

If we disregard (to a sufficient approximation) the actual deviation of the mean selenoid from a sphere, equations (2) of Section II reveal that the selenographic coordinates β_P, λ_P follow from the (reduced) measured rectangular coordinates ξ_P, η_P of P by means of the equations

$$\left.\begin{array}{l} \sin\beta_P = \eta_P, \\[2mm] \sin\lambda_P = \xi_P(1-\eta^2_P)^{-\frac{1}{2}}; \end{array}\right\} \quad (27)$$

and will, therefore, be affected by the errors $\delta\eta_P$, $\delta\xi_P$ inherent in the measurements of these coordinates by amounts $\delta\beta_P$, $\delta\lambda_P$ as given by

$$\delta\beta_P = \frac{\delta\eta_P}{\sqrt{1-\eta^2_P}} = \frac{\delta\eta_P}{\cos\beta_P}; \quad (28)$$

$$\left.\begin{array}{l} \delta\lambda_P = \dfrac{(1-\eta^2_P)\delta\xi_P + \xi_P\,\eta_P\,\delta\eta_P}{(1-\eta^2_P)\sqrt{1-\eta^2_P-\xi^2_P}} \\[4mm] \quad = \dfrac{\delta\xi_P}{\cos\beta_P\cos\lambda_P} + \dfrac{\sin\beta_P\sin\lambda_P}{\cos^2\beta_P\cos\lambda_P}\delta\eta_P. \end{array}\right\} \quad (29)$$

Inasmuch as the foregoing expressions for $\delta\beta_P$ as well as $\delta\lambda_P$ contain terms which grow beyond any limit as β_P and (or) λ_P approach 90° regardless of the smallness of the errors $\delta\xi_P$ or $\delta\eta_P$ in the measured rectangular coordinates, it follows that the selenographic coordinates of any point of the lunar surface, based on terrestrial measurements, are bound to be subject to errors growing progressively toward the limb of the Moon; and these errors may, in turn, affect adversely also the accuracy of the determination of the heights h of the lunar mountains by the shadow method.

In order to assess the magnitude of the errors δh arising from this source, let us return to the fundamental equation (6), and consider the auxiliary quantity Ω as defined by equations (7) or (15). The selenographic coordinates of point P enter (6) through the angles Ω and ν, as defined by equations (17) and (19). Since, however, the quantities $\cos\eta$ as well as $X\cos\gamma$ on the right-hand side of (15) are very small

† It should also be mentioned that the selenographic co-ordinates of P occurring in equations (17) and (19) refer, strictly speaking, to the point at which the rays from the centre of the apparent solar disk are tangent to shadow-casting obstacles. Should —as may frequently be the case—the profile of this obstacle be convex, the seleno-graphic position of the tangent point may shift somewhat with time in the course of a sunrise. The anticipated displacements arising from this cause are, however, likely to be in most cases too small (less than one minute of arc) to be significant in this connection.

in comparison with $X \operatorname{cosec} \pi$ (and, moreover, the angle ν seldom exceeds a few degrees, thus rendering $\cos \nu$ very nearly a constant), it follows that the error in h due to the uncertainty in the selenographic position of the measured point should be essentially equal to

$$\delta h = k\{X \operatorname{cosec} \pi \operatorname{cosec} \theta \tan \mu\}\delta(\sin \nu) \qquad (30)$$

where, by (19),

$$\delta(\sin \nu) = \{\sin \beta_\odot \cos \beta_P - \cos \beta_\odot \sin \beta_P \cos(\lambda_\odot - \lambda_P)\}\delta\beta_P$$
$$+ \{\cos \beta_\odot \cos \beta_P \sin(\lambda_\odot - \lambda_P)\}\delta\lambda_P. \qquad (31)$$

The foregoing equations make it evident that, in the proximity of the lunar limb, the errors $\delta\beta_P$, $\delta\lambda_P$ and, consequently, δh may become so large as to invalidate the entire present approach to the determination of the heights of the lunar mountains; and in order to investigate effectively the limb regions another method must be sought. This is, fortunately, made possible by the fact that—on account of libration—the lunar regions lying within a peripheral belt of approximately 7° in width are, from time to time, seen in projection against the dark background of the sky (or the bright background of the solar disk during the eclipses) and their profiles can be accurately measured. Following some early exploratory work by Hayn (1914a), a comprehensive atlas of lunar profiles has more recently been published by Weimer (1952). This atlas contains 72 charts of the limb profiles, based upon more than 3000 negatives secured at the Paris Observatory by Loewy and Puiseux between 1894 and 1909. An even more extensive study of the lunar limb regions by Watts and his collaborators at the U.S. Naval Observatory at Washington is approaching completion. Parallel studies of the silhouettes of the lunar limb as seen against the background of the Sun during partial lunar eclipses (cf. Whitwell 1929; Fujinami, 1952; Fujinami, Ina and Kawai, 1954; Kristenson, 1954, etc.), dependent as they are on the libration angle obtaining at each particular eclipse, are much more limited in scope and cannot compete with the limb measurements at night.

Throughout all our preceding discussion of the geometry underlying the determination of lunar altitudes we have tacitly assumed that the shadow of a peak at P (Fig. 11) falls on a smooth sphere. The lunar surface is, however, by no means smooth in detail; and the shadow method should, in principle, enable us to ascertain, not only the altitude of each eminence above the surrounding landscape, but also any irregularity of the ground on which the shadows are cast. As the study of such irregularities is, in fact, inseparably connected with that of any major features of the lunar landscape, it remains for us to consider the effects which surface irregularities are bound to exert on the geometrical analysis developed earlier in this section.

In order to do so, let us return to Fig. 11 and suppose that the actual distance from the Moon's centre at the point S is, not k, but $k+\delta k$, where δk denotes a local deviation from the mean Moon-level (i.e. a difference in level between the foot of the mountain and the tip of the shadow). If so, equations (1) or (2) as given earlier in this chapter continue to hold good irrespective of surface irregularities; but equations (3) and (4) should be replaced by

$$(k+\delta k)\sin \omega = s \cos \nu \tag{32}$$

and

$$(h+k)\cos \nu = (k+\delta k)\cos(\nu-\omega), \tag{33}$$

respectively, equation (5) then assumes the form

$$h+k = s \sin \nu +\{(k+\delta k)^2 - (s \cos \nu)^2\}^{\frac{1}{2}}; \tag{34}$$

and ignoring squares of δk (as well as their cross-products with other small quantities) we find that equation (6) should be essentially replaced by

$$(h/k) = \Omega \tan \nu + (\delta k/k) - \tfrac{1}{2}\Omega^2 - \ldots \; , \tag{35}$$

where Ω continues to be defined by (7).

Should the shadow of our eminence at P be cast on a smooth sphere, the observed angular shadow length μ should appear as a smooth function of the time, characteristic of the height h of the peak and its position on the lunar surface. If, however, the landscape is uneven, a plot of μ versus the time will show irregular oscillations. Suppose that we draw a smooth curve by free-hand through such irregularities which we shall use for a determination of h above the mean Moon-level, and denote by $\delta \mu$ the deviations of the shadow lengths, actually measured at specific points S, from the smooth curve. If so, it follows at once from (35) that, to sufficient approximation,

$$\delta k = -(r \cosec \theta \sin \nu)\delta \mu, \tag{36}$$

where r, θ, and ν continue to be given by the equations (13) and (18)–(19).

In conclusion of the present section dealing with the geometry of the shadows cast by sunlit lunar mountains, we must also confess that, for the sake of simplicity, we have so far tacitly assumed the Sun to act as an illuminating point-source of light. In reality, of course, the apparent angular diameter of the Sun as seen from the Moon amounts to very approximately half a degree; and this fact is bound to provide all lunar shadows with a penumbral band, even in the complete absence of any atmosphere, consisting of regions in which a part of the solar disk would appear to be set for the observer on the ground. The intensity of illumination at any point of the penumbral zone should clearly be given by the brightness of the visible segment of the Sun; and as this will vary from full light to complete darkness over a strip whose width should depend on the altitude of the rising (or setting) Sun—becoming the greater, the lower the shadow-casting obstacle—micro-densitometric tracing of lunar shadows should furnish much more dependable information on their extent than any visual settings possible with a micrometer. In order to enable us to make proper use of such micro-densitometric records, however, it is necessary first to ascertain the theoretical distribution of light to be expected within the penumbral zone—a task which can be approached in the following manner.

As on Fig. 11, let S denote the point of shadow cast by the peak P illuminated by a light source in the position of the Sun. Allowing now this source of light to possess an angular semi-diameter $\rho_\odot = 15'59''\cdot6$ appropriate for the Sun, the widths $f_{1,2}$ of the penumbral zones on either side of S (arising from the finite angular size of the illuminating source) will clearly be given by

$$f_{1,2} = \frac{s \sin \rho_\odot}{\sin(\nu \pm \rho_\odot)} \tag{37}$$

in the SP'-direction (cf. again Fig. 11); and their projections $f'_{1,2}$ on a plane tangent to the lunar surface at S become

$$f'_{1,2} = \frac{s \sin \rho_\odot}{\sin(\rho_\odot - \omega \pm \nu)}; \tag{38}$$

the upper and lower sign in the denominators referring to the parts of the penumbra interior and exterior to S, respectively. The total width of the penumbral zone then becomes equal to

$$f_1' + f_2' = \frac{2 \sin \rho_\odot \cos \nu \sin (\rho_\odot - \omega)}{\sin(\rho_\odot - \omega + \nu)\sin(\rho_\odot - \omega - \nu)}, \tag{39}$$

and the angle ν continues to be given by equation (19), while s, ω follow from (3) and (4).

Let, moreover, the position of any point within the penumbral zone of the lunar surface in the direction of incident sunlight be characterized by the single coordinate x, measured positively outwards from S, and expressed in terms of $f'_{1,2}$ taken as unity in the respective negative and positive range—i.e. normalized so as to vary from -1 at the first touch of sunrise, to $+1$ when the whole disk of the Sun becomes visible to the observer. If so, and if the horizon of the lunar landscape acts like a straight occulting edge (or, which is more likely, its angular horizontal irregularities are small in comparison with the solar apparent semi-diameter), then it can be proved (cf., e.g. Kopal, 1959) that the actual illumination $I(x)$ at any point x of the penumbra should vary as

$$\pi I^U(x) = I(1)(\pi - \cos^{-1}x + x\sqrt{1-x^2}) \tag{40}$$

if the apparent solar disk were uniformly bright, and

$$4I^D(x) = I(1)(1+x)^2(2-x) \tag{41}$$

if it were completely darkened at the limb.

In actual fact, the solar disk is known to be partially darkened towards the limb; and in the yellow ($\lambda = 0.56\mu$) we should accordingly expect that, very approximately,

$$7I(x) = 3I^U(x) + 4I^D(x). \tag{42}$$

The essential characteristics of the expected distribution of light is the fact that —for both I^U as well as I^D and, therefore, $I(x)$—its inflection point obtains at $x = 0$.† The variation of intensity in the penumbral shadow turns out, therefore, to be most rapid when the centre of the apparent solar disk just rises above the horizon at S. This is indeed a very useful fact, which greatly facilitates the reductions of micro-densitometric tracings of lunar shadows.

What would happen if the shadow-casting obstacle were so low (like the lunar wrinkle-ridges, for instance) that almost the entire width of the visible shadow would represent a penumbra? The measurement of the shadow profiles would then cease to have any meaning; but the unevenness of even a gently undulating ground can, in principle, be established from the photometric measurements of surface brightness, which should be (essentially) proportional to the cosine of the angle between the incident sunlight and the surface normal; as the former direction is a known function of the time, the measured surface brightness can then indicate the ground slope. This method was worked out by van Diggelen (1951) under the direction of M. Minnaert, and applied by him to the determination of the profiles of lunar wrinkle-ridges in the region of Mare Imbrium from plates secured by Minnaert with the 40-inch refractor of the Yerkes Observatory. The results showed that it is possible to measure photometrically the cross-sections of individual ridges between 100–200 metres in height, whose slopes were inclined

---

† This would, moreover, continue to be true for any distribution of brightness over the apparent solar disk—provided only that it remains radially-symmetrical.

only by 1–2 degrees, with an accuracy surpassing that of the shadow
measurements attempted later by Fielder (1958) in the same region.

IV. Formations on the Lunar Surface

In the preceding two sections of this chapter we got briefly acquainted
with some fundamentals of the methods by which the positions and
heights (or slopes) of any irregularities or landmarks on the surface of
the Moon can be ascertained by observations from the Earth. The
aim of the present section will be to give a survey of the principal
kinds of the formations encountered on the Moon and to summarize
the properties of their prototypes.

Even to the naked eye the face of the Moon is diversified with
distinct markings, which stand out expressively on composite photographs—such as shown on the accompanying Fig. 13—on account of
their different reflectivity. A cursory glance reveals that, by and
large, the lunar surface consists of two types of ground: one type,
rough and broken, is comparatively bright (reflecting, in places, as
much as 20 or 30% of incident sunlight); the other is darker (reflecting,
on the average, but 6–7%), much smoother, and frequently so flat as
to simulate the free surface of a liquid. The first type of ground can
be generally referred to as "mountains". They occupy large continuous
areas—particularly in the southern hemisphere of the Moon—covering
a total of little less than two-thirds of the visible side of our satellite,
but (according to recent Russian photographs, as shown in Fig. 14)
over 90% of its far side. The flatlands (or "maria", as they were mis-
named in the early days of telescopic astronomy) occupy the rest.
They are, on the whole, remarkably uniform in reflectivity and general
appearance—whether they be small or large.

A more detailed inspection of the lunar surface reveals a great diversity of formations and structures, no two of which are exactly alike.
However, the dominant type of formation among them, and by far
the most numerous in any part of the Moon, appear to be the ring-like
walled enclosures commonly called the *craters*. The form of their
ramparts is, in general, only approximately circular, and frequently
exhibits distinct polygonal (hexagonal) structure (cf. Fig. 10). They
occur almost everywhere on the Moon—in mountainous regions as
well as the maria—in very great numbers (giving the lunar surface
an appearance of a pock-marked face) and range widely in size. More
than 300,000 of craters with diameters in excess of one km are estimated
to be seen on the visible hemisphere of the Moon alone; and those
smaller still are probably too many to be counted.

Fig. 13. Synoptic view of the visible side of the Moon (after Urey).

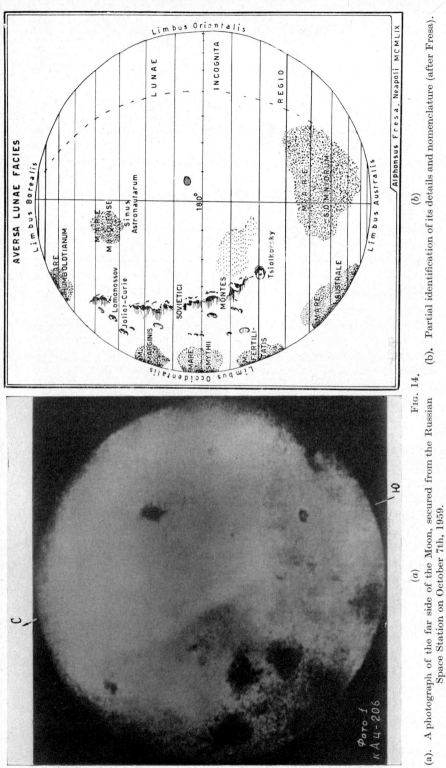

FIG. 14.

(a). A photograph of the far side of the Moon, secured from the Russian
Space Station on October 7th, 1959. (b). Partial identification of its details and nomenclature (after Fresa).

(a)   (b)

The largest of these craters—like Clavius (Fig. 15) or the Hell plain on the western shores of Mare Nubium (Fig. 16)—attain diameters in excess of 230 km; their ramparts rise 1000–2000 m above the surrounding landscape, and 3000–4000 m above their floor bottoms. Even these need not, however, be the largest formations of their kind; for it is at least possible that some of the circular maria—like Mare Crisium, with its surrounding mountains—may be closely allied to the craters; and the same may be true of the Mare Serenitatis (bordered on three sides by the Caucasus, Haemus, and Taurus mountains). It is even possible that the great mountain chains of the lunar Alps and Apennines are, in fact, nothing but broken and incomplete ramparts of a gigantic crater whose floor is the Mare Imbrium, some 700 km in diameter.

There are altogether five distinct craters on the Moon whose dimensions exceed 200 km—Clavius, the Hell plain, Grimaldi, Schickard, Humboldt—and an additional 32 objects with diameters between 100–200 km. No two are exactly alike. However, apart from individual distinguishing features, most craters possess also many characteristics in common. First, their distribution in size ranges continuously from the largest specimens mentioned above down to the smallest pits discernible with our telescopes; and the topographical distribution of craters (of all sizes) on the surface of the Moon appears to be entirely at random.

Secondly, the altitudes of the rims of the lunar craters are, in general, very small in comparison with their absolute dimensions, and their floors are depressed considerably below the level of the surrounding landscape. The height of the ramparts above the floor of the craters appears to be statistically correlated with the diameters of the respective craters (the so-called "Ebert's rule"); and the volume of the central depressions seems, in many cases, to come close to the volume of the ramparts encircling them (the "Schröter's rule")—suggesting that the material contained in the rims may have been displaced from the crust by forces which produced the crater pit. Very small craters do not appear to possess almost any ramparts at all, and represent mere depressions sunken in the lunar surface.

Third, many medium-size craters (with diameters between 50–100 km) are characterized by central peaks, whose altitude may exceed the depression of the floor bottom, but does not attain the height of the surrounding ramparts. An example of this type of formation is represented by the crater Theophilus (Fig. 17), approximately 100 km in size, whose profile (investigated by McMath, Petrie and Sawyer (1937) by the shadow method) is shown on the accompanying Fig. 18. The dimensions and heights of several representative examples of the

FIG. 15. Sunset over the crater Clavius (Mt. Wilson and Palomar Observatory photograph).

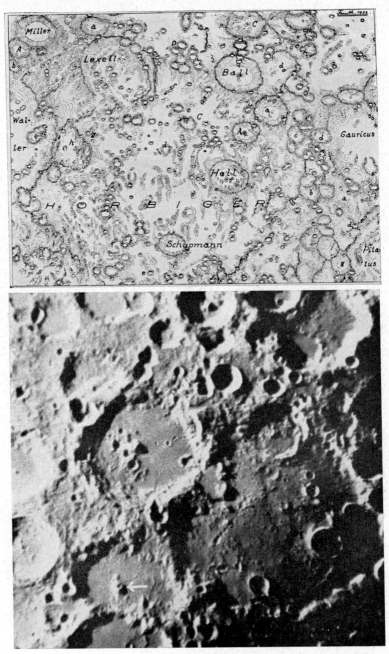

Fig. 16. A chart of the south-central portion of the lunar disk, prepared in 1932 by Philipp Fauth on the basis of his visual observations (top; reproduced by courtesy of *Sky and Telescope*, **19**, 23, 1959), as compared with a Pic-du-Midi photograph of the same region (below).

The Hell Plain was designated (privately) by Fauth on his chart as "Hörbiger", and the low-walled crater labelled "Schupmann" is generally known as Hell B.

A white arrow on the photograph indicates the position of the hill-top crater Regiomontanus A.

A comparison of the above drawing with the photograph illustrates vividly the merits and drawbacks of the finest of visual mapping work as compared with the photographic registration.

Fig. 17. Sunset over the crater Theophilus (Yerkes Observatory photograph).

FIG. 18.

lunar crater relative to the curvature of the surface of the Moon are shown on the accompanying Fig. 19. Such are the dimensions of the large ones in comparison with their heights that an observer standing at the centre of Clavius of several other large craters would not see their ramparts at all—the curvature of the lunar surface would depress even their rims completely below his horizon.

Lastly, a small number of medium-size craters—like Copernicus (90 km; see Fig. 20), Tycho (86 km), Aristarchus (46 km), or Kepler (34 km)—exhibit a radial system of bright rays diverging from the central formation to distances (in the case of Tycho) of a few thousand

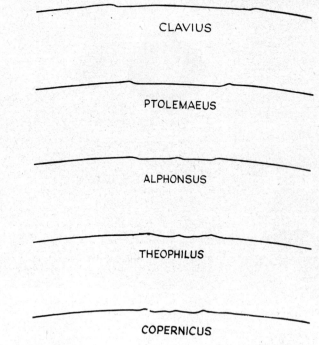

CLAVIUS

PTOLEMAEUS

ALPHONSUS

THEOPHILUS

COPERNICUS

FIG. 19.

Fig. 20. The crater Copernicus and the surrounding plains of the Oceanus Procellarum (Mt. Wilson Observatory photograph).

kilometres. These rays—vividly reminiscent of some kind of splash phenomena—are completely flat (they do not cast any shadows) and their material possesses considerably higher reflectivity than the lunar landscape on which they are spread.

Not all lunar craters, to be sure, conform to Ebert's or Schröter's empirical rules. A conspicuous exception to them is represented by the so-called "hill-top" craters—some of which occur on central peaks of larger craters (like Eratosthenes, etc.), but others entirely on their own. A typical example of this class of objects can be seen rising from the floor of the crater Regiomontanus (cf. again Fig. 16; marked on the plate with a white arrow). An investigation, by Turner (1959), of its shape by the shadow method as outlined in the preceding section led, however, again to a very flat profile as shown on the accompanying Fig. 21. Our hill-top crater Regiomontanus A turns out to be a hill

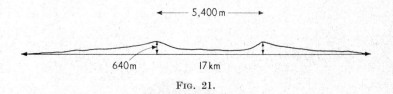

FIG. 21.

rising barely 640 metres above its surroundings, and the actual crater on its top possesses a diameter of approximately 5 km. Its base of some 100 km in circumference renders the whole formation not unlike (and, in fact, smaller than) the well-known terrestrial volcano Krakatoa off the coast of Java.

Extensive lists of the dimensions of lunar craters, with such indications of their height and depth as are available, have been compiled in recent times by Blackhall (1929), MacDonald (1929, 1931), Baldwin (1949), Schrutka-Rechtenstamm (1954), and others. As far as heights are concerned, however, the data collected in the foregoing publications are still based on the early visual measurements of Mädler and Schmidt, which are subject to considerable uncertainty and likely to be superseded by measurements of more appropriate photographic records in the near future.

The lunar craters do not, on the average, bear obvious analogy to any terrestrial formations (for more detailed discussion of this problem, cf. Chapter 8); and the same appears to be true of the lunar mountain chains—like the Alps or the Apennines (cf. again Fig. 13)—as well. Their general appearance indicates, if anything, that they were formed by upthrust rather than folding or any other known terrestrial orogenetic process. The highest peak of the Apennines, Mt. Huyghens, attains an altitude of approximately 5500 m above the plains of the Mare Imbrium to the East of it. The highest mountains found on the surface of the Moon—the Leibnitz and Doerfel Mountains—are located in the limb regions near the south pole of our satellite; and their altitudes have recently been determined by Watts (private communication) to 5970 and 5600 m, respectively. The highest lunar mountains attain, therefore, the altitudes of Kilimanjaro or Mount McKinley, but fall far short of those of the terrestrial Himalayan giants. When one considers, however, the fact that the Moon is approximately one-quarter in size of the Earth, the proportional height of surface unevennesses on the Moon appears, indeed, to be considerably greater than it is on the surface of the Earth.

Are these and other lunar mountains steep? Perhaps the main result of accurate lunar topography by the shadow method, as described in the preceding section (cf. also MacDonald, 1932 and 1940), has been the realization that most lunar slopes are not inclined more than a few degrees to the horizontal, and that large steep slopes (of 10° or more) of appreciable size appear to be conspicuous by their absence. The initial impression of raggedness, gained by a cursory glance at photographs of the sunrise or sunset on the Moon, largely disappears when the appropriate altitude of the Sun above the horizon is duly taken into account. When, in addition, we recall the large curvature of a relatively small lunar globe†, we cannot escape the conclusion that the horizontal panorama visible from most points on the Moon would be rather dull and unimpressive, with generally a very few landmarks on which the traveller's eye could safely rest in search of orientation.

In order to demonstrate this on a few specific examples, let us turn to the accompanying Fig. 22 taking us to the western bay of Mare Imbrium (which bears the poetical name of Palus Nebularum). The specific object of our inspection will be the mountain Piton (marked with a white arrow)—a solitary cliff rising from the surrounding plains and casting a long shadow in the rays of the setting Sun at last quarter. Thus viewed, the mountain produces an impression of a steep rock; but nothing could be farther from the truth. When the shadow of this mountain was recently measured and analyzed by Rackham (1959), it transpired that an observer standing at the tip of the shadow on the Moon would see it as shown on the accompanying Fig. 23. Although

---

† For the lunar globe of 3476 km in diameter, an object of 3000 m in altitude would disappear completely below the observer's horizon at a distance of 102 km; an object of 300 m in height (Eiffel Tower, Empire State Building) would disappear at 32 km; and a man of average height 160 cm, at 2500 m.

FIG. 22. Sunset over the western part of Mare Imbrium (Pic-du-Midi Observatory photograph). Craters Archimedes, Aristillus and Autolycus (top). The white arrow indicates the position of Piton; and the broken oval marks the limits of its visibility from the lunar surface.

Piton is found to attain an altitude of over 2300 metres, its base of 28 km is so wide as to give it an appearance of a large hill rather than any kind of a lunar Matterhorn. Such is, moreover, the curvature of the lunar surface that even the top of Piton would set completely below the horizon of an observer standing on the Moon at a distance of approximately 90 km (marked on Fig. 22 by a broken white line); anyone standing outside the area of this oval would see nothing of the mountain at all.

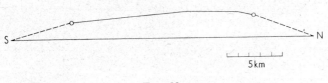

FIG. 23.

In order to provide a further example of the essential flatness of the lunar surface, let us turn to the south-eastern part of Mare Tranquilitatis, the topography of which was recently studied by Turner (1959). When we consider the altitudes of the walls of various craters in this region (whose photograph is reproduced in Fig. 24) in connection with the known curvature of the lunar surface, what would be the horizontal panorama confronting an observer on the Moon who stands at (say) points marked by X and Y on the figure ? The answer as found by Turner is diagrammatically shown on the accompanying Fig. 25. We note that the observer standing at X would see nothing at all above the flat outline of his western horizon; and his eastern horizon would reveal only the low outlines of the nearby crater Arago B. But even from the point Y—in the immediate neighbourhood of the craters Ritter and Dionysius—the horizontal panorama would by no means loom impressive.

The remaining surface formations—such as the domes, rills or faults —deserve only a brief descriptive mention in the present survey of lunar topography. The domes, analogous perhaps to the terrestrial laccoliths (which, in turn, represent certain arrested stages of volcanism) occur on the Moon in considerable numbers. The reader can distinguish many of them inside the Hell plain (Fig. 16), ranging from 2–3 km in size, and rising to heights of 200–300 metres. The rills on the Moon are likewise ubiquitous—witness the examples given on Fig. 26—and many hundreds of them have been detected so far. They are shallow gorges, sometimes a few hundred kilometres in length, but not more than a few kilometres in width and quite shallow (of the order of 300–

Fig. 24.   Sunrise over the eastern part of Mare Tranquilitatis (Pic-du-Midi Observatory photograph), with the vantage points X and Y marked in white.

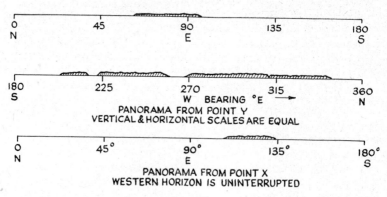

PANORAMA FROM POINT Y
VERTICAL & HORIZONTAL SCALES ARE EQUAL

PANORAMA FROM POINT X
WESTERN HORIZON IS UNINTERRUPTED

Fig. 25.

500 metres at most). Their origin and way of formation are as yet unknown; and the same is true of the cliffs—such as the famous Straight Wall in the western part of Mare Nubium (Fig. 27). The latter runs from south-west to north-east on the Moon for a distance

FIG. 26. Rills on the Moon in the Hyginus region (Pic-du-Midi Observatory photograph).

of some 100 km; and according to Ashbrook (1960), its height (i.e. the difference between the mean altitude of the right and left side of the cliff) is about 200 metres.

The foregoing paragraphs contain only a brief account of the diversity of formations encountered on the lunar surface, and of their salient features; a more complete or systematic description of the lunar face

Fig. 27. The Straight Wall in the western part of Mare Nubium on the Moon at sunrise (left) and sunset (right). Pic-du-Midi Observatory photographs.

would require a separate volume rather than a chapter. What is so arresting about this face, to render a detailed study of its topography scientifically worth while? The Moon is a very old body—probably not less than 4,500 million years of age—and has been a close companion of the Earth since the days of its formation. The permanent absence of any air or water on the Moon makes it, moreover, virtually certain that most parts of the composite fossil record exhibited by its familiar features must be of very ancient date—its oldest landmarks being, perhaps, not far removed in time from the days of the origin of our solar system. On the Earth (or other planets) all landmarks of comparable age must have fallen prey to the joint action of their oceans and atmospheres, and been obliterated aeons ago. However, as any changes on the Moon can proceed only at an exceedingly slow rate, its present wrinkled and pockmarked face must still bear scars and traces of many events which have taken place in the inner precincts of the solar system since the days of its formation; and if so, their correct interpretation holds indeed a rich scientific prize. This is, however, not the place to follow it up in any detail; and the reader interested in these implications of selenography will find many of the answers in the subsequent Chapters 8 and 13.

References

Ashbrook, J. (1960). *Publ. Astr. Soc. Pacif.* **72**, 1955.

Atkinson, R. d'E. (1951). *Mon. Not. R. Astr. Soc.* **111**, 448.

Baldwin, R. B. (1949). "The Face of the Moon". Chicago, pp. 120–123.

Banachiewicz, Th. (1955). *Trans. I.A.U.* **7**, 174.

Beer, W. and Mädler, J. H. (1837). "Der Mond". Berlin.

Belkovich, I. V. (1949). *Bull. Engelhardt Obs.* No. 24.

Blackhall, J. (1929). *J. Brit. Astr. Ass.* **39**, A245.

Fielder, G. (1958). *Mon. Not. R. Astr. Soc.* **118**, 547.

Franz, J. (1889). *Astr. Beob. Königsberg*, **38**, Nr. 1.

Franz, J. (1899). *Astr. Beob. Königsberg*, **38**, Nr. 5.

Franz, J. (1901). *Mitt. Sternw. Univ. Breslau*, Nr. 1.

Franz, J. (1906). *S.B. Preuss. Akad. Wiss.*

Fujinami, S. (1952). *Publ. Astr. Soc. Japan*, **4**, 115.

Fujinami, S., Ina, T., and Kawai, S. (1954). *Publ. Astr. Soc. Japan*, **6**, 67.

Galilei, Galileo (1610). "Nuncius Sidereus". Padua.

Hartwig, E. (1880). "Beitrag zur Bestimmung der Physischen Libration des Mondes". Karlsruhe.

Hayn, F. (1902–14). "Selenographische Koordinaten" I–IV, in *Abh. König. Sachs. Ges. Wiss. Leipzig*.

Hayn, F. (1914). *Astr. Nachr.* **199**, 261.

Hayn, F. (1914a). *Abh. König. Sachs. Ges. Wiss. Leipzig*, **33**, 3.

Herschel, W. (1780). *Phil. Trans.* **70**, 507.

Herschel, W. (1912). "Scientific Papers," Vol. 1, p. 5. London.

Hevelius, J. (1647). "Selenographia". Danzig.

Kopal, Z. (1959). "Close Binary Systems". London and New York, p. 207.

Kopal, Z. (1960). *Proc. First Int. Space Symposium*, Amsterdam, 5, 1123.

Koziel, K. (1948–49). *Acta Astr.* (a) 4, 61–193.

Kristenson, H. (1954). *Ark. Astr.* 1, 411.

MacDonald, T. L. (1929). *J. Brit. Astr. Ass.* 39, 314.

MacDonald, T. L. (1931). *J. Brit. Astr. Ass.* 41, 172, 228, 367.

MacDonald, T. L. (1932). *J. Brit. Astr. Ass.* 42, 291.

MacDonald, T. L. (1940). *J. Brit. Astr. Ass.* 50, 160.

McMath, R. R., Petrie, R. M. and Sawyer, H. E. (1937). *Publ. Univ. Obs. Michigan*, 6, 67.

Nefedjev, A. A. (1950). *Astr. Circ. Acad. Sci. U.S.S.R.*, No. 98–99.

Rackham, T. W. (1959). *Astr. Contr. Univ. Manchester*, Ser. III, No. 71.

Saunder, S. A. (1905). *Mem. R. Astr.* Soc. 57, Pt. 1 (cf. also *Mon. Not. R. Astr. Soc.* 65, 458).

Saunder, S. A. (1911). *Mem. R. Astr. Soc.* 60, Pt. 1.

Schmidt, J. F. J. (1878). "Die Charte der Gebirge des Mondes". Berlin.

Schröter, J. H. (1791). "Selenotopographische Fragmente", I. Lilienthal.

Schröter, J. H. (1802). "Selenotopographische Fragmente", II. Göttingen.

Schrutka-Rechtenstamm, G. (1954). *S.B. Öst. Akad. Wiss.* (Math.-Naturw. Klasse, Abt. II), 163, 179.

Schrutka-Rechtenstamm, G. (1956). *S.B. Öst. Akad. Wiss.* (Math-Naturw. Klasse, Abt. II), 165, 97.

Schrutka-Rechtenstamm, G. (1958). *S.B. Öst. Akad. Wiss.* (Math.-Naturw. Klasse, Abt. II), 167, 71.

Schrutka-Rechtenstamm, G. and Hopmann, J. (1958). *S.B. Öst. Akad. Wiss.* (Math.-Naturw. Klasse, Abt. II), 167, 283.

Turner, G. (1959). *Astr. Contr. Univ. Manchester*, Ser. III, No. 72.

Van Diggelen, J. (1951). *Bull. Astr. Insts. Netherlds*, 11, 283.

Watts, C. B. (1955). *Trans. I.A.U.* 9, 268; cf. also *Astr. J.* 60, 443.

Weimer, T. (1948). *C.R. Acad. Sci., Paris*, 226, 559.

Weimer, T. (1952). *Atlas des Profils Lunaires* (Publ. Obs. de Paris). Cf. also *C.R. Acad. Sci., Paris*, 230, 1934.

Weimer, T. (1954). *Bull. Astr.* 17, 271.

Wesley, W. H., and Blagg, M. A. (1935). "I.A.U. Map of the Moon". London, 1935.

Whitwell, T. (1929). *J. Brit. Astr. Ass.* 39, 255.

Yakovkin, A. A. (1950). *Kiev Obs. Publ.* No. 3.

Yakovkin, A. A. and Belkovich, I. V. (1935). *Astr. Nachr.* 256, 305.

Chapter 8

Interpretation of Lunar Craters†

Eugene M. Shoemaker

I. Introduction... 283
II. Crater-forming Processes....................................... 285
   A. Geological Trend of Inquiry................................ 286
   B. Terrestrial Crater-forming Processes........................ 289
III. Maars.. 291
   A. Surface Features of Maars................................. 292
   B. Subsurface Structure of Maars............................. 295
   C. Mechanics of Maar-forming Eruptions....................... 298
   D. Possible Maars and Other Volcanoes on the Moon............... 301
IV. Impact Craters 307
   A. Form and Structure of Impact Craters 307
   B. Eroded Structures of Probable Impact Origin 314
   C. Similarity between Impact Craters and Nuclear Explosion Craters.. 315
   D. Mechanics of Large Meteorite Impact in Rock................. 317
   E. Comparison of Maars and Meteorite Impact Craters 321
V. Ballistics of Copernicus... 323
   A. Ray Pattern of Copernicus 325
   B. Cratering Theory and Exterior Ballistics...................... 329
   C. Interior Ballistics... 335
   D. Angle of Impact.. 341
VI. History of the Copernicus Region.............................. 344
   A. Stratigraphy of the Copernicus Region........................ 346
   B. Correlation of the Lunar and Geologic Time Scales.............. 347
   C. Structure and Structural History of the Copernicus Region...... 348
     References... 351

I. Introduction

The dominant surface features of the Moon are approximately circular depressions, which may be designated by the general term crater. Employed in this way, the word crater is used in its original sense—a cup-shaped topographic feature—after the Greek root κρατερ (cup or bowl)‡. Solution of the origin of the lunar craters is fundamental to the unravelling of the history of the Moon and may shed much light on the history of the terrestrial planets as well.

Most geological and probably most selenological processes are too

† Publication authorized by the Director, U.S. Geological Survey.

‡ Despite the special niche in an elaborate classification assigned to the term crater by selenographers, and whatever connotations of volcanism this word may have had to various authors in the past, the meaning of crater has become much more general in current scientific literature; here it is employed as an inclusive descriptive term without prejudice as to mode of origin.

complex to be safely deduced from first principles. On the other hand, we may reasonably expect the same physical laws to apply on the Moon as on Earth, and we may also expect the rocks of the Moon to share some of the same range of chemical and physical properties as the rocks of the Earth. Undoubtedly there are differences—probably critical differences—in the physical, chemical, and historical setting of the surface of the Earth and Moon, and, indeed, there are striking differences in their topography. But if the problem is approached by analogy, attention may be focused on those features which are similar or the same in two different environments; the closer the comparison that can be made, the stronger is the argument.

There is nothing new in the thesis that close comparison of lunar features with possible terrestrial homologues will prove fruitful, for it has been followed in lunar studies since the time of Galileo. The justification for taking it up anew is that our understanding of terrestrial phenomena relevant to the Moon has advanced greatly over the course of the years and particularly in the last two decades. In applying analogical reasoning, moreover, great care must be exercised in scaling. This has been the major single pitfall in past comparisons of the features either of the Earth or of experimental models with those of the Moon. A jump of one order of magnitude in linear dimension and sometimes more has commonly been made in comparing terrestrial craters with lunar craters, and a jump of six orders of magnitude is commonly made in going from model experiments to the Moon.†

In the pages that follow, the characteristics and origin of terrestrial features that resemble lunar craters are first reviewed and criteria are established by which results of various crater-forming processes on the Moon might be distinguished. The history of a selected region is then examined in the light of these criteria.

It would be impossible to take cognizance of all the pertinent geological and astronomical literature in a paper of this scope. I shall draw primarily, therefore, on personal research on the mechanics of maars and of meteorite impact craters and illustrate the discussion, where appropriate, with geological and experimental features with which I have had a direct acquaintance through field work. No attempt is made to explain all the surface features of the Moon. Rather, a few examples are analysed in detail consonant with the present state of the art in lunar telescopic observation and photography and in space exploration.

† A first approximation to many of the scaling relations can be made from elementary considerations of dimensional analysis. A paper by Hubbert (1937) gives an excellent introduction to the scaling or modelling relations of the physical properties of rocks.

II. Crater-forming Processes

In his biography of G. K. Gilbert, the American geomorphologist W. M. Davis wrote (1926, pp. 185–186):

"It has been remarked that the majority of astronomers explain the craters of the moon by volcanic eruption—that is, by an essentially geological process—while a considerable number of geologists are inclined to explain them by the impact of bodies falling upon the moon—that is, by an essentially astronomical process. This suggests that each group of scientists find the craters so difficult to explain by processes with which they are professionally familiar that they have recourse to a process belonging in another field than their own, with which they are probably imperfectly acquainted, and with which they therefore feel freer to take liberties."

Since the time of Davis' writing, the division of opinion appears to have shifted, and the literature prior to 1900 reveals that a volcanic origin of the craters had been the prevailing consensus of both groups of scientists. It is nevertheless true that the selenological contributions of geologists and the selenological papers written by astronomers, have comprised two somewhat independent bodies of literature, at least after the time of the great naturalists such as von Humboldt and of the astronomer-volcanologist, Julius Schmidt.

Probably both volcanic and impact hypotheses for the origin of the lunar craters are nearly as old as the discovery of the craters by Galileo in 1610. Robert Hooke (1665, p. 243) compared the lunar craters with those formed on the surface of boiling alabaster and with craters formed by dropping bullets on wet clay, but he rejected the impact analogy because "it would be difficult to imagine whence those bodies should come". By the beginning of the 19th century a volcanic origin for the lunar craters appears to have been nearly universally accepted among the scientists of the time. A volcanic origin had been championed by Kant (1785), and the astronomer Herschel (1787) had even reported what he believed to be observations of volcanic eruptions on the Moon. But it should be recalled that the extraterrestrial origin of meteorites was not then generally accepted. After the meteorite shower at L'Aigle in France in 1803, which awakened widespread interest in meteorites, the impact hypothesis for the origin of the lunar craters was revived by Gruithuisen (1829), who also appears to have anticipated the planetesimal accretion hypothesis for the origin of the Moon. Many of Gruithuisen's views were extreme, however, and most of the principal selenologists continued to accept, without apparent hesitation, some form of volcanism as the crater-forming process.

The later history of astronomical thought on the origin of lunar surface features has been reviewed repeatedly (Nevill, 1876; Goodacre, 1931; Baldwin, 1949; Wilkins and Moore, 1955) and need not be repeated in detail here. It is appropriate, on the other hand, to trace briefly the evolution of thought in papers written from the geological point of view, which are less well known. An excellent earlier review of the geological viewpoint was given by Wegener (1921).

A. Geological Trend of Inquiry

A distinct geological line of thought on lunar craters may be considered to have begun with the rise of the science of volcanology. J. B. A. L. L. Élie de Beaumont explained the lunar craters in terms of von Buch's now rejected theory of "craters of elevation", whereby calderas and certain other types of volcanic craters were considered to have been formed by updoming of horizontally deposited layers of volcanic material around a central depression. He compared a large circular basin on the island of Ceylon with lunar craters (Élie de Beaumont, 1831), and later published (Élie de Beaumont, 1843) an extensive list of crater-form terrestrial features with which lunar craters might be compared. Most of the terrestrial craters on this list were of volcanic origin, but the largest, the Bohemian basin, about 120 miles across is a roughly circular region ringed with mountains of non-volcanic origin. It was originally compared by Galileo with the craters of the Moon.

After an expedition to the Hawaiian Islands, the American geologist Dana (1846) compared the craters of the Moon with the calderas and other features associated with the Hawaiian shield volcanoes. Much later the astronomer W. H. Pickering (1906) repeated this comparison in more detail. The English volcanologist G. P. Scrope (1862, p. 233) appears to have been the first to point out similarities between lunar craters and the maars of the Phlegraean fields, near the Bay of Naples. Again, the suggestion of the geologist was later elaborated by astronomers, in this case by Nasmyth and Carpenter (1885). Von Humboldt (1863, p. 155) reasserted von Buch's theory of "craters of elevation" with reference to the craters of the Moon in his encyclopedic work, "Cosmos", though he recognized a disparity in form and size between the lunar craters and most terrestrial volcanic craters.

A fundamental advance in the study of the origin of the Moon's surface features was made in 1893 by G. K. Gilbert, then Chief Geologist of the United States Geological Survey. Gilbert (1893) reviewed the characteristics of lunar craters and of various types of terrestrial volcanic craters and concluded that the differences in form, and to a lesser extent differences in size, between lunar and terrestrial craters were so great that a volcanic origin for the lunar craters seemed improbable. He did, however, recognize a possible analogy between the smaller lunar craters and terrestrial volcanoes of the maar type. With this as a point of departure, Gilbert proceeded to develop an impact hypothesis for the origin of the lunar craters, which was based on some acute telescopic observations of the Moon and upon laboratory experiments. Four authors of whom he was cognizant had preceded Gilbert with an impact hypothesis: the astronomer R. A. Proctor (1873, and 1878), who later abandoned the idea, according to Mary Proctor (1928, p. 83); the architect Meydenbauer (1877 and 1882); and the architect and the theologian, August and Heinrich Thiersch, son and father, who wrote under the pseudonym "Asterios" (1879).

Gilbert felt that the predominantly circular or nearly circular form of the lunar craters required special explanation under the impact hypothesis, as impacts at other than vertical incidence had produced elliptical craters in his experiments. To alleviate this difficulty he devised an ingenious "moonlet" theory in which the craters were assumed to have been formed by the infall or sweeping up of smaller satellites of the Earth. From the theory he obtained a frequency distribution for the angle of incidence with a mode at vertical incidence. The underlying assumptions of this theory foreshadow the Moulton-Chamberlain hypothesis of planetesimal accretion, and Gilbert pointed out this implication, though he refrained from developing it. One of the major contributions in Gilbert's paper is the recognition of a radiating system of linear topographic features surrounding Mare Imbrium, which he termed "Imbrium sculpture ". He considered the circular maria as simply the largest members of the whole class of craters. In the detailed application of the impact hypothesis to the explanation of various features of the lunar surface, Gilbert's paper is remarkably modern in viewpoint when compared with the papers of such latter-day authors as Baldwin (1949), Urey (1951), and Kuiper (1954).

But Gilbert's views were too advanced for his time, and they were soon attacked by the geologists Branco (1895, pp. 280–314) and Eduard Suess (1895). At the close of the 19th century the consensus among both geologists and astronomers was still firmly in favour of volcanic origin of the craters.

The principal lunar crater-forming processes advocated by geologists since 1900 may be roughly classified into four major categories, following the German writers: (1) *Blasenhypothese*—bubble or steam blast or volcanic explosion hypothesis; (2) *Vulkanhypothese*—volcanic hypothesis or, more strictly, the caldera hypothesis; (3) *Gezeitenhypothese*—

tidal hypothesis, and (4) *Aufsturzhypothese*—impact hypothesis. The first three categories may all be considered varieties of volcanic hypotheses and no sharp separation can be made between them.

The *Blasenhypothese*, conceived in its extreme form by Robert Hooke as the bursting of gigantic bubbles, supposes some form of violent escape of gas from the lunar interior. In a more realistic form the hypothesis involves simply a sudden release or explosion of steam or volcanic gas from some place beneath the lunar surface. In this form it has been applied to some or all of the lunar craters by Sacco (1907), Dahmer (1911*a*, 1911*b*, 1912, 1938, and 1952), and Mohorovičić (1928). The *Blasenhypothese* may also be considered to include the maar type of volcanism, which involves violent gaseous eruptions and will be described below in more detail. In this form it has been supported by Branco (1894 and 1915), Eduard Suess (1909), von Wolff (1914), F. E. Suess (1917), and many others.

Most supporters of the *Vulkanhypothese* compare the lunar craters with terrestrial calderas. On the one extreme the comparison is with calderas formed during violent eruptions, such as Krakatoa, and on the other extreme the comparison is with calderas formed simply by quiescent subsidence, such as the summit calderas of the Hawaiian shield volcanoes. Besides Branco, the elder and younger Suess, and von Wolff, the list of advocates of some form of volcanic hypothesis for the origin of most lunar craters includes Simoens (1906), Günther (1911), Krejčí-Graf (1928 and 1959), Forbes (1929), Matoušek (1924*a*, 1924*b*, and 1930), Spurr (1944), Sacco (1948), Escher (1949 and 1955), Viete (1952), von Bülow (1954 and 1957), Jeffreys (1959, pp. 372–377), and Green and Poldervaart (1960). European geologists, in particular, appear to favour some combination of volcanic hypotheses to explain the majority of lunar craters.

At the quiescent extreme, the *Vulkanhypothese* shares many features with the *Gezeitenhypothese* or tidal hypothesis, developed by Faye (1881), Ebert (1890), Hannay (1892), and Pickering (1903). Under the *Gezeitenhypothese* it is assumed that the Moon was once fluid except for a thin crust. Tides raised by the Earth's attraction are supposed to have fractured the crust, permitting a part of the fluid interior to flow out on the surface and then to recede again with the passage of the tide. A part of the fluid congeals on the surface with each high tide and a circular rampart is thus built up around each locus of outflow. Among geologists, this hypothesis was received with some favour by Eduard Suess (1895 and 1909), but has not been seriously considered by others, except to the extent that tides can trigger volcanic activity (Ower, 1929).

The *Aufsturzhypothese*, or impact hypothesis, which received its most important early development from Gilbert, has been supported by Wegener (1920, 1921, and 1922), Spencer (1937), Fairchild (1938), Daly (1946), Dietz (1946), and Quiring (1946) as well as many astronomers. F. E. Wright, who undertook the most extensive and painstaking investigations of the Moon of all 20th century geologists, recognized merits in both volcanic and impact hypotheses but appears to have leaned toward volcanism to explain most of the lunar craters (Wright, 1927, p. 452, and in press). Unfortunately, with the interruption of World War II, Wright did not live to publish the bulk of his results and conclusions. N. S. Shaler (1903) and E. H. L. Schwarz (1909) advocated impact for the origin of the circular maria but turned to volcanism and other mechanisms to explain the other craters. In later papers, Schwarz (1927 and 1928) developed a "torsion cylinder" hypothesis, the mechanics of which are somewhat obscure, for the lunar craters and certain terrestrial craters.

Many other ideas, which are hardly profitable to review from a geological point of view, have been advanced to explain the lunar craters, such as the "ice" or "snow" hypothesis of Ericsson (1886) and Peal (1886), and the "vortex" or "sun spot" hypothesis of Rozet (1846) and Miller (1898). The latter, which might also be called the "convection current" hypothesis, has been revived in a more sophisticated form by the astrophysicist J. Wasiutyński, (1946) and supposes a fluid moon in which there are internal currents or a fluid moon with a thin crust. Craters are supposedly formed over individual convection cells.

It should be noted that a hypothesis of the astronomers Tomkins (1927) and Marshall (1943), in which lunar craters are supposed to have formed by the quiescent opening or collapse of the summit of a dome raised over a laccolith or blister of molten rock, closely resembles von Buch's old "craters of elevation" theory for the origin of terrestrial craters. The so-called lunar domes with summit craters, cited by Marshall as formed in this fashion, probably have, as will be shown, more direct terrestrial analogues.

B. TERRESTRIAL CRATER-FORMING PROCESSES

Terrestrial craters are formed by a wide variety of processes, but terrestrial craters of only two general classes closely resemble the majority of lunar craters: (1) the maar type of volcanic crater, and (2) meteorite impact craters. These two kinds of craters are sufficiently similar in gross external form to have frequently been confused, one for the other. In fact, a volcanic or cryptovolcanic origin has been

U

proposed for nearly every major impact structure recognized up to the last few years.

Although most proponents of the volcanic origin of lunar craters have considered terrestrial calderas as homologues of the larger lunar craters, the majority of calderas differ from most lunar craters in several important respects. Only the most important need be mentioned at this point. Most calderas occupy the site of the central part of a volcanic edifice; the floor of the caldera is commonly higher than the level of the terrain surrounding the edifice (Reck and others, 1936; Williams, 1941). Lunar craters, on the other hand, in which the floor is higher than the terrain surrounding the crater rim are extremely rare. This discussion will be restricted chiefly to terrestrial features that closely resemble lunar craters.

In thus limiting the discussion, a separation has been drawn between calderas and maars, but the separation is not everywhere clear-cut in the field. Some craters in Mexico, for example, which I consider to be of the maar type (Galbraith, 1959) have been referred to by Jahns (1959) as calderas. The distinction depends upon minor but perhaps critical differences in interpretation of the history and mechanics of the craters. Most crater-form depressions referred to as calderas are considerably larger than maars.

As used by most present-day volcanologists, the term caldera is applied to large, more or less circular depressions which have been formed by the collapse of the summit of a pre-existing volcanic pile, commonly a cone-shaped volcano. The caldera is usually formed at a late stage in the history of the volcano, and the collapse or subsidence of the summit is commonly, but not always, accompanied by violent eruptions. As defined by Williams (1941), the caldera is larger than any individual eruptive vent.

A maar, on the other hand, is opened by piecemeal spalling and slumping of the walls of a volcanic vent during most of the eruptive history of the volcano. The smaller fragments are entrained in out-rushing gas and distributed far and wide around the crater; a low rim of ejecta is generally formed, which is repeatedly engulfed on the inner edge by the ever-widening crater.

It is, of course, possible to have a combination of various crater-forming processes operative at a single volcanic vent, and late stage collapse or subsidence is also a common event in the history of some maars. Therefore the classification of certain volcanic craters will necessarily depend on the somewhat arbitrary decision or personal preference of the investigator. It should also be noted that there is no unanimous agreement among volcanologists on the details of the mechanics of calderas or of maars. The theory of Escher (1929 and 1930) for the Krakatoa caldera resembles the theory presented here for volcanoes of the maar type.

On one point, on the other hand, there is now nearly unanimous agreement among close students of calderas. A caldera is formed by subsidence rather than by ejection of the rocks from the space occupied by the surface depression. The association of violent awe-inspiring eruptions, atmospheric waves and sea waves, with the collapse of the Krakatoa caldera in 1883 led to the widespread popular misconception, bolstered by the Royal Society report (Judd, 1888) that the volcano literally blew its top off. But a simple inspection of the ejected debris shows that this did not happen (Verbeek, 1886; Stehn, 1929). Most of the ejected material consists of pumice—frothy glass formed from new magma. There are far too few fragments of the old lavas of which the volcano was built to account quantitatively for the volume of rock which disappeared from the summit of the volcano during the eruption. A similar situation exists for nearly every other caldera of the Krakatoa type for which quantitative estimates of the ejecta have been made (Williams, 1941; van Bemmelen, 1929).

It is highly improbable that any volcanic eruption, although it may be classed as "explosive" by volcanologists, can be likened to the detonation of high explosives. The volcanic process commonly called explosive is simply the rapid discharge of gas, usually through some pre-existing orifice or vent. When rapidly moving volcanic gas, accelerated along a conduit by a moderate pressure gradient (Einarsson, 1950), encounters the relatively static air above the vent, visible shock waves may be generated in the atmosphere (Perret, 1912). The noise is often deafening but, despite the auditory similarity to a chemical explosion, the volcanic mechanism, as will be shown, is basically different.

III. Maars

"Maar" is a German or Rhinelander word applied to a number of small lakes that occupy volcanic craters in the dissected plateau of the Eifel region of Germany. As used by the German cartographers and geologists, "maar" or "dry maar" has also been employed to designate other similar volcanic craters in the Eifel even though they are not occupied by lakes (Hopmann, Frechen, and Knetsch, 1956). The craters are circular to elliptical or somewhat irregular depressions excavated in the Eifel plateau. They range from 70 to about 1500 m in greatest diameter, measured from rim crest to rim crest, and from about 10 to about 200 m deep, measured from the highest point on the rim to the lowest point in the crater. Most of the craters are partially encompassed by an inconspicuous low ridge of ejecta composed partly of volcanic ash and lapilli and partly of pieces of pre-existing nonvolcanic rocks from which the crater and underlying vent have been excavated.

The term "maar" or "maar-type volcano" has been very generally applied to volcanic craters scattered around the world which are similar to the German maars. Cotton (1952, pp. 258–267) has proposed the term "ubehebe" for the dry maar and "tuff ring" for the maar encircled by a higher rim of ejecta than is found at the Eifel maars. Here they will all be referred to simply as maars.

A. Surface Features of a Maar

For purposes of detailed description it is appropriate to take the Zuñi Salt Lake crater of western New Mexico (Darton, 1905) because it resembles closely in gross form a number of lunar craters of larger scale. The crater is a depression in the moderately irregular surface of the southern part of the Colorado Plateau and is encompassed by a low rim like the Eifel maars (Fig. 1). In the central part of the floor of the crater is a shallow saline lake from which rise two small basaltic cinder cones. The crater is about 2000 m across and the surface of the lake lies about 50 m below the general level of the surrounding terrain. The rim of the crater, which is of uneven height, rises about 125 m above the crater floor.

The rim is formed of bedded ejecta resting on nearly flat-lying older rocks. Mixed pieces of sandstone, shale, limestone, basalt and old crystalline rocks are found in the ejecta as well as lapilli of basalt, which represent drops of lava thrown out of the crater as the rim was being built up. Some of the sandstone, shale, and basalt fragments have been derived from beds exposed in the walls of the crater, but other rock fragments have been derived from considerably greater depth. The outer slopes of the rim are smooth and mostly gentle; the maximum gradient near the crest is about 30° and at the outer extremity the rim merges imperceptibly with the surrounding countryside. The deposit of ejecta thus forms a conical sheet which tapers gradually to a feather edge at the outer perimeter. In total volume the sheet would be insufficient to fill the crater, and the volume of pieces of rock in the sheet that are derived from the space occupied by the crater is a very small fraction of the volume of the crater.

The crater walls are irregular, steeply sloping surfaces underlain chiefly by sandstone and shale capped by the ejecta sheet of the rim. A basalt flow beneath the ejecta crops out as a low cliff on one side

FIG. 1. Zuñi Salt Lake, New Mexico; a maar with central cinder cones. Photograph by John S. Shelton.

of the crater. Sandstone, shale, and basalt, together with parts of the ejecta sheet, have dropped into the crater in a series of fault blocks (not described by Darton) along the west side, locally forming a series of terraces. The detailed features of the walls have been sculptured by erosion.

The crater floor is built up of coalescing small fans of alluvial detritus, derived by erosion of the walls and, in the centre, lake beds of undetermined thickness. The cinder cones, which represent the latest phase of volcanism at the crater, have been built upon the lake beds and rise to heights of about 50 m above the lake surface. A small crater in the centre of the largest cone descends to lake level.

Zuñi Salt Lake is a fairly representative maar, though the presence of cinder cones in the centre is unusual. Only one other maar with a central cone, the Wau en Namus of Libya (Viete, 1952, p. 475), has come to my attention. The Afton craters of southern New Mexico (Lee, 1907; Reiche, 1940) are more eroded and filled in than the Zuñi Salt Lake crater, but also exhibit the downfaulting or collapse along the crater wall. Well-developed bedding in the ejecta of the rim, which is a normal feature of maar rim deposits, led Reiche to interpret the beds in the largest of the Afton craters as fluviatile in origin. A decisive characteristic which shows such beds to have formed by fallout of ejecta, however, is the pronounced deformation of the beds under the larger blocks (Shoemaker, 1957). Such blocks in rare cases, such as in the rim of a maar in Puebla, Mexico (Ordoñez, 1905), are as much as 3 m across; the average grain size of the ejecta of maar rims commonly lies between about 5 and 10 mm.

Another feature of the bedding in the rim deposits that is characteristic of uneroded maars but also occurs at other volcanic craters is the draping of the bedding over the crest of the rim. This feature is well illustrated at several craters in Puebla. On the outer slopes of the rim the bedding is subparallel with the gently sloping upper surface of the ejecta deposit. Inward-dipping beds are found in some places on the inner slopes or walls of the craters as well. In general, the inward-dipping beds lie at angles close to the angle of repose of the material when it fell, ordinarily between 30° and 40°. Individual beds may be traced up the crater walls, over the crest of the rim, and down the outer slope. Generally only a thin layer of such beds, representing the last showers of ejecta, is draped over the rim crest. Lower beds in the rim deposit are most commonly truncated at the crater wall. The thin layer of inward-dipping ash or ejecta is quickly stripped away by erosion, but where preserved, it shows that the crater had attained nearly its final form prior to the last ejecta showers.

Draped bedding and inward-dipping ejecta may be found at the

Pulvermaar in the Eifel and the Cerro Colorado crater of the Pinacate region of Mexico (Jahns, 1959), but in these regions where the rim deposits are typically rather thin, the walls of the craters are more commonly bare bedrock. At the Diamond Head, Punch Bowl, and other maars on the island of Oahu, Hawaii (Stearns and Vaksvik, 1935), and at Crater Hill and other maars at Auckland, New Zealand (Firth, 1930), on the other hand, the walls of the craters are formed entirely of ejecta deposits. In these latter cases the floors of the present craters have been filled about to the level of the surrounding terrain or actually lie at a little higher level.

A crater of the maar type at Soda Lake, Nevada (Russell, 1885, pp. 73–76), has formed on the bed of the Pleistocene Lake Lahontan, after the lake had dried up. Fragments of the lake sediments, including shells of fresh-water invertebrates, are present in the ejecta of the crater rim. Evidently a similar occurrence of shells led Scrope (1862) to conclude that the maars of the Phlegraean fields in Italy were actually formed under water.

B. Subsurface Structure of Maars

In order to demonstrate the origin of maars it is necessary to know the relation of such craters to the underlying volcanic vents and to know the structure of the vents. One of the best places to examine these relations is in the Hopi Buttes region of the Navajo Indian Reservation, Arizona (Hack, 1942; Shoemaker, 1956; Shoemaker, and Roach and Byers, in press). Here some 300 maars of Pliocene age are well exposed in varying stages of denudation, more than are known in an area of comparable size in any other part of the world.

In the Hopi Buttes, the craters are found to be the surface features of funnel-shaped volcanic vents filled with a variable assemblage of blocks of old sedimentary rocks derived from the vent walls, basaltic tuff, tuff-breccia and agglomerate, fine-grained generally well-bedded clastic and carbonate rocks formed of sediments laid down in the craters, and intrusive and extrusive alkalic basalt. The vent walls generally slope gently (less than 45°) inward in the upper part where they cut soft Pliocene lake beds, and more steeply (more than 45°) where they cut well indurated Mesozoic rocks lower down. The walls cleanly truncate the older rocks, which are nearly flat-lying well-bedded sandstone and shale; the beds are deformed in only a few places. A volcanic vent with these characteristics has been called a diatreme by Daubrée (1891), who coined and applied the term to closely similar vents in Scotland and Germany as well as to the kimberlite pipes of South Africa.

Some of the diamond-bearing kimberlite pipes of South Africa, which are slightly different but closely related to the Hopi Buttes diatremes, have been completely explored by mining over vertical distances of

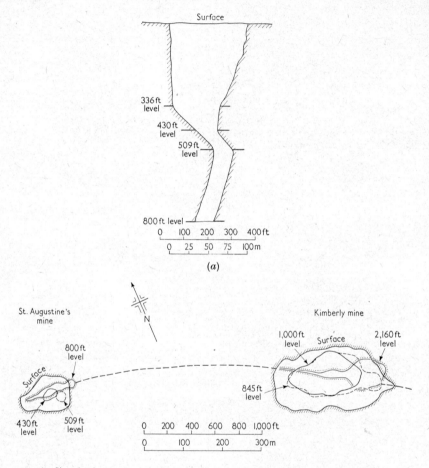

Plan showing contours of Kimberly and St. Augustine pipes. (after Wagner, 1914)

(b)

FIG. 2. St. Augustine's and Kimberley Mines, South Africa. (a) Section through St. Augustine's pipe in a northwest direction (after Wagner, 1914). (b) Plan showing contours of Kimberley and St. Augustine pipes (after Wagner, 1914).

more than 500 m (Fig. 2). They taper gradually downward into bodies increasingly elliptical in plan with depth; at the greatest depths reached by mining some pipes are elongated to dike-like forms. Kimberlite (serpentine breccia) diatremes of the northern part of the Navajo

Indian Reservation, which are exposed at a deeper level of erosion than the diatremes of the Hopi Buttes, exhibit a variety of forms at depths of several hundred to about 2000 m below the surface of eruption (Fig. 3). They range from mere local enlarged openings along dikes, as at Red Mesa (Fig. 3), to irregular pipe-like bodies with complex internal structure as at Mule's Ear (Fig. 3). These diatremes, at the level at

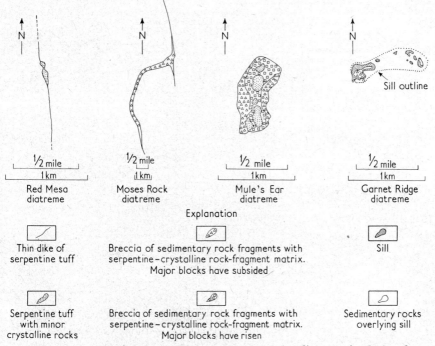

½ mile	½ mile	½ mile	½ mile
1 km	1 km	1 km	1 km
Red Mesa diatreme	Moses Rock diatreme	Mule's Ear diatreme	Garnet Ridge diatreme

Explanation

Thin dike of serpentine tuff

Breccia of sedimentary rock fragments with serpentine–crystalline rock-fragment matrix. Major blocks have subsided

Sill

Serpentine tuff with minor crystalline rocks

Breccia of sedimentary rock fragments with serpentine–crystalline rock-fragment matrix. Major blocks have risen

Sedimentary rocks overlying sill

FIG. 3. Diagrammatic plan views of four serpentine-bearing diatremes in the northern part of the Navajo Indian Reservation, Arizona.

which they are exposed, are filled entirely with fragments of serpentine, ultrabasic rocks, and pieces of rock derived from the vent walls. Blocks of sedimentary rocks, some more than 40 m across, have dropped down the vent from the horizons at which they were derived, in places as much as 1500 m. Other pieces, generally much smaller in size, have come from great depth, some probably from below the Earth's crust. Pieces that have gone down are intimately mixed with pieces that have come up, but in the Mule's Ear diatreme the largest pieces that have gone down are concentrated along the wall of the vent and the center is filled mainly with pieces that have come up. The general mixing of fragments from different sources is a common feature of diatremes.

C. MECHANICS OF MAAR-FORMING ERUPTIONS

One of the few maars that has been observed in eruption and reported in the literature is the Nilahue maar, which was opened up in
the Riñinahue volcanic field of southern Chile during the summer of
1955 (Müller and Veyl, 1957).

The entire eruptive history at Nilahue spanned about $3\frac{1}{2}$ months.
The initial volcanic activity consisted of violent gaseous discharges of
about 20 to 30 minutes' duration interrupted by periods of complete
quiescence. The duration of the gas discharges and intervening
quiescent intervals gradually became longer during the life of the
volcano. Ejecta, consisting mainly of new lava and subordinate pieces
of older rock, were carried to heights of about 5 to 8 km by the gas
discharges and showered down over an area extending more than
200 km from the volcano.

Stratigraphic relations of the ejecta of other maar-type volcanoes
suggest that most of them are similarly short lived.

Steam clearly plays an important role in maar formation but there is
no agreement as to the source of the water and the steps in its transformation to the gas phase. Some volcanologists, such as Stearns
(Stearns and Vaksvik, 1935, pp. 15–16), have emphasized the importance
of ground water in maar formation. There seems no reason to doubt
that ground water has played the key role in rare "explosive" eruptions
at Kilauea, Hawaii (Jaggar and Finch, 1924; Stearns, 1925), and
possibly in the formation of Hawaiian maars and in other unusual
eruptions as at Tarawera, New Zealand, in 1886 (Smith, 1887; Thomas,
1888). On the other hand many maars, such as those of the Eifel and
Hopi Buttes, are associated with alkalic basalts that are characteristically rich in water and other volatile rock constituents. The gas phase
given off in the eruptions at these craters may have been derived
chiefly, if not entirely, from the basaltic magma. Here we will examine
the eruptive mechanism for a magma that is saturated with volatiles
at the onset of eruption. This is probably the only case that will have
application to lunar craters.

The initial stages of opening of a maar-producing vent can only be
inferred. Suppose that a magma rich in dissolved volatile constituents
is ascending through the Earth's crust along pre-existing fractures or
along new fractures propagated by the intruding magma. The events
that will take place will be controlled by the vertical pressure gradient
in the crust, which in turn is a direct function of the superincumbent
load of rocks. For simplicity of discussion the rock pressure will be
taken to be hydrostatic. The ascending magma ultimately reaches a
level where the rock pressure is equal to the partial vapour pressure

of the magma. Exsolution or boiling of gas should begin in the magma intruded above this level.

One of the mechanical properties of rocks which is important to the next stage of the maar formation process is their very low tensile strength. Tensile fractures may be propagated in rocks by fluids moving along them under pressures only slightly exceeding, or in some cases even less than, the lithostatic or overburden pressure (Odé, 1956; Hubbert and Willis, 1957). This fact is well known from the practice of hydraulic fracturing to increase oil recovery in certain oil well operations. Depending on the supply and viscosity of the fluid, the fractures may be propagated very rapidly. If sufficient gas were evolved from a boiling magma to transmit pressure from the magma to the overlying regions of lower rock pressure, a fracture could be propagated up the lithostatic pressure gradient to the surface. Through this fracture the gas could then escape. During the initial propagation of the fracture there is a slight overpressure on the walls which forces them apart, but once the fracture is opened to the point where the gas begins to move along it at appreciable velocity there is actually a drop of pressure from the rock in the wall to the moving fluid.

Turning now to the upper tip of boiling magma, if the gas is drained rapidly away up the fracture, there will be a drop in pressure on the upper surface of the magma or at the level where froth or bubbles are beginning to form in the magma. A decompressional wave will therefore be propagated down the column of magma which will permit boiling to occur in a lower level in the magma column. If the gas exsolves sufficiently rapidly so that the formation of bubbles keeps pace with the wave front, the conditions of wave propagation would be somewhat analogous to those for deflagration waves in burning gases. Material would be accelerated upward, in the direction opposite to the propagation direction of the decompressional wave, at a velocity governed by the pressure difference across the wave front. Boiling would descend to the depth where the pressure on the low pressure side of the wave front just equals the vapor pressure of the magma. The physical condition of the material on the low pressure side of the wave front would be complex and probably would change rapidly as it moves up the vent. The bubbles would expand as the froth moves into regions of ever decreasing pressure, ultimately coalescing to form a gaseous continuum with entrained bits of partly degassed magma.

Decompressional waves would also be propagated into the walls of the fracture and the walls of the boiling part of the magma column, permitting rock to spall and become entrained in the moving gas-liquid system. The entire gas-liquid-solid melangé can be described as a complex fluidized system (Matheson and others, 1949). Depending on the velocity and density of the system, individual particles may either rise or sink or maintain their level in the vent. Some initial widening of the vent probably takes place by simple abrasion of the walls by the entrained debris, but spalling (plucking) is probably the main process which opens the fracture along a channel which soon localizes most of the flow. Along the length of the channel the pressure drop across the walls will tend to be greatest where the channel is narrowest (Venturi effect). At great depth the spalling may be sudden and violent, as in the case of rock bursts in deep mines, but near the surface it may be a more gentle slumping. By these processes the vent is cored out, probably much after the fashion of the gas coring observed by Perret (1924, pp. 62–69) in the 1906 eruption of Vesuvius.

Periodicity in the gas discharge, such as was observed at Nilahue, could be due to a number of causes. In the simplest case, a periodic discharge would occur if there were a continuous slow upwelling of magma uniformly charged with dissolved volatiles. Each time the top of the fresh magma reached a certain critical level, boiling would begin. The upper part of the column would be removed as a fluidized system, after which the vent would be choked with the unexpelled debris. The whole repetitive mechanism may be similar in some respects to that of a geyser.

The simplest maars are the orifices of vents opened by gas-coring. The floors of the craters, initially, are formed by the debris left at the end of the last eruption. Most of the material expelled from the vent is carried so high by the high velocity jet of gas that it falls far from the crater, but a small fraction falls locally to form an ejecta deposit on the rim. The lower the velocity of the gas jets, the higher is the ejecta deposit of the rim.

The distribution of ejecta around the crater follows a probability function governed by the variable velocities and characteristics of successive jets, atmospheric winds, the frequency distribution of grain size, drag coefficients of the ejecta, and many other factors. The ejecta form a blanket-like deposit with diffuse margins and an original upper surface that is generally smooth down nearly to the scale of the individual fragments. Fragments from all sources in the vent are generally indiscriminately mingled in the ejecta.

In many of the Hopi Buttes maars, particularly the larger ones, the gas-coring phase of the volcanic activity was followed by a period of subsidence or withdrawal of material down the vent. Thick deposits of fluviatile and lacustrine beds were laid down in places on the subsiding vent debris and some of the craters were greatly enlarged by slumping of the crater walls. The causes of the subsidence are not fully understood but are probably related to the presence of a fluid column of magma occupying the vent at depth. In about half the Hopi Buttes maars the volcanic activity culminated in the quiescent upwelling of lava that filled the craters and commonly piled up to form low lava domes, in some places spilling over or cutting through the ejecta rims to form short flows.

D. POSSIBLE MAARS AND OTHER VOLCANOES ON THE MOON

A nearly universal feature of maars, where they occur in considerable number as in the Eifel and the Hopi Buttes, is their tendency to be aligned in chains or rows. In the Hopi Buttes, dikes may be found in places between the craters, but more commonly there is no geologic feature connecting the craters along a given row at the surface. The alignment is probably due to some major fissure at depth along which the magma rose. In some places this fissure may be an old structure in the Earth's crust; in others the fissure may have been propagated by the magma itself (Anderson, 1951, pp. 22–28).

On the Moon, chains of small craters are common; most writers have supposed them to be of volcanic origin. There appear to be several different types of crater chains which should be examined separately.

A row composed of both small individual craters and small domes in the centre of Hell plain, pointed out by Alter (1957, p. 249), is similar to the chains of craters and domes of the Hopi Buttes, but is of slightly larger scale. Individual craters and domes are as much as 4 km across and are spaced from about 1 to 10 km apart. The entire chain, which forms a smooth arc, is more than 100 km long; in the Hopi Buttes, individual craters and domes are rarely more than 2 km across and the identifiable crater chains are not more than about 20 km long. The relative relief of the craters and domes on Hell plain, though not precisely known, appears to be comparable to the Pliocene relief in the Hopi Buttes. No visible surface features appear to connect the craters and domes in this chain on Hell plain, but higher resolution than has been achieved to date might reveal some.

A frequently cited chain of craters extending northeast of Stadius, between Copernicus and Eratosthenes (Fig. 4), appears to be of a slightly different type. The interpretation of this crater chain is complicated by the presence of numerous other small craters in the vicinity which are directly related to the large crater Copernicus. Craters that appear to belong strictly to the chain range from about 3 to 5 km across. Some occur individually, but most are adjacent to or merge with other craters in the chain. At the north end, a line of contiguous craters passes northward into a rill, a long narrow trench. These craters are characterized by a distinct rim rising above the surrounding terrain except on the sides on which they are contiguous with other craters. They are staggered somewhat irregularly along the curving course of the chain over a distance of about 130 km. This chain might be compared with the chain of craters extending from Daun to Bad Bertrich in the Eifel. Again the scale of the lunar craters is somewhat larger. None of the craters in the Eifel chain much exceeds 1 km in diameter and the whole chain is only about 18 km in length.

Lunar rills, with which some crater chains are associated, may not have any close terrestrial counterparts. It is likely, however, that the original surface features associated with the Moses Rock diatreme (Fig. 3) resembled the cratered rill at the north end of the Stadius chain or, to take an example at a larger scale, the great Hyginus cleft (Fig. 5). A major crater was probably located above the sharp bend in the Moses Rock diatreme just as the crater Hyginus occurs at the bend in the great lunar cleft. The Hyginus cleft, however, is about 15 times larger than the Moses Rock diatreme and associated dike system. A closer analogy may exist between the Moses Rock diatreme and some of the Triesnecker rills (Fig. 5). Both the diatreme and Triesnecker rills show branching. Some of the broader lunar rills or clefts, such as Hyginus and the nearby Ariadeus rill, may be complex structures that are part diatreme and part graben. Perhaps the closest terrestrial homologues of the narrower rills are the Icelandic *gjá*, great fissures in the lava fields, some of which are tens of kilometres long.

Certain small craters along rills in the floor of the large lunar crater Alphonsus are surrounded by diffuse dark haloes extending out 4–5 km from the edges of the small craters. The occurrence of these craters along the rills shows that they are probably related to processes that have taken place within the Moon. They are of the form and size of ordinary terrestrial maars and the dark haloes may well be thin deposits of dark volcanic ash.

A number of similar dark halo craters are scattered individually in the region around Copernicus (Fig. 6) and a few occur near Theophilus. These may correspond to isolated terrestrial maars such as Zuñi Salt Lake. The largest crater with a dark halo, which occurs south of Copernicus and west of Fauth (Fig. 6), is about 5 km in diameter. In all cases the dark halo is nearly symmetrically distributed about the crater and has a diffuse outer margin.

Other features in the vicinity of Copernicus resemble other types of terrestrial volcanoes. A number of well-known symmetrical hills rising from the Oceanus Procellarum near its western edge, just north of Hortensius (Fig. 6), have been referred to in the astronomical literature as domes. They are about 7–9 km across, a few hundred metres high, and most have a small crater, less than 1 km in diameter, in the summit. In all discernible respects they appear to be small shield volcanoes, as was concluded long ago by Pickering (1906, p. 156–157), who discovered the first such object in the Mare Nubium. Many similar objects have been noticed by Kuiper (1959a, p. 308–309), and others in parts of the Oceanus Procellarum between Copernicus and Kepler.

Midway between Hortensius and Copernicus (Fig. 6) is another symmetrical hill, about 5–6 km across and at least several hundred meters high, with a conspicuous crater more than 1 km across in its summit. This feature resembles a small stratovolcano. It is perhaps the best example of its type to be seen in the subterrestrial hemisphere of the Moon. Other hills with summit craters are known, but their origin may be more complex.

The largest craters that occur along well defined chains are about 15 km in diameter.† Hyginus, which is 10 km in diameter, is one of the largest. Perhaps the largest occurs in a spectacular chain just northwest of Almanon. These craters have the approximate shape of maars, but if they occurred on Earth they would probably be referred to as calderas simply because of their large size. The largest terrestrial craters that I consider to be maars are about 5 km in diameter.

The great majority of lunar chain craters of the types described are similar in size to most terrestrial maars. Many are close to the limit of resolution in existing good lunar photographs (about 1 km in diameter). All of the lunar forms that resemble terrestrial shield and stratovolcanoes are of moderate dimensions, and most are perhaps slightly smaller than the average for their possible terrestrial counterparts. These facts suggest that volcanic processes, and in particular crater-forming volcanic processes, have operated on about the same linear scale on the Moon as on the Earth.

---

† The question of what constitutes a chain will be left in abeyance here. A straight or curved line may be drawn through any two craters, and among the thousands of visible craters on the Moon there must be a large number of instances where three or more craters are approximately aligned as a result of a fortuitous combination of unrelated causes. Calculation of the probability that any particular arrangement of craters may occur by a chance combination of certain events necessarily entails a priori assumptions, the validity of which are not readily tested. It must be remembered that finding any specified arrangement of craters is, a priori, highly improbable.

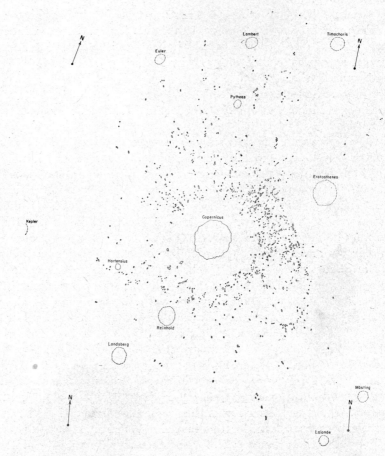

FIG. 4(a).   Secondary impact craters of the Copernican ray system.

FIG. 4(*b*). Base photograph of the Copernicus region taken by F. G. Pease with the 100-in Hooker telescope in 1929, Mount Wilson Observatory.

x

FIG. 5. Photograph of the Hyginus region of the Moon. (Observatoire du Pic-du-Midi).

IV. Impact Craters

The list of terrestrial craters of probable impact origin (Spencer, 1933; Boon and Albritton, 1938; Leonard, 1946; Hardy, 1954) now grows at the rate of about one a year (for some recent additions to the list see Karpoff, 1953; Beals, Ferguson, and Landau, 1956; Beals, 1958). Additions to the list fall into two categories, (1) previously undescribed craters, and (2) previously known craters for which evidence of impact origin has been found or for which such evidence has been strengthened. The growth of this list is likely to continue, perhaps to accelerate. Meteorite impact, however, has not yet been generally acknowledged as a process capable of or responsible for the formation of Earth features of more than modest size and number. This fact, as much as any other, has profoundly influenced past discussions of the origin of the craters of the Moon. The process of recognition of impact craters, therefore, begins on the Earth.

A. FORM AND STRUCTURE OF IMPACT CRATERS

The best known and first widely recognized meteorite impact crater in the world is Meteor Crater, Arizona.† The crater occurs in a region underlain by nearly flat-lying sedimentary rocks of contrasting lithology, and it has been possible to determine the structure of the crater in detail (Shoemaker, 1960a, and in press). For this reason it is appropriate to use Meteor Crater, Arizona, as an example for detailed description and analysis.

Meteor Crater lies in the southern part of the Colorado Plateau in an area of low relief and generally excellent exposures. The crater is a bowl-shaped depression 200 m deep, a little over 1 km wide, encompassed by a ridge or rim that rises about 30–60 m above the surrounding plain. As computed by Gilbert (1896, p. 9), the volume of the rim will just fill the depression. The rim is composed of rock debris and alluvium resting on disturbed dolomitic limestone, shale, and sandstone strata. Beds exposed in the walls of the crater include, in ascending order, light coloured sandstone and dolomite of Permian age, and red sandstone and mudstone of Triassic age. The debris of the rim has been found by mapping to be rudely stratified as well; each mappable stratum is composed chiefly of fragments from one of the underlying formations and the fragmental strata lie in a sequence the inverse of that of the underlying formations from which they are derived (Fig. 7). Pieces of rock making up the debris range in size

† Meteor Crater, Arizona, has been named the Barringer Meteorite Crater by the Meteoritical Society in honour of D. M. Barringer, who contributed most heavily in establishing the impact origin of the crater.

from microscopic splinters to great angular blocks more than 30 m across.

The surface of the surrounding part of the Colorado Plateau has been eroded since Meteor Crater was formed, and in the vicinity of the crater has been lowered, on the average, about 15 m. In most places,

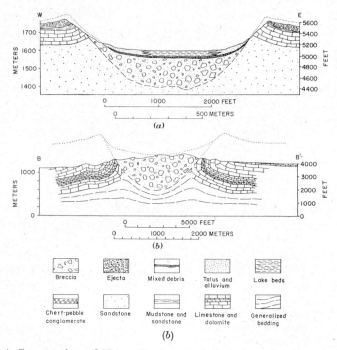

(a)

(b)

(b)

FIG. 7(a). Cross sections of Meteor Crater, Arizona, and (b) Sierra Madera, Texas.

the debris has been stripped down to a resistant layer formed by fragments of dolomite. Thin patches of late Pleistocene and Recent alluvium, composed mainly of detritus derived from the debris, rest on this stripped surface. The initial features of the crater rim, therefore, are not preserved, but the present topography of the rim affords important clues to its original appearance (Fig. 8). Today it has a peculiar hummocky rolling surface and it is likely that the original surface of the debris was similarly hummocky. Beyond a distance of about 1 km from the crater only scattered isolated fragments of debris remain.

Beds of the older formations exposed in the crater walls dip gently outward low in the crater and generally more steeply outward close to the contact with the debris of the rim. Along the north and east

FIG. 8. Meteor Crater, Arizona; an aerial view from the southeast. Photograph by John S. Shelton.

walls of the crater the uppermost red beds locally are folded back on themselves, the upper limb of the fold consisting of a flap that has been rotated in places more than 180° away from the crater (Fig. 7). At one place the flap grades outward into debris. Rocks now represented by the debris of the rim have been peeled back from the area of the crater, somewhat like the petals of a blossoming flower.

The upturned strata are broken by small nearly vertical faults of scissors type of displacement and a number of small thrust faults. Displacement on the vertical faults generally increases towards the centre of the crater. Regional jointing has controlled the shape of the crater, which is somewhat "square" in outline; the diagonals of the "square" coincide with the trend of two main sets of regional joints. The largest vertical faults, which are parallel with the regional joints, occur in the "corners" of the crater. Along one side there are also a few inward-dipping normal faults concentric with the crater wall.

The floor of the crater is underlain by talus and alluvium that interfinger toward the centre with lake beds about 30 m thick. These sediments rest, in turn, on a layer of mixed debris about 10 m thick that appears to have been formed by fallout of ejecta thrown to great height. The debris is composed of mixed fragments of the older sedimentary formations, some highly sheared and sintered, and contains sparse oxidized meteoritic iron. Though this layer apparently has not been preserved outside the crater, similar materials occur in the alluvium and as lag on the rim.

Beneath the mixed debris layer is a lens of breccia about 200 m thick, which has been partly explored by shafts and by about two dozen deep drill holes sunk by Barringer and his associates in the central part of the crater (Barringer, 1905, 1910, 1914; Tilghman, 1905). Along the upper outer margins of the lens the breccia is composed chiefly of large blocks of dolomite, but under the central part of the crater floor the breccia is made up chiefly of shattered twisted blocks of light-coloured sandstone and subordinate finer grained pieces of sheared and sintered rocks. The dolomite blocks of the upper edge of the breccia lens have been displaced downward against the sandstone in the crater walls. Meteoritic iron is dispersed in the breccia chiefly as microscopic spheres in drops of sintered dolomite, which appear to be most abundant near the base of the breccia. The sintered material constitutes not more than a few per cent of the breccia.

Recently the new mineral coesite, which had previously been known from the laboratory, has been found to be a major constituent of some of the sheared and sintered rock fragments at the crater (Chao, Shoemaker, and Madsen, 1960). Coesite is a dense polymorph of silica which has been synthesized only under hydrostatic pressures exceeding 20,000 atmospheres (Boyd and England, 1960). Its occurrence at Meteor Crater is evidently the result of strong shock such as would be generated by hypervelocity impact. Coesite-bearing fragments occur in the breccia lens, in the layer of mixed debris interpreted as fallout, and also in the alluvium on the crater rim.

A small meteorite crater about 200 m across, the largest of a group of small craters near Odessa, Texas, exhibits structural features differing from those found at the Arizona crater (Hardy, 1953). The Odessa crater has been formed in nearly flat-lying Cretaceous beds of the Edwards Plateau (Sellards and Evans, 1941). In the walls of the crater these beds are buckled in a tight asymmetric anticline. Under the centre of the crater is a lens of fragmented and pulverized rock that appears to correspond to the breccia lens at Meteor Crater, Arizona.

Prior to exploratory excavation, the Odessa crater had been nearly obliterated as a topographic feature by erosion of the rim and filling of the central part with about 30 m of Pleistocene and Recent sediments. The general erosion of the plateau surface since the crater was formed is about the same as at Meteor Crater, Arizona. Both features are of late Pleistocene age. The meteoritic material at the Odessa crater is closely similar to the ordinary Canyon Diablo irons of the Arizona crater (Lord, 1941; Beck and La Paz, 1951), and it may be that the meteorites that formed each crater are part of the same fall.

The largest terrestrial crater for which there is now strong evidence of impact origin is the Ries basin or Rieskessel of southern Germany. It is a broad shallow basin between the Schwäbian and Franken Alb that has attracted the attention of the German geologists for well over 100 years. The idea that the Ries might be an impact crater was first set forth by Werner (1904) and later elaborated by Stutzer (1936). But the consensus of the principal investigators of the Ries, as summarized by Dorn (1948), has been that the Ries was formed by some sort of volcanic explosion.

The Ries basin or crater is of mid-Tertiary age and has been greatly modified by erosion and sedimentation. Originally the crater measured about 27 to 29 km from rim to rim. Miocene lake beds up to 300 m thick have been deposited on the crater floor (Reich and Horrix, 1955). Present maximum relief between the centre of the basin and the southern rim is about 200 m and the original relief must have been more than 500 m. The original topography within the crater comprised a central depression about 12 km across, now filled with sediments, surrounded by an irregular shelf from which rose scattered hills.

Breccias, chiefly of old crystalline rocks, are exposed on some of these hills where they rise above the floor of the Ries today.

The walls of the crater and crest of the rim (the *Schollen- und Schuppen-Zone* of Bentz, 1927) are underlain by breccia and an imbricate series of thrust sheets composed chiefly of Upper Jurassic limestones that cap the Alb (Nathan, 1925, 1935; Dehm, 1932; Gerstlauer, 1940; Schröder and Dehm, 1950; and Triebs, 1950). Beyond, extending tens of kilometres to the south in the region described by Branco (1902) as the *Vorries*, are great masses of limestone breccia resting on the undisturbed limestone cap of the Alb and, at the outer limit, on Oligocene sediments. One far flung fragment of limestone, measuring nearly half a metre in diameter, was found 60 km from the crater (Reuter, 1925). In places in the *Vorries* and the *Schollen- und Schuppen-Zone*, breccias composed chiefly of Lower Jurassic and Triassic sedimentary rocks or of rocks from the crystalline basement complex rest on the breccias of Upper Jurassic limestone and the thrust slices. Locally fragments of Triassic rocks and crystalline rocks are mixed in about equal proportion. Similar breccias were found in a deep drill hole under the lake beds near the centre of the Ries. Branco (1902) and later Bentz (1925) long ago concluded that the key to solving the origin of the Ries lay in explaining the mode of emplacement of these unusual breccias.

The most remarkable aspect of the geology of the Ries is a supposed volcanic breccia or tuff that has been called *suevit* (Sauer, 1901). It occurs both inside the crater and on the rim and *Vorries*. The *suevit* consists of a wide variety of rock fragments, most of them crystalline rocks from the basement complex, in general shattered or partially sintered, as well as bombs and smaller fragments of glass that all German authors have agreed are of a conventional igneous or magmatic origin. The glass bombs invariably carry fragments of sintered or partially sintered rocks that are recognizably derived from the crystalline basement. Some of the bombs have extraordinary shapes for volcanic ejecta such as thin sheets that have been tightly folded or curled on the edges. While this manuscript was in preparation some of the sintered material in the *suevit* was found to contain coesite (Shoemaker and Chao, 1960, Pecora, 1960, p. 19) and the Ries was thus established as the world's second locality for this high pressure polymorph of silica.

The *suevit* has been commonly assumed to have erupted from numerous widely scattered vents and, because the *suevit* can locally be seen to rest on the other breccias, the eruptions have been interpreted as one of the latest events in the development of the Ries. On the basis of about a week's field study, I believe that the *suevit* can be interpreted to rest everywhere on the other breccias; local steep contacts of *suevit* with other breccia within the crater are probably due to faulting or inward slumping of the breccias along the crater walls. The sum of evidence indicates that the glassy material of the *suevit* has been fused by shock; the patches of *suevit* that have been preserved from erosion appear to be remnants of a layer that is analogous to the mixed debris or fallout layer preserved in Meteor Crater, Arizona.

Structurally the Ries is utterly unlike any caldera or crater of demonstrable volcanic origin. Indeed, *suevit* is the only material at the Ries that resembles volcanic rock. Kranz (1911, 1934) has attempted to explain the Ries in terms of one large volcanic explosion, but, as Reck has pointed out (Williams, 1941, p. 303), no masses of rock even approaching the size of the thrust slices of the *Schollen- und Schuppen-Zone* have ever been ejected in the most violent historic volcanic eruptions. To explain the thrust slices, a variety of complicated hypotheses have been invented that involve first an uplift or doming of the central part of the Ries and a later subsidence. All of the major structural features of the crater and the ejecta, on the other hand, appear to have a straightforward explanation in terms of hypervelocity impact mechanics.

A much smaller crater that has been generally agreed by Branco and Fraas (1905) and later workers to be closely related to the Rieskessel is the Steinheim basin. The Steinheim lies on the Schwäbian Alb about 30 km southwest of the Ries and is also partly filled with Miocene lake beds. Within the limits of error of paleontological dating the two craters are of the same age. The present Steinheim basin is about $2\frac{1}{2}$ km across and 80 m deep. It has been considerably modified by erosion and breaching of the crater rim by a through-flowing stream as well as by sedimentation on the crater floor. It is of interest as the only terrestrial crater so far recognized of probable or possible impact origin that exhibits a well-defined central hill. The walls of the crater are underlain by breccia of Jurassic limestone, and the central hill is underlain by highly disturbed but poorly exposed Jurassic rocks including some beds or rock fragments derived from lower horizons than any of the fragments in the breccia along walls. Branco and Fraas (1905) inferred that the Steinheim basin is an explosion crater of cryptic (hidden) volcanic origin; no direct evidence of volcanism is present at the crater. Exposures are not sufficient to determine how closely the structure of the Steinheim basin compares with that of demonstrated meteorite impact craters, but what is known of the structure is compatible with an impact origin. It seems possible, if not likely, that the Steinheim basin was formed by impact of a part of a larger object, the main impact of which produced the Rieskessel.

B. Eroded Structures of Probable Impact Origin

A complex feature that may be interpreted as the subsurface structure of an ancient impact crater is well exposed at Sierra Madera, Texas, a hill, or small mountain on the southern edge of the Edwards Plateau (Fig. 7). This is one of a number of localities in the United States, exhibiting a community of structural features, that have been called "cryptovolcanic" (Bucher, 1936) or "cryptoexplosion" in origin (Dietz, 1959 and 1960). Boon and Albritton (1937, pp. 60–62) originally suggested that the structure at Sierra Madera was produced by meteorite impact, on the basis of mapping by King (1930, pp. 123–125). This suggestion has been considerably strengthened by information from three deep drill holes and by re-examination of the central part of the structure.

King mapped Sierra Madera as a complex dome with steeply dipping to nearly vertical and even overturned beds near the centre encompassed by partially concentric folds. The steeply dipping older rocks at the centre of the structure are found on close examination to be individual blocks in a lens of a giant breccia nested in a cup of peeled back and locally overturned beds (Fig. 7). A drill hole somewhat off of the centre of the breccia lens shows that, beneath the breccia, the structural relief on an anhydrite marker bed is only a few hundred feet.†

The age of the Sierra Madera structure is not known. Cretaceous as well as Permian beds appear to be deformed and a considerable thickness of Cretaceous rocks would be required to restore the crater suggested in Fig. 7. A pre-Pleistocene age seems required to account for the regional denudation since the structure was formed. In all probability the structure is of Tertiary age. Much more work needs to be done at Sierra Madera, and a detailed geologic study will probably increase the understanding of similar geologic features.

Other structures referred to as "cryptovolcanic" or "cryptoexplosion" structures have also been mapped as domes surrounded by concentric folds, but the exposures are rarely adequate to support this interpretation. The domes are inferred more from the fact that the oldest rocks are found near the centre than from observable field relations. The oldest rocks indeed are generally found near the centres of the structures, but where quarries have been opened up or drill core obtained, as at Wells Creek Basin, Tennessee (Wilson, 1953, pp. 766–768),

---

† I am indebted to Mr. Addison Young for identification and correlation of the anhydrite bed.

these rocks have turned out to be fragments in a breccia similar to that at Sierra Madera. Upheaval Dome, Utah, which was called cryptovolcanic by Bucher (1936, pp. 1064–1066), has a well-exposed broken dome in the centre, but this structure is probably a salt dome (McKnight, 1940, pp. 124–128; Joesting and Plouff, 1958) and not related to structures of the Sierra Madera type. Each geologic feature that appears to belong to the "cryptoexplosion" category must be examined on its own merits.

The largest known structure that appears to be of the Sierra Madera type is the so-called Vredefort "dome" of South Africa (Hall and Molengraaff, 1925; Nel, 1927) which is 70 to 90 km across. The centre of the Vredefort structure is also occupied by a great mass of brecciated rock. Boon and Albritton (1937, pp. 62–64) and later Daly (1947) suggested that the Vredefort structure was formed by impact, but South African geologists appear to prefer more conventional geologic interpretations of its origin (Brock, 1951).

C. SIMILARITY BETWEEN IMPACT CRATERS AND NUCLEAR EXPLOSION CRATERS

Most of the principal structural features of large meteorite impact craters are reproduced in one or the other of two craters formed by underground explosions of nuclear devices in alluvium of Yucca Flat, Nevada (Shoemaker, 1960a). Detonation of a 1·2 kiloton device at about 6 m depth produced a crater about 80 m in diameter and 15 m deep (the Jangle U experiment).† A device of the same yield detonated in the same medium at a depth of about 20 meters produced a crater about 100 m in diameter and about 30 meters deep (Teapot Ess experiment). Different structures were produced in the rims of the two craters but both are underlain by a lens of breccia.

The Teapot Ess crater is a fairly close model at about 1/11 scale of Meteor Crater, Arizona. Beds of the alluvium are turned up and overturned along the wall of the crater and ejecta fragments are stacked on the rim roughly in an order inverted from the order of the beds from which the pieces are derived. The Jangle U crater is approximately a half-scale model of the main meteorite crater at Odessa, Texas. Beds are buckled in an asymmetric anticline beneath the rim. The anticline is sheared off at the top and the crest of the rim is formed of large slabs of ejected alluvium. These slabs may correspond, on a small scale, to the great thrust sheets of the *Schollen- und Schuppen-Zone* of the Ries. The post-shot topography of the outer flanks of the rim of both the Jangle U and Teapot Ess craters was characteristically

† 1 kiloton is equivalent to 10^{12} calories or $4·186 \times 10^{19}$ ergs total yield.

hummocky, resembling, on a small scale, the hummocky terrain on the rim of Meteor Crater, Arizona.

From the nuclear explosion craters it can be seen that the surface and structural features of impact craters can be produced by strong shocks originating at shallow depths beneath the surface of the ground and also that the structures formed depend upon the depth of the origin of the shock. Comparably strong shocks are produced by hyper-velocity impact. It may be anticipated that the structure of large meteorite craters will depend upon the depth of penetration of the meteorite, the total energy released, and the nature of the target rocks.

It would be erroneous to conclude from the structural similarities to explosion craters, however, that meteorite craters are produced by explosion of the meteorite. The concept of explosion of the meteorite or of rock heated by impact goes back at least to Merrill (1908, pp. 494–495) and has been elaborated by Ives (1919), Gifford (1924, 1930) and Moulton (1931), followed by many authors in the ensuing decades, notably Baldwin (1949) and Gilvarry and Hill (1956). So widely has this concept been described that craters of inferred high-velocity impact origin are now commonly referred to as explosion craters. In the form developed by Ives and Gifford, the concept of explosion of the meteorite was derived by computing the specific kinetic energy of meteorites travelling in the known range of geocentric velocities of meteors and equating this kinetic energy to specific internal energy in the meteorite at the moment of impact. The specific internal energy was thus found to exceed the enthalpy of vaporization for any solid at atmospheric pressure, and it was concluded that the meteorite would explode.

The error in such a calculation lies in the neglect of the partition of energy in the shock waves generated by the impact and in neglect of the equations of state of the shocked materials. Very high specific energies are produced by hypervelocity impact, but these are the consequence rather than the cause of the shocks which produce the craters. In fact, the fraction of the energy which is retained thermally by material engulfed by shock is unavailable for further propagation of the shock. For the same total energy, the higher the initial specific energy the smaller will be the crater. Vaporization of the meteorite or target rocks would not, therefore, facilitate the opening up of an impact crater, except possibly where the rocks are especially rich in volatile constituents. We may properly speak of meteorite impact craters as explosion craters in the sense that materials fly out of the craters. But in this sense the pits formed by raindrops on soft mud are also explosion craters. It would be better if the term "explosion" were dropped with reference to hypervelocity impact mechanics.

D. Mechanics of Large Meteorite Impact in Rock

When a meteorite strikes the ground at speeds greater than a few km/sec, two shocks are propagated away from the impact interface; one shock advances into the ground and the other shock races back into the meteorite.† The material between the shocks is compressed and its velocity is changed as it is engulfed by the shock fronts. In the general case, where the shape of the meteorite is irregular and the surface of the ground is irregular, the conditions and motion of material between the shocks immediately following impingement are extremely complex. We will touch briefly on some of these complexities later.

The net effect as the shocks advance into the ground and back into the meteorite will be that most of the ground engulfed by shock is accelerated down and outward away from the oncoming body and most of the meteorite engulfed by shock is decelerated and flows in directions paralleling the flow of the underlying shocked rock. Part of the kinetic energy of the meteorite engulfed by shock is converted to internal energy in the meteorite, and part is transferred as kinetic and internal energy to the shocked rock ahead of the meteorite.

A precise calculation of the motion and energy changes of the shocked material would depend upon specifying the shape of the meteorite and target and, for all except the simplest shapes, is beyond present mathematical analysis. A solution in closed form, however, may be readily obtained for the one dimensional case of a semi-infinite meteorite striking a semi-infinite target along a plane interface and in a direction perpendicular to the interface; in addition, Bjork (1958) has obtained a number of specific solutions for the impact along a plane interface of a right circular cylinder of steel into a semi-infinite steel target by numerical integration of the hydrodynamic equations.

It is helpful to examine results for the one dimensional case in order to visualize the conditions of the shocked material and the way in which the energy is partitioned. In this case the two shock fronts are infinite plane surfaces and the material between them has a uniform pressure and velocity. This pressure and velocity and the velocities of the two shocks are each simple functions of the initial velocity of the meteorite, the initial densities of the meteorite and target, and the compression by shock of the meteorite and target. A set of numerical solutions has been obtained for the meteorite and rocks at Meteor Crater, Arizona, for impact velocities of 10, 15, and 20 km/sec by treating the target rocks as a homogeneous system, employing the

† It is not necessary that the speed of the impacting body exceed the acoustic velocity in the target or the meteorite in order to produce a shock.

experimental equation of state for iron, and estimating an average equation of state for the rocks (Shoemaker, 1960a, p. 429).

For purposes of illustration, the solutions for only one impact velocity need be examined. Consider the meteorite an infinite plate of iron of thickness T striking the ground at 15 km/sec, the approximate median velocity at which meteorites enter the Earth's atmosphere (Whipple and Hughes, 1955). The pressure between the shocks will be 4·5 Mb and at this pressure the rocks will be compressed 58% and the meteorite will be compressed 43%. At the moment the shock into the meteorite reaches the back side of the plate, the shock into the ground is moving at a speed of 17·2 km/sec and will have advanced a distance of 1·48 T from the original ground surface; the leading face of the meteorite will have penetrated a distance of 0·87 T below the original ground surface and the back side a distance of 0·30 T; the centre of gravity of the compressed system will be 0·78 T beneath the original ground surface and the whole compressed system of rock and meteorite will have a velocity of 10·0 km/sec into the ground. This is the moment of greatest compression of the meteorite. The kinetic energy of the whole compressed system will be $\frac{2}{3}$ and the internal energy $\frac{1}{3}$ of the original kinetic energy of the meteorite. About $\frac{2}{3}$ of the internal energy will be in the compressed rock and $\frac{1}{3}$ in the compressed meteorite and about 53% of the total energy will have been transferred from the meteorite to the compressed rock.

When the shock hits the back side of the plate a tensional or rarefaction wave will be reflected back into the meteorite. The velocity of the meteorite behind the rarefaction will still be about 5·1 km/sec *into the ground*. At the moment the rarefaction reaches the leading face of the meteorite, the shock into the ground will have penetrated about 3·0 T into the ground; the leading face of the meteorite will have penetrated 1·8 T and the back side about 0·8 T beneath the original surface of the ground. The centre of gravity of the moving system will be 1·8 T underground. About 88% of the original kinetic energy of the meteorite will have been transferred to the compressed rock ahead of the meteorite, where the energy will be equally divided into an internal and a kinetic fraction. The compressed rock will still be moving into the ground at 10·0 km/sec.

A meteorite differs importantly from an infinite plate, but these numerical results establish several major qualitative facts about hypervelocity impact. First they show that, by compression alone, an iron meteorite at typical geocentric velocities would penetrate in its entirety below the surface of a target composed of ordinary silicate rocks. Secondly, they show that, even after reflection of a rarefaction from the back side, the meteorite will not necessarily fly apart but that the whole meteorite may continue to move into the ground. Third, it may be seen that the major part of the original energy of the meteorite is transferred to the shocked rock ahead of the meteorite at a very early stage of penetration. And finally, for the velocity and conditions illustrated, the internal energy of the meteorite never exceeds $\frac{1}{7}$ of the original kinetic energy, and only a fraction of this internal energy will be trapped thermally. A major part of this internal energy is released by expansion of the meteorite behind the rarefaction and contributes to further propagation of the shock into the rock.

The data of Altshuler and others (1958) on the equation of state of iron make it possible to calculate the minimum impact velocity at which the meteorite would have been largely fused by shock at Meteor Crater, Arizona. This velocity was found to be 9·4 km/sec (Shoemaker, in press). From the fact that much of the meteorite now appears to be dispersed as minute spherical drops in fragments of sintered dolomite in the breccia under the crater it was concluded that the impact velocity was greater than 9·4 km/sec. No evidence has been recognized, however, by which it could be shown that more than a small fraction of the meteorite or rocks at Meteor Crater ever behaved as vapour.

In the case of a real meteorite, rarefaction waves are reflected from the sides, which permit lateral flow of the body to take place as well as longitudinal compression. This accentuates the flattening of the body as it penetrates the ground and introduces an additional mechanism of penetration. A rarefaction wave is also reflected from the free surface of the ground, which permits lateral flow of part of the rock engulfed by shock. Material overtaken by the rarefaction waves is deflected laterally from the path of penetration of the meteorite. Both rock and meteorite are swept aside and the meteorite becomes the liner of a transient cavity with material from the rear part of the meteorite facing the centre of the cavity. The additional penetration brought about by lateral flow may be roughly estimated from elementary theory of incompressible fluids. This kind of approximation has been justified on the basis that the pressures greatly exceed the yield strengths of the materials.

In order to compare impact craters with nuclear explosion craters it is necessary to estimate the distribution of shock energy in the walls of the initial cavity formed by the combination of compression and lateral flow of the meteorite and target rocks. This distribution can be expressed as a central point about which the total moment of the energy vanishes. In a homogeneous medium, such a point will be close to the centre of curvature of the shock front after the shock has propagated some distance from the cavity. This point will be referred to as the apparent centre or apparent origin of the shock. For 15 km/sec impact velocity, the apparent origin of the shock at Meteor Crater, Arizona, was calculated to lie between 4 to 5 diameters of the meteorite beneath the surface, measured along the path of penetration (Shoemaker, 1960a, p. 430). The structural evidence appears to require a vertical depth of about this magnitude for the apparent shock origin.

At a more advanced stage in the opening up of the crater the shock and pattern of flow produced by impact begin to resemble more and more closely the shock and flow produced by shallow nuclear explosions. The shock propagates away from the immediate vicinity of the cavity and is followed by the rarefaction reflected from the free surface of the ground. Material engulfed by the shock is accelerated in the directions of shock propagation, which at some distance from the cavity will be approximately along the radii of a sphere. Momentum is trapped in part of the material above the rarefaction wave and it will move up- ward and outward, individual fragments following ballistic trajectories. As the shock engulfs an ever-increasing volume of rock the shock strength will decrease until ultimately the shock decays to an ordinary elastic wave. The margin of the crater is determined primarily by the radial distance, at the surface, at which there is just sufficient kinetic energy in the rocks behind the reflected tensional wave for fragments to be torn loose and lofted over the rim.

The detailed mechanics of the tearing loose and ejection of pieces at the rim depend on the size of the crater and the depth of initial penetration of the meteorite. In small experimental impact craters in rock, tensile spalling roughly parallel with the rarefaction front appears to determine the shape and size of the crater; in craters the size of the Ries basin and larger, the energy required to actually heave the rocks out is the main factor that determines the size and shape of the crater. For craters of intermediate size, the structure of the rim is sensitive to the depth of the origin of the shock. At Meteor Crater, Arizona, and at the Teapot Ess nuclear explosion crater, where the scaled depth of explosion was comparatively great, the craters were formed mainly by ejection of debris. Beds are sheared off along a roughly conical surface, and the upturning of the strata in the walls of these craters can be looked upon as essentially drag along this shear surface. At the main Odessa crater and the Jangle U crater, on the other hand, where the scaled depth of the explosion was much less, outward flow and buckling in the rim was an important process in the opening up of the craters.

Outward motion of material behind the shock front, as it moves away from the cavity produced by initial penetration, is not uniform; the pressure soon drops to levels where the strength of the rocks influences the flow. Owing to divergence of the flow, the rocks stretch normal to the flow and break up by tensile fracturing. Meteoritic material and strongly shocked rock are shot out and dispersed in a large volume of broken rock that is relatively only weakly shocked, thus forming a breccia of mixed fragments. Empirically the distance from the origin or centre of the shock to the limit of the mixed breccia in explosion craters is proportional to the cube root of the total shock energy (Shoemaker, 1960b). A lens of mixed breccia, roughly proportional in depth to the radius of the crater, may be expected under every large impact crater.

The final phase of displacement of material in fairly large impact craters is the slumping back of the breccia and part of the crater walls toward the centre of the crater. At Meteor Crater, Arizona, this displacement appears to have preceded the showering down of ejecta thrown to great height, but at the Ries basin it may have occurred later. The centripetal movement of material from the crater walls produces a rise in the level of the central part of the crater floor. No sharply defined central hump is present on the floor of Meteor Crater, though a subdued off-centre ridge may be buried under the Pleistocene lake beds below what Barringer (1910; 1924, p. 11) referred to as Silica Hill. The convergent movement resulting from slumping, however, would appear to be entirely adequate to explain the formation of a central hill such as observed in the Steinheim basin.

E. COMPARISON OF MAARS AND METEORITE IMPACT CRATERS

The distinguishing features of maars and large meteorite impact craters are as follows:

(1) Both types of craters have the same gross shape and overlap in range of size. Both are primarily an excavation in the pre-existing terrain encompassed by a rim which is a constructional feature. The relative height of the rim of a maar may vary widely; in principle, the relative height of the rim of impact craters should vary within narrower limits but also varies widely. On Earth true maars are no larger than about 5 km in diameter, though much larger craters of volcanic origin are well known. (All of the larger volcanic craters, referred to as calderas, are believed to have been formed mainly by subsidence, and most are summit features of very large stratovolcanoes.) In contrast, there is no limit, in principle, to the size of impact craters and at least one terrestrial feature of possible impact origin, the Vredefort dome, is much larger than any known volcanic crater.

Y

(2) Both types of craters tend to be approximately circular in plan but may be elliptical or may have polygonal outlines controlled by pre-existing structure. The merging of two or more vents produces compound maar-type craters of irregular outline and, in crater chains, some individual craters are elongated in the direction of the chain. Except for clusters of small craters, impact craters are typically solitary and regular in outline, but in the clusters compound craters have also been found.

(3) Both maars and impact craters may have a central hill or hills, though terrestrial examples are rare.

(4) A maar is underlain by a funnel-shaped volcanic vent filled with a variable assemblage of volcanic tuff and breccia, rocks derived from the vent walls, sediments, and intrusive igneous rocks—in short, a diatreme. An impact crater is underlain by a lens of breccia or crushed, mixed rock. Rocks sintered by shock may be expected to be a universal constituent of such a breccia in large terrestrial impact craters but rarely will constitute more than a few per cent of the breccia.

(5) The country rock is cleanly truncated in the walls of a maar. Except for normal faults, the rocks are rarely deformed in any way that can be related to the opening of the crater. The rocks in the walls of an impact crater, on the other hand, are invariably deformed. Depending on the size, the depth of penetration of the meteorite, and the original structure, beds in the walls may be turned up and overturned, buckled in concentric folds, or sheared out in a series of thrust slices.

(6) Slumping or concentric normal faulting along the crater walls is a common or expectable feature of both maars and large impact craters. The faulting may produce a series of steplike terraces in the crater walls.

(7) The ejecta deposited on the rim of a maar consist both of pieces from the walls of the vent and of new volcanic material, though the new volcanic component may be sparse. Commonly wall rock fragments are present which have come from great depth beneath the crater. Fragments from all sources are generally mixed and scattered through the deposit. Fragments in excess of 3 m in diameter are extremely rare; typical median grain sizes are of the order of 1 cm or less. The ejecta are commonly thinly bedded and, in places, cross bedded.

The ejecta on the rim of an impact crater, on the other hand, except for a minor increment of meteoritic material, are composed solely of rocks excavated from the space occupied by the original crater and the underlying breccia. The fragments are generally stacked approximately in inverted order from their original position before ejection. Thus if the target rocks are initially stratified the ejecta tend to have a mirror stratification. There is no limit to the size of the individual fragments—the larger the crater the larger are the biggest pieces thrown out. An impact crater the size of an ordinary maar may have on the rim blocks more than 30 m across.

(8) The outer slopes of the rim of a maar are typically smooth. Local relief that may be present is due chiefly to irregularities in the pre-existing topography. The outer slopes of the rim of an impact crater, however, are characteristically hummocky. This is one of the most important criteria that can be used at the present time for identification of impact craters on the Moon.

V. Ballistics of Copernicus

Very few of the features useful in distinguishing an impact crater from a solitary maar on the Moon can be seen under the present limitations of telescopic observation. Much discussion on the origin of lunar craters has centred around statistics of size, shape, and distribution of the craters. By their very nature the statistical arguments are inconclusive and do not lead to the determination of the origin of a single crater. The evidence which has been adduced for the impact origin of lunar craters is thus insufficient.

Many lunar craters are larger than terrestrial maars and all the major lunar craters are larger than any known volcanic crater. But Wright (1927, p. 452) has pointed out that the low gravitational potential on the Moon would result in a far wider distribution of volcanic ejecta on the Moon than on the Earth. For the same magma, boiling would also begin at much greater depth on the Moon. These factors might favour the development of larger craters of the maar type on the Moon than on the Earth, though the size of the chain craters suggests that the influence of these factors is not great.

Baldwin (1949) has shown that the distribution of the depth as a function of the diameter of lunar craters is scattered around a curve extrapolated from data on craters produced by detonation of high explosives. The pertinence of this extrapolation is, at best, not clear. The shape and characteristics of a given crater are sensitive to the scaled depth of the charge or to the penetration of the meteorite. Most of the data on the depths of the lunar craters are old visual measurements of Beer and Mädler (1837) and Schmidt (1878), some of which have large errors. The depth–diameter ratios of lunar craters show about the same broad scatter as ratios for terrestrial volcanic craters, as has been pointed out by Green and Poldervaart (1960, pp. 17–18). In the final analysis we should not expect an especially close relation between the depth–diameter ratios of craters produced by high explosives and impact craters. Because a large amount of gas is produced, the crater mechanics of high-explosive detonation are substantially different from the crater mechanics of high-velocity impact.

There is one major feature of lunar craters observable from the Earth, however, that may permit unambiguous discrimination of

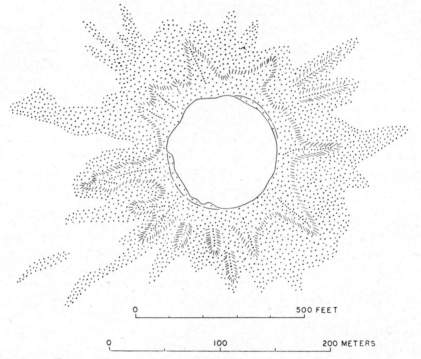

FIG. 9.   Ejection pattern at Teapot Ess nuclear explosion crater.

impact craters from volcanic craters. This feature is the distribution pattern of the ejecta. The ejecta from maars are almost invariably thrown out along high-angle trajectories and shower down in a diffuse, more or less uniform, pattern around the crater. These trajectories are the result of entrainment of the fragments in the volcanic gas jets, which are predominantly vertical. The ejecta from large impact craters, on the other hand, are thrown out along both high and low trajectories.

The ejecta pattern around all known large terrestrial impact craters, beyond the immediate vicinity of the rim, has been destroyed by erosion. The general nature of the ejecta pattern to be expected, however, is revealed by the debris deposited around nuclear explosion craters. Far flung ejecta from nearly every shallow underground explosion crater, whether the explosion is nuclear or chemical, are laid down in distinct streaks or rays (Fig. 9). The position and shape of the rays are governed, in turn, by the pattern in which the ground breaks up as it is engulfed by shock. From the ray pattern and the trajectories of the fragments that form the rays (the exterior ballistics) it is possible to reconstruct the fragmentation pattern of the ground (the interior ballistics of crater formation).

A. RAY PATTERN OF COPERNICUS

Many craters on the Moon are surrounded by a system of rays resembling the ejecta patterns around nuclear and high-explosive craters. The ray pattern of Copernicus is especially suited for detailed analysis. Copernicus is favourably located near the centre of the lunar disk; the ray system surrounding the crater is not only widespread but also extends in large part over dark, relatively smooth maria surfaces. Many of the fine details of the system can, therefore, be deciphered (Fig. 4).

The crater itself is somewhat polygonal in outline. It is about 90 km across, and about 3500 m deep, measured from rim crest to floor. The rim rises about 1000 m above the surrounding lunar surface. The interior walls of the crater comprise a series of terraces, scarps, and irregular sloping surfaces that descend stepwise from the crest to the crater floor, a roughly circular area of generally low relief 50 km in diameter. A few low peaks rise above the floor near the centre of the crater.

The outer slopes of the rim are a scaled up version of the outer slopes of the rims of the Jangle U and Teapot Ess nuclear explosion craters. To a lesser extent the rim of Copernicus resembles the rim of Meteor Crater, Arizona. Rounded hills and ridges are combined in a distinctive hummocky array that consists of humps and swales without obvious alignment near the crest of the rim and passes gradually outward into a system of elongate ridges and depressions with a vague radial alignment. The relief of the ridges gradually diminishes until it is no longer discernible at a distance of about 80 km from the crest of the rim. Beyond this distance the rim passes gradationally into the ray system.

The ray system, which extends over 500 km from Copernicus, consists mainly of arcuate and loop-shaped streaks of highly reflective material on a generally dark part of the Moon's surface. In reflectivity characteristics, the rays are essentially an extension of the crater rim and cannot be sharply delimited from it. The major arcs and loops can be locally resolved into en echelon feather-shaped elements, ranging from 15 to 50 km in length, with the long axes of the elements approximately radially arranged with respect to the centre of the crater.

The pattern of the ray system roughly resembles the pattern of lines of force in a dipole magnetic field in a plane containing the dipole. The "dipole" axis of the Copernican rays trends northwest-southeast. Major arcuate rays curve away from the axis on either side, and a large closed elliptical loop extends southwest toward Mösting.† The ray system has a rough bilateral symmetry about a line coincident with the long axis of this loop, which is perpendicular to the "dipole" axis. Within the main loop extending toward Mösting are subsidiary loops. North of Copernicus are two so-called cross-rays. Both cross-rays consist of a series of vaguely defined loops linked end to end. Near or along the "dipole" axis the rays are mainly straight and radially arranged with respect to Copernicus; in some places, only individual feather-shaped ray elements are present.

Within the rays, and preponderantly near the concave or proximal margins of the major arcs and loops, are numerous elongate depressions or gouges in the lunar surface ranging in length from the limit of telescopic resolution to about 8 km. A peculiar feature of the gouges is their alignment, which is radial from Copernicus in some places but is commonly at an angle to the radial direction. The alignment varies erratically from one gouge to the next. Visible depressions or gouges lie at the proximal ends of many ray elements, though there is not a 1:1 correspondence between gouges and distinguishable ray elements.

It is commonly stated in the literature that there is no determinable relief of the lunar surface associated with the rays. This is not strictly true. At very low angles of illumination the Moon's surface along the rays can be seen to be rough (see Kuiper, 1959a, pp. 289–291). The roughness is due, at least in part, to the presence of the gouges and very low rims around the gouges.

The interpretation is here adopted that lunar rays are thin layers of ejecta from the crater about which they are distributed. This interpretation dates back at least to the 19th century and is probably older. The gouges are interpreted as secondary impact craters formed by individual large fragments or clusters of large fragments ejected from Copernicus. Distinct ray elements are interpreted as splashes of crushed rock derived chiefly from the impact of individual large fragments or clusters of fragments. Partial verification of these interpretations is obtained if a full explanation of the ray pattern and associated gouges can be given in terms of the required ballistics.

† The astronomical convention for east and west on the Moon is opposite to the convention used for the Earth.

In order to reduce the ballistic problem of the Copernican rays to a series of discrete points that can be treated mathematically a compilation has been made of 975 secondary impact craters (Fig. 4). This is a conservative compilation and far from complete. The problem of compilation lies in finding the craters, many of which barely exceed the lower limit of resolution on good lunar photographs, and also in distinguishing secondary impact craters belonging to the ray system of Copernicus from other craters of about the same size that are common in this region. Three criteria were used to identify secondary impact craters, and no craters are included in the compilation that did not satisfy at least two of the criteria: (1) markedly elongated shape, (2) shallow depth compared to most small craters outside of ray system, (3) absence of visible rim or extremely low rim. Most small craters in the region around Copernicus that fit these criteria occur in well-defined rays or ray elements, and nearly all such craters that do not lie in the Copernican rays appear to belong to another system of secondary impact craters around the major crater Eratosthenes. The identification of the secondary impact craters is based mainly on one photograph taken by F. G. Pease at the Mount Wilson Observatory, though other photographs from Mount Wilson and Lick Observatories were used as a check.

Two deficiencies in particular should be noted in the present compilation. First, there is a gap in the area around Eratosthenes where no secondary impact craters have been plotted. This gap is due, not to the absence of craters, but to difficulty in distinguishing with certainty the secondary impact craters belonging to the Copernican ray system from craters produced by fragments ejected from Eratosthenes. All craters in the area around Eratosthenes have, therefore, been omitted. The second deficiency is a relative incompleteness of the compilation on the east side of Copernicus, as revealed by the much lower areal density of craters in that area. This defect is due to the fact that, in the principal photographs used for the compilation, the terminator lay to the west of Copernicus and the small secondary impact craters can be distinguished with much higher confidence on the side nearest the terminator.

Ranges of all the secondary impact craters plotted on Fig. 4 were measured from the Mount Wilson photographs. The distance measured was from the tip of the centremost peak on the floor of Copernicus, which is almost precisely at the centre of the circular crater floor, to the nearest point on the rim of each secondary impact crater. These measurements are strictly preliminary and have significant systematic proportional errors in certain directions. The purpose in making the measurements is simply to find the general nature of the fragmentation pattern that controlled the Copernican rays.

The frequency distribution of the secondary impact craters by range shows a sharp node near 100 miles (about 160 km) from the centre of Copernicus (Fig. 10). At greater distances the frequency drops off

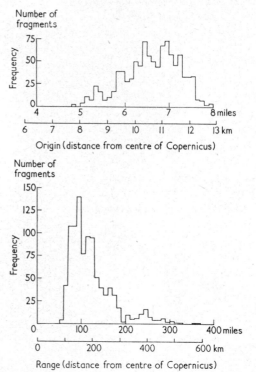

Fig. 10. Frequency distribution of secondary impact crater-forming fragments by range and by calculated original position in Copernicus.

rapidly, but the histogram reveals several subordinate maxima. Toward the outer extremity of the ray system, the frequency drops gradually to zero. Coming closer to Copernicus from the modal distance, the frequency drops off very rapidly, owing to the fact that toward the main crater the gouges in the pre-existing lunar surface tend to be covered up or smothered under an increasingly thick deposit of material making up the crater rim. The smothering effect begins about 80 km from the edge of the crater, and from this point inward there is essentially a continuous blanket of ejecta.

The problem at hand is to deduce the trajectories of the fragments or clusters of fragments that have formed the secondary impact craters and to solve for the original position of these fragments within the crater. We wish to see if the special pattern of the ray system of Copernicus can be related to a relatively simple pattern of breakup of the rocks within the area of the crater and whether this interior ballistic pattern reflects any of the structural features of the Moon's crust that can be seen in the region around Copernicus. If such a relationship can be found, it will strengthen not only the ballistic interpretation of the rays but also the general features of the crater theory upon which the numerical computations are based.

B. CRATERING THEORY AND EXTERIOR BALLISTICS

To find the trajectories for individual fragments ejected from Copernicus we require a theory of cratering that gives the relation between ejection velocities and angle of elevation of ejection. A series of approximations and idealization of the cratering problem will be used to obtain a relation in closed form.

First the shock generated by impact will be treated as having an apparent origin at a point some distance below the surface of the ground, corresponding to the centre of gravity of the energy delivered during penetration of the meteorite. This approximation becomes seriously in error within a narrow cone with an axis coincident with the penetration path, but at angles to the probable penetration path that are of interest in explaining the observable features of the Copernican rays the approximation is held to be valid within the limits of variation introduced by inhomogeneities of the surface of the Moon. The exterior ballistics can then be expressed in terms of the geometrical parameters shown on the following diagram, Fig. 11.

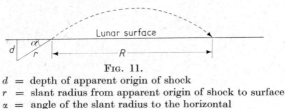

FIG. 11.

d = depth of apparent origin of shock
r = slant radius from apparent origin of shock to surface
α = angle of the slant radius to the horizontal
R = range of trajectory of ejected fragment

From the Rankine-Hugoniot conditions we have the following relations across the shock front:

$$U\rho_0 = (U-\mu)\rho, \qquad \text{(conservation of mass)} \qquad (1)$$

$$P = \rho_0 U\mu, \qquad \text{(conservation of momentum)} \quad (2)$$

$$e = (1/\rho_0 - 1/\rho)P/2, \text{(conservation of energy)} \qquad (3)$$

where U is the shock velocity, μ is the particle velocity behind the shock front, ρ_0 is the initial density of the lunar crust, ρ is the density behind the shock front, P is the pressure increment across the shock front, and e is the internal energy increment across the shock front. Combining equations (1), (2), and (3) we have

$$e = (\tfrac{1}{2})\mu^2. \tag{4}$$

Now we shall make an approximation employed successfully by Griggs and Teller (1956, pp. 8–9) to predict shock arrival times in the Jangle U underground explosion in the region of strong shock,

$$E = 2eM, \tag{5}$$

where E is the total shock energy and M is the mass engulfed by shock. This approximation can be derived by assuming that the energy is uniformly distributed in the material behind the shock. Such a distribution is impossible, but the relation gives a fair approximation for the rates of decay of energy, pressure, and shock and particle velocities for shock propagation in rock and leads to a cube root scaling law for the crater diameters. E can be written as

$$E = (\tfrac{1}{2})mv^2, \tag{6}$$

where m is the mass of the meteorite or impacting bolide and v is its velocity. Combining (4), (5), and (6) we have

$$\frac{v^2}{\mu^2} = \frac{2M}{m}. \tag{7}$$

Partly for algebraic simplicity M will be taken as

$$M = (4/3)\pi r^3 \rho_r, \tag{8}$$

where ρ_r is the initial density of the lunar crustal material. This relation preserves cube-root scaling and will minimize the estimate of v. We also may write

$$m = (4/3)\pi x^3 \rho_m, \tag{9}$$

where x is the radius of the bolide, ρ_m its density, and

$$r = \frac{d}{\sin \alpha}. \tag{10}$$

Combining (7), (8), (9), and (10) we have

$$v = \mu \sqrt{\frac{2\rho_r}{\rho_m}} \cdot \frac{1}{\sin^{3/2}\alpha} \left(\frac{d}{x}\right)^{3/2}. \tag{11}$$

For an elastic wave the particle velocity for a point on the surface would be $2\mu \sin \alpha$, but the velocity of a large fragment ejected from a rock surface by shock will be close to μ. This means simply that the kinetic energy imparted by the rarefaction wave reflected from the ground surface is minor, and that the angle of ejection of a fragment from the horizontal lunar surface would be close to α. These relations are consistent with experimental results that have been obtained from large underground explosions.

In order to evaluate equation (11) numerically we must make some assumptions about $\rho_r \rho_m$ and d/x, and an accessory relationship is required relating μ and α. Some minimum requirements of this accessory relationship can be drawn from the ray system of Copernicus.

First, from (4), (5), and (8) we have

$$\mu = \sqrt{\frac{3E}{4\pi\rho_r r^3}}. \tag{12}$$

For a first approximation let us ignore radial variation in the lunar gravitational potential and the departure of the lunar surface from a sphere, and employ the simple classical ballistic formula

$$R = \frac{\mu^2 \sin 2\alpha}{g}, \tag{13}$$

where g is the gravitational acceleration at the surface of the Moon (167 cm/sec^2). We will return to a more precise treatment of the trajectory later. Substituting (10) and (12) into equation (13) we have

$$R = \frac{3E \sin^3\alpha \sin 2\alpha}{4\pi\rho_r d^3 g}, \tag{14}$$

where

$$\frac{3E}{4\pi\rho_r d^3 g} = K \text{ (a constant)}.$$

Now the greatest distance that the Copernican rays can be traced is a little more than 500 km. In order to set a minimum value for v, let us suppose that this distance actually represents the greatest range of fragments. This supposition is demonstrably false, but we will examine it in more detail later. Under this supposition there are two possible trajectories for any range less than the maximum: one for ejection angles higher than the ejection angle for the maximum range, and one for lower ejection angles. For the maximum range we have

$$\frac{dR}{d\alpha} = K(\cos\alpha 4 \sin^3\alpha \cos \alpha - \sin^4\alpha \sin \alpha) = 0, \tag{15}$$

$$\cos \alpha_{max} = \sqrt{1/5}, \quad \alpha_{max} = 63°26'. \qquad (16)$$

Substituting the value of α obtained in (16) and $R = 500$ km into equation (13)

$$\mu = \sqrt{\frac{167 \times 5 \times 10^7}{0.80}} \text{cm/sec} = 1.02 \text{ km/sec}. \qquad (17)$$

We are now in a position to evaluate minimum values of v from equation (11). For Meteor Crater, Arizona, a value of d/x of about 8 to 10 was found for $\rho_r/\rho_m = \frac{1}{3}$ and $v = 15$ km/sec (Shoemaker, 1960a, p. 430). For the surface of the Moon and likely compositions of the impacting bolide, values of ρ_r/ρ_m between $\frac{1}{2}$ and 1 are more probable. For these higher ratios of the densities lower values of d/x may be anticipated for the same impact velocities. Let us adopt two pairs of values for numerical evaluation (a) $\rho_r/\rho_m = \frac{1}{2}$, $d/x = 4$; and (b) $\rho_r/\rho_m = 1$, $d/x = 2$. For the velocities that are derived from equation (11), these pairs of values are realistic for the case of Copernicus. Substituting pair (a) in (11)

$$(a) \qquad v = \frac{1.02 \times 8}{0.846} \text{km/sec} = 9.6 \text{ km/sec} \qquad (18)$$

and

$$(b) \qquad v = \frac{1.02 \times 1.414 \times 2.83}{0.846} = 4.8 \text{ km/sec}. \qquad (19)$$

The interesting fact about these results is that the cratering and ballistic theory presented here leads to the conclusion that the bolide that formed Copernicus was probably an independent member of the solar system, and not a planetesimal or moonlet orbiting around the Earth (cf. Kuiper, 1954, pp. 1108–1111). The value 4·8 km/sec for the impact velocity obtained in (19) is a minimum.

It may be noticed from (14) that the range, as defined, can be made independent of the total energy E and the size of the crater, if the linear dimensions of the shock scale as the cube root of the energy. Thus we would expect practically just as long trajectories from small craters formed by small bolides as from large craters formed by large bolides if the impact velocities are similar. But, in point of fact, there is a rough correlation between size of crater and length of observable rays on the Moon. This can be interpreted to mean that the rays are visible only to the point where the areal density of ejected material is so sparse that it can no longer be photographed or seen, and smaller craters have shorter observable rays because the quantity of ejected debris is less. When examined closely, it may be seen that the rays die out gradually. There is rarely any suggestion of increase in ray density near the end, such as would be predicted by the maximum range hypothesis. Thus the Copernican rays are formed only by material ejected at low angles and the material ejected at high angles went into escape trajectories.

Employing equation (14) the total range R_T of a fragment from the epicentre of the shock may be written as

$$R_T = K \sin^3\alpha \sin 2\alpha + \frac{d}{\tan \alpha}. \tag{20}$$

From the form of equation (20) it may be seen that the total range, as defined, must pass through a minimum. For a large crater this minimum will be slightly less than the radius of the initial crater produced by ejection of material. At decreasing angles of α, sufficiently low that the total range starts to rise due to rapid increase of the second term, pieces will no longer be thrown out of the crater but will be simply displaced a short distance laterally. A *Schollen- und Schuppen-Zone* or series of thrust sheets may be formed at angles of α where the total range passes through the minimum. In a large crater the final radius of the crater is increased by slumping.

From equation (12) we may write

$$\mu_2{}^2 = \frac{\sin^3\alpha_2}{\sin^3\alpha_1}\mu_1{}^2, \tag{21}$$

Thus, if d and any pair of values of μ and α are specified, we may draw a curve for R_T. By successive approximation it may be found that an ejection velocity of $0\cdot4$ km/sec for an ejection angle of $12°$ will lead to the formation of a crater of the lateral dimensions of Copernicus if the centre of gravity of the energy released is at $3\cdot2$ km (2 miles) depth. The crater is taken as having been enlarged 25 km by slumping, as measured by the cumulative width of the terraces on the crater walls. From equation (11) the impact velocity is found to be 17 km/sec. At this velocity the centre of gravity of the energy released will be about equal to the linear dimensions of the bolide if the bolide is composed of the same material as the surface of the Moon (calculated from methods given by Shoemaker, 1960a). Adopting $d/x = 2$ and a density of 3 for the impacting bolide, the kinetic energy is found to be $7\cdot5 \times 10^{28}$ ergs or $1\cdot8 \times 10^9$ kilotons TNT equivalent. This may be compared with $1\cdot2$ kilotons for the Jangle U experiment; the cube root of the ratio of the energies is $1\cdot14 \times 10^3$. As the ratio of the diameters of the two craters is $1\cdot1 \times 10^3$, the crater theory employed here gives good

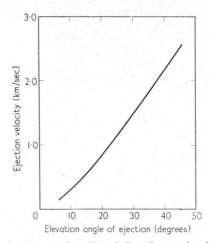

FIG. 12. Ejection velocity as a function of elevation angle of ejection for Copernicus.

agreement with the empirical cube-root scaling law for the diameters of nuclear craters (Glasstone, 1957, p. 198). It should be noted that the scaled depth for the Jangle U shot is slightly greater than that calculated for Copernicus.

The precise equation for the range of the trajectory on a spherical body can be written in the form

$$\phi = \tan^{-1}\frac{\mu^2 \sin \alpha \cos \alpha}{lg - \mu^2 \cos^2\alpha}, \tag{22}$$

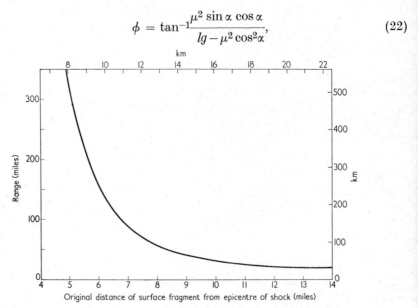

FIG. 13. Range of fragments as a function of original position in crater (Copernicus).

where ϕ is half the angular distance of travel along the surface and l is the radius of the sphere (Giamboni, 1959). For ranges up to 100 km, or about 3° on the lunar surface, the error of equation (13) is small.

Given $\mu = 0.4$ km/sec at 12° ejection angle, the ejection velocity may be specified for all ejection angles from equation (20) (see Fig. 12). From equation (22) and the tangent of α, the range of individual fragments initially at the surface may then be expressed as a function of the distance of these fragments from the epicentre of the shock (Fig. 13).

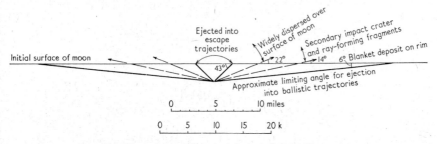

FIG. 14.   Provenance of material ejected from Copernicus.

Fragments ejected at angles ranging from about 6° to 14° form the continuous ejecta blanket mantling the rim of Copernicus. The ejected fragments follow a series of overarching trajectories, as required to form the inverted stratigraphy of the rim at Meteor Crater, Arizona. Fragments ejected at angles ranging from about 14° to about 22° form secondary impact craters (the gouges) and the rays (Fig. 14). Between ejection angles of 22° and 43° the smaller volume of material ejected is so widely scattered over the surface of the Moon that it is lost. Above 43° the fragments are ejected into escape trajectories.

C. INTERIOR BALLISTICS

The formation of rays depends upon a departure from the idealized crater model in the real case. Fragments are not ejected precisely along the radii from the apparent shock origin, but are thrown out in distinct clusters or clots. The shape and orientation of these clots as they are first formed in the crater can be found by using the theoretical trajectories to replace the fragments in their approximate original positions.

In order to plot positions within Copernicus for the approximate original loci of the fragments that produced the secondary impact craters, the provisional hypothesis is made that each secondary impact crater was formed by one main fragment and that the fragments all came from a near surface layer. By use of the curve on Fig. 13 all the fragments are then transposed back into Copernicus along radii from the central point, which is taken as the shock epicentre. In the provisional transposition, the fragments are all found to originate from a circular belt around the shock epicentre (Fig. 15) with an inside radius

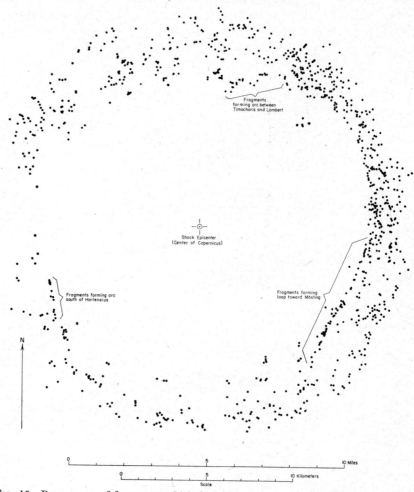

FIG. 15. Provenance of fragments which formed the secondary impact craters in the ray system of Copernicus.

just under 8 km (5 miles) and an outside diameter of 13 km (8 miles). The farthest thrown fragments are derived from the inner margin of the belt.

The large loop-shaped ray extending toward Mösting is found to have originated from a linear cluster of fragments about 7 km long within Copernicus. The trend of this cluster is essentially parallel with the "dipole" axis of the whole ray system. It is also parallel with a northwest-trending linear system of prominent ridges in the Carpathian Mountains and with the dominant trend of linear topographic features in the general vicinity of Copernicus (Fig. 6). These ridges and linear features are structural elements of the lunar crust that at least in part clearly predate the formation of Copernicus, as will be shown in a later section. The fragmentation pattern thus appears to have been influenced by pre-existing lines of weakness; individual clots of fragments evidently pulled apart along faults and fractures already present in the lunar crust. The linear cluster of fragments that formed the loop-shaped ray toward Mösting is interpreted as a pre-existing structural block that maintained its identity momentarily as it was engulfed by shock. In this way the major features of the ray pattern, the "dipole" axis and axis of symmetry, are controlled by the dominant structural grain of the lunar crust in the vicinity of Copernicus.

Subordinate structural trends also influenced the ray pattern. A prominent arc-like ray that curves around just north of Hortensius is derived from a linear cluster of fragments parallel with a subordinate set of north-northwest trending linear features north of Copernicus and a north-northwest trending set of terraces on the eastern crater wall (Fig. 6). Other linear clusters are also present in the interior ballistic pattern which are parallel with other linear structures in the crater wall and the region around Copernicus.

The significance of these results is that a simple genetic relationship between the main features of the Copernican ray pattern and other observable features of the lunar crust is found by use of the idealized theory of crater formation. The theory accounts quantitatively for both the crater dimensions and the distribution of ejecta. The transposition of rays into linear fragment clusters, however, is not a sensitive test of precision of the computed trajectories. The main features of the interior ballistic pattern would not be significantly changed by minor modification of the relation between the angle of elevation and ejection velocity that was derived from a series of approximations.

We may return now to examine the provisional hypothesis that all the secondary impact crater-forming fragments were derived from a near-surface layer. Material derived from deep positions close to the origin of the shock will be ejected at the same angles as fragments close to the surface. As the near-surface fragments are farthest from the shock origin along any given slant radius and therefore experienced the lowest peak shock pressure, it is reasonable to expect the largest

z

fragments to have come from near the surface. The question is whether any fragments or clusters of fragments large enough to form secondary impact craters may have originated at significant depth beneath the surface. The frequency distribution of the secondary impact crater-forming fragments and the reconstructed internal ballistic pattern provides some evidence bearing on this question.

The radial frequency distribution of fragments, after transposition into the crater, shows a series of pronounced maxima and minima that correspond to maxima and minima in the original range frequency distribution of the secondary impact craters (Fig. 10). This distribution has been broken down into three sectors around Copernicus (Fig. 16), and the individual maxima may then be identified with major rays or belts of secondary impact craters. In nearly all cases it is found that a maximum in one sector coincides fairly closely in radial position with a maximum in one of the other sectors. Such a coincidence suggests that the interior fragmentation pattern has elements of concentric symmetry around the shock epicentre. A concentric pattern would be found if the lunar crust were layered and clusters of fragments were formed by the separation or pulling apart of layers. This implies that clusters which are separated radially in the fragmentation pattern as plotted on Fig. 15 may actually have been separated vertically in the crater.

Some features of the ray pattern seem easiest to explain by a combination of vertical and horizontal separation of fragment clusters. The very long ray trending north between Timocharis and Lambert, for example, is intersected or joined by two east-west trending cross-rays, one that crosses north of Pytheas, and one that runs just north of Turner. The greatest density of visible secondary impact craters along the north-south ray occurs near the intersections. Such relations could be explained as follows: The north-trending ray was formed by an elongate cluster of fragments with the approximate shape and orientation shown on Fig. 15, but one end of the cluster originally lay at a deeper level than the other in the lunar crust and more than two separable layers were included in the cluster. The uneven distribution of secondary impact craters along the ray would be due to the tendency of the fragments of each layer to hang together momentarily on ejection. This interpretation implies that the fragments of the Turner cross-ray are derived from a different layer than those of the Pytheas cross-ray.

It is not immediately evident which of the two cross-rays, in this interpretation, would represent the deeper layer. Shock propagation theory suggests that, along a given slant radius, the upper layer should have the higher ejection velocity, in which case the Pytheas cross-ray would represent the higher layer. Empirical evidence from high-explosives cratering experiments, on the other hand, suggests that along certain slant radii fragments from the deeper layer would go farther (Sakharov and others, 1959). The high explosives data may

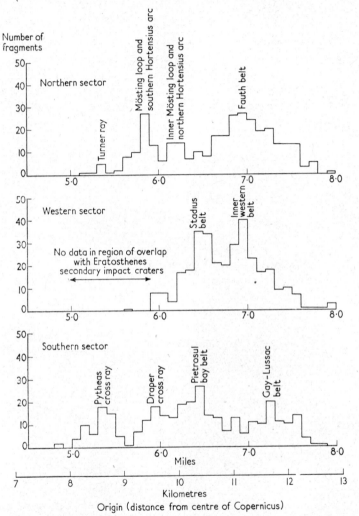

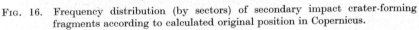

FIG. 16. Frequency distribution (by sectors) of secondary impact crater-forming fragments according to calculated original position in Copernicus.

not be applicable because the fragments are ejected more by the impulse derived from expansion of the explosion gases than by the shock.

Keeping in mind the factors that may influence fragmentation, we may examine the question of the actual size of the fragments that formed the secondary impact craters. A total of at least 975 fragments are derived from an annular segment of the lunar crust with an area of about 330 km², and an unknown depth. If the fragments are assumed to be of equidimensional shape and all derived from one layer, the maximum mean diameter of the fragments would be about 600 m. If the depth from which the large fragments are derived were about three times the mean diameter of the fragments, then the maximum mean diameter would be closer to 1 km. But probably very few, if any, of the fragments that formed the secondary impact craters were as much as a kilometer across. In the first place, a mean diameter of a little less than 1 km would require that essentially all the material ejected at ray-forming angles (Fig. 14) was in large fragments, whereas empirical data on the size frequency distribution of fragments produced by shock shows that about 50% of the material will be in size classes more than an order of magnitude smaller than the maximum size. Secondly, there is a much larger number of secondary impact craters in the visible size range than has actually been compiled. A better guide to the actual size of the fragments is probably provided by the length of cluster of fragments that was ejected towards Mösting to form the loop-shaped ray. At least 50 fragments were derived from a cluster which was only 7 km long. The mean size of the fragments that formed the visible secondary impact craters in the loop-shaped ray was probably in the range of 100 to 200 m in diameter.

These results have an immediate bearing on the origin of the elongate secondary impact craters. Many of the elongate secondary impact craters are oriented at angles to the radial direction from Copernicus and thus cannot be attributed simply to plowing or skidding of the low-angle missile on the lunar surface. Arbitrarily oriented craters could be formed by arbitrarily oriented elongate fragments, but the length required for the fragments is unreasonably great, for some of the secondary impact craters are more than 5 km long. All of the markedly elongate craters are, therefore, probably compound craters formed by the impact of two or more fragments travelling closely together. All gradations can be found, especially along the inner margin of the ray system between short chains of secondary impact craters and compound craters in which the partially merged components can still be recognized. The formation of these chains and compound craters is simply a smaller scale manifestation of the phenomenon of clustering of fragments which is responsible for the broad scale pattern of the rays. Ejection of fragments from large primary impact craters thus provides another mechanism in addition to volcanism by which chains of small craters can be formed on the Moon.

D. Angle of Impact

It is appropriate at this point to return to some questions that were set aside in the discussion of the mechanics of impact and to review the effects of variation of angle of impact, in particular, on the distribution of ejecta.

By ignoring the gravitational attraction of the Moon, Gilbert (1893, pp. 263 and 268) showed that the frequency function dP for the zenith angle of incidence i for bodies approaching from random directions is

$$dP = 2 \sin i \cos i \, di = 2 \sin 2i \, di.$$

The angle of incidence of maximum frequency would therefore be 45°. It may readily be shown that this result is more general, and still applies even when the gravitational attraction of the Moon is taken into account.† In the case of craters formed by the impact of asteroids,

† The case of impact on a massless sphere can be stated as follows. Consider a meteoroid approaching a sphere of radius r from a random direction. Within a circle of the radius of the sphere all points of intersection of the path of the meteoroid with a plane perpendicular to the path are equally probable, and the total probability P is given by

$$P = \pi r^2 = 1.$$

The differential probability or frequency with which the meteoroid will pass through a point at a distance x from the centre of this circle, where $0 \leqslant x \leqslant r$, is

$$dP = 2\pi x dx,$$

and

$$x = r \sin i,$$

where i is the zenith angle of incidence with the sphere (Fig. 17(b)). As

$$dx = r \cos i \, di,$$

then

$$dP = 2\pi r \sin i \, r \cos i \, di = 2\pi r^2 \sin 2i \, di = \sin 2i \, di.$$

In the case of a meteoroid approaching a gravitating body (a homogeneous sphere with mass) from a random direction, the total probability P that the meteoroid intersects a plane perpendicular to the path of the meteoroid within the capture cross-section of radius R is

$$P = \pi R^2 = 1,$$

and the differential probability with which the meteoroid will pass through a point at a distance x from the centre of the capture cross-section, where $0 \leqslant x \leqslant R$, is

$$dP = 2\pi x dx.$$

From conservation of angular momentum we have

$$mx V_\infty = mr V_n,$$

Footnote continued on pp. 342 and 343.

as is indicated for Copernicus by the calculated impact velocity, we will be most frequently concerned with angles of incidence around 45° and instances of vertical incidence have a vanishing probability of occurrence. It should be noticed that very low angles of impact may also be expected to have been of infrequent occurrence.

where m is the mass of the meteoroid, V_∞ is the velocity of the meteoroid at infinite distance from the sphere, V_n is the tangential component of the velocity of the meteoroid at the moment of impact and r is the radius of the sphere (Fig. 17(a)). If V_r is the

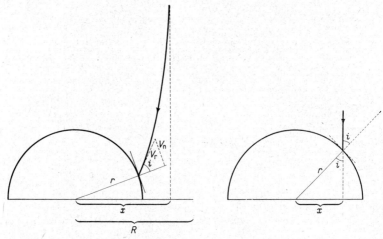

(a) Homogeneous sphere with mass   (b) Massless sphere

FIG. 17 (a) and (b). Diagrams illustrating angle of incidence of bodies approaching a sphere from a random direction.

velocity of the meteoroid at the moment of impact and i the zenith angle of incidence,

$$V_n = \sin i \, V_r,$$

$$x = \frac{r V_r \sin i}{V_\infty},$$

$$dx = \frac{r V_r \cos i \, di}{V_\infty},$$

and

$$dP = 2\pi \left(\frac{r V_r \sin i}{V_\infty} \right) \left(\frac{r V_r \cos i \, di}{V_\infty} \right) = \frac{\pi r^2 V_r^2}{V_\infty^2} \sin 2i \, di.$$

But at

$$\sin i = 1, \, x = R,$$

and thus

$$R = \frac{r V_r}{V_\infty}.$$

Small scale hypervelocity experiments show that in the vertical impact of a sphere on a plane surface a small amount of material is ejected, in the beginning stages of penetration, at very flat angles to the surface at velocities exceeding the impact velocity (Charters, 1960). This high speed ejection is evidently due to a jetting effect similar to that produced in the collapse of wedge-shaped liners of shaped charges (Birkhoff et al., 1948). As the penetration proceeds, larger amounts of material are ejected at progressively steeper angles and lower velocities, and in the case of impact into metals the bulk of the material is ejected at angles ranging from about 45° to 65° from the horizontal. This ejection occurs mainly under conditions of hydrodynamic flow; a similar flow regime and mechanics of ejection should prevail for the initial stages of penetration of a large meteorite or asteroid into a rock surface. It is only during the later stages of penetration and cratering that the angle of ejection should decline again as the crater opens up, as indicated in the analysis presented in the preceding pages. At a certain stage of penetration the trend of variation in the angle of ejection is reversed, and there should remain a conical region around the path of penetration, an excluded or forbidden region, through which no fragments may be expected to be ejected.

A pronounced effect on the ray pattern around an impact crater should be found when the zenith angle of incidence is so high that one side of the excluded region becomes parallel or nearly parallel with the Moon's surface. An excluded area for rays would then be expected in the ray pattern around the crater. The ray pattern of Proclus, which has an area with no rays through an arc of about 150° on the southeast side of the crater, is perhaps an example of an ejecta pattern produced by impact at a very high zenith angle. The effect of impact approaching the limiting case of grazing incidence may be illustrated by the highly elliptical crater Pickering, which has just two prominent nearly parallel rays, one extending from each side of the crater in a direction parallel with the long axis of the ellipse. At angles of incidence where the sum of the zenith angle and half the apex angle of the conical excluded region are somewhat less than 90° the ray pattern would probably be asymmetrical, the longest rays extending in the direction

---

Therefore

$$\frac{\pi r^2 V_r{}^2}{V_\infty{}^2} = 1,$$

and

$$dP = \sin 2i \, di.$$

in which the impacting body is travelling and the shortest rays in the opposite direction. The ray pattern of Tycho may illustrate this effect.

At the modal angle of impact (45°) the effect of the direction of approach of the bolide on the ray pattern probably becomes negligible. The ejecta most strongly influenced by the asymmetrical flow produced by the oblique penetration are thrown out in escape trajectories. Ray-forming fragments are ejected at greater distances from the path of penetration where the configuration of the shock becomes more nearly symmetrical. The most that can be said from a ray pattern in which the rays extend about equally far in all directions, as in the case of Copernicus, is that the zenith angle of impact was probably not unusually high. Probably the principal effect of increase in the zenith angle of impact is simply to reduce the depth of the apparent origin of the shock.

VI. History of the Copernicus Region

Conclusions as to the origin of Copernicus have wide application, because Copernicus is a member of a large class of lunar craters characterized by a number of distinctive features. The principal feature that unites members of this class is the topography of the rim. The hummocky rim of Copernicus is closely simulated many times over at other craters of similar and smaller size. In general, the ratio of the width of the hummocky terrain to the diameter of the crater decreases with decreasing size of the crater. Around some craters almost all the rim terrain is made up of a nearly random arrangement of hummocks typical of the rim crest at Copernicus; around others the rim is marked by a strong radial or subradial pattern of low ridges typical of the peripheral zone of the rim of Copernicus. Visible gouges or secondary impact craters surround the rims of all such craters approaching Copernicus in size. The interior walls of these craters are almost invariably terraced, the floors are irregular, and nearly all have a central peak or peaks.

Many craters with this group of characteristics are the foci of prominent ray patterns, but many others are entirely unaccompanied by rays. Eratosthenes (Fig. 4) is a good example of a crater that exhibits all the principal topographic features of Copernicus and is surrounded by a well-developed pattern of gouges but lacks rays. Where it is not overlapped by Copernican rays, the rim and floor of Eratosthenes have relatively low reflectivity.

All gradations may be observed in the brightness of the rim and associated rays of craters of the Copernicus type. Copernicus, Aristillus, and Theophilus illustrate a sequence of craters accompanied by rays ranging from bright to faint. The rays of Aristillus are plainly visible but not as bright as those of Copernicus; the rays of Theophilus are very faint, though its secondary impact craters are widely distributed and as numerous as those of Copernicus. The reflectivity of the rim of Theophilus approaches that of Eratosthenes. It is highly probable that this sequence is one of increasing age of the craters. Wherever a rayless crater of the Copernicus type or a crater with very faint rays occurs in an area with bright rays from some other crater, the bright ray pattern is in all cases superimposed on the darker crater or faint ray pattern; in no instance is a darker ray pattern or rim deposit of a crater of the Copernicus type superimposed on a bright ray. Some process or combination of processes is evidently at work on the lunar surface that causes fading of the rays and other parts of the Moon's surface with high reflectivity. Most of the brightest parts of the Moon's surface are the steepest slopes, where fresh material might be continually exposed by mass movement. Darkening of the surficial materials by radiation damage and mixing of the thin layer of ray material with underlying dark material by micrometeorite bombardment are processes that might well contribute to ray fading.

It is concluded that all craters that exhibit the general topographic features of Copernicus, particularly the hummocky rim and surrounding gouges, are of impact origin.

Other craters of much larger and much smaller size are probably of impact origin as well. Kuiper (1959b, p. 1717) has drawn attention to a class of small craters of conical shape or the shape of a truncated cone which he compares with the South African kimberlite pipes, a comparison first made by Eduard Suess (1909, p. 596; 1895, pp. 46–47). An example of such a crater is Hortensius (Fig. 4). Most of these craters have low or inconspicuous rims. The steep inner walls are generally very bright, and some, but not all, have associated rays. It must be borne in mind that the interior and exterior ballistics of impact craters obey different scaling laws and small impact craters on the Moon may have very low rims owing to the wide distribution of the small amount of material ejected. The similarity of the rim of Copernicus to the rims of the much smaller Arizona Meteor Crater and the nuclear explosion craters is partly fortuitous, and is a consequence of the difference in the gravitational potential at the surface of the Moon and Earth which tends to compensate for the difference in size. The presence of rays around some of the conical craters indicates that most craters in this class are probably of impact origin.

At the other extreme of size, the extent of the continuous ejecta deposit of the rim around a very large impact crater tends to be greater in proportion to the diameter of the crater than in the case of Copernicus. As first pointed out by Gilbert (1893, pp. 275–279) Mare Imbrium is partially encompassed by what appears to be an immense sheet of ejecta that extends over a substantial fraction of the visible surface of the Moon. The topography of this sheet is distinctively hummocky in detail, but it is draped over diverse topographic features, some of great size. Mare Imbrium, the apparent source of this sheet of ejecta, or a part of the Mare, evidently represents the largest crater of impact origin on the Moon.

A. STRATIGRAPHY OF THE COPERNICUS REGION

In the Copernicus region the surface of the Moon is built up mainly of an overlapping series of deposits of ejecta. These deposits, together with layers of material of probable volcanic origin, constitute a stratigraphic succession from which the relative sequence of events in the history of this region can be determined. The deposits have been grouped into five stratigraphic systems: (1) pre-Imbrian, (2) Imbrian, (3) Procellarian, (4) Eratosthenian, and (5) Copernican, which correspond to five intervals of time (Fig. 6).

The Imbrian system: the stratigraphically lowest and oldest system that is widely exposed in the Copernicus region, is made up mainly of the deposit of ejecta derived from the region of Mare Imbrium. The deposit is characterized by a gently rolling "pimply" and "pockmarked" topography that has a shagreen appearance at certain phases. Locally it exhibits a peculiar dark faintly greenish colouration. It has been deposited on a surface of considerable relief that includes old craters and, in the Carpathian Mountains, a series of linear ridges and valleys. The Imbrian ejecta tends to fill in the old craters and valleys and is probably several thousand feet thick where it fills some of these pre-existing depressions, but it is evidently thin where it is draped across the crests of old crater rims and certain high ridges, as indicated by the relative sharpness of form of these features. Some materials of pre-Imbrian age may be locally exposed in areas indicated on Fig. 6.

Material which underlies the relatively smooth dark floors of the Oceanus Procellarum, Mare Imbrium, and Sinus Aestuum rests stratigraphically on the Imbrian system. This material, together with the domes resembling basaltic shield volcanoes, make up the Procellarian system. In reflectivity, the mare floors are indistinguishable from the volcano-shaped domes, and the mare material is probably composed chiefly of dark volcanic flows, though, except for the domes, typical volcanic features are not readily visible on the maria.

The rim deposits of rayless craters of the Copernicus type are superimposed upon the Imbrian and Procellarian systems. The most extensive of these deposits in the Copernicus region are associated with the craters Eratosthenes, Reinhold, and Landsberg; the whole group of these deposits is taken as the Eratosthenian system. The material making up the narrow rims of rayless conical and truncated cone-shaped craters of the Hortensius type is also included in the Eratosthenian system. These various craters probably have a wide range in age, but all are post-Imbrian and the rim deposits of most rest on the Procellarian. Nearly all are overlapped by Copernican rays.

The Copernican system includes the rays and ejecta deposits of Copernicus and several smaller ray craters, notably Hortensius and a bright ray crater east of Gambart. Among the stratigraphically highest units in the region are the rim deposits of the dark halo craters, which are superposed on the ejecta and rays of Copernicus. These have also been included in the Copernican system.

B. Correlation of the Lunar and Geologic Time Scales

An approximate idea of the correlation of the lunar stratigraphy and the lunar time scale used here with the geologic time scale may be obtained by comparison of the areal density of impact structures and comparison of rates of impact. The areal density of craters interpreted to be of primary impact origin that are superposed on the Procellarian has been examined by R. J. Hackman of the U.S. Geological Survey. He finds that primary impact craters of Eratosthenian and Copernican age that are large enough to be distinguished on photographs (minimum diameter slightly less than one mile) range in density from about $0 \cdot 24$ per $1000 \, km^2$ in Mare Crisium to about $0 \cdot 53$ per $1000 \, km^2$ in Mare Nubium, and average about $0 \cdot 45$ per $1000 \, km^2$ for all the readily visible mare surfaces. If we suppose the end of Procellarian time to have been very early in Earth–Moon history, say $4 \cdot 5$ billion years ago (Patterson, Tilton, and Inghram, 1955), then the mean rate of impact since that time of objects large enough to form craters that may be distinguished photographically is about $0 \cdot 1$ per $1000 \, km^2$ per billion years. The rate of impact of objects large enough to form craters 3 km in diameter would be about $0 \cdot 05$ per $1000 \, km^2$ per billion years.

This rate may be compared with that calculated from the areal density of known probable impact structures (structures of the Sierra Madera type) of about $0 \cdot 01$ per $1000 \, km^2$ in the central United States, in an area that is geologically favourable for the recognition of impact structures. Most of these structures probably correspond to craters about 3 km in diameter or larger. The average age of the beds exposed in this area is of the order of 300 million years. The rate of impact of objects large enough to form the known structures of the Sierra Madera type in this area is therefore about 0·04 per 1000 km^2 per billion years. This figure is likely to be a minimum because of incompleteness of detailed geologic information on this region and because of the loss from the geologic record of impact events due to erosion. Account must also be taken of the fact that the rate of impact on the Earth should be higher than on the Moon because of the Earth's greater gravitational attraction. For objects entering the Earth's atmosphere at 15 km/sec, the rate of impact on the Earth would be about 2·2 times greater than on the Moon, if the direction of approach were truly random. Several other corrections must be applied, which will be the subject of a separate paper.

When all the factors and uncertainties are considered, the data appear consistent with the hypothesis that the end of Procellarian time is not far removed from the beginning of geologic time and that the rate of impact has been fairly constant since Procellarian time. This hypothesis is in accord with the concept that the objects which formed the Eratosthenian and Copernican impact craters were asteroids, as suggested by the solution for the impact velocity for the bolide which formed Copernicus. It is also possible that some craters may have been formed by the impact of comets.

If the rate of impact has remained steady since the end of the Procellarian (the beginning of the Eratosthenian) we may estimate the age of Copernicus. There are two recognizable craters of probable primary impact origin superimposed on the crater and ejecta rim of Copernicus, an area of about 50,000 km^2. At a rate of 0·1 craters per 1000 km^2 per billion years, this would correspond to an age of about half a billion years for Copernicus. In terms of the geologic time scale this would place Copernicus approximately in the early Paleozoic. The fading of the rays is apparently a slow process. As the rays of Copernicus are toward the brighter end of the range of brightness, the beginning of Copernican time (the age of the faintest rays) is probably well back in Precambrian. On the basis of the relative number of craters, it appears likely that Eratosthenian time covers somewhat more than half of all lunar history.

C. Structure and Structural History of the Copernicus Region

The structure of the Copernicus region comprises old pre-Imbrium structures, now buried under Imbrian and later strata, folds in the Procellarian, rills and structures of probable volcanic origin of Procellarian or later age, and structures associated with individual craters of the Copernicus and Hortensius type of Eratosthenian and Copernican age.

Pre-Imbrian structures are reflected by the prominent linear ridge and valley topography of the Carpathian Mountains. This topography is a small part of the extensive pattern of linear features termed Imbrian Sculpture by Gilbert (1893, pp. 275–282), the origin of which has been discussed extensively in recent years (Baldwin, 1949, pp. 201–212; Urey, 1951, pp. 220–228; von Bülow, 1957; Kuiper, 1959a, p. 310). Trenches, ridges, and scarps in this pattern tend to be approximately aligned along a series of great circles that intersect in the northern part of the Mare Imbrium. The ridges and troughs of the Carpathians are layered over by rocks of the Imbrian system and plunge beneath the Procellarian along the northern margin of Mare Imbrium. Individual ridges that rise above the level of the surrounding Imbrian ejecta are the prominent features of the Carpathians. It is possible that some displacement has occurred along some of these ridges since the Imbrian system was deposited, but there is no apparent displacement of the Procellarian where it overlaps the ridges and valleys along a series of promontories and bays that constitute the mountain front.

To get the full evidence on the origin of the Imbrian sculpture it is necessary to go far beyond the Copernicus region. Gilbert interpreted the large troughs as furrows, plowed by low-angle ejecta; Suess (1895, pp. 38–39) advanced the explanation that they were fissures or graben. Aside from the fact that the trajectories and strength of the ejecta required for the plowing of such furrows are improbable, offsets in the walls of the troughs and ridges show that they are more likely to be fault scarps. It appears highly probable that the Imbrian sculpture is the topographic expression of a radiating set of normal faults that were formed during dilation of the lunar crust by divergent flow behind the shock front generated by the impact that produced the Imbrian ejecta. The ridges of the Carpathians are thus interpreted as horsts; probably they were scarcely formed before they were partially buried by ejecta.

Other linear structures (which have been plotted by R. J. Hackman) also appear to be buried under the Imbrian and higher strata in the Copernicus region (Fig. 6). They are reflected in the alignment of subdued linear topographic features, most of which are best seen stereoscopically. The tectonic fabric, or pattern of faults and fractures, in the pre-Imbrian of this region is probably complex and the product of numerous structural events besides the impact which produced Imbrian ejecta.

A significant hiatus in time appears to have intervened between the deposition of the Imbrian ejecta and the formation of the Procellarian system, but the evidence for this again lies largely outside of the Copernicus region. The ejecta of several craters that are superposed on the Imbrian ejecta are overlapped by the Procellarian; one of the best examples is the crater Archimedes which lies on the western margin of Mare Imbrium.

Several structural features occur on the maria, in addition to the volcano-shaped features, which may be related closely in time to the emplacement of the Procellarian. These include braided and en echelon systems of low amplitude anticlines or ridges and low scarps that may be monoclines or flow fronts. These features may be chiefly surficial and related to the fluid dynamics of emplacement of the Procellarian system rather than to any broad pattern of stress that affected all or a major segment of the Moon.

A rill on the southwest side of Stadius and the chain crater-rill system north of Stadius (Fig. 6) may be late Procellarian in age or Eratosthenian. They are overlapped by Copernican ejecta and rays.

The structure of craters of Eratosthenian and Copernican ages shown on Fig. 6 is based partly on the observable topography of the craters and is partly inferred from data on terrestrial impact and explosion craters. Copernicus itself is the best example. The well-defined scarps in the crater wall are taken to be normal faults forming the slip surfaces of great slump blocks. These scarps are distinctly linear and show preferred orientations that are probably controlled by pre-Imbrian structure. The outline of the crater, which is somewhat polygonal, has been controlled by the slump faulting. The floor of the crater is inferred to be underlain by a breccia comparable to the breccia of Sierra Madera or perhaps the central breccia of the Vredefort dome. Its depth, shown in the cross-section, is estimated from an empirical scaling relation determined from breccias formed by chemical and nuclear explosions (Shoemaker, 1960b), a scaling relation that fits the dimensions of the breccia at Meteor Crater, Arizona. The central peaks of Copernicus are thought to have been raised up in the centre in response to the centripetal slumping of the crater walls. Large Eratosthenian craters have been interpreted in the same way as Copernicus.

Among the latest structural events in the Copernicus region were the formation of the dark-halo craters, here interpreted as maars. If the correlation that has been presented of the lunar time scale is approximately correct, volcanism appears to have been spread over most of lunar history, though apparently it has changed in character with time. Because of the spatial association of dark-halo craters with Copernicus and the very similar crater Theophilus, there is a suggestion that the later maar-producing volcanism was triggered by impact.

REFERENCES

Alter, Dinsmore (1957). The nature of the domes and small craters of the moon. *Publ. Astr. Soc. Pacif.* **69**, No. 408, 245–251.

Al'tshuler, L. V., Krupnikov, K. K., Ledenev, B. N., Zhuchikhin, V. I. and Brazhnik, M. I. (1958). Dynamical compressibility and equation of state for iron under high pressure (in Russian). *Soviet J. Exp. Theor. Phys.* **7**, 606–614; translated from Russian in *J. Exp. Theor. Phys.* **34**, No. 4, 874–885, 1958.

Anderson, E. M. (1951). "The Dynamics of Faulting and Dyke Formation with Application to Britain", 2nd edition, Oliver and Boyd, Edinburgh, 206 pp.

Baldwin, R. B. (1949). "The Face of the Moon", Chicago University Press, Chicago, 239 pp.

Barringer, D. M. (1905). Coon Mountain and its crater. *Proc. Nat. Acad. Sci., Wash.* **57**, 861–886.

Barringer, D. M. (1910). "Meteor Crater (formerly called Coon Mountain or Coon Butte) in Northern Central Arizona". Published by the Author, Philadelphia, Pa., 24 pp.

Barringer, D. M. (1914). Further notes on Meteor Crater, Arizona. *Proc. Nat. Acad. Sci., Wash.* **66**, 556–565.

Barringer, D. M. (1924). Volcanoes—or cosmic shell holes; a discussion of the origin of the craters on the Moon and of other features of her surface. *Sci. Amer.* **131**, No. 1, 10–11, 62–63; No. 2, 102, 142–144.

Beals, C. S. (1958). Fossil meteorite craters, *Sci. Amer.* **199**, No. 1, 32–39.

Beals, C. S., Ferguson, G. M. and Landau, A. (1956). A search for analogies between lunar and terrestrial topography on photographs of the Canadian shield, *Roy. Astr. Soc. J.* **2**, 203–211, 250–261.

Beck, C. W. and La Paz, Lincoln (1951). The Odessa, Texas, siderite (ECN = +1025, 318) *Pop. Astr.* **59**, 145–151.

Beer, Wilhelm, and Mädler, J. H. (1837). Der Mond nach seinen kosmischen und individuellen Verhältnissen, oder Allgemeine vergleichende Selenographie. Berlin, Simon Schropp, 412 pp.

Bemmelen, R. W. van (1929). Het Caldera probleem [The caldera problem]. *De Mijningenieur*, No. 4, pp. 8–15.

Bentz, Alfred (1925). Die Entstehung der "Bunter Breccie", das Zentral Problem in Nördlinger Ries und Steinheimer Becken. *Zbl. Miner.*, Abt. B., pp. 97–104, 141–145.

Bentz, Alfred (1927). Geologische Beobachtungen am westlichen Riesrand. Stuttgart, *Dtsch. Geol. Gesell. Z.* **79**, 405–438.

Birkhoff, Garrett, MacDougal, D. P., Pugh, E. M., and Taylor, Sir Geoffrey (1948). Explosives with lined cavities. *J. Appl. Phys.* **19**, 563–581.

Bjork, R. L. (1958). Effects of a meteoroid impact on steel and aluminium in space. 10th *Int. Astronaut. Congr.*, London, 1958; preprint, 24 pp.

Boon, J. D., and Albritton, C. C., Jr. (1937). Meteorite scars in ancient rocks. *Field & Lab.* **5**, No. 2, 53–64.

Boon, J. D., and Albritton, C. C., Jr. (1938). Established and supposed examples of meteoritic craters and structures. *Field & Lab.* **6**, No. 2, 44–56.

Boyd, F. R., and England, J. L. (1960). The quartz-coesite transition. *Geophys. Res. J.* **65**, No. 2, 749–756.

Branco, Wilhelm (1895). Schwabens 125 Vulkan-Embryonen und deren Tufferfüllte Ausbruchsröhren; das grösste Maargebiet der Erde: *Wurttemb. Jhefte,* **50**, 505–997 and **51** (1895), 1–337.

Branco, Wilhelm (1902). Das vulkanische Vorries und seine Beziehung zum vulkanischen Ries bei Nördlingen. Berlin, 1902, Phys.-Math. Kl. *Abh. 1, Preuss. Akad. Wiss.*, 1–132.

Branco, Wilhelm (1915). Die vier Entwicklungas tadiem des Vulkanismus. Berlin, *S. B. Preuss. Akad. Wiss.* 59–76.

Branco, Wilhelm, and Fraas, E. (1905). Das kryptovulcanische Becken von Steimheim. Berlin, 1905, Phys. Math. Kl. *Abh. 1, Preuss. Akad. Wiss.*, 1–64.

Brock, B. B. (1951). The Vredefort Ring. *Proc. Geol. Soc. S. Afr.* **53**, 131–157.

Bucher, W. H. (1936). Cryptovolcanic structures in the United States. 16th Internat. Geol. Cong., United States 1933, Rept. **2**, 1055–1084.

Bülow, Kurd von (1954). Die Urkruste des Mondes und der Erde. *Wiss. Z. Univ. Rostock Vg.* 4, *Math.-Naturw. Reihe No. 1.*

Bülow, Kurd von (1957). Tektonische Analyse der Mondrinde. *Geologie (Berlin),* **6**, 565–609.

Chao, E. C. T., Shoemaker, E. M., and Madsen, B. M. (1960). First natural occurrence of coesite. *Science,* **132**, No. 3421, 220–222.

Charters, A. C. (1960). High-speed impact. *Sci. Amer.* **203**, No. 4, 128–140.

Cotton, C. A. (1952). "Volcanoes as Landscape Forms", 1st edition, revised, John Wiley and Sons, Inc., New York, 416 pp.

Dahmer, Georg (1911a). Ein neuer Versuch zur Deutung der Mondoberfläche auf experimenteller Grundlage. *Geol. Rdsch.* **2**, No. 7, 437–440.

Dahmer, Georg (1911b). Die Gebilde der Mondoberfläche. *Neues Jb. Min. Geol. Paläont.* **1**, 89–113.

Dahmer, Georg (1912). Die Entstehung der Kraterfelder des Mondes. *Neues Jb. Min. Geol. Paläont.* **2**, 42–44.

Dahmer, Georg (1938). Zur Dampfstosstheorie des Mondreliefs; Ist das Dampftoss-Experiment bloss ein "Modellversuch"? *Geol. Rdsch.* **29**, No. 1, 72–83.

Dahmer, Georg (1952). Die Dampfstosstheorie zur Deutung der Mondkrater. *Naturw. Rdsch.* **5**, No. 11, 458–461.

Daly, R. A. (1946). Origin of the moon and its topography, *Proc. Amer. Phil. Soc.* **90**, No. 2, 104–119.

Daly, R. A. (1947). Vredefort ring-structure of South Africa. *J. Geol.* **55**, No. 3, Pt. 1, 125–145.

Dana, J. D. (1846). On the volcanoes of the moon, *Amer. J. Sci.* Ser. 2, **2**, 335–353.

Darton, N. H. (1905). The Zuñi Salt Lake, *J. Geol.* **13**, 185–193.

Daubrée, Auguste (1891). Recherches Expérimentales sur le rôle possible des gaz à hautes températures, doués de très fortes pressions et animés d'un mouvement fort rapide dans divers phénomènes géologiques. *Bull. Soc. Géol. France* 3rd Ser., **19**, 313–354.

Davis, W. M. (1926). Biographical memoir of Grove Karl Gilbert, 1843–1918. *Mem. Nat. Acad. Sci.* **21**, 5th Mem., 303 pp.

Dehm, Richard (1932). Geologische Untersuchungen im Ries: Das Gebiet des Blattes Monheim. *Neues Jb. Min. Geol. Paläont.* B.–Bd. **67**, Sect. B, 139–256.

Dietz, R. S. (1946). The meteoritic impact origin of the moon's surface features. *J. Geol.* **54**, No. 6, 359–375.

Dietz, R. S. (1959). Shatter cones in cryptoexplosion structures (meteorite impact?). *J. Geol.* **67**, No. 5, 496–505.

Dietz, R. S. (1960). Meteorite impact suggested by shatter cones in rock. *Science*, **131**, No. 3416, 1781–1784.

Dorn, Paul (1948). Ein Jahrhundert Riesgeologie: Berlin. *Dtsch. Geol. Ges. Z.* **100**, 348–365.

Ebert, H. (1890). Ein Vorlesungversuch aus dem Gebiete der physikalischen Geographie (Bildung der Schlammvulkane und der Mondringgebirge). *Ann. Phys. Chem. Neue Folge* **41**, 351–362.

Einarsson, Trausti (1950). The eruption of Hekla 1947–1948. **IV**, 5; The basic mechanism of volcanic eruptions and the ultimate causes of volcanism. *Rit. Visind. Isl.* (Soc. Sci. Islandica), Reykjavík, 30 pp.

Élie de Beaumont, J.B.A.L.L. (1831). Sur les rapports qui existent entre le relief du sol de l'île de Ceylon et de celui de certaines masses de montagnes qu'on aperçoit sur la surface de la Lune. *Ann. Sci. Nat.* **22**, 88–96.

Élie de Beaumont, J.B.A.L.L. (1843). Comparaison entre les masses montagneuses annulaires de la Terre et de la Lune. *C. R. Acad. Sci., Paris*, **16**, 1032–1035.

Ericsson, John (1886). The lunar surface and its temperature: *Nature, Lond.* **34**, 248–251.

Escher, B. G. (1929). On the formation of Calderas. *Leid. Geol. Meded.* **3**, 183–219.

Escher, B. G. (1930). On the formation of Calderas. *IV Pacif. Sci. Cong., Proc.* **2**, 571–589.

Escher, B. G. (1949). Origin of the asymmetrical shape of the earth's surface and its consequences upon volcanism on earth and moon. *Bull. Amer. Geol. Soc.* **60**, No. 2, 352–362.

Escher, B. G. (1955). Three caldera-shaped accidents; volcanic calderas, meteoric scars and lunar cirques, *Int. Volcan. Ser.* 2, **16**, 55–70.

Fairchild, H. L. (1938). Selenology and cosmogeology; cosmic and geologic import of the lunar features. *Science* n.s., **88**, No. 2294, 555–562.

Faye, H. A. (1881). Les volcans de la lune. *Rev. Sci.* ser. 3, **1**, 130–138.

Firth, C. W. (1930). The Geology of the North-west portion of Manukau County, Auckland. *Trans. Proc. N.Z. Inst.* **61**, 85–137.

Forbes, V. S. (1929). The moon and radioactivity. *Geol. Mag.* **66**, 57–65. Reprinted with additions, 1931, *Smithson. Inst. Ann. Rept.* (1930), 207–217.

Galbraith, F. W. (1959). Craters of the Pinacates: Arizona Geol. Soc., "Southern Arizona Guidebook 2", pp. 161–164.

Gerstlauer, K. (1940). Geologische Untersuchungen im Ries: Das Gebiet des Blattes Offingen: München, *Abh. Geol. Landesuntersuch. Bayer. Oberberg.* **35**.

Giamboni, L. A. (1959). Lunar rays: their formation and age. *Astrophys. J.* **130**, 324–335.

Gifford, A. C. (1924). The mountains of the Moon. *N.Z. J. Sci. Tech.* **7**, 129–142.

Gifford, A. C. (1930). The origin of the surface features of the Moon. *N.Z. J. Sci. Tech.* **11**, 319–327.

Gilbert, G. K. (1893). The moon's face; a study of the origin of its features. *Bull. Phil. Soc. Wash.* **12**, 241–292.

Gilbert, G. K. (1896). The origin of hypotheses, illustrated by the discussion of a topographic problem. *Science*, n.s. **3**, 1–13.

Gilvarry, J. J., and Hill, J. E. (1956). The impact of large meteorites. *Astrophys. J.* **124**, No. 3, 610–622.

Glasstone, Samuel, ed. (1957). "The Effects of Nuclear Weapons". Washington D.C., U.S. Atomic Energy Commission, 579 pp.

Goodacre, Walter (1931). "The Moon, with a Description of Its Surface Formations." Published by the author, Bournemouth, England, 364 pp.

Green, Jack, and Poldervaart, Arie (1960). Lunar defluidization and its implications, XXI Internat. Geol. Cong. Rept. of Sessions, Pt. 21, 15–33.

Griggs, D. T., and Teller, Edward (1956). Deep underground test shots. California Univ. Radiation Lab. Rept. 4659, 9 pp.

Gruithuisen, F. von P. (1829). "Analekten Erd- und Himmels-Kunde", München, 2.

Günther, Siegmund (1911). "Vergleichende Mond- und Erd-kunde". Braunschweig, F. Vieweg und Sohn, 193 pp.

Hack, J. T. (1942). Sedimentation and volcanism in the Hopi Buttes, Arizona: *Bull. Amer. Geol. Soc.* **53**, No. 2, 335–372.

Hall, A. L. and Molengraaff, G.A.F. (1925). The Vredefort Mountain land in the southern Transvaal and the northern Orange Free State. *Verh. Akad. Wet. Amst.* Sect. 2, No. 3, Pt. 24, No. 1–183.

Hannay, J. B. (1892). Formation of lunar volcanoes. *Nature, Lond.* **47**, 7–8.

Hardy, C. T. (1953). Structural dissimilarity of Meteor Crater and Odessa meteorite crater. *Bull. Amer. Ass. Petrol. Geol.* **37**, 2580.

Hardy, C. T. (1954). Major craters attributed to meteoritic impact. *Bull. Amer. Ass. Petrol. Geol.* **38**, No. 5, 917–923.

Herschel, William (1787). An account of three volcanoes in the Moon. *Phil. Trans.* p. 229.

Hooke, Robert (1665). "Micrographia", London, J. Martyn and J. Allestry, 246 pp.

Hopmann, Michael, Frechen, Josef, and Knetsch, Georg (1956). "Die Vulkanische Eifel". Bonn, Wilhelm Stollfuss Verlag, 143 pp.

Hubbert, M. K. (1937). Theory of scale models as applied to the study of geologic structures. *Bull. Amer. Geol. Soc.* **48**, No. 10, 1459–1519.

Hubbert, M. K. and Willis, D. G. (1957). Mechanics of hydraulic fracturing. *Trans. Amer. Inst. Mining Engrs.* **210**, 153–168.

Humbolt, Alexander von (1863). "Cosmos: A Sketch of a Physical Description of the Universe", vol. 4 (translated from German by E. C. Otté and B. H. Paul). New York, Harper and Brothers, 234 pp.

Ives, H. E. (1919). Some large-scale experiments imitating the craters of the moon. *Astrophys. J.* **10**, 245–250.

Jaggar, T. A., Jr. and Finch, R. H. (1924). The explosive eruption of Kilauea in Hawaii. *Amer. J. Sci.* 5th ser., **8**, 353–374.

Jahns, R. H. (1959). Collapse depressions of the Pinacate volcanic field, Sonora, Mexico. Arizona Geol. Soc., "Southern Arizona Guidebook 2", 165–184.

Jeffreys, Harold (1959). "The Earth: its Origin, History and Physical Constitution", 4th edition. Cambridge Univ. Press, 420 pp.

Joesting, H. R. and Plouff, Donald (1958). Geophysical studies of the Upheaval Dome area, San Juan County, Utah, *in* "Guidebook to the Geology of the Paradox Basin." Intermountain Assoc. Petroleum Geologists, 9th Ann. Field Conf., 86–92.

Judd, J. W. (1888). The eruption of Krakatoa and subsequent phenomena. "Report of the Krakatoa Committee of the Royal Society, Pt. I", London, Trübner and Co.

Kant, J. (1785). Die Vulkane im Monde: Leipzig Naturwiss. Schriften von J. Kant, (Insel- Verlag) 1912, 425–433.

Karpoff, Roman (1953). The meteorite crater of Talemzane in southern Algeria. Meteorites 1, 31–38.

King, P. B. (1930). "The geology of the Glass Mountains, Texas. Pt. 1, Descriptive geology". Texas Univ. Bull. 3038, 167 pp.

Kranz, Walter (1911). Das Nördlinger Riesproblem: Stuttgart. Jb. Oberhein. Geol. Ver. N.F.1, 32–35.

Kranz, Walter (1934). Fünfte Fortsetzung der Beiträge zum Nördlinger Ries-Problem. Zbl. Miner. pt. B, No. 6, 262–271.

Krejčí-Graf, Karl (1928) Der Bau des Mondes. Natur u. Mus. Rep. 58, No. 8, 337–346; No. 9, 395–405; No. 10, 449–460; No. 11, 510–518.

Krejčí-Graf, Karl (1959). Der Bau der Mondoberfläche im Vergleich mit der Erde Daten und Deutung. Astronautica Acta, 5, Nos. 3–4, 163–223.

Kuiper, G. P. (1954). On the origin of the lunar surface features. Proc. Nat. Acad. Sci. Wash. 40, No. 12, 1096–1112.

Kuiper, G. P. (1959a). The exploration of the moon, in "Vistas in Astronautics", 2nd Annual Astronaut. Symposium. New York, Pergamon Press, Vol. 2, 273–312.

Kuiper, G. P. (1945b). The moon. J. Geophys. Res. 64, 1713–1719.

Lee, W. T. (1907). Afton craters of southern New Mexico. Bull. Amer. Geol. Soc. 18, 211–220.

Leonard, F. C. (1946). Authenticated meteoritic craters of the world, in "A Catalog of Provisional Coordinate Numbers for the Meteorite Falls of the World". Albuquerque, New Mexico Univ. Pub. Meteoritics No. 1, New Mexico Univ. Press.

Lord, J. O. (1941). Metal structure in Odessa, Texas, and Canyon Diablo, Arizona, meteorites. Pop. Astr. 49, 493–500.

Marshall, R. K. (1943). Origin of the lunar craters, a summary. Pop. Astr. 51, 415–424.

Matheson, G. L., Herbst, W. A., Holt, P. H. and others (1949). Dynamics of fluid-solid systems. Fifteenth annual chemical engineering symposium; Division of Industrial and Engineering Chemistry, American Chemical Society. Industr. Engng. Chem. 41, No. 6, 1099–1250.

Matoušek, Otakar (1924a). Study in comparative cosmic geology, I. The district of Sinus Iridium on the moon (in Czech, with English summary). Riše Hvězd 5, 1–12.

Matoušek, Otakar (1924b). Studien aus der vergleichenden Kosmischen Geologie; Die Gegend Sinus Iridium am Monde. Zbl. Miner. Geol. Paläont. No. 1, 10–17.

Matoušek, Otakar (1930). Tectonics of the moon. Pan-Amer. Geol. 54, No. 2, 81–86.

McKnight, E. T. (1940). Geology of area between Green and Colorado Rivers, Grand and San Juan Counties, Utah Bull. U.S. Geol. Survey, 908, 147 pp.

Merrill, G. P. (1908). The meteor crater of Canyon Diablo, Arizona; its history, origin, and associated meteoritic ions. Smithson. Inst. Misc. Coll. 50, 461–498.

Meydenbauer, A. (1877). Über die Bildung der Mondoberfläche. *Sirius Lpz.* **10,** 180.

Meydenbauer, A. (1882). Die Gebilde der Mondoberfläche. *Sirius Lpz.* **15,** 59–64.

Miller, Ephraim (1898). A new theory of the surface markings of the moon. *Trans. Kansas Acad. Sci.* **15,** 10–13.

Mohorovičič, Stepan, (1928). Experimentelle Untersuchugen über die Entstehung der Mondkrater, ein neuer Beitrag zur Explosionshypothese (Croatian with German summary). *Archiv za Hemiju i Farmaciju, Zagreb,* **2,** 66–76.

Moulton, F. R. (1931). "Astronomy". New York, MacMillan Co., 549 pp.

Müller, G. and Veyl, G. (1957). The birth of Nilahue, a new maar type volcano at Riñinahue, Chile. XX Internat. Geol. Cong. Rept., Sect. 1, 375–396.

Nathan, Hans (1925). Geologische Untersuchungun im Ries. Das Gebiet des Blattes Möttingen. *Neues Jb. Miner. Geol. Paläont.* B.-Bd. **53,** B, 31–97.

Nathan, Hans (1935). Geologische Untersuchungen im Ries. Das Gebiet des Blattes Ederheim: München. *Abh. Geol. Landesuntersuch. Bayer. Oberberg.* No. 19, 24 pp.

Nasmyth, J. H. and Carpenter, J. (1885). "The Moon". New York, Scribner and Welford.

Nel, L. T. (1927). The geology of the country around Vredefort; an explanation of the geological map. South Africa Dept. Mines and Industries, Geol. Survey, 134 pp.

Nevill, E. N. (Neison, Edmund, pseudonym) (1876). "The Moon and the Condition and Configurations of its Surface". London, Longmans, Green and Co., 576 pp.

Odé, Hans (1956). A note concerning the mechanism of artificial and natural hydraulic fracture systems. *Colo. Sch. Min. Quart.* **51,** No. 3, 19–29.

Ordoñez, Ezequiel (1905). Los Xalapazlos del Estado de Puebla. *Parerg. Inst. Geol. Mex.* **1,** 295–344.

Ower, L. H. (1929). The moon and radioactivity. *Geol. Mag.* **66,** 192.

Patterson, C. C., Tilton, G. R. and Inghram, M. G. (1955). Age of the earth. *Science,* **121,** 69–75.

Peal, S. E. (1886). Lunar glaciation. *Nature Lond.,* **35,** 100–101.

Pecora, W. T. (1960). Coesite craters and space geology. *Geotimes* **5,** No. 2, 16–19, 32.

Perret, F. A. (1912). The flashing arcs: a volcanic phenomenon. *Amer. J. Sci.* Ser. 4, **34,** 329–333.

Perret, F. A. (1924). The Vesuvius eruption of 1906; study of a volcanic cycle. Carnegie Inst. Wash., Publ. No. 339, 151 pp.

Pickering, W. H. (1903). "The Moon; a Summary of the Existing Knowledge of our Satellite with a Complete Photographic Atlas". New York, Doubleday, Page and Co., 103 pp.

Pickering, W. H. (1906). Lunar and Hawaiian physical features compared. *Mem. Amer. Acad. Arts Sci.* **13,** 149–179.

Proctor, Mary (1928). "Romance of the Moon". New York, Harper & Bros., 262 pp.

Proctor, R. A. (1873). "The Moon, her Motions, Aspect, Scenery and Physical Condition". Manchester, Alfred Brothers, 394 pp. (Second Edition, 1878, London, Longmans, Green and Company, 314 pp.).

Quiring, Heinrich (1946). Gedanken über Alter, Zusammensetzung und Entstehung des Mondes: *Z. Dtsch. Geol. Ges.* **98,** 172–187.

Reck, Hans, ed. (1936). Santorin, der Werdegang eines Inselvulkans und sein Ausbruch 1925–1928. Berlin, Dietrich Reimer, 3 vols.

Reich, Hermann, and Horrix Wilhelm (1955). Geophysikalische Untersuchungen im Ries und Vorries und deren geologische Deutung. Hannover, Beihefte zum *Geol. Jb.* No. 19, 119 pp.

Reiche, Parry (1940). The origin of Kilbourne Hole, New Mexico. *Amer. J. Sci.* **238,** No. 3, 212–225.

Reuter, Lothar (1925). Die Verbreitung jurassischer Kalkblocke aus dem Ries im sudbayr. Diluvialgebiet: *Jber. Mit. Oberrhein. Geol.* N.F. **14,** 191–218.

Rozet, M. le Capitaine (1846). Sur la sélénologie. *C.R. Acad. Sci., Paris,* **22,** 470–474.

Russell, I. C. (1885). Geological history of Lake Lahontan, a Quaternary lake of northwestern Nevada. U.S. Geol. Survey Mon. 11, 288 pp.

Sacco, Federico (1907). "Essai Schématique de Sélénologie". Turin, G. Clausen-H. Rinck suco., 47 pp.

Sacco, Federico (1948). Considérations sur la genèse lunaire. *Bull. Belge. Géol. Pal. Hydr.* **57,** Pt. 2, 240–245.

Sakharov, V. N., Kolesnikov-Svinarev, V.I., Nazarenko, V.A. and Zabidarov, E.I. (1959). Local distribution of earth thrown up by underground explosions. *C.R. Acad. Sci. U.R.S.S.* **124,** 21–22.

Sauer, Adolf (1901). Petrographische Studien an den Lavabrocken aus dem Ries: *Jb. Vaterl. Naturk. Württembg.* **57.**

Schmidt, J. F. J. (1878). "Die Charte der Gebrige des Mondes". Berlin, Dietrich Reimer, 303 pp.

Schröder, Jöachim and Dehm, Richard (1950). Geologische Untersuchungen im Ries. *Abh. Naturw. Ver. Schwaben e. V. in Augsburg,* **5,** 147 pp.

Schwarz, E. H. L. (1909). The probability of large meteorites having fallen upon the earth. *J. Geol.* **17,** 124–135.

Schwarz, E. H. L. (1927). Cauldrons of subsidence. *Geol. Mag.* **56,** 449–457.

Schwarz, E. H. L. (1928). Terrestrial and lunar faults compared. *J. Geol.* **36,** No. 2, 97–112.

Scrope, G. P. (1862). "Volcanoes". London, Longman, Green, Longmans and Robert, 490 pp.

Sellards, E. H., and Evans, G. L. (1941). Statement of progress of investigation at Odessa meteor craters. Texas Univ., Bur. Econ. Geology, 12 pp.

Shaler, N. S. (1903). A comparison of the features of the earth and moon: *Smithson. Contrib. Knowl.* **34,** No. 1438, 1–130.

Shoemaker, E. M. (1956). Occurrence of uranium in diatremes on the Navajo and Hopi reservations, Arizona, New Mexico, and Utah; *in* Page, L. R., Stocking, H. E. and Smith, H. B., Contributions to the geology of uranium and thorium by the United States Geological Survey and Atomic Energy Commission for the United Nations International Conference on Peaceful Uses of Atomic Energy, Geneva, Switzerland 1955; U.S. Geol. Survey Prof. Paper 300, 179–185.

Shoemaker, E. M. (1957). Primary structures of maar rims and their bearing on the origin of Kilbourne Hole and Zuñi Salt Lake, New Mexico (abs.). *Bull Amer. Geol. Soc.* **68,** No. 12, Pt. 2, 1846.

Shoemaker, E. M. (1960a). Penetration mechanics of high velocity meteorites, illustrated by Meteor Crater, Arizona. XXI Internat. Geol. Congr. Rept., Pt. 18, 418–434.

Shoemaker, E. M. (1960b). Brecciation and mixing of rock by strong shock. *U.S. Geol. Survey Prof. Paper* 400-B, 423–425.

Shoemaker, E. M. (in press). Impact mechanics at Meteor Crater, Arizona, *in* Kuiper, G.P., ed., "The Solar System", Chicago, Chicago Univ. Press, Vol. 4, Pt. 2.

Shoemaker, E. M., Roach, C. H. and Byers, F. M., Jr. (in press). Diatremes and Cenozoic geology of the Hopi Buttes region, Arizona. *Bull Amer. Geol. Soc.*

Shoemaker, E. M., and Chao, E. C. T. (1960). Origin of the Ries basin, Bavaria, Germany (abs.). *Bull. Amer. Geol. Soc.* **71**, 2111–2112.

Simeons, G. (1906). À propos d'une récente tentative de comparaison entre la constitution de la terre et celle de la lune. *Bull. Soc. Belge Geol. Pal. Hydr.* **19**, Proc.-verb. 204–215.

Smith, S. P. (1887). The Eruption of Tarawera. A Report to the Surveyor-General. Wellington, New Zealand Government Printer, 84 pp.

Spencer, L. J. (1933). Meteorite craters as topographical features on the earth's surface. *Geog. J.* **81**, No. 3, 227–248.

Spencer, L. J. (1937). Meteorites and the craters on the moon. *Nature, Lond.* **139**, No. 3520, 655–657.

Spurr, J. E. (1944). "Geology Applied to Selenology": Vol. 1 "The Imbrian Plain Region of the Moon". The Science Press Printing Co., Lancaster, Pa., 112 pp.

Stearns, H. T. (1925). The explosive phase of Kilauea volcano, Hawaii, in 1924. *Bull. Volcan.* **5/6**, 193–208.

Stearns, H. T. and Vaksvik, K. N. (1935). Geology and ground-water resources of the island of Oahu, Hawaii. Hawaii Terr. Dept. Public Lands Div. *Hydrogr. Bull.* **1**, 479 pp.

Stehn, C. E. (1929). The geology and volcanism of the Krakatau group. IV Pacif. Sci. Congr., Java, 55 pp.

Stutzer, Otto (1936). "Meteor-Crater", Arizona und Nördlinger Ries. *Z. Dtsch. Geol. Ges.* **88**, No. 8, 510–523.

Suess, Eduard (1895). Einige Bemerkungen über den Mond. *S.B. Akad. Wiss. Wien. Math.-Naturwiss Kl.* **104**, Pt. 1, No. 2, 21–54.

Suess, Eduard (1909). "The Face of the Earth", Volume IV (English translation). Oxford, Clarendon Press, 673 pp.

Suess, F. E. (1917). Gestalten der Mondoberfläche. *Geol. Gesell. Wien Mitt.* **10**. 218–248.

Thiersch, August, and Thiersch, H. W. J. (Asterios) (1899). "Die Physiognomie des Mondes". Nördlingen.

Thomas, A. P. W. (1888). Report on the eruption of Tarawera and Rotomahana, New Zealand. Government Printer, Wellington, New Zealand, 74 pp.

Tilghman, B. C. (1905). Coone Butte, Arizona. *Proc. Philad. Acad. Nat. Sci.* **57**, 887–914.

Tomkins, H. G. (1927). The igneous origins of some of the lunar formations. *J. Brit. Astr. Ass.* **37**, No. 5, 161.

Treibs, Walter (1950). Geologische Untersuchungen im Ries; das Gebiet des Blattes Otting. *München Geol. Bavar.* **3**, 52 pp.

Urey, H. C. (1951). The origin and development of the Earth and other terrestrial planets. *Geochim. et Cosmochim. Acta.* **1**, 209–277.

Verbeek, R. D. M. (1886). "Krakatau". Batavia, Imprimerie de l'Etat, 567 pp. and Atlas in 2 volumes.

Viete, Gunter (1952). Geologie und Mondoberfläche. *Die Bergakad. Freiberg*, **4**, No. 12, 470–482.

Wagner, P. A. (1914). The diamond fields of Southern Africa. *The Transvaal Leader*, Johannesburg, Union of South Africa, 347 pp.

Wasiutyński, Jeremi (1946). Studies on hydrodynamics and structure of stars and planets. *Astrophys. Norvegica*, **4**, 497 pp.

Wegener, Alfred (1920). Die Aufsturzhypothese der Mondkrater. *Sirius Lpz.* **53**, 189.

Wegener, Alfred (1921). Die Entstehung der Mondkrater. Braunschweig, Sammlung Vieweg, Tayesfragen. *Natur. u. Tech.* **55**, 48 pp.

Wegener, Alfred (1922). Versuche zur Aufsturztheorie der Mondkrater. *S. Nova Acta Leop. Carol.* **106**, No. 2, 107–118.

Werner, E. (1904). Das Ries in der Schwäb.-fränk. *Blätter Schwäb. Albver.*

Whipple F. L., and Hughes R. F. (1955). On the velocities and orbits of meteors, fireballs and meteorites. *J. Atmos. Terres. Phys.* Suppl. 2, 149–156.

Wilkins, H. P., and Moore, P. A. (1955). "The Moon", London, Faber & Faber Ltd., 388 pp. Also MacMillan and Co. Inc., New York.

Williams, Howel (1941). Calderas and their origin. *Calif. Univ. Bull. Geol. Sci.* **25**, No. 6, 239–346.

Wilson, C. W. (1953). Wilcox deposits in explosion craters, Stewart County, Tennessee, and their relations to origin and age of Wells Creek Basin structure. *Bull. Amer. Geol. Soc.* **64**, No. 7, 753–768.

Wolff, F. L. von (1914). *Der Vulkanismus.* Stuttgart, Ferdinand Enke, Verlag, Allgemeiner Teil, Pt. 2, **1**, 301–711.

Wright, F. E. (1927). Gravity on the earth and on the moon. *Sci. Mon. N.Y.* **24**, 448–462.

Wright, F. E. (in press). The surface of the Moon. In "The Solar System" (G. P. Kuiper, ed.), Vol. 4, Planets and Comets, Pt. II. Chicago Univ. Press, Chicago. Ill.

Chapter 9

Physical Observations of the Lunar Surface

N. A. Kozyrev

I. Introduction. 361
II. Observations by Dinsmore Alter. 363
III. Spectral Observations of Alphonsus on 3rd November, 1958. 363
IV. Spectral Observations of Alphonsus on 23rd October, 1959. 375
V. Conclusions. 382

I. Introduction

There are good reasons for supposing that the basic pattern of the lunar surface was formed gradually, by the action of physical processes produced by the Moon's internal energy. Morphological analysis shows that both sinking and expansion have taken place in the lunar crust at different times.

The existence of tilted and semi-submerged "ghost" craters on the edges of the seas proves that an enormous area of the crust sank in these places, followed by the effusion of molten masses. The remarkable valley in the Lunar Alps, about 10–15 km wide and more than 100 km long, and similar smaller hills are examples of a raising of the lunar crust accompanied by considerable expansion. Such tectonic processes must also have been connected with volcanic activity, traces of which can actually be detected in many morphological features. Thus, the cosmic history of the Moon is similar to the geological history of the Earth. Physical processes of an endogenous character are taking place on Earth even today. The question arises whether the Moon still retains any internal energy or the possibility of active physical processes.

The topography of the Moon has been studied most carefully for two hundred years, and there are numerous reports claiming that changes have been observed in details of the lunar landscape. However, there is no doubt that the vast majority of these reports are false. Actually the visibility of lunar details depends a great deal on the conditions under which they are illuminated by the Sun; hence, apparent changes may easily be taken for real ones. The most noteworthy changes observed in the lunar landscape are the disappearance of Linné's crater on the eastern side of the Mare Serenitatis and the appearance of the dark crater Hyginus N to the north of Hyginus crater, which is situated almost at the centre of the lunar disk. Schmidt reported from Athens in 1866 that he had seen a bright spot about 6 seconds in diameter, not the ordinary deep crater as Linné was observed in 1841. Linné appears today as Schmidt saw it. The previous appearance of Linné, in the shape of an ordinary crater, is corroborated by Lohrmann's and Mädler's maps, where it was used as a cartographical point. The appearance of the gap Hyginus N. (i.e. a crater without a wall), was reported by Klein in 1877. A study of earlier maps, sketches and photographs and also the evidence of E. Neison and other authorities of the period indicates that the crater Hyginus N is, in fact, a new formation.

Nevertheless, there is widespread scepticism about these observations in present-day astronomical literature. In his book "Unser Mond", Fauth (1936) argued in considerable detail that the disappearance of Linné and the appearance of Hyginus N were illusory. We should bear in mind, however, that many contemporaries of Schmidt and Klein accepted these changes as genuine; and in spite of the fact that the details of their arguments have not been preserved, their opinions should carry considerable weight. All the same, we are bound to admit that so far there is not a single scientifically attested proof of any changes in the lunar landscape during our epoch. This conclusion does not conflict with the possibility of intensive tectonic activity on the Moon even at the present time. Indeed, we should remember that a nautical mile (i.e. 1·85 km on the Moon) corresponds to only one second of arc: therefore, if we discount processes connected with the activity of water, air and life on Earth, it would be very difficult, looking from the Moon, to detect for certain any changes in the Earth's landscape during the period of our investigations.

Now, although we cannot strictly verify the consequences of tectonic processes because the lunar surface has not been sufficiently studied, we can try to establish the existence of the processes themselves from concomitant physical phenomena. Such a phenomenon may, for example, be the luminescence of gases released from the Moon's interior. Since the Moon has no atmosphere, and particularly no free oxygen, gases cannot ignite and give off light and heat such as terrestrial volcanoes do. However, since hard solar radiation has free access to the surface, the volcanic gases should be able to emit a cold fluorescent light. This luminescence should be observable most easily on the edge of the lunar disk or close to the terminator where, because of the inclination of the Sun's rays, the brightness of the background becomes greatly reduced. In this connection, special interest attaches to indications given by various observers that a haze has appeared, temporarily obscuring details at the bottom of some craters. An objective basis for the possibility of such phenomena was first obtained by the American astronomer, Dinsmore Alter.

II. Observations by Dinsmore Alter

Near the last quarter, on the 26th October, 1956, working in the Cassegrain focus of the 60-inch reflector at Mount Wilson Observatory, Alter obtained four pairs of photographs of the craters Alphonsus and the neighbouring Arzachel. Each pair consisted of photographs taken immediately one after the other on ordinary plates and without a filter (i.e. in violet-blue rays), and in infra-red rays with a filter transmitting $\lambda > 7200$ Å. One of these pairs of photographs is reproduced on Fig. 1. Because of the scattering of light in the Earth's atmosphere, all the details on the violet picture had considerably less contrast than those in the infra-red picture. Alter drew attention to the fact that the fissures in the west half of the Alphonsus crater (the lower one on Fig. 1) appear to be much more blurred in the violet light than the fissures in the crater Arzachel. This difference recurred throughout the whole series of photographs, which was obtained in 1 hour and 15 minutes. Apparently, in the crater of Alphonsus itself there was an additional cause that decreased the contrast in the violet rays. It is possible that in the western part of Alphonsus a temporary emission of gas took place.

On the Moon an atmospheric haze cannot be created by the ordinary Rayleigh scattering. In fact, this would require a quantity of molecules of the order of 10^{24} per square centimetre of the surface. But if the gases can fluoresce under the action of the Sun's hard radiation, all that is needed to create a haze is a column of gas capable of absorbing an appreciable amount of this radiation. We may suppose, therefore, that a column of gas of the order of 10^{15} molecules (i.e. of density about 10^{-10} of that in the terrestrial atmosphere) will create a fluorescence which might substantially reduce the visibility of details. Alter's photographs do not, of course, give a sufficient basis upon which to judge the correctness of this interpretation. Even the effect itself, noted by Alter, might easily be called into question. But a direct and rigorous proof of physical lunar processes may be obtained by spectrographic analysis. By such a method it should be possible to establish and investigate the additional features introduced by any physical phenomenon and superposing on ordinary solar spectrum, as reflected from the lunar surface.

III. Spectral Observations of Alphonsus on 3rd November, 1958

In the autumn of 1958 the author began to make systematic spectral investigations of details of the lunar surface near the terminator.

FIG. 1(a). A photograph of the crater Alphonsus taken with the 60-inch reflector of the Mount Wilson Observatory on October 26th, 1956, by Dr. Dinsmore Alter (blue light).

FIG. 1(b).   A photograph of the crater Alphonsus taken with the 60-inch reflector of
the Mount Wilson Observatory on October 26th, 1956, by Dr. Dinsmore Alter (red light).

These investigations were carried out with the 50-inch reflector of the Crimean Astrophysical Observatory, by use of a prism spectograph, with a camera giving linear dispersion of about 23 Å mm at $H\gamma$. The scale of the spectrogram was 10 seconds per mm, and the scale of the image on the slit was 8 seconds per mm. Spectrograms were obtained with a slit width of 0·05 mm on Kodak 103 aF plates. All the photographs were photometrically standardized by use of a wedge photometer. Stimulated by Alter's observations, we made a special point of obtaining the spectra of details inside the crater Alphonsus. Figure 2 shows the position and length of the slit of the spectrograph when the spectrum was photographed on 3 November, 1958.

The crater Alphonsus (whose selenographic co-ordinates are $\lambda = -5°$ and $\beta = -23°$) is situated on the western shore of the Mare Nubium, and is at the centre of a distinctive group of three craters situated along the meridian. The northern member in this group is Ptolemaeus and the southern one Arzachel. The diameter of Alphonsus is approximately 120 km. Its central peak rises to 1400 m above the western part of the base and 1200 m above the eastern part.† A distinctive feature of Alphonsus is the mountain ridge running along the diameter of the crater in a direction close to the meridian. This ridge, which is especially well developed in the southern part of the crater, runs somewhat more easterly than the central peak. Owing to a western branch that runs towards the central peak, there is a sizeable valley on its eastern side. It is a most interesting fact that in the neighbourhood of Alphonsus there are a number of breaks and fissures running parallel with its axial ridge. The "Straight Wall" fault, which can be seen in the upper right-hand corner of Fig. 2, runs in the same direction. The group of craters which we are examining is of ancient origin, but these breaks and fissures at the base of the craters are more recent formations and show a high tectonic activity in this area at a later time.

On the 3rd of November 1958, we took a spectrogram exposed from 3 hr 00 min to 3 hr 30 min U.T., showing the fluorescence of gases issuing from the central peak of Alphonsus. Whilst this picture was being taken, and guided on the slit of the spectrograph, the central peak appeared brighter and whiter than usual. Suddenly, for a period of less than a minute, the brightness of the peak dropped to normal. The exposure was then stopped immediately and the next one followed from 3 hr 30 min to 3 hr 40 min, with the slit in the same position. This spectrogram confirmed our visual impression: it showed a spectrum of the crater now in its normal state. At about 1 hr U.T. the same

† Subsequent measurements by Turner (Astr. Contr. Univ. Manchester, Ser. III, No. 67, 1959) reduced this height to 934 ± 10 metres.   [Editor.

night, before taking these pictures, we obtained another spectrogram through cloud, showing no traces of gas emission at all.† Therefore, this gas emission must have lasted for not more than $2\frac{1}{2}$ hours and not less than half an hour. The following night (3rd–4th November) we managed to take two further spectrograms of Alphonsus. These showed that the crater continued to remain in its normal state. The last quarter began on the evening of 4th November and Alphonsus ceased to be accessible to observation.

FIG. 2. Photograph of a group of the craters Ptolemy, Alphonsus and Arzachel, showing the position of the slit during the author's spectrographic observations on November 3rd, 1958.

The two spectrograms of Alphonsus taken from 3 hr 00 min to 3 hr 40 min are reproduced on Fig. 3. The spectra of the eastern and western walls of the crater and the spectrum of the central peak and its shadow can be seen distinctly on these spectrograms, taken with the position of the slit as shown on Fig. 2. On the first spectrogram

† In preliminary reports the author indicated that the central peak in this spectrogram appeared noticeably fainter in the violet and this may be explained by an ejection of dust—volcanic ash. Subsequent detailed study of the spectrum has shown this to be incorrect.

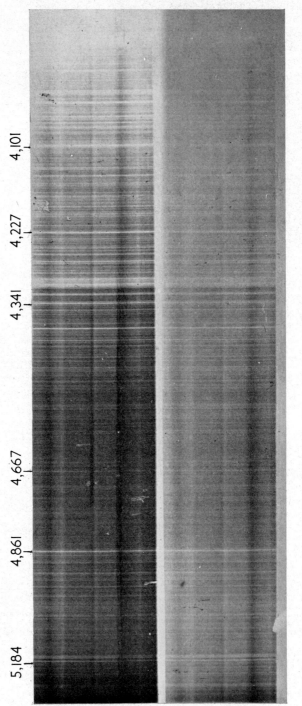
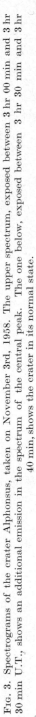

FIG. 3. Spectrograms of the crater Alphonsus, taken on November 3rd, 1958. The upper spectrum, exposed between 3 hr 00 min and 3 hr 30 min U.T., shows an additional emission in the spectrum of the central peak. The one below, exposed between 3 hr 30 min and 3 hr 40 min, shows the crater in its normal state.

it can be seen at once that the ordinary spectrum of the central peak has been covered by an additional emission. The most distinctive feature of this additional emission is a group of bands with a comparatively sharp red edge at about 4740 Å. The brightness of these bands reached 40% of the peak's normal brightness in the same wavelengths. On the short-wave side one can still see a broad system of faint bands caused by this emission group, with a maximum brightness of about 4400 Å. The presence of emission here is supported by the faintness of a Fraunhofer line of 4384 Å which is quite distinct on the spectrogram. An intense band with a sharp edge at about 4740 Å is typical of the spectra of cometary heads. There can be no doubt that it is basically a band in the Swan resonance series of the diatomic molecules of carbon (C_2).

The emission spectrum of the central peak was very carefully investigated microphotometrically by Dr. A. A. Kalinyak at Pulkovo. The accompanying Fig. 4 gives the results of these measurements in the short-wave end of the spectrum. The intensity of the additional emission is plotted along the axis of the ordinates, and expressed in fractions of the intensity of the continuous spectrum of the central peak. The results of two separate sets of measurements are shown as circles and dots. The random distribution of circles near the zero line on the lower diagram gives some idea of the exactitude of these microphotometric measurements. The corresponding distribution of circles and dots in the fundamental band with an edge of 4740 Å shows the real structure of this band. The maxima we have here may be compared with vibration changes (1·0), (2·1), (3·2) in the band of C_2: 4737, 4715 and 4698 Å. But the whole band is much more complicated and extends farther to the short-wave end of the spectrum than the ordinary band of C_2. In interpreting this band it is very important to note that the entire emission from 4640 to 4740 Å is displaced towards the Sun with respect to the central peak and to the position of the other bands. This displacement is quite visible on the spectrogram (Fig. 3) and is confirmed by the microphotometric measurements as given on Fig. 5. These measurements were carried out in the direction of the slit. Measurements in the spectral domain of λ 4740 to H_β, where there is clearly no emission, enables us to obtain the normal background brightness of the central peak, shown at the top of the diagram.

The middle curve on Fig. 5 was obtained by deducting the normal background brightness from the brightness of the peak in the domain of weak emission (4575–4610 Å). The maximum on this curve completely coincides with the position of the maximum in the normal

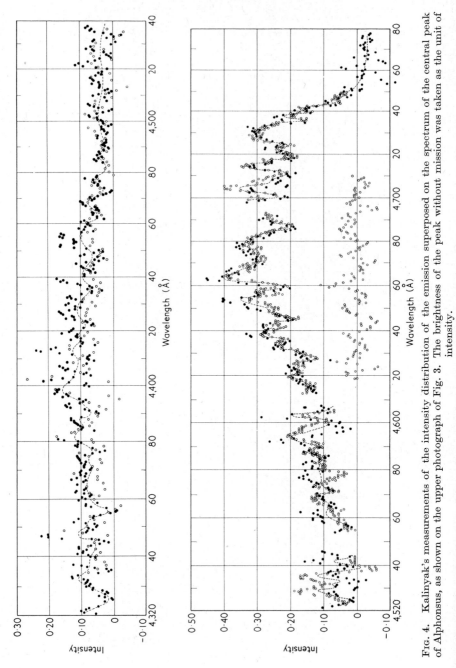

FIG. 4. Kalinyak's measurements of the intensity distribution of the emission superposed on the spectrum of the central peak of Alphonsus, as shown on the upper photograph of Fig. 3. The brightness of the peak without emission was taken as the unit of intensity.

profile of the central peak. But the emission in the bright part of the band along the sections 4670, 4730, 4737 Å gives an equal displacement of the brightness maximum in the direction of the Sun. The central section of additional emission is represented by the lower curve, which shows a shift equal to 1″·2 or 2 kilometres on the lunar surface. The most probable explanation of this result is as follows: Gases consisting of complex molecules giving off a faint emission were

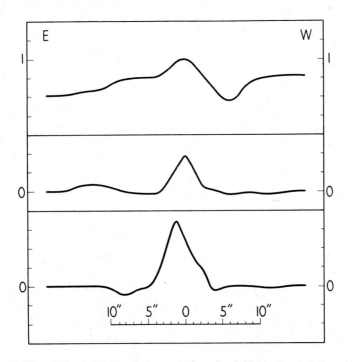

FIG. 5. Profiles of the intensity of the central peak of Alphonsus and the additional emission along the slit of the spectrograph. The top curve gives the profile of the peak in its normal state. The curve at the centre shows a section of weak additional emission (λ 4620, 4580 Å); and the bottom curve, a section of the additional emission in the bright part of the λ 4740 Å band (the average of sections in the light of λλ 4740, 4730, and 4660 Å bands). The unit of intensity is the maximum intensity of the central peak.

released from the central peak of Alphonsus. They were transparent to solar radiation which caused them. But the Sun's hard radiation, destroying these complex molecules and forming radicals, only penetrated the outward side of the gas cloud turned towards the Sun. From this point of view, all the bright band of 4740 Å must have the same chemical nature, i.e. must constitute an emission of the molecules of C_2. It is possible that the radiation of the radical of C_2 at the moment of its formation produces a system of bands displaced by perturbations of the molecular structure; and the combination of this spectrum with the ordinary spectrum of C_2 may produce the complex structure of the band shown on Fig. 4. This kind of structure is not found in the spectra of cometary heads. This can be understood if we bear in mind that the spectrum under investigation must be similar to that of the nucleus of a comet, in which gases are released, and not that of a cometary head.

According to Kalinyak's measurements, the Swan long-wave band 5165 is not found in the spectrum. Figure 6 gives the results of these measurements, in the part of the spectrum from 5100 to 5700 Å. Only two bands stand out clearly here, with maxima of 5470 and 5630 Å. It is possible that the latter is a Swan band, formed by vibration changes (0·1), (1·2), (2·3): 5636, 5585, 5541 Å.

At the short-wave end of the spectrum between 4300Å and H_δ practically no emission can be detected. According to the author's measurements, some weak emission bands may be present to the violet of H_δ, which may be identified with bands of C_3 in the cometary spectra (maximum brightness 4050 Å). But this conclusion was not supported by Kalinyak's measurements, and the question remains open. Although the spectrum was very much under-exposed in ultra-violet, we can still hold for certain that the emission band of CN molecules at 3883 Å, which is very bright in cometary spectra, is absent. This is bound to be true if there is considerably less likelihood of photo-dissociation of the parent molecules with the formation of CN than that of C_2. If so, then in the area where the gases are released the quantity of CN may prove insufficient to cause any appreciable emission. This adduces a further proof that the critical spectrum of Alphonsus must be similar to that of a cometary nucleus, not a cometary head.

Now let us compare the surface brightness of the observed fluorescence with that of the comets. Near the full Moon the reflectivity of the central peak of Alphonsus attains a value of about 0.15, i.e. approximately twice the average reflectivity of the lunar surface. During the period of our observations the height of the Sun above the horizon of Alphonsus was 18°. According to the data collected by V. A. Fedorets at Kharkov, the reflectivity of the central peak for that height of the Sun is reduced to a tenth of its reflectivity at full Moon. If we assume that, at all wavelengths, the flourescence of escaping gases added, on the average, 10% of the peak's brightness, then the surface brightness of the observed flourescence is equal to one-fiftieth

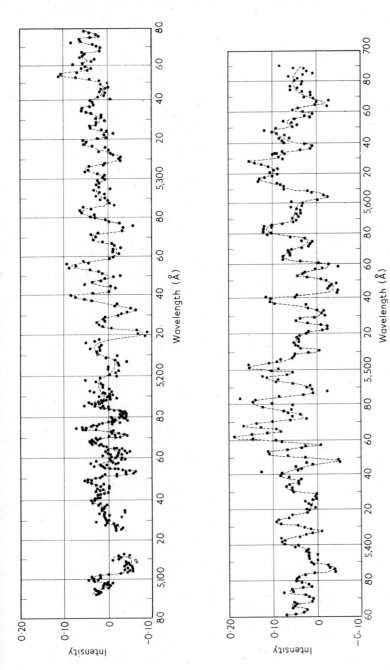
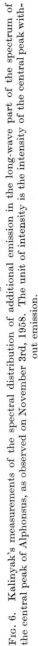

FIG. 6. Kalinyak's measurements of the spectral distribution of additional emission in the long-wave part of the spectrum of the central peak of Alphonsus, as observed on November 3rd, 1958. The unit of intensity is the intensity of the central peak without emission.

of the Moon's average surface brightness when it is full. Since the brightness of a full Moon is known to be $-5\cdot5$ magnitudes per square minute, the surface brightness of the flourescence should be of the order of -1 stellar magnitude per square minute. But the surface brightness of cometary heads is about a ninth magnitude per square minute. Therefore, the surface brightness of the observed flourescence must have been ten thousand times greater than that of a cometary head; and, if we compare the intensity of the bands of C_2 in the spectra of Alphonsus and of a cometary head, then (since the radiation in the latter is mainly due to the Swan bands) this ratio must be decreased by at least one order.

On the basis of the photometric data given above we may assert that the gases were in fact released from the centre of the peak of Alphonsus. This process lasted for about an hour. Let us now try to estimate the total quantity of gas expelled during this process. The simplest and most reliable estimate can be made by utilizing the fact that the observed gas cloud was opaque to the Sun's shortwave radiation, which caused the photo-dissociation of the molecules. For such processes the absorption coefficient per molecule must be of the order of $10^{-15} - 10^{-16}$. We may assert, therefore, that there were no fewer than 10^{15} molecules in the path of the solar rays in a column with a cross-section of 1 cm^2. In order to obtain the actual quantity, we must probably increase this figure by one order. As is shown by the photometric profiles on Fig. 5, that part of the gas cloud which we observed had a diameter of about 3–5 km; thus, taking an area of cloud cross-section to be 10^{11} cm^2, we get a value of the order of 10^{27} for the total quantity of molecules constituting it. The density of the gas is of the order of 10^{11} particles per cm^3. At this density, the mean free path must be about one kilometre, i.e. about the size of the cloud itself. The velocities of gas escape cannot be very different from thermal velocities (i.e. several hundred metres per second). There-fore, once the gases ceased to escape, the cloud must have dispersed within several seconds. This means that during this time, while the cloud was stationary, 10^{27} molecules must have been released. The full quantity of molecules released throughout the whole process is 10^{30}. Thus, during this process which we observed, the lunar interior gave off about a hundred thousand cubic metres of gas at the terre-strial atmospheric pressure, which is a very small quantity in compari-son with the cubic kilometres of gas released when terrestrial volcanoes erupt. This comparison indicates the low level of activity of the process; and if so, one could hardly expect to find it to have caused any appreci-able changes in the landscape. Observations at large observatories did not confirm a report by Wilkins and Bruin that a new small reddish spot (not observed before November) appeared on 19th November 1958, near the central peak of Alphonsus on its south side. A report by Poppendiek and Bond that they had visually observed a large gas cloud about 30 km in diameter above the central peak on 19th November, 1958, at 4 hr U.T. (*Publ. A.S.P.*, **71**, 233, 1959) is probably also incorrect. This report conflicts with that of Haas (*l.c.*, p. 236), who observed Alphonsus at this same time with a considerably larger instrument and saw nothing unusual.

On the 19th November, 1959 at 4 hr U.T. the rising Sun was just beginning to illuminate the central peak and the adjacent heights. Under these conditions, it is very easy to mistake an isolated cliff illuminated by low Sun for a gas cloud. From personal experience the author is well aware of the possibility of such an error. When Sinus Iridum was close to the terminator, it acquired a completely isolated light spot of a peculiar shade which looked like a gas cloud. Only by examining a photograph of the spectrum of this spot was this found not to be so.

IV. Spectral Observations of Alphonsus on 23rd October, 1959

In the autumn of 1959 the author continued his investigation of the active regions of the lunar surface using the spectroscopic method with the 50-inch reflector at the Crimean Astrophysical Observatory. Despite the variety of objects thus examined, the usual solar spectrum of light reflected by the lunar surface was found on each of the photographs. This was how the spectrum of Alphonsus appeared when taken on 11th October, near the first quarter. The circumstances in which these observations were made were exactly the same as in the previous year, except that immediately after the slit the collimator of the spectrograph was provided with a prism giving full internal reflection and used to enlarge stellar spectra. For technical reasons we had to take spectra of the lunar surface with this prism, decreasing the length of the slit by almost a half, and turning the image with respect to the direction of dispersion.

On the 23rd October, when images were very good, we obtained a spectrum of Alphonsus exposed from 2 hr 10 min to 2 hr 25 min U.T. (exposure 15 min), and this again showed the crater to be in an unusual state. Unfortunately, during the guiding we did not visually notice any peculiarities in the appearance of the crater. Therefore, the photograph was not repeated and the only other spectrum photographed that night was that of Aristarchus. The following night was

overcast, and on 25th October Alphonsus was no longer illuminated by the Sun.

The circumstances under which we obtained the spectra this year
and in 1958 were very similar. The Sun was setting, at an altitude
of 19° above the horizon of Alphonsus. The direction of the slit differed
only by 4° from that shown on Fig. 2, in a more perpendicular position

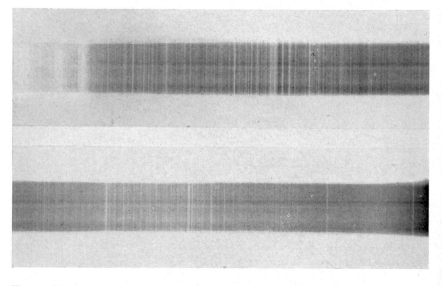

Fig. 7. The spectrograms of Alphonsus, taken by the author on October 23rd, 1959.

to the axial ridge of the crater. The impression of the violet and red
part in the spectrum of Alphonsus on 23rd October is reproduced on
Fig. 7. Because the length of the slit was decreased, the spectrogram
refers only to the west side of the crater illuminated by the Sun, and
the bottom of the east rampart almost exactly up to the shadow.
In the centre is the spectrum of the area around the central peak and
its shadow. A striking feature is the peculiar character of the spectrum
of this area in the red, beginning beyond the triplet Mg 5184 Å and
clearly marked behind the line Na 5895 Å and beyond. What is especially noticeable here is a bright detail of a very small section (1".2)
which is not visible in the short-wave part of the spectrum. This
detail stands out a good deal more clearly in longer wavelengths. It
is located 6" (i.e. 11 km) from the shadow in the direction of the Sun,
hence towards the east. In this part of the spectrum the shadow is
very short and is preceded, on the sunlit side, by a small increase in
brightness, considerably weaker than that of the central peak. All this

can be seen clearly from a direct comparison between the short-wave and the red end of the spectrum, as in the lower spectrum on Fig. 8. The upper part of Fig. 8 shows a comparison of this spectrum with that of Alphonsus in 1958. The fine detail in the red part of the spectrum obtained in 1959 shows the excellence of the images at the time of observation. At the same time, the comparison of spectra on Fig. 8

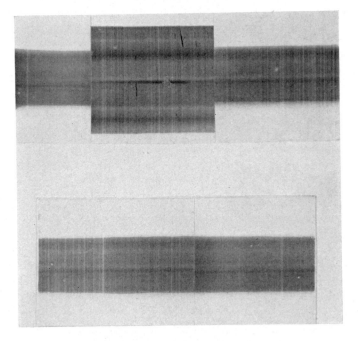

Fig. 8   (above): A comparison of the spectra of Alphonsus taken on November 3rd, 1958 (inset) and on October 23rd, 1959, (below): comparison of the long- and short-wave parts of the spectrum of Alphonsus taken on October 23rd, 1959. A spectrum of the sunlit rampart of the crater can serve for the purpose of comparison.

reveals that the area of the central peak and the shadow are wider in the short-wave end than on the spectrum taken in 1958. Hence, the 1959 spectrum appears to be anomalous at short waves.

In an interpretation of this complex spectrum, it is natural to start by measuring the amount of contrast in the bright red detail as a function of the wavelength. The results of the respective microphoto-metric measurements are shown on the accompanying Fig. 9. Its upper part gives the brightness as measured with respect to the brightness of the crater floor in the direction of the Sun. Its lower part shows

the measurements of the brightness of the details with respect to the
area of the crater lying in the direction of the shadow. The significant
diagram is the upper one, since it gives the change in contrast of the
detail in relation to the normal lunar surface—undisturbed by any
physical processes. Starting from wavelengths between 5300–5400 Å
we find a uniform increase in contrast which we can trace up to 6600 Å
on the photograph. This uniform increase is most likely due to thermal

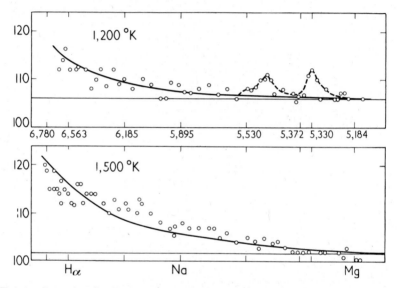

Fig. 9.   Intensity distribution in the spectrum of the red glow observed in Alphonsus
on October 23rd, 1959. The upper curve gives the intensity distribution with respect to
that at the floor of the crater; and the bottom curve gives the same distribution in comparison with that prevailing in the shadow.

radiation. In this range the intensity of the solar spectrum only
drops by 20% to the red side. This decrease in brightness is probably
fully balanced by an increase of the albedo of the lunar surface on the
red side of the spectrum. Hence we may assume that the relative
brightness of the spectrum is the same for the whole section of spectrum
under consideration. Then, as is shown by the curve on the diagram,
the uniformity of contrast is entirely in agreement with the radiation
of a black body at a temperature of 1200° K. On the short-wave side
there appear some irregularities in contrast, as shown by a dotted
line, and these may be explained by the presence of some emission
bands. These bands continue further in the direction of shorter wavelengths. No emission bands are found in the lower diagram on Fig.
9. This means that there is emission not only above the bright red

detail, but also above the whole area of the lunar surface from the detail to the shadow. Because of this, the brightness of the spectrum in the comparison used in this diagram is reduced to the red side of the spectrum where there is no additional emission. As a result, we have an artificial increase in the contrast of the red detail, representing an improbably high temperature of 1500° K.

The explanation of this red detail as caused by thermal radiation can be verified by calculating the temperature according to an absolute value of radiation energy. If $x = 1·44/\lambda T$, then an application of Wien's law to the case of the red detail leads to an equation of the form

$$e_{([}^{-x} = 2·1 \times 10^{-5} A_{h\odot} \ K(e^x - 1)^{-1}.$$

The numerical coefficient in this expression is the dilution factor of solar radiation over the distance between the Moon and the Sun; $A_{h\odot}$ stands for the albedo of the spectrum in comparison with that of the crater floor when the Sun is at a height $h_\odot$ during the observations; K is the contrast of the red detail in the wavelength selected. Let us carry out our calculations by assuming that $\lambda = 6500$ Å. In the parts of the spectrum between the Fraunhofer lines the Sun's colour temperature will be $T_\odot = 6700°$. If $h_\odot = 19°$ we may take the albedo of the crater-base in the red rays to be $A_{h\odot} = 0·015$. In accordance with the upper diagram on Fig. 8 the contrast is taken as $K = 0·08$. If so, the foregoing equation can be solved to yield $x = 20·7$ leading to $T = 1080°$ K—in close agreement with the previously determined colour temperature of 1200°. In actual fact, the unsteadiness of seeing and guiding errors are bound to decrease the contrast of the detail, thus causing a decrease in black-body temperature. Since, however, the factor decreasing the contrast does not depend on wavelength, the colour temperature comes out correct, regardless of these errors. To obtain an energy temperature of 1200°, the contrast must be almost 8 times greater than that measured. Consequently, the actual extent of the phenomenon which gave rise to the emission could not have been 2 km, but only about 300 metres. Evidently, during the exposure, the slit of the spectrograph intercepted a lava flow of this width. Lava from terrestrial volcanoes retains its plasticity up to 700° C or 1000° K. But on leaving the volcano, its temperature is of the order of 1400° K. The figure of 1200° K as the calculated temperature of the red detail on the Moon agrees so closely with these facts that there can be little doubt we are correct in identifying the detail as a lava flow.

The short shadow in the red part of the spectrum and the small contrast of its elevation show that the slit did not pass across the central peak. During the guiding, the brightest object in the centre of the crater was placed in the centre of the slit. In this case the object was probably a gas cloud producing an emission at wavelengths shorter than 5400–5300 Å. The slit passed near the foot of the central peak from the south where the heights of Alphonsus' axial ridge cast a noticeable, but foreshortened, shadow. This position of the slit is shown on Fig. 10. Eleven kilometres from the limit of the shadow in the direction of the slit we find the position of the lava flow almost exactly on the eastern crest of the branch in the axial ridge more on its inner (i.e. western) slope. Here on the eastern ridge, slightly to the east, there is a hill resembling the cone of a volcano. It is possible that this hill is actually a volcano and that its eruption caused the phenomena we observed.

Above the lava flow and all the valley formed by the fork in the axial ridge, gases were released, producing an emission. At wave lengths below 5400–5300 Å the emission bands are so close that they give the impression of a continuous spectrum. However, a careful study of the spectrum reproduced on Fig. 7, reveals shifts of altitude in different parts, indications of irregular brightness and blurring of the Fraunhofer lines. Unfortunately, the spectrum has no clear signs of emission—such as bands of radicals (for example, of C_2). This is probably connected with other chemical compounds of the gases. Actually, the gases released in this instance may have been of the fumarolic type; but in terrestrial conditions the fumaroli have a chemical composition different from that of gases released from the crater of an erupting volcano. An interesting feature of the spectrum we obtained in the increase in width of the shadow in the short-wave end of the spectrum. Evidently the gas cloud cast additional shadow. This is further borne out by the fact that the width of the shadow shows irregular changes throughout the whole spectrum. If the light is completely dispersed, there can be no shadow from the gas-cloud. This requires true absorption involving the transformation of visible light into long-wave radiation. True absorption is usually due to molecular collisions, which is impossible in this case because of the low density of the gas. The observation of a shadow in these conditions shows that, when the structure of the molecules is complex, a mechanism similar to collisions is able to take place among the molecules; and this causes visible light to be transformed into infra-red radiation.

On the dark side of the Moon, not illuminated by the Sun, the surface heated to 1200° K should prove a fairly bright object for infra-red photographic plates. Let us suppose that we are observing such a surface measuring one square kilometre. One square second of the lunar

FIG. 10.   The probable position of the slit of the spectrograph during the exposure of
the spectrum taken on October 23rd, 1959.   The physical processes whose imprint was
recorded on that spectrogram were most likely caused by volcanic activity of the subsidiary peak marked with the arrow.

surface at full Moon radiates as a star of $+3 \cdot 5$ magnitude. But the brightness during the phase when we observed Alphonsus was $2 \cdot 5$ magnitudes smaller. This gives us the 6th stellar magnitude per square second. For wavelengths around 8000 Å, a surface heated to $1200°$ K should be approximately 50 times brighter than the lunar surface in this particular phase and the same wavelengths. Hence, a surface area of 1 km^2 should radiate like a star of the spectral class type G of 4th or 5th magnitude. On 26th October, using infra-red plates with a filter, we took direct photographs of the dark side of the Moon in the region of Alphonsus. The conditions at the time of observation were such that we should have been able to obtain an object of the brightness expected. The results of the observations were negative. We must presume that by 26th October, the lava flow in Alphonsus had already ceased and cooled off.

In its external features the spectrum obtained on 23rd October, 1959, seems less significant than the one taken on 3rd November, 1958. But the analysis given above shows that on 23rd October, 1959, a considerably more active volcanic process took place in Alphonsus, at least equal in scale to large eruptions of terrestrial volcanoes. It is possible that the phenomena we observed were similar to the 1912 eruption of the volcano Katmai in Alaska, when the famous valley of 10,000 smokes was formed by the lava flow. Our observations show that the axial ridge of the Alphonsus crater is in the stage of formation at the present epoch.

V. Conclusions

When the lunar interior gives off gases their molecules, which have thermal velocities of the order of hundreds of metres per second, must acquire (after photo-dissociation) velocities of about 1–2 km per sec, as do molecules in a cometary head. The parabolic velocity of escape from the Moon is only $2 \cdot 4$ km/sec. Hence, the gases which are released must disperse and escape almost instantaneously. An occasional release of gases from the Moon's interior cannot, therefore, cause any noticeable atmosphere to accumulate round it; and the hard solar radiation, corpuscles or micrometeorites, are not necessary to blow it away. Actually, in this case, the penetration of particles is bound to produce an effect similar to a depth charge where the energy is transmitted to large masses of gas. As a result, the separate molecules would not acquire velocities necessary for escape.

When lava comes out on the lunar surface, the gases absorbed into it must be discharged very violently due to the absence of any atmospheric pressure. Hence, we may expect to find spongy structures of the pumice type widespread on the Moon. Under vacuum conditions, such structures must have—as they are observed to possess on the lunar surface—a very small coefficient of heat conductivity, which is one hundredth or a thousandth of that of solid terrestrial rocks. An accumulation of such spongy structures will be conducive to the development of magmatic centres. This produces an interesting and somewhat paradoxical conclusion: the absence of atmosphere, which brought about the formation of spongy structures, severely decreases the heat loss, thereby helping an accumulation of the internal energy, and the development of orogenic processes.

It is no accident that the gases are given off precisely from the central peak of the crater Alphonsus. It is probable that the peak of this crater has a funnel, i.e. it is a genuine volcano. If so, we may conjecture that the central peaks of lunar craters have the same origin as the cones of terrestrial ones and are, therefore, accumulated formations. The craters themselves bear a similarity to the calderas of terrestrial volcanoes, which were formed as depressions when a magmatic centre became exhausted. The large diameter of lunar craters, almost one order of magnitude greater than the size of terrestrial calderas, may be accounted for by the fact that the gravity of the Moon is six times smaller than it is on the Earth.

The spectroscopic observations described in this chapter should go a long way towards establishing the fact that the Moon, even at the present time, has sufficient internal energy for orogenic processes. This result clearly shows that the history of the formation of the lunar landscape may, in fact, be mainly the history of the internal processes of the Moon's cosmic existence; while external influences may have been of secondary importance and, in particular, the role played by meteorite impacts scarcely more significant than in the formation of the known terrestrial features.

CHAPTER 10

The Luminescence of the Lunar Surface

J. F. GRAINGER AND J. RING

I. Introduction.. 385
II. Historical Survey... 385
III. Observations of Line Profiles.. 393
IV. Photometric Accuracy Requirements....................................... 397
V. The Ideal Luminescence Spectrophotometer................................ 399
VI. Conclusions... 404
References.. 404

I. Introduction

It is well known that the Earth-Moon system is under continuous bombardment by high energy electro-magnetic and corpuscular radiations from the Sun. Our knowledge of these radiations has, in recent years, been considerably extended by means of rockets and satellites which have transported instruments beyond the Earth's atmosphere. It is interesting to consider what effect these radiations will have on the surface of the Moon, unprotected by any layer of air and, consequently, exposed to their full intensity. One phenomenon which may confidently be expected is that of photoelectric emission by some of the lunar surface material. This effect is giving rise to serious considerations as to whether the Moon may be expected to have a net electric charge. However, a less spectacular, though perhaps potentially more important, consequence of the solar bombardment may be that of *luminescence* of the lunar surface rocks. Such a phenomenon, in which the solar U.V. radiation, X-rays and proton streams are caused to give up their energy for re-radiation in the form of visible light, could be made the basis of a continuous monitoring service, using the Moon as a ready-made space-borne wavelength converter. These ideas are beginning to look more feasible in the light of recent experiments and the present chapter will survey the available information on this subject.

II. Historical Survey

The first reference to the luminescence of the Moon's surface appears to have been made by Link (1946). In this work he referred to the well-known phenomenon that a lunar eclipse is never completely dark.

2C 385

Most astronomical texts mention this in passing and dismiss it as being due to light reaching the Moon by refraction through the Earth's atmosphere. Link discussed, in particular, the optical density of the penumbras of lunar eclipses and remarked (*loc. cit.*): ". . . Comparison with observations is very interesting. There are some eclipses whose penumbral densities correspond with the theoretical value, or are perhaps a little greater. But some eclipses furnish penumbral densities which are weaker than the theoretical values. . . . This excess illumination would at first sight be explicable by the supplement provided by the part of the Sun visible due to refraction; but from the quantitative point of view this explanation does not account for the observed facts, unless one supposes an improbable structure for the atmosphere between 20 and 80 km. altitude." Link suggested that the excess light is provided by luminescence of the lunar surface stimulated by ultra-violet or corpuscular radiations from the Sun. The important point of his argument was that these radiations follow different paths from the optical radiation and are, therefore, not so severely eclipsed. Their effect is greatly enhanced under such circumstances, and so the excess light is more easily detected during an eclipse. In his first paper Link used data from five eclipses, ranging from 1931 to 1942, but deduced nothing save the plausibility of the hypothesis of lunar luminescence.

However, the year 1947 saw Link becoming much more definite on the existence of luminescence (Link, 1947a, b). In the first of these papers he recounted his photometric theory of lunar eclipses (Link, 1933) and extended it to deal with the penumbra, hitherto neglected. He took account of atmospheric absorption, diffusion and refraction and indicated that the effect of ozone (which he neglected) could only be to absorb. Having thus arrived at a good theory of the illumination to be expected in the penumbra, he compared the theory with ten eclipses, ranging from 1921 to 1945. Some of the eclipses were definitely lighter than theory suggested, whilst there were also "normal" and "dark" eclipses. Link continued: "As in our theory the ozone absorption was neglected, the 'dark' eclipses ought to be considered normal whilst the others are affected by a source of supplementary illumination which diminishes the theoretical density." After re-stating the hypothesis of lunar luminescence, he showed that it would only require a luminescent power of 2 to 3 stilb/watt, for the lunar surface, to account for the observations. This is an order of magnitude lower than that of commercially produced luminophors and so quite reasonable.

If the excess light is indeed caused by luminescence stimulated by radiations from the outer layers of the solar atmosphere and the inner corona, then we may expect the relative excess of light to behave as follows. We may conveniently suppose the illumination in the penumbra to consist of two components: $I_1(\tau)$ being due to optical radiation coming from the solar disk, and $I_2(\tau)$ being due to degeneration of radiation coming from the Sun's outer regions and corona; τ is a parameter describing the position of the point considered in the penumbra. The illumination in the penumbra is expressed in terms of that of the fully lit region outside the eclipse. If I_1° and I_2° are the values of $I_1(\tau)$ and $I_2(\tau)$ in this condition, then the illumination in the penumbra is

$$\frac{I_1(\tau)+I_2(\tau)}{I_1^0+I_2^0}.$$

The theoretical illumination is, on the other hand,

$$\frac{I_1(\tau)}{I_1^0};$$

and so the excess of light may be represented by

$$\Delta(\tau) = \frac{I_1(\tau)+I_2(\tau)}{I_1^0+I_2^0} - \frac{I_1(\tau)}{I_1^0}$$

$$= \frac{I_2(\tau)I_1^0-I_2^0I_1(\tau)}{I_1^0(I_1^0+I_2^0)}.$$

Expressing $I_1(\tau)$ and $I_2(\tau)$ in terms of their final values by introducing the dimensionless parameters $\alpha(\tau) = I_1(\tau)/I_1^{\circ}$ and $\beta(\tau) = I_2(\tau)/I_2^{\circ}$ we obtain

$$\Delta(\tau) = \frac{I_2^0}{I_1^0+I_2^0}\,(\beta-\alpha).$$

We can see qualitatively how α and β behave by an inspection of Fig. 1. In (a) we see the Sun from a position in the penumbra with small τ, in which the illumination due to the corona is already well advanced, but that due to optical radiation is only just beginning (i.e., for $\tau = \tau_1$, $\beta > \alpha$, and $\Delta(\tau_1) > 0$).

In (b) the Earth's limb is dichotomising the Sun-corona system and the two components of penumbral illumination have each reached half their final value. Thus $\beta = \alpha$ and $\Delta(\tau_2) = 0$.

In (c) the Sun is almost completely visible, but the corona is still significantly eclipsed and so $\beta < \alpha$ and $\Delta(\tau_3) < 0$. Thus, a graph of excess relative penumbral illumination against a positional co-ordinate in the penumbra should show an inversion at about that value of the co-ordinate corresponding to the eclipse being half total. Link showed that the mean curve for his sample of eclipses did indeed behave in this way, though with some considerable spread in individual cases which he attributed to the fact that the corona does not maintain the same shape as time goes on, introducing asymmetries with respect to the centre of the Sun's disk. This behaviour is strongly in favour of the extra light being produced by a mechanism involving the outer regions of the Sun, and luminescence seems the only satisfactory one.

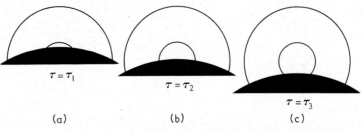

FIG. 1. Three stages of a lunar eclipse as seen from the Moon.

Clearly, from the observed behaviour of $\Delta(\tau)$ and knowledge of $I_1°$, an estimate of $I_2°$ can be obtained. In this way Link arrived at a figure of 10% for the proportion of lunar light accounted for by luminescence. Link also drew attention to the possible luminescent effect of the solar corpuscular radiation and suggested an attempt to correlate the penumbral fluctuations with terrestrial magnetic perturbations. In the 1947 paper, evidence of such a correlation was inconclusive.

Since the luminescent component varies markedly from one eclipse to another, being frequently 10% of the optical radiation, it might reasonably be expected that the light of the un-eclipsed Moon should undergo measurable fluctuations. Link pointed out the difficulties of making such measurements, but suggested that other results (Rougier, 1933) seemed to prove the existence of such fluctuations. In fact, the 1947 papers did report briefly the establishment of a correlation between the lunar light level and solar constant variations. This was dealt with more fully in a paper published by Link in 1951, in which he called attention to the fact that Abbot and his collaborators at the Smithsonian Institute (Abbot, 1942) found variations in the solar constant of the order of 1%. A search for similar changes in the light reflected by the planets did not confirm these variations.

The Moon, however, had never been made the subject of such experiments and Link decided to try to use Rougier's results for this purpose. These consisted of an extended series of photoelectric measurements of the Moon at a wavelength of 4400 Å. Great care was taken to eliminate all extraneous effects, and the result was a curve giving the mean overall magnitude of the Moon as a function of phase angle. The curve possessed two slightly different branches, one for increasing phase, the other for decreasing. Each individual value of the overall magnitude could then be compared with the mean value corresponding to its phase—obtained from the curve—and the departure Δm obtained. The values of the solar constant c were obtained from Abbot's results, and the corresponding fluctuations Δc were calculated as $(c - 1 \cdot 945)$. Link plotted Δc against Δm and obtained a correlation coefficient of $r = -0 \cdot 438 \pm 0 \cdot 082$. An important point emerges when we consider the quantities $\Delta m/m$ and $\Delta c/c$ in relation to each other. It appears that a variation in the solar constant produces a change about thirty times greater in the light of the Moon. Clearly this cannot be a simple reflection of the variation of the solar constant. Again the hypothesis of luminescence can come to the rescue, since it will depend on the U.V. and X-ray output from the Sun. Now it was known (Abbot, 1942) that the ratio of spectral variations to solar constant fluctuations increased towards the short wavelength end of the spectrum. In fact, even at 3500 Å, this ratio had reached about 6:1. Thus in the U.V. and X-ray regions, variations of 30:1 would not seem unreasonable (especially bearing in mind the ionospheric electron density fluctuations which may be 100 times greater than the solar variations) and these would be translated into visible fluctuations by the suggested luminescence process. Link displayed his results in an alternative way, by plotting Δm and Δc each as functions of time in the 27 day rotation period. The correlation was again apparent, but an interesting fact emerged in the form of a time-lag of about a day between the solar constant variation and the associated variation in the Moon's magnitude. In view of this lag, it is tempting to attribute the luminescence to corpuscular stimulation.

Little more can be deduced about the luminescence unless some much more reliable method of investigation can be found. So far we have seen that the phenomenon seems likely, both from the behaviour of eclipses and from the overall brightness fluctuations. However, data such as these take a very long time to accumulate and both suffer from the severe disadvantage that they require the calculation and removal of the effects of the Earth's atmosphere, always an uncertain procedure and especially treacherous when small deviations from theory are being sought.

For the answer to these difficulties, we must again turn to a paper by Link (1950), in which he reported an idea which arose in conversation with Brück, Kiepenheuer, Dufay and others.

Here the briefest reference was made to the effect of luminescence on the Fraunhofer lines of the Moon's spectrum. The idea was again mentioned in slightly greater detail in a later paper (Link 1951) in which Link wrote:

"The central intensity of Fraunhofer lines is usually of the order of 0·1 of the continuum level. If, therefore, the light diffused by the Moon contains a component of luminescent origin, the central intensity of

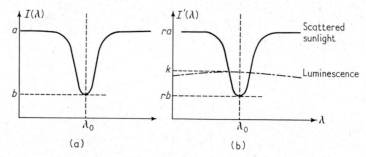

FIG. 2.   Theoretical profiles of absorption lines in the absence (a) and presence (b) of luminescence.

the line may suffer variations from 0·1 to about 0·2. Measurements of this type made by the same instrument on the Sun and on the Moon would doubtless permit the easy detection of such variations in the strong lines $H\alpha$, K and H, for example."

We see in this statement the beauty of the method, since both the continuum and the base of the line are equally affected by terrestrial atmospheric phenomena. Their ratio is therefore unaffected. The amount by which the ratio in the lunar spectrum differs from that for the same line in the solar spectrum is thus a measure of the luminescent radiation. We can express this quantitatively as follows. Let us suppose that in the wavelength interval λ to $\lambda + d\lambda$, the flux of solar energy at the Earth's surface is $I(\lambda)d\lambda$. A Fraunhofer line at wavelength λ_0 will show up in a graph of $I(\lambda)$ against λ as indicated in Fig. 2(a). Let us define the depth of the line as

$$R = \frac{\text{Deepest level}}{\text{Continuum level}}$$

In the case of the Sun we have

$$R_S = \frac{b}{a}.$$

(1)

In the absence of luminescence, the light received from the Moon is simply the sunlight incident upon it, attenuated by a constant factor r. Thus in the lunar spectrum the same lines will appear, and their depth will be

$$R_M = \frac{rb}{ra} = R_S. \tag{2}$$

However, in the presence of luminescence, there will be an additional amount of light k which we may suppose constant over the width of the Fraunhofer line, for even if the luminescence spectrum has the usual banded structure, these bands are likely to be at least fifty times as wide as the Fraunhofer line (see the dotted line of Fig. 2(b)). In this case the depth of the line in the lunar spectrum will be

$$R_M = \frac{rb+k}{ra+k} \neq R_S. \tag{3}$$

We can express the amount of luminescence k in terms of the continuum level in the absence of luminescence (a simple relation exists between this and the observed continuum) by means of the dimensionless parameter ρ defined by

$$k = \rho ra. \tag{4}$$

Equation (3) can then be rewritten as

$$R_M = \frac{b+\rho a}{a(1+\rho)} \tag{5}$$

or

$$R_M = \frac{R_S+\rho}{(1+\rho)}. \tag{6}$$

A solution of (6) then gives

$$\rho = \frac{R_S-R_M}{R_M-1}. \tag{7}$$

Thus the measurement of R_S and R_M is sufficient to give the percentage luminescence. By consent of the subsequent literature, this process has become known as "The Method of Line depths". Link did not evaluate the expression for ρ, nor perform the experiments necessary to test the method. In fact, with the exception of a paper written jointly with Široký in 1951 (Link and Široký, 1951) in which further photometric evidence for the excess of light in the penumbra was presented, Link had nothing further to say on the subject until three papers in the period 1958 to 1960, which are improvements of his eclipse methods and have been superseded by the line depth results.

The next stage in the story of the investigation of lunar luminescence takes us to 1956–57. This period saw the almost simultaneous publication of three papers on the subject, two by Dubois and one by Kozyrev. The first of Dubois' papers (Dubois, 1956) was semi-popular in nature. It reviewed the conditions prevailing in the space around the Moon and pointed out the likelihood of luminescence, bearing in mind that in many parts of the world (e.g. Arizona, California, Spain, France, etc.) there are exposed beds of materials which would luminesce if suitably stimulated. The Moon's low albedo would make it easier to detect any such parasitic illumination against the background of the scattered light. As evidence of the actual existence of luminescence he called attention to Link's work on eclipse penumbrae, but pointed out that this method of measurement is not capable of giving high accuracy and, of course, can only be performed when there is an eclipse.† In the light of these considerations Dubois adopted the method of line depths. The actual expression for the luminescence was not derived in that paper, though it was clearly known to him since he performed some laboratory experiments to test its validity.

Before proceeding with the application of the method to the Moon, Dubois posed himself the question: "If, in the study of lunar spectra, we find a diminution in the depth of certain lines in comparison with solar spectra, can we then conclude that this alteration is attributable to luminescence?" It might be simpler to ask what other explanations there could be. Dubois suggested two possibilities: one that the lunar reflection coefficient has sharp discontinuities at the exact wavelengths of the Fraunhofer lines; the other that the parasitic illumination may be due to scattering, either from the Earth's atmosphere illuminated by the Moon, or inside the instrument itself.

The first of these he dismissed immediately as artificial. The second, he seemed to think, might have some effect, but could be allowed for (in the case of atmospheric scattering) or carefully eliminated in the instrument. However, it is difficult to see how the light scattered by the atmosphere could alter the line profiles, since it would have the same spectrum.

Having decided that luminescence was a reasonable working hypothesis, Dubois described observations on many lunar regions with a

† In connection with this limitation on frequency of observation, mention should be made of a suggestion in Link's 1951 paper. In Link's words: ". . . one might ask oneself if the penumbral phenomenon would not be observable outside eclipses, on the terminator. A simple calculation shows that in the most favourable case there would be a region of 1″ around the place, where the increase of brightness would be observable. Bearing in mind the image agitation due to 'seeing', the possibility of this type of observation appears to us to be minimal".

variety of dispersive powers. He pointed out the inherent difficulty
of photographic photometry in that the emulsion response is logarithmic and that the plates whose exposure places them on the linear part
of the "γ-curve" are just those of low dispersion, thus not permitting
very accurate depth measurements. In spite of these difficulties,
". . . certain definite regions of the lunar surface seem to present a
certain fluorescence".

He later made extensive observations by this method. These,
together with Kozyrev's work are discussed in the next section.

III. Observations of Line Profiles

It occurred to Kozyrev that the absence of a lunar atmosphere
could lead to luminescence of the surface (Kozyrev, 1956). With this
in view he searched the spectrum of the dark region of the Moon, but
found only that of the ashen light. From this observation he concluded that the Moon has zero or negligible magnetic field, and hence
the charged particles emitted by the Sun must strike the Moon's
surface according to the same geometrical laws as the electro-magnetic
radiation. Any luminescence phenomena would, of necessity, superpose
on the reflected sunlight and would, therefore, be difficult to observe.

He noted Link's evidence for luminescence—lunar eclipse penumbras
and the correlation of overall magnitude variations with fluctuations
in the solar constant—but pointed out the need for a more systematic
method of investigation, especially if the luminescence spectrum were
to be obtained. He concluded that photometry of the continua of the
lunar and solar spectra could only detect a luminescent spectrum
consisting of narrow emission lines. "But usually luminescent spectra
of minerals consist of wide bands which, when superimposed on the
reflected solar spectrum, cannot be distinguished with certainty from
the characteristic features of the spectral curve of reflection of the
Moon's surface". He therefore utilized the method of line-depths on
plates taken in the autumn of 1955 with the 50-inch reflector of the
Crimean Astrophysical Observatory and a spectrograph of 50 Å/mm
dispersion. His spectral resolution was about 2·5 Å and the region on
the Moon covered by his slit was about 2″ in width. In order to obtain
accurate observations of luminescent intensity he restricted his measurements to lines broad enough to be well resolved. For this reason he
used the H and K lines of CaII which had the further advantage of
being in a spectral region where the solar continuum would be least
likely to mask a given luminescent intensity. He studied the Maria
Serenitatis and Imbrium; the central mountainous region, the craters

Aristarchus, Plato, Schickard and Copernicus and Wood's Spot. Of these regions only Aristarchus gave a positive result. From his observed profile he deduced a luminescent intensity of about 13% on a particular night when the effect was very pronounced. It should be noted, however, that the deepest portion of his profile, where the effect should be most marked, gave an anomaly which was attributed to a systematic error of the photographic process. From the difference in intensity at the H and K lines he decided that the doublet was located on the falling edge of an ultra-violet band. He discovered a discontinuity in the lunar continuum in this region which matched the intensity derived from the profiles of the H and K lines, and thus felt justified in attributing the whole discontinuity to luminescence. Figure 3 shows the

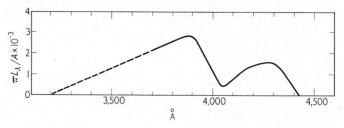

FIG. 3. Luminescent spectrum of Aristarchus (Kozyrev, 1956)

results obtained on October 4th, 1955, when abnormally strong luminescence was observed, approximately four times the normal intensity. From this large fluctuation he deduced that it could not be caused by ultra-violet radiation from the reversing layer, which is known to be stable; and having dismissed chromospheric ultra-violet lines and coronal U.V. and X-radiation on the grounds of insufficient intensity, he decided that the effect was probably caused by corpuscular streams. On the assumption of 12 keV protons he derived a value for the flux density of 5×10^3 particles/cm^3 on the basis of a luminescence efficiency of 10% and a reflection coefficient of 0·05.

Kozyrev pointed out that these spectra cannot be used to identify the luminophor, since the presence of small traces of impurity can radically change the character of a luminescence spectrum. From the variations of intensity with the Sun-Moon-Earth angle he concluded that the luminescent material was situated at the bottom of fine irregularities in the ray system.

The only other detailed luminescence observations came from Dubois who has been using the method of line depths since 1949, with a variety of instruments. (Dubois, 1957, 1959). His best observations appear to have been made with high-dispersion spectrographs at Utrecht and Arcetri. He employed slit widths corresponding to as little as 0·2 Å, which allowed him to use many more lines than Kozyrev. However, he only quotes luminescence measurements on the Fraunhofer lines: $H\alpha$, D, E, F, G. In general, he was prevented from observations in the violet and U.V. by the characteristics of his spectrographs, which makes comparison with Kozyrev's results rather difficult.

Dubois has observed about 90 lunar regions, of which he claims that about half exhibit significant luminescence. His results are given in Table I and show values of ρ between 3 and 25%.

TABLE I

Luminescent intensities in various lunar regions after Dubois (1959)

Lunar Region Observed	Values of ρ for different colours:				
	Red 6563	Yellow 5893	Green 5200	Blue 4861	Violet 4300
South-west Limb Lat. 45°S		0·14	0·20	0·04	
Region between the Maria Serenitatis and Pluvium (Lat. 30°N, Long. 8°W)		0·05			0·06
Centre of Sinus Medii	0·12			0·10	
Mare Tranquilitatis (Lat. 0°, Long. 28°W)	?	0·14			
Mare Foecunditatis (Lat. 0°, Long. 50°W)	0·08	0·10		?	
Floor of crater Regiomontanus	0·25	0·13		0·05	
Mare Crisium		0·15	0·20	0·08	
Mare Frigoris (Western Region)		0·06	0·07	?	0·04
Region around Lat. 12°S, Long. 60°W	0·07	0·10			0·03
Mare Vaporum	0·12	0·07		0·14	
Oceanus Procellarum (Central and South-western region)	0·20				0·10

It is interesting to note that a few of these regions, showing luminescence at 4300 Å, were observed by Kozyrev who obtained a negative result.

He claimed also to have used a number of weaker lines together with continuum measurements to investigate the fine structure of the luminescence bands, but it is difficult to discover from his published work exactly how he arrived at the detailed curves he shows (Fig. 4).

The method of continuum measurements essentially assumes a knowledge of the behaviour of the lunar reflection coefficient with wavelength; whilst this quantity may be established at those wavelengths for which line-depth luminescences are available, the authors agree with Kozyrev that to interpolate between these points may lead to dubious results. Dubois bases his interpolations on the fact that different regions of the Moon, in wavelength ranges where they do not luminesce, give very similar curves of intensity versus wavelength. He then plots such curves for the luminescent regions and whilst ignoring slow changes with wavelength, interprets the more rapid changes as due to luminescence. Since, however, the amplitudes of both these types of variation are of the same order of magnitude, and

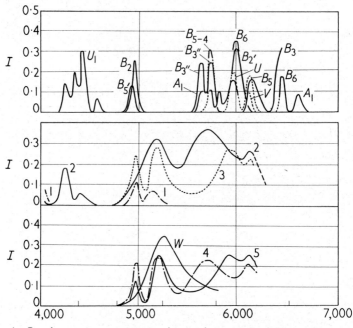

FIG. 4. Luminescent spectra at various points on the lunar surface. A—Arcetri; B—Bordeaux; U—Utrecht; B_3 and B_3'—dark regions between Mare Nubium and Mare Humorum; B_3 and B_3''—bright regions between Mare Vaporum and Mare Nubium; B_4—Sinus Medii, Mare Vaporum; B_5—bright region between Mare Vaporum and Mare Serenitatis; B_6—centre of Mare Serenitatis; 1—region near the limb in the west of Mare Crisium; 2—centre of Mare Crisium; 3—west of Mare Frigoris; 4—Aristoteles; 5—centre of Palus Nebularum; W—synthetic willemite (Dubois 1959).

the photometric accuracy of his results is low, one cannot place too much reliance on band structure derived in this way. Nevertheless, he finds that these results are in substantial agreement with those found from his line-depth measurements.

Dubois also found fluctuations in the intensity of luminescence which he attributed to variations in the stimulating radiation from the Sun. He has attempted to correlate these fluctuations with the critical frequency of the ionosphere and with the value of the Earth's magnetic field in an endeavour to distinguish between ultra-violet radiation and corpuscular streams as stimulants. The conclusions reached are that both agencies play a part and are of different relative importance for various regions of the Moon. Some of the correlations found in this way are negative, that is to say an increase in the stimulation causes a decrease in the luminescence!

Both these observers used photographic spectrometers and do not seem to have considered fully the effect of errors inherent in photometry on their derived luminescent intensities. Since these intensities are frequently only a few per cent of the continuum, it is necessary to perform a detailed analysis of the photometric accuracy required from an ideal instrument.

IV. Photometric Accuracy Requirements

A consideration of equation (7) leads to an error $\delta\rho$ in ρ, given by

$$(\delta\rho)^2 = \left(\frac{1+\rho}{1-R_S}\right)^2 [(1+\rho)^2 \delta R_M{}^2 + \delta R_S{}^2]$$

reducing to

$$\left(\frac{\delta\rho}{\rho}\right)^2 = \left[\frac{1+\rho}{\rho(1-R_S)}\right]^2 [(\rho+R_S)^2 + R_S{}^2]f^2, \tag{8}$$

where f is the fractional error in R_M and R_S, as defined by

$$\delta R_M = f\,R_M,$$
$$\delta R_S = f\,R_S.$$

With a photographic spectrograph there are several sources of error leading to δR_M and δR_S. We have seen from Kozyrev's work that the Eberhard effect may lead to a spurious change in line depth. In any event the accuracy in a measured intensity from a plate will seldom be better than 5% and the lack of dynamic range in the photographic process may give larger errors at the bottom of a deep line. If we accept the accuracy of 5% in an intensity measurement, then a ratio can be measured at best to 7%.

It is clear that for a significant difference of line-depth the ratios R_M and R_S must differ by at least $2\delta R$. This leads to a minimum detectable luminescence of

$$\rho_{min.} = \frac{0 \cdot 14 R_S}{1 - 1 \cdot 14 R_S}.$$

Thus values of R_S of $0 \cdot 1$, $0 \cdot 2$ and $0 \cdot 5$ give $\rho_{min.}$ of $1 \cdot 5\%$, 4% and 16% respectively. Even to *detect* a typical luminescence ($\sim 10\%$)

necessitates the use of solar lines with at least 60% absorption at the resolution employed.

However, equation (8) permits us to calculate the fractional error in ρ as a function of ρ and R_S. Typical values are given in Table II.

TABLE II

Table of Fractional Errors in ρ

R_S ρ in %	0·1	0·2	0·3	0·4	0·5	0·6
5	0·29	0·59	0·76	>1	>1	>1
10	0·19	0·35	0·55	0·82	>1	>1
15	0·16	0·27	0·41	0·60	0·88	>1
20	0·15	0·23	0·35	0·50	0·72	>1

It is clear from this that the above minimum detectable amounts will not in fact be of any value quantitatively owing to their large uncertainties. They should only be recorded as "luminescence detected but not accurately measurable".

If, however, we can somehow make the error in R_S negligible compared with that in R_M —which should after all be possible, since the solar lines do not fluctuate and can, therefore, be measured many times —then the expression for $\delta\rho$ becomes

$$\delta\rho = \frac{(1+\rho)^2}{1-R_S}\,\delta R_M,$$

which on being expressed in terms of $\delta R_M/R_M$ assumes the form

$$\delta\rho = \frac{(1+\rho)(\rho+R_S)}{1-R_S}\cdot\frac{\delta R_M}{R_M}.$$

If we can also increase the accuracy of R_M to about $1\tfrac{1}{2}\%$ then we can write the fractional error in ρ as

$$\frac{\delta\rho}{\rho} = \frac{3\,(1+\rho)}{200\rho}\,\frac{\rho+R_S}{1-R_S}.$$

Substituting again typical figures of $\rho = 10\%$ and $R_S = 0\cdot1$, we obtain

$$\frac{\delta\rho}{\rho} = 0\cdot04,$$

a result revealing that, a luminescence of 10% can be determined as

$$0.10 \pm 0.04,$$

using a line of depth 0·1. With the previous method, the fractional error was about five times larger (see Table II).

Even a luminescence of 0·01 can be found with a fractional error of about 0·2 using a line with $R_S = 0·1$, whereas previously it was below the limit of detectability.

The very act of observing the lines produces an apparent profile which is shallower than the true one, owing to the finite resolving power of the spectrometer. Whilst it is easily shown that the apparent profiles are still related to the luminescent intensity by the same equation, this effect necessarily increases the uncertainty in the result. Thus the ideal spectrometer should be more than adequate to resolve the narrowest line of interest.

The only possible way of achieving these improvements, and also removing the severe limitations on dynamic range which the photographic plate presents, is to use a spectrometer of high dispersion with a photoelectric device as detector. An instrument incorporating these advantages will be described in the next section.

V. The Ideal Luminescence Spectrophotometer

The observations described above have been used to arrive at a specification for an ideal instrument to observe lunar luminescence. If the spectrum is to be explored thoroughly many lines must be studied; and to allow reasonable photometric accuracy the spectrometer should completely resolve them. This suggests an instrumental profile of about 0·2 Å, which should correspond to the smallest details seen on the Moon, (i.e. the slit should subtend about 1 sec of arc on the sky). If the luminescent intensity is only a few per cent of the scattered sunlight, the photometry must not have errors greater than 1%.

Let us consider an idealized astronomical spectrometer as shown on Fig. 5. Light from the telescope mirror (diameter D_0) forms an image in the plane of the entrance slit. The size of this image will be the product of the focal length (F_0) of the telescope and the angle subtended by the object (the detail on the Moon being investigated). Let S and H represent the width and length of the entrance slit; F_c, the focal length of the collimator; and D_c, the aperture of the dispersing element. The angular dispersion $d\theta/d\lambda$, of this element is represented by D. The wavelength range given by the slit width will be

$$\delta\lambda = \frac{\delta\theta}{D} = \frac{S}{F_c D}. \tag{9}$$

The region studied on the Moon will be rectangular, with sides of angular extent

$$\alpha_H = \frac{H}{F_0}, \qquad \alpha_S = \frac{S}{F_0}. \tag{10}$$

If one wishes to study the lunar surface in the greatest detail, α_S and α_H will both be about 1 sec of arc, but for certain features (rays, for example) the slit may be placed along the object studied with a consequent increase in permissible slit length resulting in a greater signal. Equations (9) and (10) lead to the relation

$$\alpha_S = \frac{F_c D}{F_0}\delta\lambda \quad \text{or} \quad D = \frac{\alpha_S F_0}{\delta\lambda F_c} = \frac{\alpha_S D_0}{\delta\lambda D_c}$$

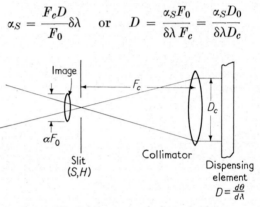

FIG. 5. Idealized astronomical spectrometer.

assuming that the focal ratios of telescope and collimator are equal. The flux of light ϕ from this object must be as high as possible to allow a short time of observation.

If B is the brightness of the lunar surface (photons/Å/sq. cm/sec/ster) then

$$\phi = \tfrac{1}{4}B\alpha_S\alpha_H\pi D_0^2\delta\lambda.$$

If we fix α_S ($= \alpha_H$) and $\delta\lambda$ at 1 sec of arc and 0·2 Å respectively, we see that (if D is expressed in seconds per Å)

$$D = 5\frac{D_0}{D_c}$$

and

$$\phi = \frac{B\pi}{20}D_0^2.$$

Thus the flux of light will increase with the area of the telescope mirror but to match a given telescope we will need to reach a certain product of diameter of dispersing element and dispersive power. If we consider a 50-inch mirror, we find that a grating of about 4″ diameter with a blaze angle of approximately 30° is required.

It has been shown that the low photometric accuracy of the photographic plate makes it of doubtful value in these observations. However, the photomultiplier cell can easily give an accuracy of 1%; and since the number of spectral elements to be investigated is only of the order of one or two hundred, its overall sensitivity will be comparable with that of the plate. (The photocell will be about one hundred times more sensitive, but the spectral elements must be explored sequentially and not simultaneously as with the plate.) The dark current of the cell will set the limit to the flux required, but the following calculation shows that with the instrument considered the flux is sufficient. The Moon can be regarded as having a brightness of $+3^m \cdot 5$ per square second of arc. One may assume a flux of some $1 \cdot 2 \times 10^5$ photons/sec/Å from an object of this size into a 50-inch mirror, leading to a rate of $2 \cdot 5 \times 10^4$ photons/sec into $0 \cdot 2$ Å. If the cell has a quantum efficiency of 10%, we may expect a photo-current of 4×10^{-10} A at the collector as compared with a dark current of the order of 10^{-12} A from a selected cell cooled with solid carbon dioxide. An integration time of ten seconds will reduce photon shot noise below the assumed uncertainty of 1%.

This calculation suggests that a d.c. amplifier and recorder can be used to display the line profiles as the spectrum is scanned across the exit slit of the spectrometer. Previous experiments have shown that the worst problem with such a photoelectric monochromator arises from scintillation, but with an extended object this is unlikely to cause trouble. In any case, the difficulty can be overcome by taking the ratio of the intensity measured at the exit slit to that entering the spectrometer.

The first instrument designed specifically to study lunar luminescence was constructed by the authors in 1959. The dispersing element is a Bausch and Lomb grating (135 × 110 mm, No. 33–53–18–36) mounted in the Fastie-Ebert system (Fastie, 1952). This spectrometer is designed for the Newtonian focus of the 125 cm diameter telescope at Asiago, and has a relative aperture of $f/5$. The theoretical resolving power of the grating is 320,000 in 2nd order, which leads to a minimum instrumental width of $0 \cdot 01$ Å at 4000 Å. Since it will normally operate with equal entrance and exit slit widths equivalent to $0 \cdot 2$ Å, the instrumental profile should be triangular, with good suppression of the wings. The focal length is 24 inches, giving a dispersion of 5 Å/mm at 4100 Å (the effective 2nd order blazed wavelength). A compromise between mechanical stability and lightness has been effected by mounting the two mirrors and the grating on the end plates of a magnesium alloy cylinder. A photomultiplier cell with a tri-alkali cathode (E.M.I. type No. 9588) is mounted behind the exit slit and can be cooled with solid CO_2. The grating is turned by a motor-driven micrometer screw which pushes an arm attached to the grating cell. Gears allow scanning

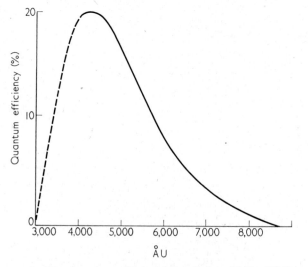

FIG. 6. Wavelength sensitivity of the photomultiplier (EMI 9588)

speeds between $\frac{1}{10}$ Å/min and $\frac{1}{2}$ Å/min. The electronic system comprises an AVO d.c. amplifier (type 1388B) and a potentiometric recorder; full scale deflection can be obtained from a current of 3×10^{-13} A (corresponding to a light flux at the photomultiplier cathode of a few tens of photons per second). The wavelength sensitivity of the photocell (Fig. 6) allows the range from 3500 to 6500 Å to be investigated. The spherical mirrors are figured to better than $\lambda/4$, but the combination of the small focal ratio and large off-axis angle (7°) gives rise to a flare around an astigmatic line focus. The flare is reduced significantly on stopping the instrument down to $f/7$. In addition, the mounting of the optical components inside the ends of the cylinder makes the instrument somewhat difficult to align. To overcome these difficulties, a second instrument is being constructed with the mirrors working in a Newtonian arrangement and mounted on a base plate (Fig. 7). The Newtonian mirrors entail no further loss of light since the Newtonian mirror of the telescope shadows them. This improved spectrometer will be more convenient to operate and should give a better optical performance.

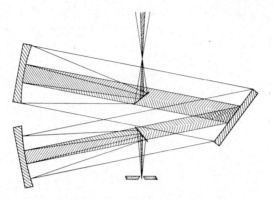

FIG. 7.   Improved luminescence spectrometer.

It will be used during the winter of 1960–61 to survey the complete lunar disk over a wide spectral range.

Preliminary scans have been made of lunar line profiles using a 7-inch objective lens at the Jodrell Bank Experimental Station. A typical scan is shown on the accompanying Fig. 8.

In addition to this observational programme, laboratory investigations of luminescence are in progress in the Faculty of Technology of

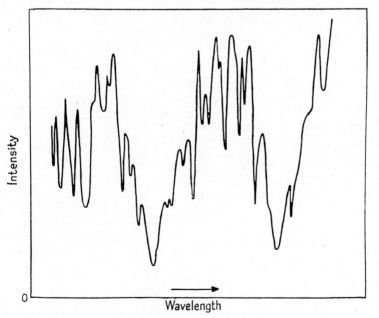

FIG. 8.   *H* and *K* line profiles in moonlight.

the University of Manchester. Typical powdered rock and meteoritic dust will be exposed in vacuum to fluxes of protons, electrons and ultra-violet radiation, and their luminescent spectrum measured by means of a photoelectric spectrometer. These experiments cannot positively identify the nature of lunar surface materials for the reasons mentioned earlier, but should yield important information about the efficiency of the various luminescence processes. It will be interesting also to see to what extent charge transfer can influence the mobility of the dust.

VI. Conclusions

Observations of several distinct characteristics of moonlight all point to the same conclusion—namely, the existence of luminescent regions on the lunar surface. Photometry of lunar eclipses, whilst strongly suggesting the existence of this phenomenon, is not a convenient method of investigation because of the infrequency of observations. Overall magnitude measurements call for extreme accuracy of photometry, and have best served to confirm the existence of some parasitic light by showing that the fluctuations of brightness are too large to be accounted for by any simple reflection effect.

The line depth method used by Dubois and Kozyrev has been shown to be a very powerful technique which is independent of atmospheric transparency and can be used to display the spectrum of the luminescence. We have shown that the photometric errors of photographic spectrometry have severely limited the application of this method so far and that recourse must be made to photoelectric techniques if it is to be fully exploited.

A spectrometer has been constructed specifically for this purpose and it is intended to obtain detailed spectra of the luminescence from a large number of points on the lunar surface. Complementary laboratory investigations will provide the information on quantum efficiencies necessary to an interpretation of these observations. In this way we hope ultimately to arrive at a better understanding of the nature of solar radiations in the vicinity of the Earth-Moon system.

References

Abbot, C. G. (1942). *Ann. Astrophys. Obs. Smithson. Instn.* **6**, 85.
Dubois, J. (1956). *Astronomie*, **70**, 225.
Dubois, J. (1957). *J. Phys.* **18**, 13S.
Dubois, J. (1959). *Rozp. Czech. Acad. Sci.* **69**, Pt. 6.
Fastie, W. (1952). *J. Opt. Soc. Amer.* **42**, 641.

Kozyrev, N. A. (1956). *Izv. Crimean Astrophys. Obs.* **16**, 148.
Link, F. (1933). *Bull. Astr.* **8**, 77.
Link, F. (1946). *C.R. Acad. Sci., Paris*, **223**, 976.
Link, F. (1947a). *Čas. Pěst. Math.* **72**, 65.
Link, F. (1947b). *Colloq. Int. Cent. Nat. Rech. Sci.* p. 308.
Link, F. (1950). *Trans. Int. Astr. Un.* **7**, 135.
Link, F. (1951). *Bull. Centr. Astr. Inst. Czech.* **2**, 131.
Link, F., and Siroky, J. (1951). *Bull. Astr. Inst. Czech.* **2**, 86.
Rougier, G. (1933). *Ann. Obs. Strasbourg*, **2**, 3.

CHAPTER 11

Temperatures on the Lunar Surface

WILLIAM M. SINTON

    I. Early Infrared Measurements of the Moon....................... 407
   II. Infrared Measurements of Lunar Temperatures................... 407
  III. Temperature of Moon in Eclipse................................ 411
   IV. Theoretical Analysis of the Surface Temperature Variation.......... 413
    V. Analysis of the Surface Temperature Variation During an Eclipse.. 417
   VI. Temperature Dependence of Thermal Conductivity and Specific Heat 418
  VII. Microwave and Millimetre-wave Observations..................... 419
 VIII. Interpretation of Microwave Temperatures....................... 421
   IX. Comparison of Measurements at Different Wavelengths............ 424
    X. Departures of Observations from the Theory and Model........... 426
       References.. 427

I. Early Infrared Measurements of the Moon

Lord Rosse was the first person to make a measurement of the temperature of the Moon. He began his measurements as early as 1868 and employed his 3-foot reflector at Parsontown (Rosse, 1869, 1870, 1872). The technique he employed became essentially that adopted by all observers of planetary radiation up until 1952. Two thermopiles, placed side by side at the focus of the telescope, were connected in opposition to the galvanometer. One of the thermopiles received the total light from the entire disk of the Moon while the other received sky light. He then eliminated the Moon's emitted energy with a glass plate. The difference of the deflections, after the latter deflection was corrected for reflection losses of the glass plate, gave the thermal emission. At full Moon the fraction transmitted by the glass was 15%. With reasonable assumptions about the atmospheric transmission and the albedo of the Moon, this yields 397°K for the effective temperature, in agreement with temperatures obtained by later observers. He also determined the variation of the Moon's total heat radiation with phase angle and this differs but little from later measurements by Pettit (1935). Subsequent observations of lunar heat were made by Langley (1884, 1887) and Very (1898, 1906).

II. Infrared Measurements of Lunar Temperatures

Pettit and Nicholson (1930) at the Mount Wilson Observatory did the most significant work on the temperature of the Moon. Very sensitive and delicate thermocouples were employed, and these were fitted with a rock-salt window on one side and a glass window on the other side to enable viewing of the telescopic image and the thermo-junctions. The two junctions were connected in electrical opposition to provide freedom from changes in ambient temperature. For most of the work a microscope cover glass was used as a filter to eliminate the heat radiation of the Moon. A galvanometer indicated the current produced in the junctions.

Many of the observations were made at the 100-inch telescope. For lunar work one receiver was focused on the Moon; the other was exposed to the sky. The thermocouples were exposed both with and without the cover glass. The difference, after correcting for reflection losses, gave the heat radiation beyond the cut-off of the cover glass at about 5μ. Calibration of the sensitivity of the equipment was made from observations of stars of well-known temperatures. Correction for absorption by the atmosphere was made in two steps. The fraction absorbed in regions where the atmosphere is opaque is calculated for each temperature. The part absorbed in the transparent regions was determined by plotting the log of deflection against the air mass during the observation.

Pettit and Nicholson established the maximum observed temperature of the lunar surface (407°K at the centre of the full Moon) and the minimum (120°K at the centre of the dark hemisphere). However, they found that the temperature of the subsolar point was not constant, but varied according to its position on the disk, as shown in the polar diagram of Fig. 1, which gives the total energy radiated as a function of the angle from the normal to the surface. They found that although the temperature of the subsolar point was 407°K at full Moon, it was only 358°K at quarter-phase; this phenomenon is a result of the roughness of the surface and will be discussed more later.

Since the subsolar point does not radiate as a Lambert surface with equal apparent temperature in all directions, we would like to calculate the temperature of a surface that emits in accordance with Lambert's law and would give the same total radiation as emitted by the subsolar point. Pettit and Nicholson found 391°K for this temperature. They compared the $1\cdot93$ cal cm^{-2}min^{-1} emission of the subsolar point with the theoretical emission obtained from the insolation. They took the solar constant to be $1\cdot95$ cal cm^{-2}min^{-1}; the amount of energy reflected by the Moon they measured as $0\cdot24$ cal cm^{-2}min^{-1}; and of the amount absorbed they assumed that $0\cdot1$ cal cm^{-2}min^{-1} was conducted inward at the subsolar point. This left only $1\cdot61$ cal cm^{-2}min^{-1} to be re-emitted compared to the observed $1\cdot93$ cal cm^{-2}min^{-1}. They assumed the difference of about 20% was due to an error in the transmission of the Earth's atmosphere used in the reduction. As we will see, in the theoretical analysis of the surface, only about 0·01 cal is conducted into the surface. There is also reason to believe that the solar constant is nearer 2·00 cal cm^{-2}min^{-1} (Stair *et al.* 1954). Their difference of

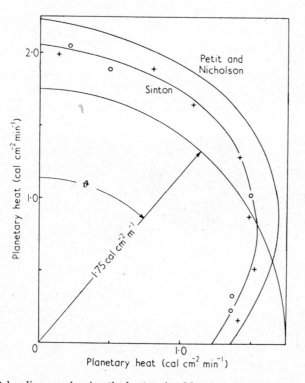

FIG. 1. Polar diagram showing the heat emitted by the subsolar point of the Moon as a function of the angle ϑ from the normal to the surface. Crosses and circles designate measurements before and after full Moon, respectively.

0·32 is reduced to 0·18 cal cm^{-2}min^{-1} which may have been produced by an erroneous transmission.

At Lowell Observatory we have been measuring the Moon using the most modern infrared techniques. We use the procedure of chopping rather than opposing junctions to eliminate drift; a narrow-band filter at 8·8μ where the atmosphere has high transparency; and a new procedure for evaluating atmospheric transmission that uses the square-root law (Sinton, 1959; Sinton and Strong, 1960). This square-root relation gives a more accurate determination of transmission.

The Lowell measurements are also shown on Fig. 1, and compared to Pettit and Nicholson we find about 5% less emission. The discrepancy between the theoretical total emission and the observed is now only 5%, and the temperature of the mean spherically emitting surface is 389°K.

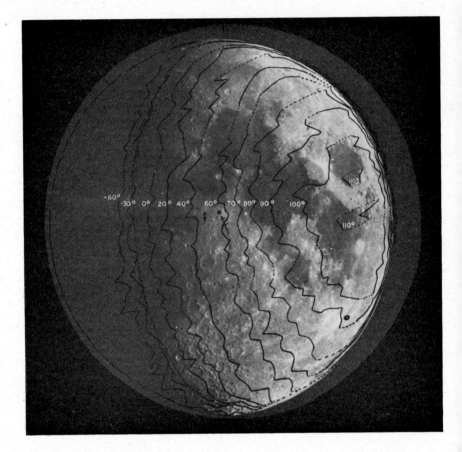

FIG. 2. Map of lunar isotherms on a simultaneous photograph of Moon.

The temperature at "midnight" is much less well determined. We have measured this temperature on several nights at Lowell (Sinton, 1959) and found 122 ± 3°K, which compares well with Pettit and Nicholson's 120 ± 5°K. However, we do not have observations at various obliquities in order to make an analysis as we did for the subsolar point.

Figure 2 shows one of the isothermal maps that recently have been made at Lowell (Geoffrion *et al.* 1960). The map was made by scanning the Moon in a television-like raster obtained from astronomical motions. Rotation of the Earth carried the telescope and receiver across the Moon in about 2 minutes to make the horizontal scans. Every 3 minutes the telescope was moved ahead to produce another scan. The vertical scanning was produced by the Moon's motion in declination. When the Moon is near the celestial equator, only about 3 hours are required to observe the whole Moon. The resolution employed has been about 25 seconds of arc and is commensurate with the distance between scans. About 60 scans in all are obtained.

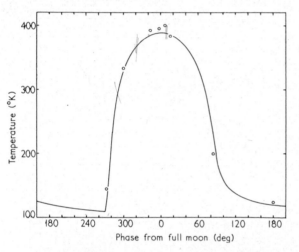

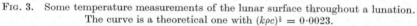

Fig. 3.   Some temperature measurements of the lunar surface throughout a lunation. The curve is a theoretical one with $(kpc)^{\frac{1}{2}} = 0 \cdot 0023$.

We may concentrate our attention on the measurements made at or near normal incidence of a point near the centre of the disk and establish the variation of the temperature throughout a lunation. From the maps of isotherms recently made at Lowell, we have taken some points on the illuminated part of the Moon and combined these with the measurement of the "midnight" temperature mentioned above, with the result shown on Fig. 3. Observations are being continued to complete this curve.

III. Temperature of Moon in Eclipse

Perhaps the most important single piece of information comes from measurements of the course of lunar temperatures during a total eclipse. Pettit and Nicholson (1930) measured a point only 48 seconds from the south limb during the eclipse of June 14th, 1927 (Fig. 4a). Pettit (1940) measured an area near the centre of the Moon's disk during the eclipse of October 27th, 1939 (Fig. 4b). Strong and Sinton (unpublished observations) made drift curves across the Moon's face

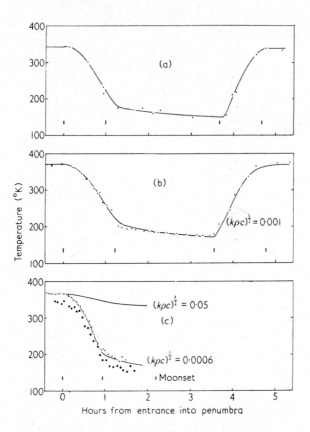

FIG. 4. Temperature measurements of lunar eclipses. (a) June 14, 1927 observed by Pettit and Nicholson. The curve is one drawn through the points. (b) October 27, 1939 observed by Pettit. The curve is a theoretical one computed by Wesselink. (c) July 26, 1953 observed by Strong and Sinton. The curves are theoretical ones taken from Jaeger. The large dots are for a point 2′ from the east limb and the small dots are for a point 9′ from the east limb. The vertical marks on the diagrams indicate the times of entering and leaving the penumbra and umbra.

during the eclipse of July 26th, 1953. All of these measurements are characterized by an extremely rapid change in temperature during the penumbral phase of the eclipse. In the hour that it takes a point on the Moon to move through the penumbra of the Earth's shadow, the temperature plummets from 374°K (the effective mean-spherical subsolar temperature obtained by Pettit and Nicholson is given) to about 200°K or lower at the beginning of totality. The Mount Wilson observations show that the temperature then proceeds to decline slowly until sunlight again falls on the Moon at the end of totality. The temperature rises very rapidly and by the end of the eclipse it is back to its starting point.

The measurements of Strong and Sinton also show an interesting effect when comparing the measurements of the limb to those of the centre. They chose five points from their drift curves corresponding to five lunar regions. Two of the regions (I and V) were 2' from the east and west limbs. Region III was in the centre of the disk and regions II and IV were between I and V, respectively, and the centre. Figure 4c shows the measurements of regions I and II. The central regions II, III, and IV, followed quite well the curve of Pettit for the 1939 eclipse and attained a temperature of 213°K at the commencement of totality. The limb regions, on the other hand, were much colder at the beginning of totality (190°K) and compare with the 174°K attained at a point closer to the limb in the 1927 eclipse. It may be argued that these limb regions were colder to begin with, but a little consideration will show that they have lost a much larger fraction of their total heat than the central regions. The significance of the limb effect will be discussed later; for first we need to gain an understanding of thermal conduction into the Moon's surface.

IV. Theoretical Analysis of the Surface Temperature Variation

We now proceed to develop a theory of the surface temperature of the Moon following the work of Epstein (1929), Jaeger (1953a), and Wesselink (1948). We will then compare this model with the observational data already presented.

The surface of the Moon is imagined as a homogeneous, semi-infinite solid material characterized by a thermal conductivity k, a density ρ, and a specific heat c. In such a material the temperature T at any depth x below the surface and at time t may be found from the one-dimensional heat-conduction equation,

$$\frac{\partial T}{\partial t} = \frac{k}{\rho c} \frac{\partial^2 T}{\partial x^2}. \tag{1}$$

The heat flux outward at any point is given by the equation,

$$F = k \frac{\partial T}{\partial x}. \tag{2}$$

In the case of the Moon, the surface receives heat I from the Sun and eventually re-radiates this to space. The boundary condition that must be obeyed is

$$\sigma T_0{}^4 = I + F_0 , \tag{3}$$

where σ is the Stefan-Boltzmann constant, and the subscript zero signifies the surface. We assume that during the half period when the Sun is shining on the surface the insolation is given by

$$I = \frac{G}{r^2}(1 - A)\cos 2\pi(t/P), \tag{4}$$

where G is the solar constant, r is the distance from the Sun in astronomical units, P is the period of rotation of the Moon, and A is the albedo of the surface. During the other half, when that part of the lunar surface is turned from the Sun, I is zero.

The solution of the equations cannot be found by Fourier series because of the non-linearity of the radiation term in the boundary condition. Wesselink has found one solution by a method of numerical integration. It is, however, tedious to do by hand but can probably be readily adapted to machine computation.

Jaeger, on the other hand, has found an easier iterative method, wherein a solution is first assumed and then modified according to where it is seen to fail.

For a given environmental situation involving a definite insolation and rotation period, there is a family of solutions which are given parametrically by the thermal inertia $(k\rho c)^{\frac{1}{2}}$. The thermal inertia measures the resistance of the surface to a change in temperature; the greater the value of $(k\rho c)^{\frac{1}{2}}$, the smaller is the temperature variation.

On Fig. 5 we present the curves of surface temperatures that have been computed. The thermal inertias are given in calories, centigrade degrees, and c.g.s. units. The curves with inertias of $0·001$, $0·002$, $0·004$, $0·008$, and $0·05$ have been taken from Jaeger, and the two remaining curves have been computed by the present author, one by each method. In computing the curves, the solar constant was assumed so as to make the maximum temperature $370°K$. In one of the previous sections we saw that this should be raised to $389°K$; this can readily be done by means of the homologous transformation that has been given by Wesselink.

If we substitute,

$$\left.\begin{array}{ll} T = \alpha T_* & x = \beta\alpha^{-3}x_* \\ (k\rho c)^{\frac{1}{2}} = \beta(k\rho c)^{\frac{1}{2}}_* & I = \alpha^4 I_* \\ t = \beta^2\alpha^{-6}t_* & F = \alpha^4 F_* , \end{array}\right\} \tag{5}$$

then the starred quantities are also solutions to equations (1) to (4). Since these transformations can change the time scale as well as the insolation, the solutions given on Fig. 5 can be used for other atmosphereless planets having different rotation periods and distances from the Sun. For our present case, to correct the temperature scale, we

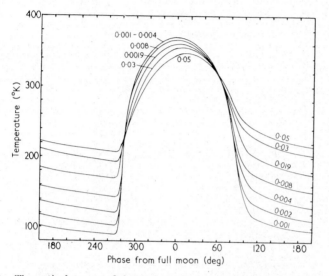

FIG. 5. Theoretical curves of the surface temperature variation for different values of the parameter $(k\rho c)^{\frac{1}{2}}$.

do not desire a change in time scale, and therefore $\beta^2 = \alpha^6$. The ratio of the temperatures, 389/370, gives $\alpha = 1\cdot05$ and $\beta = 1\cdot16$. The curve given on Fig. 3 is the transformed curve from Fig. 5 where the thermal inertia was $0\cdot002$. It may be seen that this gives a reasonably good fit to the experimental points. However, the critical "midnight" point is not accurately determined, and smaller inertias are indicated by eclipse observations.

The agreement shown on Fig. 1 demonstrates that our model of the Moon's surface works tolerably well and that the thermal inertia of the surface is very low. A search through tables of constants reveals that ordinary rocks, such as granite and basalt, have inertias near $0\cdot05$. Dry soils and sands range between $0\cdot01$ and $0\cdot02$. Pumice has one of the smallest inertias of natural materials but it is still of the order of $0\cdot004$. Even pumice does not offer an adequate explanation of the low inertia of the lunar surface.

But the reason that granulated natural materials do not have a sufficiently low conductivity is that their conductivity is greatly raised by air in the interstices. Smoluchowski (1910, 1911) investigated the thermal conductivity of powders at gas pressures down to a good vacuum. At a high vacuum the conductivity for an average of 11 grain sizes smaller than 0·1 mm was $k = 3 \times 10^{-6}$ cal cm^{-1}sec^{-1}(°C)$^{-1}$. If we combine this with a density of 1·5 and a specific heat of 0·2, typical of most rocks and minerals, we find $(k\rho c)^{\frac{1}{2}} = 0·001$. Powdered material or dusts in a vacuum therefore appear to offer a satisfactory explanation of the very low thermal inertia of the lunar surface.

Beneath the surface a thermal wave is propagated downward and satisfies equation (1). Here, we may use Fourier analysis, and the solution found at the surface is resolved into such a series. The surface variation is expressed as

$$T(0, t) = \sum_{n=0}^{\infty} T_n \cos(2\pi n t / P + \epsilon_n). \tag{6}$$

At any depth x below the surface, the temperature becomes

$$T(\xi, t) = \sum_{n=0}^{\infty} T_n e^{-2\pi\xi n^{\frac{1}{2}}} \cos(2\pi n t / P - 2\pi n^{\frac{1}{2}}\xi + \epsilon_n), \tag{7}$$

where $\xi = x/l$, and l is the wavelength of the fundamental wave given by $l = 2(\pi P k/\rho c)$. Equation (7) does not contain the diffusivity $k/\rho c$ explicitly but only through l so if we concentrate on ξ, we do not need to know the diffusivity. Each component wave is propagated into the material with a strong attenuation coefficient given by $2\pi n^{\frac{1}{2}}$. Since the wavelength of each component is $n^{-\frac{1}{2}}$, in one wavelength the wave is reduced to $e^{-2\pi}$ of its amplitude.

Using $(k\rho c)^{\frac{1}{2}} = 0·001$, we evaluate the T_n and ϵ_n and find the values given in Table I. We note that the fundamental wave lags behind the phase of the Moon by 6°. This phase shift is produced by the slow decay of the lunar temperature during the "night".

TABLE I

Fourier Series Parameters for Lunar Surface

n	T_n	ϵ_n
0	210°K	—
1	157	−6°
2	34	+6
3	30	159

The equation for the heat flux becomes in terms of ξ,

$$F = (4\pi P)^{-\frac{1}{2}}(k\rho c)^{\frac{1}{2}}\frac{\partial T}{\partial \xi},$$

and it too does not contain the diffusivity explicitly but only the inertia. At the surface the flux outward becomes

$$F_0 = \left(\frac{\pi}{P}\right)^{\frac{1}{2}}(k\rho c)^{\frac{1}{2}}\sum_{n=0}^{\infty}n^{\frac{1}{2}}T_n \cos\left(2\pi\frac{nt}{P}+\epsilon_n+\frac{\pi}{4}\right).$$

For the case $(k\rho c)^{\frac{1}{2}} = 0\cdot001$ and at $t = 0$ we find $F_0 = 0\cdot0077$ cal cm^{-2}min^{-1}, which we used in the comparison of the observed and theoretical temperature of the subsolar point.

Although the homogeneous model appears to give satisfactory agreement with the lunation infrared measures, a two-component model is suggested by some other observations. Jaeger (1953b) has given the surface temperature variation expected of a model consisting of a homogeneous base of rock or pumice with an inertia of $0\cdot05$ or $0\cdot008$ that is overlain by a thin "skin" of dust. He gives a parameter $D = T^{\frac{1}{2}}(k\rho c)^{-\frac{1}{2}}k'/d'$ where the unprimed quantities refer to the base material and k' and d' refer to the conductivity and thickness of the layer. He finds a satisfactory agreement with the observed lunation temperature curve with either $(k\rho c)^{\frac{1}{2}} = 0\cdot05$ or $0\cdot008$ and a $D = 0\cdot1$ or $0\cdot625$. If $(k'\rho'c')^{\frac{1}{2}} = 0\cdot001$ with $\rho' = 1\cdot8$ and $c' = 0\cdot2$, then $d = 0\cdot89$ cm. The present author believes that, at the moment, the observations are not of sufficient quality to decide between the two models.

V. Analysis of the Surface Temperature Variation During an Eclipse

Equations (1), (2), and (3) are applicable to the temperature change during an eclipse. Here, of course, the changes are much more rapid and I decreases from its largest value to zero within about an hour. Depending on the magnitude of the eclipse, the duration of totality may last up to 3 hours, and then emergence occurs in the same time as the initial penumbral phase.

Solutions may be found by numerical integration and such have been found by Wesselink and Jaeger for the homogeneous one-constituent model. Figure 4b shows the curve calculated by Wesselink for an inertia of $0\cdot001$, and reasonable agreement is found with the eclipse observations of Pettit in 1939. Pettit has assumed that the temperature before the eclipse was 370°K and the equipment was not otherwise calibrated. If we want to take 389°K for this temperature,

2E

we may use the transformation given before. The temperatures will be raised by 1·05 and the inertia will be raised to 0·0012.

It is seen in Figure 4b that the general range of the variation is correct, but that during totality the observed curve is much flatter than the computed. Jaeger and Harper (1950) have resolved this disagreement with the layer model described in the previous section. They have found for a thickness of 0·17 cm of dust with $(k'\rho'c')^{\frac{1}{2}} = 0\cdot00097$ overlying a base material having $(k\rho c)^{\frac{1}{2}} = 0\cdot01$ that better agreement with Pettit's observed curve is obtained. The data of Strong and Sinton appear to show greater slope in the umbral portion of the eclipse, but they employed a rather large aperture (3′·8) and smoothing effects may possibly be responsible for this.

Figure 4c shows a curve for homogeneous material with an inertia of 0·05. It is obvious that in the areas which have so far been observed there is a negligible amount of bare rock or lava. Strong and Sinton's measurements were taken from drift curves across the Moon and no regions with persisting warmth were found in these curves. We may say that the most part of the Moon's surface is covered by dust.

During the eclipse of March 13, 1960, Shorthill, Borough, and Conley (1960) discovered that the craters Aristarchus, Copernicus, and Tycho were warmer than their surroundings during totality. They estimated that Tycho was warmer by 40 to 60° Sinton (1960), observing during the eclipse of September 5, 1960, found that the temperature of Tycho was 238° K during totality. It did not seem to cool below this value and the general shape of the curve agreed with some of the curves of Jaeger and Harper (1950) for a layer of dust on top of rock. Sinton (1960) found that a layer of dust 0·3 mm thick on top of rock would satisfy the observations.

VI. Temperature Dependence of Thermal Conductivity and Specific Heat

So far it has been assumed that the thermal conductivity and specific heat are independent of the temperature. Both Wesselink and Jaeger have commented that these properties are not constant but both will decrease at low temperatures. Some evidence has been shown by Muncey (1958) that, for materials similar to those expected on the Moon, the conductivity and specific heat are proportional to absolute temperature. Equation (1) becomes with this substitution

$$\frac{\partial V}{\partial t} = \frac{k}{\rho c} \frac{\partial^2 V}{\partial x^2},$$

where $V = T^2$. We see that the same equation results but in terms of T^2. If we know the surface temperature variation, we can then find a solution beneath the surface by making a Fourier expansion of V. The constant term will give the time average of T^2 and this, rather than the average of T, will be constant with depth.

The solution of the surface variation again involves a non-linear term, and so has to be performed by numerical integration or other non-analytic methods. The writer is not aware that this solution has yet been made. Muncey has stated that one can expect the thermal inertia to be near 0·003 rather than 0·001 at a temperature of 300°K. The actual variation of surface temperature is not expected to be greatly different from what has been derived for the constant thermal inertia since the limits of the variation are established by observation. In the discussion that follows we will use the theory that has been developed for constant inertia, but reference will again be made to variation of the parameters when the microwave observations are compared with the infrared measurements.

VII. Microwave and Millimetre-wave Observations

The first microwave observation of thermal radiation from the Moon was made by Dicke and Beringer (1946). They made only one measurement at 1·25 cm wavelength. This was followed by extensive measurements of Piddington and Minnett (1949) at the same wavelength. Their antenna beam width at half-power points was $\pm \frac{3}{8}°$ and so it averaged over most of the lunar disk. Calibration of the antenna-receiving system was made by using a resistive termination of a wave guide which could be heated. They found that the equivalent antenna temperature followed a nearly sinusoidal variation given by

$$T = 39 \cdot 0 + 6 \cdot 6 \cos\left(\frac{2\pi}{P}t - \frac{\pi}{4}\right).$$

They have reduced their measurements to an average along the equator of the Moon. Using the antenna beam width and an assumed lunar emissivity of 0·90 they have corrected their temperatures to the variation at the equator. They obtained the equatorial temperature

$$T = 249 + 52 \cdot 0 \cos\left(\frac{2\pi}{P}t - \frac{\pi}{4}\right).$$

A number of later investigators have followed their lead and the lunar temperature has been observed in a wide range of wavelengths.

TABLE II

Microwave Temperatures of the Moon

Investigator	Ref.	λ	T_0'	T_1'	ψ	Emissivity assumed
Salomonovich	1958	0·8 cm	197 ± 20°K	32°K	40°	1
Gibson	1958	0·86	180 ± 18	30	39	1
Piddington and Minnett	1949	1·25	249 ± 13	52	45	0·9
Troitsky and Zelenskaya	1955	3·2	170 ± 34	<12	—	1
Akabane	1955	10	315 ± 50	36	45	1
Mezger and Strassl	1959	20·5	250 ± 30	<5	—	1
Seeger, Westerhout, and Conway	1957	75	185	<18	—	1

Where a monthly variation has been found it has nearly always been sinusoidal. Table II gives the constants that they have found in the following relation for the equatorial temperature.

$$T = T_0' + T_1' \cos\left(\frac{2\pi}{P}t - \psi\right).$$

Gibson (1958) had a beam width of only 0·2° and found definite asymmetry in drift curves across the Moon. He also found that the periodic variation of the lunar temperature was definitely non-sinusoidal and was similar to the theoretical curves of Jaeger that are given in the next section. The parameters given in Table II are the results of the author's analysis of Gibson's published curves.

Akabane (private communication) did not make a correction for the change in the apparent size of the Moon. This correction has been applied to his value of T_1' in Table II.

Microwave temperature measurements that have been made by other investigators, who did not secure sufficient material to trace an apparent temperature variation, are not listed in Table II. Most of these are at longer wavelength than 10 cm, and variation is probably negligible there. Westerhout (1958) observed on a single day at 21 cm, and found 245°K. Denisse and Le Roux (1957) found a temperature of 298°K at 33 cm. Coates (1959, 1960) made observations at 4·3 mm and found at the centre of the Moon at phase angles of 257°, 306°, and 100°, from full Moon, the apparent temperatures of 182°, 243°, and 245°K, respectively. The beam width was 6·7 minutes of arc.

Sinton (1955) observed with essentially optical techniques in a band centred at $\lambda = 0 \cdot 15$ cm. His beam width included the whole Moon. Effective temperatures ranged from 120°K near new Moon to a mean temperature of 336°K near full Moon. Much scatter was present and calibration, which was by means of solar observations, was difficult. But the measurements serve to show approximate agreement with the infrared measurements at 10μ.

Sinton (1956) also observed the total lunar eclipse of January 18th, 1954. He found that the initially observed temperature of 300°K dropped to about 170°K during the eclipse. Moreover, the observed temperature variation appeared to lag behind the optical eclipse by an hour. Thus the characteristics of 1·5 mm lunar radiation are somewhere between the infrared and the microwave behaviour. For a long-period variation in insolation, such as throughout a lunation, the apparent temperature variation is large and nearly in phase; while for a rapid variation, as during an eclipse, there is a small lag and the range of variation is reduced from that which is observed at 10μ. On the other hand, microwave observations of eclipses have always shown no change in apparent temperature (Gibson, 1958; Mezger and Strassl, 1959).

At Lowell Observatory the author, during the eclipse of March 13th, 1960, attempted to confirm the earlier 0·15 cm eclipse observations. The observed area was now restricted to 6′, and measurements were made of Mare Tranquilitatis. The signal-to-noise ratio was, however, much poorer than in 1954 and many clouds with more humid atmosphere hindered the observations. The data seem to show no variation during the eclipse, thereby casting some doubt on the previously found variation. Until further observations have been made, the earlier data will be used.

VIII. Interpretation of Microwave Temperatures

The small amplitude of variation and the phase lag of the microwave measures demonstrate that the radiation is arising from below the surface of the Moon. We have seen that the surface variation produces a thermal wave that propagates into the Moon with a rapid attenuation of amplitude. If we confine our attention to the radiation arising from a thin layer below the surface, the emission will have a phase lag characterized by the time for the thermal wave to propagate to this level and an amplitude variation corresponding to the temperature variation at this level. Actually, the emission comes partly from all levels and the apparent variation is the summation of the emission from these levels.

On Fig. 6 the radiation per unit solid angle and cm^2 arising at angle ϑ from a layer $d\xi = dx/l$ in the medium with absorption coefficient $\alpha = \alpha'/l$ and index of refraction n is, by Kirchhoff's law $n^2 B(\lambda, T)\alpha' \sec\vartheta d\xi$, where $B(\lambda,T)$ is the Planck's function. In the microwaves $B(\lambda,T)$ is approximated very well by the expression $CT\lambda^{-4}$, where C is constant. The emission suffers absorption of the amount

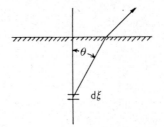

FIG. 6.   The emission at angle ϑ to the normal from a layer of thickness $d\xi$ beneath the surface of the Moon.

$1 - e^{-\alpha'\xi\sec\vartheta}$ in reaching the surface. Just above the surface the radiation will be given by

$$I = (1 - R)\alpha'\sec\vartheta \int_0^\infty B(\lambda, T)e^{-\alpha'\xi\sec\vartheta}d\xi, \qquad (8)$$

where R is the Fresnel reflection loss. Using the approximate expression for $B(\lambda,T)$ we find that the apparent microwave temperature is

$$T_a = \frac{I}{C\lambda^{-4}} = (1 - R)\alpha'\sec\vartheta \int_0^\infty T(\xi)e^{-\alpha'\xi\sec\vartheta}d\xi. \qquad (9)$$

In this discussion, by employing the reduced depth ξ, we have kept our attention upon quantities that are measurable from the emitted radiation. We continue this idea by introducing the mass absorption coefficient $\mu = \alpha/\rho$, in terms of which $\alpha' = (2\mu/C)(\pi P) \frac{1}{2}(k\rho c)^{\frac{1}{2}}$. Substituting this into (9) we have only the inertia, which we already know; the period of the Moon; the mass absorption coefficient, which does not depend on the state of division of the lunar matter; and the specific heat, which may be guessed fairly closely. From tables of specific heats it is seen that nearly all minerals and rocks have specific heats close to 0·2, with a dispersion less than 10%.

The expression (7) may be used for the temperature below the surface. Evaluating the integral in (9) we obtain for the apparent temperature, an expression of the form

$$T_a = (1-R)T_0 + (1-R) \sum_{n=1}^{\infty} T_n \frac{\cos[2\pi(nt/P) + \epsilon_n - \phi_n]}{(1 + 2\delta_n + 2\delta_n^2)^{\frac{1}{2}}},$$

where δ_n has been written for $(C/\mu\sec\vartheta)(n\pi/P)^{\frac{1}{2}}(k\rho c)^{-\frac{1}{2}}$ and $\phi_n = \tan^{-1} \delta_n/(1 + \delta_n)$. We have already seen from the observations that, generally, only the fundamental term is necessary in the summation. The strong attenuation of the overtone thermal waves makes others unimportant except at very short wavelengths. Furthermore, the maximum ϕ_n that is possible is $45°$. Since the fundamental wave already lags $6°$ behind the phase of insolation, the maximum possible lag from full Moon for observations of the centre of the lunar disk is $51°$. We may use either the observations of the ϕ, or the observations of the amplitudes of the fundamental waves to derive the mass absorption coefficient for different wavelengths. We take $(k\rho c)^{\frac{1}{2}} = 0.001$, $c = 0.2$, and $P = 2.55 \times 10^6$ sec. For observations of the centre of the disk sec $\vartheta = 1$. If observations extend over the entire visible disk and the dielectric constant is 5, then (sec $\vartheta)_{av}$ is only 1.05. In any event, the mean is not larger than 2. To eliminate possible calibration errors and the necessity of assuming an emissivity, we take the observed T_1'/T_0' and set it equal to $(1 + 2\delta + 2\delta^2)^{-\frac{1}{2}} T_1/T_0 = 0.748(1 + 2\delta + 2\delta^2)^{-\frac{1}{2}}$. Table III gives the μ's derived by the amplitude and phase lag methods. If the thermal inertia is 0.002, as indicated by lunation measures, instead of 0.001, then the values in Table III are all reduced to about one-half those given.

TABLE III

Mass Absorption Coefficients

Observers	λ	μ, (Amplitude Method)	μ, (Phase Method)
Salomonovich	0.8 cm	0.082 cm^{2}g^{-1}	0.107 cm^{2}g^{-1}
Gibson	0.86	0.083	0.119
Piddington and Minnett	1.25	0.107	0.045
Troitsky and Zelenskaya	3.2	<0.03	—
Akabane	10	0.052	0.045
Mezger and Strassl	20.5	<0.008	—
Seeger, Westerhout, and Conway	33	<0.044	—

Gibson has compared his observations with Jaeger's calculations for a homogeneous surface, as the observations show the presence of higher harmonics. However, the presence of the higher harmonics does not introduce any error into the determination of μ from the fundamental alone. On Fig. 7 his observations are compared with a computed curve with the parameter $C = \alpha(kP/\rho c)^{\frac{1}{2}} = (\mu/c)(k\rho c)^{\frac{1}{2}}P^{\frac{1}{2}} = 1\cdot25$. Gibson's measures have been scaled so that the average temperature is $210°K$; this has been done to avoid errors of calibration. A smaller C would doubtless fit the data better. However with $C = 1\cdot25$, $\mu = 0\cdot156$.

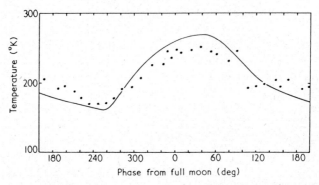

FIG. 7. Gibson's observations of lunar temperatures at $0\cdot86$ cm compared with Jaeger's theoretical curve having $C = 1\cdot25$ and $(k\rho c)^{\frac{1}{2}} = 0\cdot001$. The scale of Gibson's measurements has been increased by 17% to secure better fit.

It is possible that Akabane's observed variation is real if the Moon's surface has some resonance near 10 cm, but this is not likely. Microwave observations may possess a systematic error having the lunar period. The new Moon must be observed in the daytime and the full Moon must be observed at night. Therefore, the equipment is subjected to a temperature variation that has the period of one month.

IX. Comparison of Measurements at Different Wavelengths

The mass absorption coefficients from Table III have been plotted in Fig. 8 as a function of wavelength. Sinton (1956) has derived the mass absorption coefficient from his eclipse measurements at $0\cdot15$ cm by using some of the theoretical calculations of Wesselink. He has found $\mu = 2\cdot9$ g^{-1} cm^2 at this wavelength and this value is also given in Fig. 8.

The absorption in the millimetre region is very likely due to the strong crystal lattice vibrations occurring in the far-infrared region. The equation that relates the complex index of refraction to the crystal eigenfrequencies and damping constants is

$$(n-i\kappa)^2 = 1 + \sum_l \frac{A_l\lambda^2}{(\lambda/\lambda_l)^2 - 1 + iD_l\lambda}.$$

At wavelengths much beyond resonance this expression gives the extinction coefficient κ proportional to λ^{-1}. Since κ is defined as $4\pi\lambda\alpha$, α and μ are proportional to λ^{-2}. A line with this slope is plotted on Fig. 8 and the observations are seen to be in fair agreement with it.

Sinton also measured the mass absorption coefficients of some natural materials at $1\cdot5$ mm and found that the observed coefficient is closest to that of basalt. Recent measurements at Lowell of the

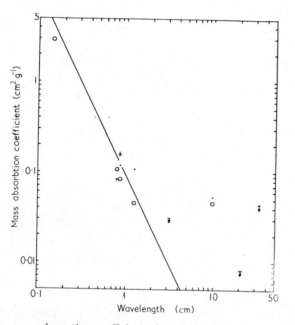

FIG. 8. The mass absorption coefficients from microwave observations at different wavelengths. Solid points are determined from the observed amplitude variation while open circles are from observed phase lags. The cross designates the value obtained from Jaeger's theoretical curve with $C = 1\cdot25$. When no significant temperature variation was found, arrows indicate the maximum permissible value. The line shows the wavelength variation expected theoretically.

mass absorption coefficients of some materials show that the Plainview and Morland stone meteorites have coefficients close to 9, while several tektites have coefficients near 2.

On Fig. 9 the average apparent temperatures at the various wavelengths have been plotted with their probable errors when these are given. In comparing these with the T_0 determined from the infrared observations, the actual temperatures should be raised about 10% to allow for the Fresnel loss at the surface. If we accept that the mean-square temperature is independent of depth, rather than the

mean temperature, then the observed mean temperature at 1 cm
would be only 1% lower than the constant temperature observed
at very long wavelengths. Obviously the measurements are not
sufficiently accurate to decide this. The mean infrared (surface)
temperature is 228° if the maximum of 389⁰ and "midnight" temperature of 120° are accepted. Then, with constancy of the mean-square
temperature, the microwave temperature should be about 16% higher
than the mean infrared or 265°. This temperature is significantly
higher than the mean microwave temperature even with the correction
for the emissivity.

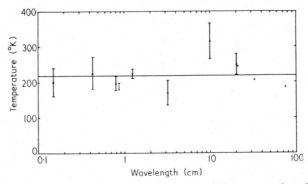

Fig. 9. Average lunar temperatures observed at different wavelengths. Probable
errors given by the various observers are shown by bars. The line is the mean of all the
measurements.

X. Departures of Observations from the Theory and Model

The model that has a layer of low thermal conductivity overlying
material having a conductivity comparable with that of rock or pumice was initially introduced to explain two discrepancies. One of
these was the rate of cooling during totality in Pettit's eclipse measurements. The data of Strong and Sinton suggest a greater cooling rate,
but their observations did not extend over a sufficiently long interval
to cast serious doubt upon the earlier work. The other reason for
introducing the new model was to explain an inconsistency between
the phase lags and the amplitude observed by Piddington and Minnett
(1949). It was not appreciated by these workers that the fundamental
thermal wave itself lagged by 6°. With this correction, the phase and
amplitude do not appear to be definitely inconsistent. At the moment
there does not seem to be much need to consider the more involved
models.

There are, however, other inconsistencies which do require an explanation. The first concerns the infrared variations found during a lunation and during an eclipse. The lunation measures require a thermal inertia close to 0·002 while the eclipse data require a value near 0·001. The variation of the conductivity and specific heat with temperature as introduced by Muncey would not explain this effect because, for the smaller temperature range occurring during an eclipse, a higher, rather than lower, average inertia would prevail than during a lunation.

The other modification which should be made is taking account of the roughness of the surface. We have evidence of its influence in two phenomena. One is the variation of the effective subsolar temperature with the angle of sight. The valleys, which cannot radiate into space through a complete hemisphere, are warmer than adjacent peaks. At a large angle to the vertical the valleys cannot be seen, and consequently a lower effective temperature is obtained as Fig. 1 shows.

Roughness also accounts for the lower inertia obtained near the limb during a lunar eclipse. Here the valleys, which cannot cool as rapidly as the peaks because of the restricted radiation angle, are again not seen. The inertia obtained from limb observations is more nearly representative of the lunar material since the peaks that are seen can radiate nearly to the full hemisphere.

It is evident that more theoretical as well as observational work is required to clear up these differences. More accurate microwave data are much desired at many wavelengths in order to obtain the absorption spectrum of the lunar surface.

References

Akabane, K. (1955) *Proc. Imp. Acad. Japan*, **31**, 161.
Coates, R. J. (1959). *Astrophys J.* **64**, 326.
Coates, R. J. (1960). Private communication.
Dicke, R. H. and Beringer, R. (1946). *Astrophys. J.* **103**, 275.
Denisse, J. F. and Le Roux, E. (1957), as quoted in Seeger, Westerhout, and Conway, 1957.
Epstein, P. S. (1929). *Phys. Rev.* **33**, 269.
Geoffrion, A., Korner, M., and Sinton, W. M. (1960). *Lowell Obs. Bull.* **5**, 1.
Gibson, J. E. (1958). *Proc. Inst. Radio Engrs*, **46**, 280.
Jaeger, J. C. (1953a). *Proc. Camb. Phil. Soc.* **49**, 355.
Jaeger, J. C., (1953b), *Aust. J. Phys.* **6**, 10.
Jaeger, J. C. and Harper, A. F. A. (1950). *Nature, Lond.* **166**, 1026.
Langley, S. P. (1884). *Mem. Nat. Acad. Sci.* **3**, 3.
Langley, S. P. (1887). *Mem. Nat. Acad. Sci.* **4**, 107.
Mezger, P. G. and Strassl, H. (1959). *Planetary Space Sci.* **1**, 213.

Muncey, R. W. (1958). *Nature, Lond.* **181**, 1459.

Pettit, E. (1935). *Astrophys. J.* **81**, 17.

Pettit, E. (1940). *Astrophys. J.* **91**, 408.

Pettit, E., and Nicholson, S. B. (1930). *Astrophys. J.* **71**, 102.

Piddington, J. H., and Minnett, H. C. (1949). *Aust. J. Sci. Res.* **A, 2**, 63.

Rosse, Lord (1869). *Proc. Roy. Soc.* **17**, 436.

Rosse, Lord (1870). *Proc. Roy. Soc.* **19**, 9.

Rosse, Lord (1872). *Proc. Roy. Soc.* **21**, 24.

Salomonovich, A. E. (1958). *Astr. J. U.S.S.R.* **35**, 129.

Seeger, C. L., Westerhout, G., and Conway, R. G. (1957) *Astrophys. J.* **126**, 585.

Shorthill, R. W., Borough, H. C., and Conley, J. M. (1960). Paper presented at the June 17, 1960 meeting of the Astr. Soc. of the Pacific.

Sinton, W. M. (1955). *J. Opt. Soc. Amer.* **45**, 975.

Sinton, W. M. (1956). *Astrophys. J.* **123**, 325.

Sinton, W. M. (1959). *Lowell Obs. Bull.* **4**, 260.

Sinton, W. M. (1960). *Lowell Obs. Bull.* **5**, 23.

Sinton, W. M., and Strong, J. (1960). *Astrophys. J.* **131**, 470.

Smoluchowski, M. (1910). *Bull. Acad. Sci. Cracovie*, **A**, 129.

Smoluchowski, M. (1911). *Bull. Acad. Sci. Cracovie*, **A**, 548. See also *Int. Crit. Tab.* **2**, 315.

Stair, R., Johnston, R. G., and Bagg, T. C. (1954). *J. Res. Nat. Bur. Stand.* **53**, 113.

Troitsky, B. S., and Zelinskaya, M. R. (1955). *Astr. J. U.S.S.R.* **32**, 550.

Very, F. W. (1898). *Astrophys. J.* **8**, 265.

Very, F. W. (1906). *Astrophys. J.* **24**, 351.

Wesselink, A. J. (1948). *Bull. Astr. Insts Netherlds*, **10**, 356.

Westerhout, G. (1958). *Bull. Astr. Insts Netherlds*, **14**, 215.

REVIEW AND INTERPRETIVE ARTICLES

Garstang, R. H. (1958). *J. Brit. Astr. Ass.* **68**, 155.

Gilvarry, J. J. (1958). *Astrophys. J.* **127**, 751.

Jaeger, J. C. (1953). *Aust. J. Phys.* **6**, 10.

Pawsey, J. L., and Bracewell, R. N. (1955) "Radio Astronomy", Chapter VIII. Oxford Univ. Press.

Chapter 12

Radio Echo Studies of the Moon

J. V. Evans

I. Introduction : the Radar Equation............................ 429
II. Factors Influencing the Intensity of the Echoes.................. 435
   A. The Variation of the Range of the Moon..................... 435
   B. Refraction Effects....................................... 436
   C. Absorption of Radio Waves................................ 437
   D. Radio Noise Reflected by the Moon........................ 437
   E. Doppler Effects... 438
III. The Directivity Factor g................................... 439
IV. The Librations of the Moon................................. 441
   A. The Libration in Latitude............................... 441
   B. The Libration in Longitude.............................. 441
   C. The Diurnal Libration................................... 441
   D. Physical Libration...................................... 442
V. Pulse Length Considerations................................. 444
VI. The Early Experiments..................................... 446
VII. The Later Experiments..................................... 452
VIII. Summary of the Results.................................... 468
IX. Discussion of the Results................................... 469
X. The Lunar Ionosphere...................................... 477
XI. Conclusion.. 477
   References.. 478

I. Introduction: the Radar Equation

The radio-echo or radar method of studying distant objects was developed principally for investigating the Earth's ionosphere before 1939. The advent of war stimulated the development of radar techniques, and the design of suitable transmitting, receiving and recording equipment. But it was not until towards the end of the war when very high power radar systems could be made, that it became possible to detect radio echoes from the Moon. Several workers (De Witt and Stodola, 1949; Bay, 1946) then attempted this experiment, without having any particular object in view, other than solving a difficult technical problem. The results obtained in these early experiments, which are reviewed in a later section of this chapter, showed certain unexpected features. In consequence, Moon-echo studies have continued until the present time, and the scattering properties of the Moon are now fairly well understood.

The reason why this work requires a high power radar system can

429

be seen from the following argument. Consider a radio transmitter driving a power P_t watts into an aerial system, which radiates equally in all directions. Then the radio flux density at a point R metres distant is

$$\text{Flux density} = \frac{P_t}{4\pi R^2} \text{ watts m.}^{-2} \tag{1}$$

To increase the flux density at the target an aerial system may be employed which directs the signals towards the target. If such an aerial system has a gain G over an isotropic radiator, the flux density at the target becomes

$$\text{Flux density} = \frac{P_t G}{4\pi R^2} \text{ watts m.}^{-2} \tag{2}$$

Where this aerial system takes the form of a reflector having an aperture A, over which the transmitter power is uniformly distributed in such a way that a plane wave is produced, the gain G is given by

$$G = \frac{4\pi A}{\lambda^2}, \tag{3}$$

where λ is the radio wavelength. For a parabolic reflector, which is perhaps the type most frequently used, the value of A should be taken as being 50% to 65% of the area across the mouth of the parabola. This is because it is not possible to arrange for all the transmitter power to be uniformly distributed over the surface of the reflector. The actual value of the efficiency as well as depending upon this effect may also be influenced by others such as (i) irregularities in the shape of the reflecting surface which cause it to depart from the true paraboloidal surface, and (ii) leakage of power through the reflecting surface, (where this is constructed of mesh and not sheet metal). Thus in equation (3) A represents the effective aperture of the aerial system.

The power radiated by the transmitting aerial forms a cone of radiation, whose angular width is termed the beamwidth. This is usually defined as the angular distance between the points which are half the power intensity observed along the axis of the beam. The beamwidth decreases as the aerial gain G is increased, and to achieve a pencil beam having an angular width comparable with the angular diameter of the Moon ($\sim \frac{1}{2}°$) a gain of the order of 200,000 would be required. At the present time only one or two aerial systems have such a high gain, and for most aerials it would be justified to assume that the flux density will be constant over the area presented by the Moon's disk. (The case where this approximation does not hold has been considered by Winter, 1956.) Thus if a is the radius of the Moon the total power intercepted by the Moon's disk is

$$\text{Power} = \frac{P_t G}{4\pi R^2} \cdot \pi a^2 \text{ watts .} \tag{4}$$

A perfectly conducting metal sphere whose radius is much greater than the radio wavelength would re-radiate all the incident energy isotropically. Since the Moon is not a metal sphere, but a body whose surface has a reflection coefficient ρ the re-radiated energy is approximately given by

$$\text{Power} \simeq \frac{P_t G}{4\pi R^2} \cdot \rho \pi a^2 \text{ watts .} \tag{5}$$

Here ρ is the reflection coefficient of any element of the surface, at normal incidence. In the case of the Moon it is probable that ρ varies over the surface. If the nature of the surface material were known with complete certainty ρ could be calculated by measuring the dielectric constant of similar materials on the Earth. Where k_1 is the dielectric constant ρ is given by

$$\rho = \frac{(\sqrt{k_1} - 1)^2}{(\sqrt{k_1} + 1)^2} . \tag{6}$$

The dielectric constant k_1 for dry terrestrial rock or powdered rock is of the order of 5, which yields a value for ρ of 0·146. Since the Moon's albedo is low (0·07) this is probably an over-estimate and a value $\rho = 0\cdot1$ will be assumed here.

The possibility that the Moon possesses a critically dense ionosphere must not be overlooked. This question will be discussed in more detail later, but it would appear from radio star occultation measurements (see Chapter 5 on "Polarization" and "Investigation of an Atmosphere"), that the lunar ionosphere does not have a density greater than 10^4 electrons cm^{-3}. Since the relationship between the number density n_e of the electrons and the corresponding critical (or plasma) frequency f_c (measured in megacycles) is

$$n_e = 1\cdot24 \times 10^4 \cdot f_c^2 , \tag{7}$$

it follows that the critical frequency for the lunar ionosphere is probably not greater than 1 Mc/s. On the other hand, radiowave frequencies of not less than about 10 Mc/s must be used in order that the waves can penetrate the Earth's ionosphere and reach the Moon.

The total power re-radiated by the Moon (equation (5)) may be scattered equally in all directions, or there may be favourable reflection back towards the Earth. This will depend upon the size and distribution of the surface irregularities, and a directivity factor g may be used to denote the gain of the Moon over an isotropic reflector when viewed from the same position as the transmitter. Possible theoretical values for g range from 1·0 when all the irregularities on the surface are assumed to be less than $\lambda/8$, to about 6 when the surface is considered to be very rough with irregularities whose average size is much greater than the radio wavelength. These theoretical models will be discussed fully later, and here it will be assumed that g has a value near unity. Hence, the flux density of the reflected radio power at the surface of the Earth is

$$\text{Flux density} = \frac{P_t G \rho g \pi a^2}{(4\pi R^2)^2} \text{ watts m.}^{-2} \tag{8}$$

If the aerial used for transmitting is also used for receiving the signals, then the power presented at the receiving input terminals is

$$P_r = \frac{P_t G A \rho g \pi a^2}{(4\pi R^2)^2} \text{ watts .} \tag{9}$$

If we insert for the gain G from (3), equation (9) becomes

$$P_r = \frac{P_t A^2 \rho g a^2}{4\lambda^2 R^4} \text{ watts .} \tag{10}$$

This power will only be observable (in a simple radar system) if it exceeds the noise power P_n developed in the receiver. This is the sum of the radio noise received from the sky by the aerial system, and that produced by the random arrival of the electrons at the anode of the first amplifying stage in the receiver. This latter component of the noise may be reduced by employing any of the special receiving devices which have been recently developed, such as the maser or reactor diode parametric amplifier. These devices produce little unwanted noise, but that due to the sky brightness cannot be eliminated. The total noise power P_n at the receiver input terminals is given by

$$P_n = [(n-1)T_0 + T_a]kb \text{ watts,} \tag{11}$$

where n is the receiver noise factor (which describes the number of times the noise power developed at the input of the receiver when terminated by a matched load at room temperature would exceed that developed in the load alone); T_0 is room temperature $\simeq 290°\text{K}$; T_a is the effective aerial temperature, which is a function of both the frequency of the radio waves and the direction in which the aerial beam is pointed; k is Boltzmann's constant ($1\cdot38 \times 10^{-23}$ watts.deg^{-1}), and b is the energy bandwidth of the receiver which may be defined as

$$b = \frac{1}{\overline{V}^2} \int_0^\infty V^2(f)df \quad \text{cps} .\tag{12}$$

Here V is the overall voltage gain of the receiver at frequency f. The variation of the aerial temperature T_a with frequency f is shown approximately on Fig. 1. The actual value of T_a observed will be higher than indicated on Fig. 1 if the aerial beam is directed towards the Sun, the plane of the galaxy or any other strong source of radio waves (such as the sources in the constellations of Cassiopeia or Cygnus). The signal to noise ratio in the receiver is

$$\frac{P_r}{P_n} = \frac{P_t A^2}{4\pi k b [(n-1)T_0 + T_a]\lambda^2} \cdot \frac{g\rho\pi a^2}{R^4} .\tag{13}$$

This is known as the radar equation, and the product $g\rho\pi a^2$ is generally replaced by a term σ which denotes the scattering cross-section of the target.

Some estimate of the performance required of a radar system to detect echoes from the Moon can be gained by assuming that $\lambda = 2\cdot5$ metres, then T_a is not very different from T_0 and equation (13) becomes

$$\left.\begin{aligned}\frac{P_r}{P_n} &= \frac{1}{4\pi k T_0} \cdot \frac{P_t A^2}{n\lambda^2 b} \cdot \frac{g\rho\pi a^2}{R^4} \\[2mm] &= 1\cdot93 \times 10^{19} \cdot \frac{P_t A^2}{n\lambda^2 b} \cdot \frac{g\rho\pi a^2}{R^4} .\end{aligned}\right\}\tag{14}$$

The mean range R to the Moon is $3\cdot844 \times 10^8$ metres, the radius $a = 1\cdot738 \times 10^6$ metres, and assuming $g = 1\cdot0$ and $\rho = 0\cdot1$ the target term

$$\frac{g\rho\pi a^2}{R^4} = 4\cdot35 \times 10^{-23}\text{m.}^{-2} .\tag{15}$$

Hence,
$$\frac{P_r}{P_n} = 8\cdot35 \times 10^{-4}\left(\frac{P_t A^2}{n\lambda^2 b}\right).\tag{16}$$

Thus the performance figure of the equipment $(P_t A^2/n\lambda^2 b) \geqslant 10^4$ for the echoes to be observable. In the early experiments this was achieved largely by reducing the receiver bandwidth b to the lowest practicable limit. Whilst it might be thought that almost any signal-to-noise ratio can be achieved by this means, this is not so. In radar systems the transmitted signals usually take the form of pulses. If these are of length τ seconds, then the transmitted waves are found to cover a band of frequencies approximately $1/\tau$ cycles wide. The actual spectrum is given by the Fourier transform of the pulse envelope, and if the band-width b is made less than this the signal-to-noise ratio will deteriorate.

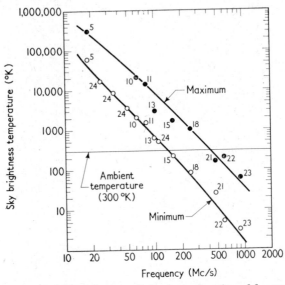

Fig. 1. The variation of the sky temperature as a function of frequency (after Kraus and Ko, 1957). The numbers adjacent to the points are reference numbers for the different observers listed by Kraus and Ko.

A theorem discovered independently by Wiener, Hansen, North and Van Vleck states that the optimum signal-to-noise ratio is achieved when the receiver bandwidth just accommodates all the frequencies in the spectrum of the transmitted signals. In most radar systems the criterion for optimum bandwidth is further complicated by such factors as the sweep frequency of the displays and the persistence of vision of the eye (Lawson and Uhlenbeck, 1950a). In practice, the frequency stability of the transmitter or receiver, and the necessity of detuning the receiver from the transmitter frequency to compensate for Doppler shifts (to be discussed later), may prevent b from being made as small as required for the optimum signal-to-noise ratio.

In many of the early experiments b was around 50 cps and λ in the region of 2·5 metres. Then, with a noise factor n of about 3, it follows from equation (16) that

$$P_t A^2 \geqslant 10^7 \text{ watts.m}^4 \qquad (17)$$

for echoes to be detectable. Hence, if a transmitter power of 10 kW were available, an aperture A of about 100 m² would also be required. Transmitter powers of this order at frequencies around 120 Mc/s, and aerial systems in the vicinity of 100 m² aperture were not developed until there was a demand for them during the war.

In the calculation outlined above no mention has been made of the influence of the Moon on the spectrum or duration of the echo. This will depend upon the scattering mechanism at the surface, and is discussed in the following sections. Also there has been no consideration of the relation of the length of the transmitter pulses to the time taken for the radio waves to travel from the front edge of the Moon to the limbs and back (11·6 milliseconds). This time is called the radar depth of the target, and the pulse length τ must exceed this if the whole surface is to be illuminated and, therefore, effective in scattering at the same time. Provided that this condition is fulfilled, then the above calculation is in the main correct. Where, however, $\tau \ll 11·6$ milliseconds there will never be a time when the entire surface is illuminated, and the target term $g\rho\pi a^2/R^4$ must be reduced by a factor which depends upon the pulse length and type of scattering which occurs at the Moon's surface.

II. Factors Influencing the Intensity of the Echoes

It can be seen from equation (14) in the previous section that, for a radar system which has been calibrated so that the equipment parameters are known, the measurement of the signal-to-noise ratio P_r/P_n for the echoes will provide a determination of the product ρg. These quantities define the way in which the Moon scatters radio waves. In attempts to measure P_r/P_n other additional factors may influence the echo intensity, and these will now be discussed.

A. The Variation of the Range of the Moon

The mean range of the Moon is about 384,400 km (235,000 miles) which produces and echo delay of 2·56 seconds. Because the Moon travels in an elliptical orbit, the actual range may vary over $\pm 8\%$ of the mean range. Thus the Moon can be considered to move in a circle about a point 384,400 km distant from the Earth. The point itself has a circular geocentric motion with a monthly period and a radius of 30,600 km, and as a result the echo power will vary by ± 30% (about ± 1 dB). The accuracy achieved in most radar experiments is insufficient for this to be detected, and Fricker *et al.* (1958) appear to be the only workers who have observed this variation of echo power during the month. Even they were unable to observe the small variations (about 0·2 dB) introduced by the rotation of the Earth. The range changes caused by the motion of the Moon relative to the Earth, and the Earth's rotation, are easily observed in the variation of the echo delay time. Such measurements of the distance of the Moon have been a subject of special study (Yaplee *et al.* 1958; Hughes, 1957) and some of the results are discussed in the first chapter on "The Motion of the Moon in Space".

B. REFRACTION EFFECTS

Radio waves do not travel from the surface of the Earth out into space along perfectly straight paths, but are subject to refraction both by the air in the troposphere, and by the Earth's ionosphere. These two sources of refraction may be considered separately. Radio waves, like light waves, are refracted by the troposphere by an amount which may be as large as 1° for observations along the horizon. The presence of water vapour in the atmosphere increases the refractive index μ for radio waves above that for light. Thus, for radio wavelengths,

$$\mu = 1 + \frac{79}{T} \times 10^{-6} \left(P - \frac{P'}{7} + \frac{4800P'}{T} \right),$$

where T is the absolute temperature, P is the atmospheric pressure in millibars and P' the partial pressure of water vapour also in millibars. At elevation angles θ greater than about 20° the refraction $\Delta\theta$ is given approximately by $(\mu - 1) \cot \theta$. For an elevation of 45°, $\Delta\theta$ is about 1 min of arc, and below 20° it is necessary to take into account the curvature of the Earth and the change in the refractive index with height. Hence, observations made with an aerial system whose beamwidth is < 1° are liable to be in error below about 10–20° elevation.

The refraction of radio waves due to the ionosphere is a function of the radio wavelength. It can only be neglected where the radio-wave frequency f exceeds the critical frequency f_c about 10 times, and the elevation angles are greater than about 10°. Kerr and Shain (1951) discuss the effect which the ionosphere might have where these conditions do not apply. Their treatment of the problem suggests that where $f \simeq 2\frac{1}{2} f_c$ the refraction can be as large as 15° for observations on the horizon. Both atmospheric and ionospheric refraction serve to increase the angle of arrival of the radio waves. Thus signals can be received from, say, an artificial Earth satellite for some time after it appears to have "set".

The ionosphere can also introduce small errors in the apparent azimuth of the Moon, where there are marked east-west gradients in the total number of electrons in the ionosphere. Smith (1952) observed apparent displacements of the positions of four radio stars at 3·7 m of about ± 20 sec of arc.

Thus, to summarize, for observations of the Moon at elevations greater than 10° with aerials employing beamwidths of > 1° atmospheric refraction can be neglected. Ionospheric refraction also can be neglected if the radio wave frequency is about 10 or more times greater than the critical frequency.

C. ABSORPTION OF RADIO WAVES

For radio wavelengths greater than about 25 cm the attenuation caused by the Earth's atmosphere is negligible. At wavelengths lying between 25 cm and about 2 cm there is some attenuation caused chiefly by oxygen ($\sim$ ·02 dB/km at 10 cm), and for wavelengths shorter than 2 cm both oxygen and water vapour cause serious attenuation due to absorption resonances (water vapour first at 1·3 cm and then oxygen at 0·5 cm where the attenuation rises to about 14 dB/km). Below about 1 mm the atmosphere is effectively opaque.

At long radio wavelengths ($\sim$ 10 metres) serious absorption can be introduced in the ionosphere where the air molecules exert a damping effect (due to collisions) on the electrons which are trying to oscillate in the presence of the electric field of the radio wave. The absorption is greatest in the D and E regions of the ionosphere (where the density of the air molecules is relatively high), but there is also serious attenuation in the F region at frequencies close to the critical frequency. Here again the influence of the ionosphere can only be neglected at frequencies of the order of 10 times the critical frequency (say 100 Mc/s). At lower frequencies the attenuation will be a function of the critical frequencies of the various ionospheric layers, and the length of the ray path through the ionosphere. (For a more complete discussion of these effects see Hanbury Brown and Lovell "The Exploration of Space by Radio" (1957).)

D. RADIO NOISE REFLECTED BY THE MOON

Radio waves generated by the Sun and arriving at the surface of the Earth after reflection by the Moon should be about 60 dB weaker than the waves arriving by direct paths. Thus it is just possible that the most intense solar outburst of radio noise could contribute to the noise level in the receiver, after reflection at the Moon (Kerr and Shain, 1957). At frequencies above about 400 Mc/s the actual thermal noise radiated by the Moon (which behaves like a black-body radiator at a temperature of about 200°K) may be an important contribution to the total receiver noise in any system which employs both a narrow aerial beam and a receiver with a low noise factor (see Chapter 11 on "Temperatures on the Lunar Surface" for details of radio-wave observations of the Moon's temperature).

E. DOPPLER EFFECTS

Because the Moon moves in an elliptical orbit it will, in general, possess a component of velocity towards the centre of the Earth. This has a maximum value

$$v_1 = \pm \frac{2\pi \times 30{,}600 \text{ km}}{28 \text{ days}} = \pm 80 \text{ metres/sec.}$$

In addition to this relative motion of the Moon and the Earth, an observer on the surface of the Earth will have a velocity component v_2 in the line of sight due to the rotation of the Earth given by

$$v_2 = \pm \frac{2\pi \text{ Earth's radius} \times \cos L \times \cos \delta \times \sin HA}{\text{Earth's rotation relative to the Moon}},$$

where L is the observer's latitude, δ the Moon's declination and HA the local hour angle. This has a maximum value on the equator of the Earth at moonrise (or moonset), when it is of the order of ± 500 metres/sec. The two components of motion may be added to give the velocity dR/dt of the observer relative to the centre of the Moon. The Doppler shift Δf of the returned signal is then simply

$$\Delta f = 2\frac{dR}{dt} \cdot \frac{1}{\lambda},$$

where the transmitter and receiver are at different locations A and B,

$$\Delta f = \frac{1}{\lambda}\left(\frac{dR_a}{dt} + \frac{dR_b}{dt}\right),$$

and dR_a/dt is given by (see Fricker et al. 1958)

$$\frac{dR_a}{dt} = \frac{R_0 - r_a \cos\psi}{R_a}\frac{dR_0}{dt} - \frac{r_a R_0}{R_a}\frac{d}{dt}(\cos\psi),$$

where R_a is the range of the centre of the Moon to the observer at A,
  R_0 is the distance between the centre of the Moon and the centre of the Earth,
  r_a is the radial distance from A to the centre of the Earth,
  ψ is the angle at the centre of the Earth between the lines drawn to A and the centre of the Moon.

For a wavelength $\lambda = 3$ metres, Δf can be as large as $\pm$ 250 cps, and where a narrow receiver bandwidth is employed some provision must be included to permit the receiver frequency to be adjusted relative to that of the transmitter. Careful measurements of the Doppler shift of the echoes have been made by Blevis (1957), Fricker et al. (1958), and Pettengill (1960) but have not yet revealed any systematic differences between the predicted and observed Doppler shifts. Thomas (1949) considered the possibility that the radius of the Earth might be determined from such observations. He concluded that the changes in the position of the effective scattering centre of the Moon would be sufficient to prevent the Doppler shift from being measured precisely. The radius of the Earth can be determined in experiments where direct range measurements of the Moon are made (Yaplee et al. 1958). It would seem possible in principle to redetermine the figure of the Earth by accurate range measurements of the Moon made at a sufficiently large number of observing sites.

III. The Directivity Factor g

It was stated in the first section that although the Moon may behave as an isotropic re-radiator of the incident radio waves (in which case $g = 1$) it could also reflect favourably in the direction of the Earth ($g > 1$). Isotropic re-radiation will only take place where the surface is smooth, i.e. all irregularities are less than about $\lambda/8$. In this case only the first few Fresnel zones at the front of the Moon are effective in scattering power to the Earth. Since at $\lambda = 3$ metres the first Fresnel zone has a radius of just over 1 km, an observer with radio-sensitive vision would see a small bright spot at the centre of the Moon.

Because the Moon is known to have a rugged terrain, most early workers considered alternative models of the scattering mechanism. Their ideas were largely influenced by the behaviour of the Moon at optical wavelengths. Thus Kerr and Shain (1951) proposed a model in which the distribution of the brightness across the Moon's disk was supposedly uniform. This type of scattering can arise where the surface irregularities have smooth sides but are themselves much larger than the wavelength. In this case the mountains near the limbs of the Moon scatter back along the line of sight and screen from view those regions which would not give favourable reflection. This form of scattering (Lommel-Seeliger) is approximately observed for light waves and Kerr and Shain (1951) deduced a value for the directivity g of 5·7 from the figures for the variation with phase of the optical brightness of the Moon given by Russell, Dugan and Stewart (1945).

Grieg, Metzger and Waer (1948) considered Lambert scattering. This type of scattering occurs where the average irregularity has a size approximately equal to the wavelength; and for a curved surface, such as the Moon's, this introduces some limb darkening. Grieg, Metzger and Waer calculated a value for g of 8/3 for this type of scattering. In Lommel-Seeliger scattering the power radiated per unit solid angle from a small element of the surface is independent of the direction. For Lambert scattering the power radiated per unit solid angle, at an angle ϕ to the normal is

$$P\phi = P_N \cos\phi,$$

where P_N is the power radiated along the normal. These two forms

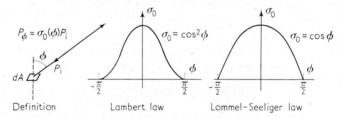

FIG. 2. The variation of the scattering cross-section σ_0 of an elemental area dA as a function of the angle between the line of sight and the normal, for both Lambert and Lommel-Seeliger scattering. P_i is the incident power and $P\phi$ the power reflected along the same ray path (after Green, 1959).

of reflection are illustrated on Fig. 2. Pettit and Nicholson (1930) observed that at infra-red wavelengths the Moon appeared to scatter according to the law

$$P\phi = \frac{0\cdot46 P_N \cos\phi}{0\cdot46 \cos\phi + \sin\phi}.$$

Winter (1956) calculated the value for g for this law, and obtained $g = 2\cdot5$.

It has so far been assumed that the directivity of the Moon is independent of the aspect from which it is viewed. The sunlight reflected from the Moon's surface has originated from many incoherent sources. Thus the optical brightness does not show any marked rapid fluctuation.

In a radar system, on the other hand, the radio waves have originated at a single coherent source. Thus if the Moon is not a smooth reflector but one having many scattering irregularities, the echo power is given by the sum of the powers returned from all the elements of the surface, added with regard to phase. Hence the echo will have an amplitude and phase depending upon the distribution of the scattering centres which determines the reinforcement and destructive interference of the reflected waves. Provided that the Moon maintains the same orientation with respect to the observer, the resulting amplitude and phase of the echo will remain constant. We can then replace the Moon with a hypothetical plane reflector which would return an echo of equivalent amplitude and phase. The distance of this hypothetical reflector from the leading edge of the Moon defines the position of the effective phase centre.

IV. The Librations of the Moon

At most times the Moon appears to be spinning relative to an observer on the Earth. This is the result of libration (cf. Chapter 2) which has four principal components:

A. The Libration in Latitude

The Moon's equator is inclined to the plane of its orbit by about $6 \cdot 5°$, and since the direction of the Moon's axis is fixed (neglecting perturbation) an observer on the Earth sees sometimes more of the Moon's northern hemisphere and sometimes more of the southern hemisphere. This libration in latitude, as it is called has a period of one sidereal month, and the rate of libration l_B has a maximum value of 3×10^{-7} radian.sec^{-1}, which occurs when the Moon crosses the nodes of its orbit.

B. The Libration in Longitude

The angular velocity of the Moon's rotation about its axis is equal to its mean geocentric angular velocity in its orbit, but because the orbit is an ellipse there will be a difference between the rotational angular velocity and the instantaneous geocentric orbital angular velocity. This leads to libration in longitude, having a rate l_L which is direct in sense at apogee, and retrograde at perigee, with a maximum value of about 4×10^{-7} radian sec^{-1}.

C. The Diurnal Libration

As the Earth rotates, an observer on its surface sees a parallactic shift between the centre of the Moon's projected disk and the true centre of the Moon. This so-called diurnal libration is always in a direct sense when the Moon is in transit, with a maximum rate l_D for a declination $\delta = 0$ of about $12 \cos L \times 10^{-7}$ radian sec^{-1} (where L is the geographic latitude of the observer).

D. PHYSICAL LIBRATION

This is a rocking produced by the variable gravitational couples exerted by the Earth and Sun on the Moon's equatorial bulge. Its maximum rate of 3×10^{-10} radian.sec^{-1} is so small that it can be neglected in comparison with the other librations.

The three main components of the libration are illustrated on Fig. 3.

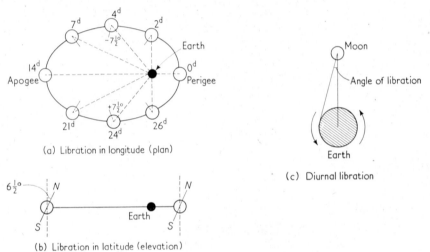

(a) Libration in longitude (plan)

(c) Diurnal libration

(b) Libration in latitude (elevation)

FIG. 3. The three principal causes of the Moon's libration.

At any instant the Moon may be considered to be spinning about an axis with a speed defined by the vector addition of the three main components l_D, l_L, and l_B. The value of the diurnal libration l_D at transit has been given and the values of l_L and l_B can be obtained with reasonable accuracy by linear interpolation of the figures listed in the Astronomical Ephemeris for the Earth's selenographic longitude and latitude. The total rate of libration l_T may then be computed by resolving l_D, l_L and l_B into components perpendicular to the line of sight. Suitable equations have been developed by Fricker et al. (1958).

The effect of the librational spin will be to alter the path lengths of the various scattering centres distributed over the surface of the Moon, with a consequent change in the phases of all the components of the reflecting signals which make up the echo. This will cause the echo amplitude to fluctuate at a rate which will depend upon l_T.

The Moon may be regarded as a flat disk which can be divided into strips parallel to the apparent axis of rotation. Each strip is in motion towards or away from the observer and returns signals whose frequency is shifted relative to the signals from the central strip because of the Doppler effect (Browne *et al.* 1956) by an amount f'. The maximum Doppler shift f'_0 (from the limbs of the Moon) is

$$f'_0 = \frac{\pm\, 2l_T a}{\lambda} \quad (a \text{ being the radius of the Moon}),$$

which for a wavelength $\lambda = 2\cdot5$ metres is at the most only of the order of $\pm\ 2$ cps. The distribution of the echo power over the range

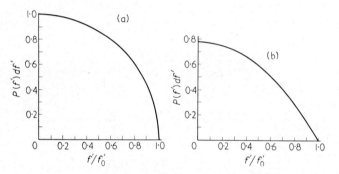

Fig. 4. The radio frequency power spectra $P(f')df'$ plotted as functions of the fractional Doppler broadening f'/f_0' for both (a) Lommel-Seeliger and (b) Lambert scattering.

$\pm f'_0$ is called the power spectrum, and is directly related to the distribution of the scattering centres over the disk. The power spectra $P(f')df'$ for Lommel-Seeliger and Lambert scattering are plotted as a function of the fractional Doppler broadening f'/f'_0 and shown on Fig. 4.

The actual instantaneous spectrum $P(f')df'$ of the echoes will depend upon the way in which the reflected signals recombine at that instant. However, by taking a time-average of the instantaneous spectra, it is possible to derive the mean distribution of the scattering centres. By choosing a high radio frequency, so that f'_0 will be large, and by making observations when l_T is at its maximum, it is just possible to measure the echo power spectrum using a narrow band receiver as a spectrum analyser. This measurement calls for extreme frequency stability throughout the system, and also the use of a C.W. bistatic radar (i.e. receiver and transmitter located at different points). Such observations have been made by Fricker *et al.* (1958) but are not as precise as the methods employed by Evans (1957a) and Pettengill (1960). For observations with simple pulsed radar equipments the

spectrum of the transmitted pulse is usually quite broad ($\propto 1/\tau$) and
not sufficiently well defined to permit the small Doppler broadening
due to the Moon's rotation to be observed.

V. Pulse Length Considerations

Apart from a brief statement in Section I, that the full scattering
area of the Moon will not be realized where the radar pulse $\ll 11\cdot6$
milliseconds, no consideration has yet been given to the fact that the
Moon is a scatterer of considerable depth. At this point it should be

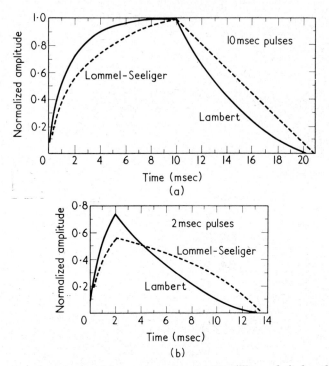

Fig. 5. The shape expected for square pulses (a) 10 milliseconds in length (b) 2 milliseconds after reflection by the Moon if the surface obeys the Lambert scattering law
(full line) or Lommel-Seeliger scattering law (broken line).

made clear that in the discussion of the value of the directivity term
g, and the spectrum of echoes in the previous sections, it has been
tacitly assumed that the complete surface is effective in scattering.
This calls for pulse lengths of at least 20 or 30 milliseconds.

The belief that the Moon is a scatterer of considerable depth, led
Grieg, Metzger and Waer (1948) to conclude that the Moon could not

be used as a reflector in a communication system. This is because for modulation frequencies greater than about 50 cps, destructive interference would take place between signals reflected from different parts of the surface, and this would tend to demodulate the reflected wave. The resulting effect would be similar to that observed in a room having poor acoustical properties, where many superimposed echoes may be heard. This "reverbebration time" will distort square 10 millisecond and 2 millisecond pulses as shown on Fig. 5. An extremely

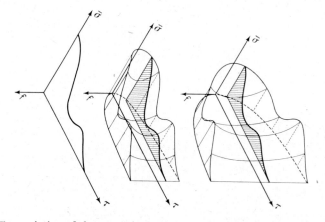

Fig. 6. The variation of the scattering cross-section σ as a function of range (τ) and frequency (f). In the lower curve the rate of libration l_T is zero and the distribution of the scattering centres can be inferred only from the echo versus time function $y(\tau)$. The other two curves show the distribution of echo power as a function of both frequency and time $y(f\tau)$ for increasing values of the rate of libration l_T. If l_T is known then the distribution of the scattering centres can be inferred from the distribution of echo power with frequency $y(f)$ (after Green, 1959).

short pulse would be returned in a manner dictated by the distribution of the scattering centres over the depth of the Moon, and hence this distribution can be inferred, either by observing the distribution of echo intensity with time $y(\tau)$ (using short transmitted pulses), or the distribution of echo intensity with frequency $y(f)$ (using long transmitter pulses).

In more general terms, at a time when the rate of libration l_T is zero (such times do occur) the average echo pattern $y(\tau)$ defines the distribution of the scattering centres. This is illustrated on Fig. 6 for a hypothetical distribution of scattering centres. Now as l_T increases the echo can be defined by a function $y(f\tau)$ which represents the average time and frequency characteristics. Two such functions are illustrated on Fig. 6 for increasing values of the total libration l_T. At any instant the distribution of echo power with time and frequency will be less smooth than illustrated on Fig. 6, due to the way in which the various scattering centres combine to form local peaks in the function $y(f\tau)$.

The accuracy with which this function can be examined with a radar system depends upon the analogous function for a single radar pulse $P(f\tau)$, known as the ambiguity function. Thus where long pulses are used, it is possible to achieve a high frequency resolution and with short pulses a high range resolution. Figure 7 illustrates this, and the ambiguity function $P(f\tau)$ is plotted for long and short pulses. Since

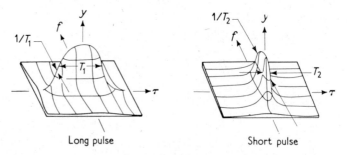

Long pulse   Short pulse

FIG. 7. The ambiguity function $P(f\tau)$ is illustrated for two pulses. In the case of the long pulse T_1 the intensity y has a narrow frequency distribution ($\sim 1/T_1$) whilst for the short pulse T_2 the frequency extent is much greater (after Green, 1959).

the transmitter pulse spectrum is approximately given by the reciprocal of the pulse length τ, it follows that it is not possible to obtain a single pulse having both small time and frequency distributions. That is, the volume under the surface $P(f\tau)$ is constant, and in the case of the Moon for radar equipments, operated at wavelengths > 10 cm, the volume under the surface $P(f\tau)$ exceeds that under the surface $y(f\tau)$. Thus it is not possible with a given equipment, by observing single pulses of fixed length, to examine the function $y(f\tau)$ by means of direct observation of the echo power both as a function of time and frequency. This explains why, in most experiments to determine the distribution of the scattering centres, either the echo power spectrum or the echo time function have been measured, and few workers have been in a position to measure both.

VI. The Early Experiments

The first group of workers to detect radio echoes from the Moon were members of the U.S. Army Signals Laboratory, under the direction of Lieut.-Colonel J. H. De Witt. They succeeded in detecting the echoes first at 11.58 a.m. on 10th January, 1946 (Webb, 1946); Mofenson, 1946), but a full account of this work was not published until 1949

(De Witt and Stodola, 1949). The parameters of their equipment were $P_t = 3$ kW (later raised to 15 kW); $f = 115 \cdot 5$ Mc/s; pulse length $\tau = 0 \cdot 2$ to $0 \cdot 5$ seconds; aerial gain $G = 24$ dB; receiver noise figure $n = 5$ dB; receiver bandwidth $b = 50$ cps. The transmitter and receiver were crystal controlled in such a way that the Doppler shifts could be compensated, but because an unwanted image signal appeared at the output of the receiver the effective noise figure was 8 dB. The aerial took the form of two army radar aerials (SCR271) mounted together on a 100-foot tower, so that observations could be made at moonrise and moonset. Due to favourable ground reflection a 12 dB increase in system sensitivity was expected at an elevation of $0 \cdot 8°$. De Witt and Stodola observed that the echo amplitudes showed marked variation from echo to echo (the interpulse period was 4 seconds), and on some days the echoes were entirely absent. The maximum echo amplitudes observed were in the region of $+ 20$ dB. Echoes of up to $+30$ dB were expected upon the basis of their calculations in which it was assumed that $g = 1$ and $\rho = 0 \cdot 17$. In fact, De Witt and Stodola assumed that the whole of the Moon was effective in scattering and yet behaved as an isotropic radiator. They suggested that the libration of the Moon was responsible for the echo fading, but could provide no evidence to substantiate this point.

The observations made by De Witt and Stodola only just preceded those of Bay (1946) who was working at the Tungsram Research Laboratory, Ujpest, Hungary, and succeeded in detecting echoes first on 6th February, 1946. Bay commenced work on this project during the summer of 1944, but because of the events of the second world war he did not succeed until 1946, by which time he had been forced to rebuild his equipment three times. The parameters of this equipment were $P_t = 3$ to 4 kW; $f = 120$ Mc/s; pulse length $\tau = \cdot 06$ sec; aerial gain $G = 20$ dB; noise figure $n = 5$ dB; receiver bandwidth $b = 200$ kc/s.

Bay did not have a crystal controlled transmitter or receiver and, in consequence, was compelled to use a wide receiver bandwidth b to accommodate the drifts in the frequency of the transmitter and receiver. He used a post detector bandwidth b' of 20 cps which gave an increase in the amplitude of the echoes of $\sim \sqrt{b/b'} = 100$. His aerial system, like that of De Witt and Stodola, was an aperture (8 metres × 6 metres) illuminated by full wave dipoles. This was mounted in such a way that it could be steered in both azimuth and elevation to follow the motion of the Moon across the sky. On the basis of calculations, in which he assumed $g = 1$, $\rho = 0 \cdot 1$, Bay concluded that the echo amplitude should be about 1/10th of the noise voltage. He constructed a bank of water voltameters and connected these by a rotary switch to the output of the receiver. The switch operated in such a way that the amount of hydrogen liberated in each voltameter would be proportional to the integrated receiver output power, corresponding to different range intervals along the timebase. In this manner he was able to detect the echoes, and concluded that the average echo amplitude was in agreement with his calculations. He was of course unable to study the fading characteristics of the echoes.

In 1949 workers at the Australian Commonwealth Scientific and Industrial Research Organization (Kerr, Shain and Higgins, 1949) commenced a series of observations using short-wave broadcast transmitters (VLC9 17·84 Mc/s, 50 kW output, or VLB5 21·54 Mc/s, 70 kW output) and conventional communications-type receivers. The transmitter was keyed by landline signals from the receiving station Hornsby 600 km distant. Transmitter pulses of (a) three successive $\frac{1}{4}$ second pulses, (b) a single pulse 2·2   seconds long, (c) 1 millisecond pulses occurring 40 per second for a period of 2·2 seconds, were all used at various times. The transmitting aerial was a 16 element broadside array constructed to direct a beam at an elevation of 9° and having a gain $G = 20$ dB. The receiving aerial took the form of an array of two rhombic aerials, which gave a gain at 21·54 Mc/s of 17 dB. Receivers were set up at other sites, including three in the United States; but because of the low frequency used this effort met with limited success. The receivers employed 70 cps predetector bandwidths b and 6 cps post detector bandwidths b', except for the observation of the 1 millisecond pulses where a 1 kc/s bandwidth was used. Kerr and Shain (1951) calculated that the post detector signal-to-noise ratio should be $+25$ dB for smooth Moon scattering ($g = 1$) and 32 dB for rough Moon scattering ($g = 5·7$). A reflection coefficient $\rho = 1·5$ was assumed. The observed mean echo intensities frequently were about $+10$ dB and only occasionally rose to $+20$ dB above the noise level. At times the echoes completely disappeared.

Despite the fact that the interpretation of their results was complicated by ionospheric effects (ionospheric refraction and possibly absorption), Kerr and Shain were able to distinguish two forms of fading. The first having a period of a few seconds was attributed to the Moon's libration; and in support of this they were able to show that the fading rate of the echoes was related to the total rate of libration l_T in almost exactly the manner that would be expected if the Moon were to behave as a uniformly bright reflector. The second fading mechanism appeared to be responsible for variations in the mean intensity of the echoes, and this had a period of the order of minutes. They suggested (wrongly, as it was later discovered) that this long-period fading might be caused by irregularities in the Earth's ionosphere which serve to defocus the aerial beam. Such irregularities are observed to cause fluctuations in the intensity of radio stars, but usually with a period much shorter than several minutes.

In support of their hypothesis that the Moon behaved as a uniformly bright reflector (they were unable to distinguish between Lommel-Seeliger and Lambert scattering), they reported that 1 millisecond pulses were elongated as would be expected, but the use of the 1 kc/s receiver bandwidth (to match this short pulse length) reduced the echo intensity, so that these echoes were never successfully photographed.

Though other workers subsequently reported successful Moon reflection experiments (Sulzer, Montgomery and Gerks, 1952; Bateman and Smith, 1953), little progress was made until Murray and Hargreaves (1954) discovered that the long-period fading, which hitherto had not been properly explained, was caused by the rotation of the plane of polarization of the radio waves in the Earth's ionosphere in the presence of the Earth's magnetic field. The radio waves after reflection at the Moon's surface suffer the same additional amount of rotation before reaching the receiving aerial system, where the intensity observed is the component of the echo electric field resolved along the direction of the dipoles. The two forms of fading are illustrated on Fig. 8, where two samples of echoes observed by Browne et al. (1956) are shown. In each sample only the echoes have been photographed. These are 1·8 seconds apart and show the rapid fading clearly. This is caused by libration, whilst the difference between the mean echo amplitudes of the two samples is due to the rotation of the plane of polarization of the radio waves. The echoes on Fig. 8(b) were observed some 14 minutes before those on Fig. 8(a).

Browne et al. (1956) showed that the total amount of rotation is a function of the integrated number of electrons per cm² column through the ionosphere $\int_0^R N dr$, and hence experiments to determine the total number of rotations of the plane of polarization of the radio waves would provide a new method of studying the ionosphere. Many such experiments have since been conducted for this purpose (Evans, 1956, 1957 b; Bauer and Daniels, 1958, 1959). Both signals reflected from the Moon, and more recently observations of the radio signals from artificial Earth satellites have been used.

Murray and Hargreaves (working at the Jodrell Bank Experimental Station, England) employed, like Bay, a frequency of 120 Mc/s and a transmitter power $P_t = 3$–4 kW (later improved to 10 kW; Browne et al. 1956). By using a crystal controlled receiver and transmitter, a receiver bandwidth of 26 cps could be employed which was found to be

2G

approximately the optimum for the pulse length (30 m.secs) used. The aerial system consisted of a stepped broadside array of 10 sections having an aperture $A = 250 \, \mathrm{m}^2$ ($G = 27$ dB) and the aerial beam was directed due south. Observations could only be made over a period

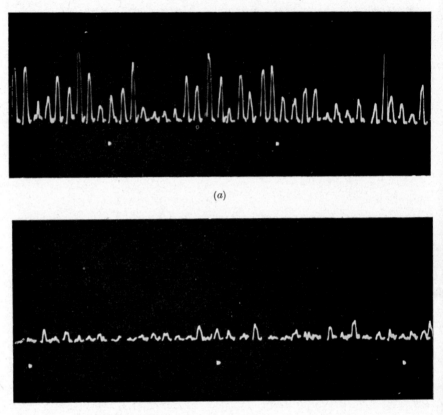

(a)

(b)

FIG. 8. Two samples of echoes observed by Browne *et al.* (1956). In each sample only the echoes have been photographed and these occur every 1·8 seconds. The dots below the traces are half minute time marks. In both (a) and (b) the echoes are fading rapidly. The echoes in (b) which were observed some 14 minutes before those in (a) are on average much weaker because of the rotation of the plane of polarization of the radio waves in the earth's ionosphere (after Brown *et al.* 1956).

of one hour around transit, and the elevation of the aerial beam could be changed from day to day to follow the variation of the declination δ of the Moon. By assuming a reflection coefficient $\rho = 0\cdot1$ and directivity term $g = 5\cdot7$ (on the basis of Kerr and Shain's results) the mean echo intensity was predicted to be 36 ± 1 dB. The maximum mean echo intensity observed was 27 ± 2 dB. Some 4 dB loss in equipment sensitivity was attributed to frequency modulation of the transmitter, but the remaining discrepancy of 5 ± 3 dB between the predicted and observed echo intensities could not be accounted for.

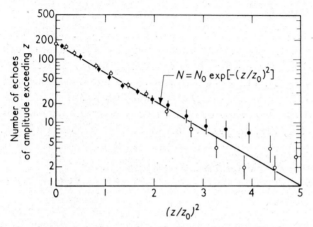

FIG. 9. In the above graph the number of echoes whose amplitude exceeds a value z is plotted as a function of the ratio of z to the r.m.s. echo amplitude z_0. The straight line shows the distribution to be expected for the Rayleigh Law (after Browne *et al.* 1956).

Browne *et al.* (1956) also showed that the individual echo amplitudes followed Rayleigh's law (see Fig. 9), as would be expected if the rapid fading was due to interference from more than about 10 individual scattering centres on the surface of the Moon (Lawson and Uhlenbeck. 1950*b*). Like Kerr and Shain, they observed that the rate of the rapid fading increased as the rate of libration l_T increased; but they could not find any clear agreement between the observed rate of fading, and that expected as a result of Lommel-Seeliger or Lambert scattering. The echo fading rate can be defined by the pulse to pulse autocorrelation coefficient $\gamma(\tau)$ given by

$$\gamma(\tau) = \frac{\overline{y(t)y(t+\tau)} - \overline{y(t)}^2}{\overline{y^2(t)} - \overline{y(t)}^2},$$

where $y(t)$ denotes the echo amplitude at time t, and the "bars" denote averages. The autocorrelation function $\gamma(\tau)$ observed at any time will depend upon the rate of libration l_T at that time. This rate of libration may be defined by the corresponding maximum Doppler broadening of the echo f'_0; hence, the function $\gamma(f'_0\tau)$ should be time-independent, and related to the power spectrum. The radio-frequency power spectrum

$P(f')df'$ of the echo is not in general the same as the video power spectrum, because cross modulation terms are introduced in the detector. Lawson and Uhlenbeck (1950c) showed how to calculate the video spectrum from the radio frequency power spectrum for both linear and square law detectors. A linear detector was used by Browne et al., for which the autocorrelation function $\gamma(f'_0\tau)$ is given approximately by the square of the Fourier cosine transform of the radio frequency power spectrum $P(f')df'$. The autocorrelation functions of echo amplitude $\gamma(f'_0\tau)$ for Lommel-Seeliger and Lambert law scattering (Fig. 4) are shown on Fig. 11. That Browne et al. could find no agreement between the observed and expected autocorrelation functions was, in part, due to the fact that the Moon does not scatter as a uniformly bright reflector, and in part to an error in their calculations.

VII. The Later Experiments

As early as 1951 workers at the U.S. Naval Research Laboratories, Washington, discovered that the Moon behaved as a "limb-darkened" scatterer of radio waves (Trexler, 1958), but had not been allowed to publish their results. Therefore, it was not until Evans (1957a) had carefully repeated the earlier work of Browne et al. (1956), and published the results of a set of experiments which showed this, that the work done at N.R.L. was published.

Using the equipment constructed by Murray and Hargreaves at Jodrell Bank, Evans made a careful measurement of the echo amplitude autocorrelation function $\gamma(f'_0\tau)$. To do this, pairs of pulses were transmitted and as the pulse separation τ was increased the fall in the correlation of the echo amplitudes was measured. The results of this work are shown on Fig. 10. On Fig. 11 they are compared with the expected autocorrelation functions for Lommel–Seeliger and Lambert scattering. It was evident that the echoes were fading much more slowly than expected; and by fitting a Gaussian curve $\exp(-1\cdot3(f'_0\tau)^2)$ to his results, Evans was able to compute the echo power spectrum which gave rise to this autocorrelation function. It will be remembered that in these experiments a linear detector was used and, hence, $\gamma(f'_0\tau)$ is the square of the Fourier cosine transform of the power spectrum $P(f')df'$. The power spectrum $P(f')df'$ computed from the results was

$$P(f') = P_{f'=0} \exp(-15\cdot3(f'/f'_0)^2).$$

This is plotted on Fig. 12 together with the power spectra for Lommel-Seeliger and Lambert scattering (Fig. 4). It can be seen that there is very little Doppler broadening of the echoes and, hence, nearly all the

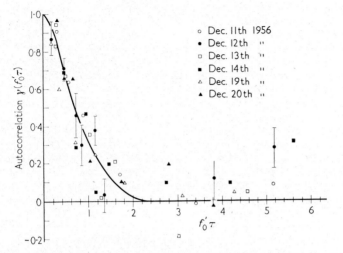

FIG. 10. The values for the autocorrelation function $\gamma(f_0'\tau)$ plotted against $f_0'\tau$ for six different nights. The full line is the mean curve through the points. Errors are shown only for December 12th but are typical (after Evans, 1957a).

scattering centres must lie within an area having a radius of only about one-third of that of the Moon. Such an area would only have a depth of 0·7 milliseconds, and Evans confirmed this "dark-limb" theory by examining the distortion produced by the Moon for 2 and 10 millisecond pulses. Unlike the pulses drawn in Fig. 5, there was no measurable pulse elongation, nor did the echo amplitude fall by more than 2 dB when the pulse length was changed from 10 to 2 milliseconds. A fall of 5 dB would have been expected if the Moon behaved as a uniformly

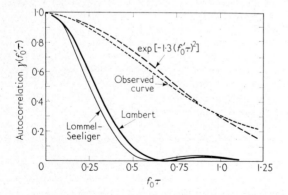

FIG. 11. The observed curve for the autocorrelation function $\gamma(f_0'\tau)$ shown (broken) together with the curves expected for the Lommel-Seeliger and Lambert scattering laws. Also shown is the fitted Gaussian function $\exp(-1\cdot3(f_0'\tau)^2)$ (after Evans, 1957a).

bright reflector. In a final experiment it was shown that to within the experimental accuracy ($\pm$ 1 msec) the echoes were returned from the leading edge of the Moon. Evans postulated that since the Lambert scattering law

$$P_\phi = P_N \cos \phi$$

gives rise to some limb darkening, then a law

$$P_\phi = P_N \cos^m \phi, \qquad\qquad m = \text{constant},$$

might be used to explain these results. By a process of numerical integration over the spherical surface the expected power spectrum

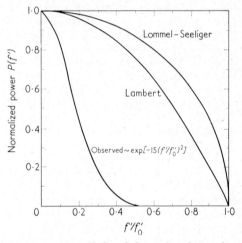

FIG. 12. The power spectrum deduced from the observed auto-correlation function $\gamma(f_0'\tau)$ shown together with the power spectra produced by the Lommel-Seeliger and Lambert scattering laws (after Evans, 1957a).

$P(f')df'$ was calculated for several values of m. The observed and theoretical power spectra were in close agreement for $m = 30$. Thus a scattering law

$$P_\phi = P_N \cos^{30} \phi$$

was proposed. However, such a law is not physically realizable since it implies that the reflection properties of the surface elements are independent of the direction from which they are illuminated. A full statement of the law of reflection would include terms depending upon the angle of incidence, and these cannot be determined solely from ground-based observations for which the angles of incidence and reflection are the same.

Whereas Evans had tackled the problem of determining the distribution of the scattering centres by measuring the echo frequency function $y(f)$, Trexler (1958) at N.R.L. chose instead to measure the time function $y(\tau)$. This required a high system sensitivity, and Trexler's equipment had the following parameters: $P_t = 1$ MW; pulse length $\tau = 12$ microsecs; frequency = 198 Mc/s; aerial gain 40 dB; receiver noise figure 2–3 dB; receiver bandwidth 250 kc/s. This aerial system was a section of a parabola of revolution having an elliptical opening 220 by 263 feet. It was formed by making a depression in the ground of the correct shape and surfacing this with a wire mesh. By an ingenious method of moving the primary feed system, observations could be made over a period of about 1 hour. The echoes obtained with this equipment (illustrated on Fig. 13) showed a large initial spike followed by an exponential tail. Some 50% of the echo power was returned in the first 50 microsec, of the pulse. This corresponds to a depth of five miles, and a region of only 210 miles in diameter. This region is about $\frac{1}{10}$th of the total radius of the Moon; and, hence, there is good agreement between these observations and the power spectrum curve of Fig. 12. The exponential tail of the echo appeared to extend some 500 microsec beyond the leading edge of the echo, but this appeared to be a function of signal-to-noise ratio, because strong echoes showed extensions out to 1000 microsec. Figure 14 shows the average distribution of the echo power as a function of time. On Fig. 15 two observed echoes are compared with the echo which would have been expected from a uniformly bright reflector.

It is clear from these experiments that radio waves are reflected by the Moon principally by a number of specular reflecting regions at the centre of the Moon's disc. These reflections predominate over the reflections from other regions normal to line of sight at greater distances. A similar result was reported by Yaplee et al. (1958) who also worked at the Naval Research Laboratories. Yaplee's equipment employed a power $P_t = 2$ MW; pulse length $\tau = 2$ microsec; frequency = 2860 Mc/s ($\lambda = 10\cdot4$ cm); and was used in conjunction with a steerable parabolic reflector aerial system, which had a diameter of 50 feet. An example of the echoes observed, with 50 microsec post detector integration, is shown on Fig. 16. In this paper it was reported that the specular-like reflection by the lunar surface was similar to that observed with airborne radar over dry sandy terrestrial deserts at normal incidence by Grant and Yaplee (1957) (see also Edison, Moore and Warner, 1959). Yaplee's work was principally directed towards making accurate range measurements, but it is of interest to find that the echo time-function $y(\tau)$ for this wavelength is no different from that observed

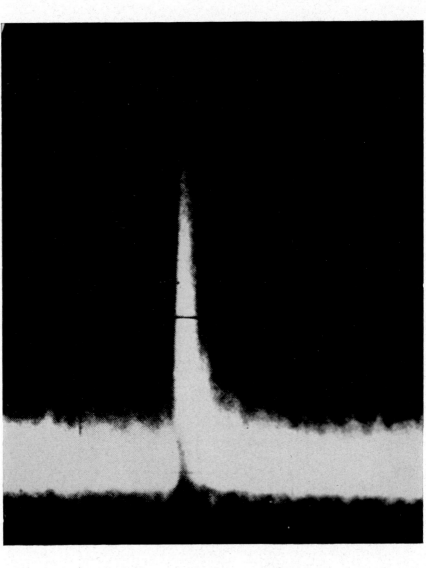

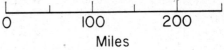

FIG. 13. The amplitude versus range display obtained by Trexler (1958) using transmitter pulses of 12 microseconds in length. The distance in miles from the leading edge of the Moon is shown on the scale below. (By permission of the Editors of *Proc. Instn Radio Engrs.*)

at metre wavelengths (2·5 and 1·5 metres). The results of Yaplee's range measurement experiments, which have been continued, are reviewed in the chapter on "The Motion of the Moon in Space".

It can be concluded from the last three reported experiments that the surface of the Moon is not densely covered with objects having sizes in the range 2·5 metres to 10 cm. Since the Moon is approximately uniformly bright at both light and infra-red wavelengths (Markov, 1958; Pettit and Nicholson, 1930) it follows that the surface must, nevertheless, be rough at wavelengths of the order of 10^{-2} cm. It is not known at what wavelength between $\lambda = 10$ cm and 10^{-2} cm the transition occurs between smooth Moon scattering and uniformly bright scattering. It seems unlikely that this information could be obtained, (with earth-based radar equipment), in view of the strong atmospheric absorption

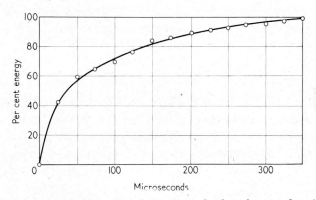

Fig. 14. The average distribution of the energy in the echo as a function of time as observed by Trexler (1958) using 12 microsecond transmitter pulses. More than 50% of the echo power is returned within the first 50 microseconds. (By permission of the Editors of *Proc. Instn Radio Engrs*.)

in this wavelength range. The possible implications of these results concerning the Moon's surface are discussed in the next section.

More recent radar experiments have added considerably to the results reviewed above. Using the 250-foot fully-steerable telescope at Jodrell Bank, Evans *et al.* (1959) were able to repeat the previous experiments at a new wavelength of 3 metres. They showed that the rate of fading of the echoes varied throughout the day in the manner expected from the known variation of the rate of libration l_T (due to the change in the diurnal libration component l_D) (see Fig. 17). The echo power spectrum at this wavelength (3 m) was not measurably different from that observed at 2·5 metres. In these experiments the long-period fading normally present due to the rotation of the radio waves in the ionosphere was eliminated by using circularly polarized

waves. Fricker *et al.* (1958) also found that the rate of the rapid fading
could be predicted from purely dynamical considerations. Their work
was conducted at a frequency of 412·85 Mc/s between two field stations
operated by the Massachusetts Institute of Technology in the United
States. A 60-foot paraboloid and a 40 kW C.W. transmitter were used

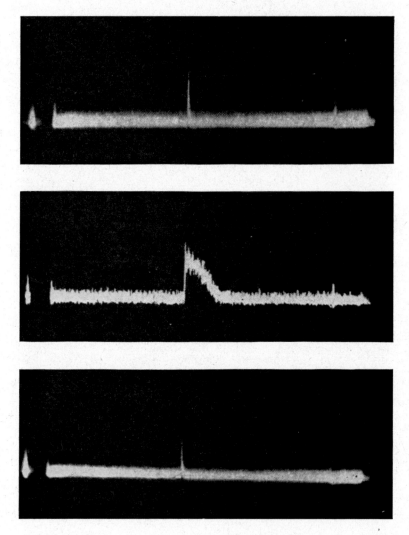

Fig. 15. At the top and bottom are the observed amplitude versus range displays
shown for comparison with the echo (centre) which would be expected from the Moon
if it were to scatter with uniform brightness, (after Trexler 1958). (By permission of
the Editors of *Proc. Instn Radio Engrs.*)

at the transmitting site, and a 28-foot paraboloid at the receiving site.
The receivers used had a noise figure of about 5 dB and their bandwidths were variable between 50 cps and 300 cps. Fricker's value for
the product $\rho g = 0 \cdot 074$ is perhaps the most accurate determination
made so far.

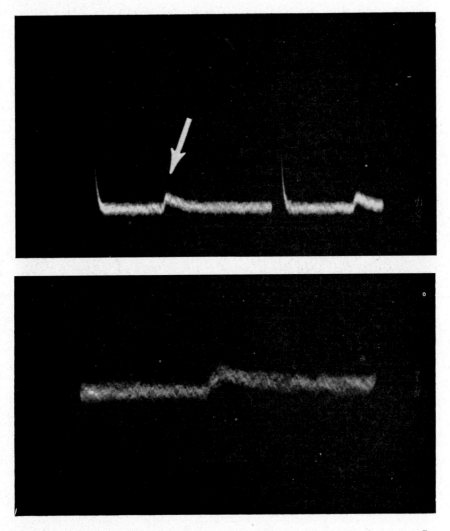

Fɪɢ. 16. The echoes observed by Yaplee *et al.* (1958) at a wavelength of 10·4 cm. In
this photograph many superimposed echoes are shown and some of the echo fluctuation
has been removed by using 50 microseconds post detector integration. (By permission
of the Editors of *Proc. Instn Radio Engrs*.)

Hey and Hughes (1959), of the Royal Radar Establishment, England, using a 45-foot parabolic aerial at a wavelength of 10 cm were able to confirm the observations of Yaplee reported above. They used a transmitter power $P_t = 2$ MW; pulse length $\tau = 5$ microseconds; receiver with noise factor $n = 9$ dB, and bandwidth $b = 500$ kc/s. An example of one of their echoes is shown on Fig. 18. By comparing the echo intensity with the inclination of the lunar surface to the line of sight at different distances from the leading edge of the echo, Hey and Hughes concluded that 50% of the echo power was returned from regions inclined at angles of less than 5°. They argue that, since the variation of echo amplitude exceeds 100%, then the phase modulation introduced by the reflecting surface is likely to be greater than 2π radians. By arguments similar to those developed by Hewish (1951, 1952) they concluded that the value of 5° for the scattering angle would be consistent with a mean scale for the phase modulation at the lunar surface of about 1 metre. That is, in a horizontal distance of about 1 metre over the surface, the reflected wave electric field pattern will, on the average, show a phase change of 2π radians. Hence, the average surface gradient must be about 1 in 20. A similar result was obtained by Hargreaves (1959) in a theoretical paper which is reviewed in the next section.

Hey and Hughes (1959) also measured the autocorrelation function $\gamma(\tau)$ for different distances from the leading edge of the echo. These are shown on Fig. 19 where it can be seen that the time over which the echo intensity is self-correlated falls with increasing distance. This is to be expected because the echoes observed at each range interval are caused by reflections from an annulus on the Moon's surface, where the radius of the annulus and consequently the Doppler broadening of the echo, increase with distance from the leading edge.

Leadabrand (1960) and his colleagues used the 142-foot radio telescope (shown on Fig. 20) at Fraserburgh in Scotland. Their equipment had a transmitter power of 130 kW, a frequency of 401 Mc/s, and a pulse length of 300 microseconds. They were able to distinguish two types of scattering element on the surface, since the sensitivity was sufficiently high to permit echoes to be seen from regions near the limbs of the Moon. Like Hey and Hughes, they noticed that these more distant echoes faded faster than those from the leading edge. This is illustrated on Fig. 21 where a section of one of the range-intensity records is shown. On Fig. 22 the range amplitude display for many superimposed echoes is presented, and the sharp leading edge echo having an exponential tail is clearly visible. In addition, there is a weaker echo which decays linearly and persists out to the limb of

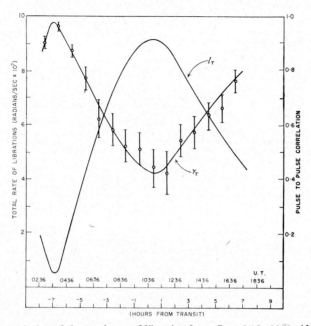

FIG. 17. The variation of the total rate of libration l_T on June 15th, 1958. Also shown is the resulting variation of the pulse to pulse correlation for echoes one second apart observed on this day (Evans *et al.* 1959).

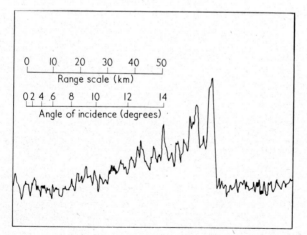

FIG. 18. An example of the echo amplitude versus range variation observed by Hey and Hughes (1959). This plot was obtained using a recording photometer from the range-intensity record made by these workers. (By permission of the Editors of Stanford University Press.)

the Moon. To explain these two components, Leadabrand *et al.* (1960) proposed a scattering law

$$P(\phi) \propto \left(\frac{\sin\phi}{\phi}\right)^{20\pm6} + \frac{1}{10}.$$

Since $\sin\phi/\phi$ raised to a high power is approximately the same as $\cos\phi$,

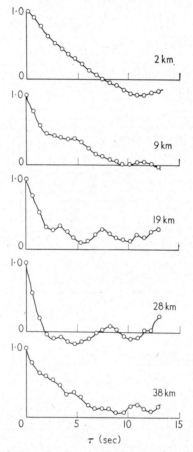

FIG. 19. The autocorrelation of echo amplitude as a function of distance from the leading edge of the Moon observed by Hey and Hughes (1959). (By permission of the Editors of Stanford University Press.)

the first term is similar to that proposed by Evans, and accounts for the large specular portion of the echo. The additional constant term represents an isotropic component not previously observed. This is suggestive of Lommel-Seeliger or Lambert scattering, and thus it would appear that, although the surface is not densely covered with irregularities of the order of a wavelength or more in size, there are a sufficient number to introduce this additional weaker part of the echo-time function.

A similar, though more detailed, experiment has recently been

FIG. 20. The 142-foot radio-telescope operated by Stanford Research Institute at Fraserburgh in Scotland.

conducted by Pettengill (1960) who employed the Millstone Hill radar equipment operated by the Massachusetts Institute of Technology. His equipment parameters were $P_t = 2 \cdot 1$ MW; pulse length $\tau = 500$ microseconds; frequency $f = 440$ Mc/s; receiver noise figure = 2 dB

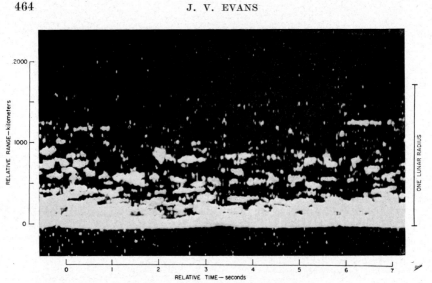

FIG. 21. A section of the intensity-modulated range display observed by Leadabrand *et al.* (1960). Echoes can be seen almost to the limbs of the Moon, but these are considerably weaker than those from the leading edge and they do not usually persist as long.

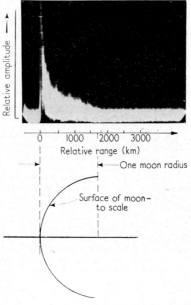

FIG. 22. The amplitude range display observed by Leadabrand *et al.* (1960). As in the earlier work a large echo which decays exponentially with range is observed at the leading edge of the Moon. In addition, a weaker echo decaying linearly out to the limbs of the Moon can be seen which is due to diffuse reflection.

and pulse repetition frequency is 33·4 cps. An 84-foot parabolic aerial system was used both for transmitting and receiving. The local oscillator and transmitter frequencies used in this equipment were derived from a single stable oscillator, so that a chain of coherent pulses could be transmitted. These had an interpulse period of greater than the depth of the Moon (11·6 msec). The echoes were examined over 26 successive 500 microsecond range intervals, and the values for echo intensity and phase at each of the range intervals were stored by a fast digital computer for a period of operation of up to 10 seconds. Because a chain of coherent pulses had been transmitted, Pettengill was able to obtain almost the same frequency resolution that would have been observed for a C.W. signal lasting 10 seconds (i.e. $\pm \frac{1}{10}$ cps). This was achieved by instructing the computer to perform a Fourier analysis of the stored amplitude and phase information to provide the power spectrum of the echoes for each of the 26 range intervals. This is analogous to the method employed by Evans; but since the additional information about the phase of the echo is available, the resulting power spectrum is the superposition of the power spectra of two halves of the visible disk (lying above and below the equator). In Evans' work all four quadrants were superimposed, and because no range information was available, the results were dominated by the strongest echoes. On the other hand, Pettengill obtained detailed distributions of echo power with frequency at different ranges and the computer was made to present these on a cathode ray tube to give a display such as that shown on Fig. 23. On this figure each horizontal line represents one of the 26 range intervals, and the abscissa is marked off in cycles of Doppler broadening. The intensity of the echo power is presented in the form of histograms for each range interval. These have been scaled relative to each other by a factor which is shown in the left hand column, in order that they can all fit the display. These scaling factors show clearly that the most intense part of the echo arises as a result of reflections near the leading edge. However, the semi-circular outline of the histograms also shows that echoes are produced at all ranges up to the limbs of the Moon. The apparent limb brightening observed for the most distant range intervals is caused by the fact that whereas the contours of equal distance are circles concentric about the centre of the disk as seen from the Earth, the contours of equal Doppler shift are lines drawn parallel to the apparent axis of librational rotation. This is illustrated on Fig. 24, and it can be seen that near the limbs large areas fall inside both sets of contours, and give rise to strong high frequency components. Pettengill also used his computer to measure the average echo intensity as a function of

2H

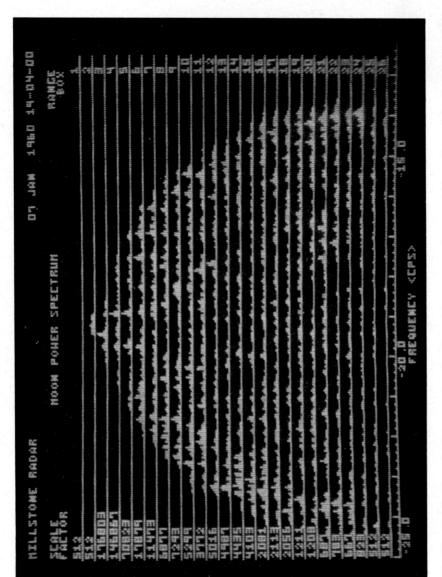

Fig. 23. The distribution of echo power as a function of frequency and range $y(f\tau)$ as observed by Pettengill (1960) using a train of coherent pulses to achieve a high frequency resolution. Each horizontal line represents one of 26 successive range intervals 500 microseconds wide. The echo intensity as a function of frequency is shown as a histo-

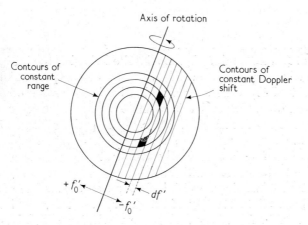

FIG. 24. The contours of equal Doppler shift due to the Moon's libration and the contours of equal range. Near the limbs large areas fall within both sets of contours giving large high frequency components at this range (see Fig. 23). Any given range and frequency co-ordinates have two corresponding positions on the Moon's surface, such as the two areas shown shaded (after Leadabrand *et al.* 1960).

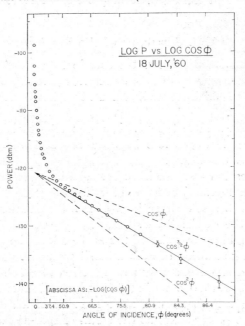

FIG. 25. The distribution of echo power observed by Pettengill (1960), plotted as a function of the log of the cosine of the angle of incidence ϕ. For values of $\phi > 50°$, the intensity of the echoes follows a law lying between the Lambert and Lommel-Seeliger scattering laws. This law is similar to that observed by Pettit and Nicholson (1930) at infrared wavelengths.

range during a period of operation lasting 16 minutes. In this way and average $y(\tau)$ function was obtained and is plotted on Fig. 25 as intensity against the cosine of the angle of incidence of the rays. As in the work of Leadabrand *et al.*, a weak echo following the initial specular component can be observed. The specular echoes predominate in the central part of the disk over a region having a radius of about half that of the Moon. Beyond this region the echo intensity conforms to the Lambert law of scattering. By comparing the relative amounts of specular and diffuse reflection, Pettengill concludes that only about 10% of the surface is sufficiently rough at this wavelength (70 cm) to give rise to Lambert scattering.

At the time of writing no visible features on the surface of the Moon have yet been related to any of the observed echoes, despite the great improvements in frequency and range resolution which have become possible. This is partly because any given set of range and frequency co-ordinates has two corresponding positions on the Moon's surface. By observing over days where there are marked changes in the orientation of the axis of libration, it may be possible to overcome this difficulty.

VIII. Summary of the Results

1. Range measurements have been made to an accuracy of 300 to 600 metres. The accuracy of measurement is partially dictated by the fading of the echo which makes it difficult to define precisely the leading edge of the Moon.

2. The Doppler shift of the echo has been determined with precision, but no measurable differences between the observed and predicted results have been reported.

3. When ionospheric effects have been eliminated, it is found that the echo amplitudes are subject to rapid fading at a rate which is proportional to the total rate of libration l_T. The distribution of echo amplitudes follows the Rayleigh law.

4. The scattering properties of the surface have been measured by observing the distribution of echo intensity with range $y(\tau)$, with frequency $y(f)$ and simultaneously as a function of range and frequency $y(f\tau)$. The results of these experiments conducted in the frequency range 100 Mc/s to 3000 Mc/s show a large measure of agreement. About 50% of the echo power arises as the result of reflections from a region at the centre of the visible disk having a radius of $\frac{1}{10}$th of that of the Moon. From the laws proposed to explain these leading edge echoes, and from considerations of echo power as a function of the inclination of the surface to the line of sight, it is clear that most of the power

is reflected from regions which are nearly perpendicular to the ray paths. Hence, the surface must be smooth and undulating and but sparsely covered with objects of the order of a wavelength in size. At ranges beyond a region bounded by a circle of about half the Moon's radius, weaker echoes have been observed which obey the Lambert scattering law. By comparing the intensity of these echoes with the stronger specular echoes it has been concluded that only about $\frac{1}{10}$th of the surface gives rise to this diffuse reflection.

5. Up to the present time there have been no reports of the association of particular radio echoes with prominent features of the lunar surface.

6. The signal-to-noise measurements of the various workers are shown in Table I (after Senior and Siegel, 1960), where the values for the product ρg are tabulated against wavelength.

TABLE I

The values of the product ρg deduced from the signal to noise measurements of various workers (after Senior and Siegel, 1960). The values for (i) and (ii) were obtained using short pulse lengths, whilst the others were determined using long pulses or C.W.

	Wavelength	ρg	Probable error
(i)	0·100 m.	4×10^{-4}	
(ii)	0·104 m.	3×10^{-4}	± 4 or 5 dB
(iii)	0·34 m.	9×10^{-2}	± 3 dB
(iv)	0·61 m.	3×10^{-2}	± 3 dB
(v)	0·73 m.	7×10^{-2}	± 3 dB
(vi)	0·75 m.	1×10^{-1}	± 3 dB
(vii)	1·00 m.	$5\text{--}9 \times 10^{-2}$	± 4 dB
(viii)	1·49 m.	7×10^{-2}	± 3 dB
(ix)	1·50 m.	$6\text{--}10 \times 10^{-2}$	± 4 dB
(x)	1·99 m.	5×10^{-2}	
(xi)	2·5 m.	1×10^{-2}	± 3 dB
(xii)	3·0 m.	1×10^{-1}	± 3 dB

IX. Discussion of the Results

No evidence exists of any marked wavelength-dependence for the values listed in Table I of the product ρg in the range 3·0 to 0·33 metres. Hence, its mean value can be taken to be $\rho g = 7\cdot6 \pm 2\cdot1 \times 10^{-2}$. It is not possible to compute the value of g without knowing the law of reflection for the surface elements. As has been stated earlier, this requires a knowledge of the way in which the power reflected along any ray path varies with the angle at which the surface is illuminated. Lambert's cosine law represents a special case in which the dependence upon the angle of incidence i and the angle of reflection ϕ are identical: namely,

$$P_{\text{reflected}} \propto \cos i \cos \phi;$$

and for this case $g = 2 \cdot 7$. Pettengill has shown that only about 10% of the surface gives rise to this type of scattering, whilst the remainder reflects in an almost specular manner (for which the directivity must be close to unity). It seems, therefore, probable, that the directivity g must be of the order of $1 \cdot 3 \pm 0 \cdot 1$ and, hence, the reflection coefficient $\rho \approx 0 \cdot 06$. By virtue of equation (6) of Section I, the value $\rho \approx 0 \cdot 06$ corresponds to a value for the dielectric constant k_1 of $2 \cdot 72$, which is close to the value observed for dry sandy soil ($k_1 = 2 \cdot 55$—see "Reference Data for Radio Engineers", 1953). Alternatively, if it is assumed that the surface is composed mainly of silicate materials which, in the solid form, have dielectric constants $k_1 \approx 5$, the above result shows that, on the average, these materials are distributed over the surface of the Moon in a manner which gives a density of about 40% of that of the same materials in bulk. Thus the surface must be broken up and porous in texture.

Senior and Siegel (1959, 1960) have considered in some detail the relation between the reflecting properties of the lunar surface and the nature of the material. They argue that the smooth nature of the surface could have been deduced from observation of the radio wave rotation fading (long period fading) introduced in the Earth's ionosphere. This is because the level of the fading is of the order of 20 dB (Browne *et al.* 1956), and hence the amount of depolarization due to multiple reflections at the Moon's surface must be small ($\gg 10\%$). Since any rough surface tends to depolarize the incident field, the surface cannot be rough (that is, covered with irregularities of the same size as the wavelength).

Senior and Siegel develop an expression for the scattering cross-section of the Moon by the following argument: A perfectly conducting smooth surface having principle radii of curvature a_1 and a_2 will have a scattering cross-section

$$\left. \begin{aligned} \sigma &= \pi a_1 a_2 \\ &= \pi a^2 \text{ when } a_1 = a_2 = a. \end{aligned} \right\} \quad (1)$$

Large smooth irregularities on such a surface would themselves have a cross-section $\sigma = A/\lambda^2$, where A is proportional to the area. A cone-like structure having small included angle would have a cross-section $\sigma = C\lambda^2$; C being a constant which is independent of the wavelength. If both types of scattering are present on the surface, the total cross-section can be written as

$$\sigma = \frac{A}{\lambda^2} + B + C\lambda^2 , \quad (2)$$

where B represents the cross-section of the unperturbed surface. This equation neglects the effect of interference between the signals from different scatterers. At the leading edge of the echo one scatterer will be responsible for the major part of the power, and hence at this point it should be expected that one of the terms A, B or C will predominate over the other two. This value for the scattering cross-section has been derived by assuming the transmitter and receiver to be at a distance $R \gg a$. Where this is not true equation (1) due to the near zone effect becomes

$$\sigma = \pi \left(\frac{aR}{a+R} \right)^2 , \tag{3}$$

where R is the range of the Moon and a is the Moon's radius.

When $a \gg R$,

$$\sigma = \pi R^2 \tag{4}$$

which is the scattering cross-section of an infinite flat plate. For $R \gg a$ we have, as before

$$\sigma = \pi a^2 .$$

Thus for either spherical or plane waves the leading term in the expansion for the cross-section of a sphere is πa^2. Since the Moon is not a conducting body, but has a reflection coefficient $\rho = |Q|^2$ given by

$$Q = \frac{1 - \sqrt{\left[\frac{\mu_0}{\mu} \left(\frac{\epsilon}{\epsilon_0} + i \frac{s}{\omega \epsilon_0} \right) \right]}}{1 + \sqrt{\left[\frac{\mu_0}{\mu} \left(\frac{\epsilon}{\epsilon_0} + i \frac{s}{\omega \epsilon_0} \right) \right]}} , \tag{5}$$

where ϵ = permittivity, μ = permeability, s = conductivity (the subscript $_0$ denotes free-space values) and ω is the angular frequency of the radio waves. Since the surface of the Moon is probably covered with dielectric materials, $s \ll \omega \epsilon_0$

and

$$Q = \frac{1 - q - iq'}{1 + q + iq'} , \tag{6}$$

where

$$q = \sqrt{\left(\frac{\mu_0 \epsilon}{\mu \epsilon_0} \right)} \quad \text{and} \quad q' = \frac{s}{2 \omega \epsilon_0} \sqrt{\left(\frac{\mu_0 \epsilon_0}{\mu \epsilon} \right)} .$$

Thus

$$|Q|^2 = \frac{(1-q)^2 + q'^2}{(1+q)^2 + q'^2} , \tag{7}$$

in which $(1 + q)^2 \gg q'^2$.

Hence

$$|Q|^2 \simeq \left(\frac{1-q}{1+q}\right)^2 + \left(\frac{q'}{1+q}\right)^2 , \qquad (8)$$

which, since $\omega = 2\pi c/\lambda$ (c being the velocity of light), leads to

$$|Q|^2 = p + \lambda^2 p' , \qquad (9)$$

where $p = \left(\frac{1-q}{1+q}\right)^2$ and $p' = \left(\frac{q}{1+q} \cdot \frac{s}{4\pi c\epsilon}\right)^2$.

To obtain the cross-section of a flat area having imperfect conductivity, the scattering cross-section for infinite conductivity must be multiplied by the value $|Q|^2$. In the case of cone-like projections the corresponding expression for $|Q|^2$ is found to have the same wavelength dependence as appears in equation (9). Since Senior and Siegel seek to show later from the available experimental results that σ is not wavelength dependent, they do not make a detailed derivation of the cross scattering area of a dielectric cone. They state that the total cross scattering area can be written in the form

$$\sigma = \frac{Ap}{\lambda^2} + (Ap' + Bp) + (Bp' + Cp)\lambda^2 + Cp'\lambda^4 . \qquad (10)$$

To compare this result with the experimental results they assume that p and p' are independent of wavelength, that is ϵ, μ and s do not vary rapidly with frequency.

In most measurements of the scattering cross-section σ there is interference between various reflecting centres and an r.m.s. echo amplitude has been calculated and then assumed to be proportional to the average value of σ. At the very front of the Moon, however, there may be a single predominant scatterer of any of the three types discussed. Senior and Siegel consider that for observations with pulse length in the range 1–5 microsec. the initial part of the echo is due to such a single scatterer. Thus if all the measurements of σ shown in Table I had been made with such pulses, the wavelength dependence of the results could be compared with that of equation (10). Since most of the results have been made with long pulses instead, they scale the values down according to a function relating echo amplitude with pulse length observed by Trexler (unpublished—privately communicated to Senior and Siegel). In this way they obtained the values of σ which would be observed with pulses of 5 microsec. or less. The results are shown in Table II.

TABLE II

In this table the scattering cross-sections which would be observed for pulses of 5 microsec. or less are shown (after Senior and Siegel, 1960).

	Wavelength	σ
(i)	0·100 m.	$4 \times 10^{-4}\pi a^2$
(ii)	0·104 m.	$3 \times 10^{-4}\pi a^2$
(iii)	0·33 m.	$5\cdot4 \times 10^{-4}\pi a^2$
(iv)	0·61 m.	$1\cdot9 \times 10^{-4}\pi a^2$
(v)	0·73 m.	$4\cdot3 \times 10^{-4}\pi a^2$
(vi)	0·75 m.	$6\cdot3 \times 10^{-4}\pi a^2$
(vii)	1·00 m.	$4\cdot7 \times 10^{-4}\pi a^2$
(viii)	1.49 m.	$4\cdot2 \times 10^{-4}\pi a^2$
(ix)	1·50 m.	$5\cdot3 \times 10^{-4}\pi a^2$
(x)	1·99 m.	$3\cdot0 \times 10^{-4}\pi a^2$
(xi)	2·5 m.	$6\cdot3 \times 10^{-4}\pi a^2$
(xii)	3·0 m.	$6\cdot3 \times 10^{-4}\pi a^2$

The errors inherent in this procedure are difficult to determine. It has, for instance, been assumed that the echo-amplitude versus pulse-length function is independent of wavelength. Also the experimental errors associated with this function are unknown. In the absence of

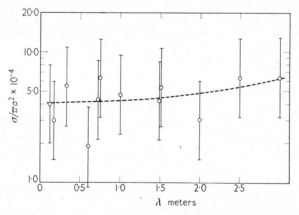

Fig. 26. The values for the ratio of the observed scattering cross-section σ to the geometric cross-section πa^2, corrected so that each measurement corresponds to that which would have been obtained with short (2–5 microsecond pulses). The full line is the best fitting curve to these points (after Senior and Siegel, 1960).

this information Senior and Siegel assume that the errors in Table II are all of the order of $\pm$ 3 dB, and they plot these results as shown on Fig. 26.

Their analysis proceeds as follows. By making a least-squares fit to the observed points and comparing this with equation (10) they find

$$Ap = -8 \cdot 94 \times 10^{-7} \times \pi a^2 \text{ metres}^4$$
$$Ap' + Bp = 4 \cdot 45 \times 10^{-4} \times \pi a^2 \text{ metres}^2$$
$$Bp' + Cp = -1 \cdot 03 \times 10^{-5} \times \pi a^2$$
$$Cp' = 3 \cdot 71 \times 10^{-6} \times \pi a^2 \text{ metres}^{-2}.$$

Since it is assumed that $\rho \neq 0$ then because Ap is small and negative A can be taken to be near zero, (i.e. small flat facets do not make large contributions). In addition, since Cp' is also small, a further wavelength dependent term can be removed, and the least-squares analysis repeated using only terms up to λ^2 whence

$$Bp = 4 \cdot 04 \times 10^{-4} \times \pi a^2 \text{ metres}, \tag{11}$$

$$Bp' + Cp = 2 \cdot 37 \times 10^{-5} \times \pi a^2. \tag{12}$$

Thus the predominant contribution to the echo is the specular reflection from the unperturbed surface, and the power reflected from cone-like objects must be a factor of 17 less for $\lambda < 1$ metre. Thus the effect of cone-like objects can also be neglected and the scattering cross-section reduces to that of a smooth sphere—i.e.

$$\sigma = \pi a^2 |Q|^2 \qquad (|Q|^2 = \rho \text{ the reflection coefficient})$$

Then from equations (11) and (12), it follows that

$$\sigma = (p + \lambda^2 p')\pi a^2,$$

where $p = 4 \cdot 04 \times 10^{-4}$ and $p' = 2 \cdot 37 \times 10^{-5} \text{m}^{-2}$, and the corresponding curve is plotted in Fig. 26. From the values of p and p' there are two solutions for the electromagnetic constants

$$\epsilon/\mu = 6 \cdot 5 \times 10^{-6} \text{ mhos}^2$$
$$s/\mu = 2 \cdot 4 \times 10^2 \text{ mhos/henry},$$

and

$$\epsilon/\mu = 7 \cdot 6 \times 10^{-6} \text{ mhos}^2.$$
$$s/\mu = 2 \cdot 7 \times 10^2 \text{ mhos/henry}.$$

Since, in the second group of equations, the value ϵ/μ exceeds the free space value, this set is taken to be correct. Because power measurements alone cannot yield explicit values of ϵ and s, it is assumed that $\mu = \mu_0$, whence

$$\epsilon = 9 \cdot 6 \times 10^{12} \text{ farads/m.} \ (= 1 \cdot 1 \epsilon_0),$$

$$s = 3 \cdot 4 \times 10^{-4} \text{ mhos/m},$$

Few materials apart from liquids or gases have a relative permittivity as low as 1·1. If it is arbitrarily assumed that $\mu = 1·4 \ \mu_0$ the value of ϵ can be raised to $1·5 \ \epsilon_0$, which would not be inconsistent with soils such as magnetite.

An alternative solution to this apparent anomaly would be if the first part of the echo were due to a smooth projection on the surface of the Moon having a radius of only $-\frac{1}{1}a$. Then $|Q|^2$ is increased by a factor of 100 and even with $\mu = \mu_0$ the permittivity becomes $1·5 \ \epsilon_0$. When considering experimental evidence such as that of Hey and Hughes (1959) (see Fig. 18) Senior and Siegel regard the first few spikes in the echo train as each being due to a single reflecting centre. Hence they argue that the many similar spikes in the first part of the echo must mean that the Moon is covered by projections having a radius $\frac{1}{10}a$, if the anomaly is to be resolved in this way: this they consider to be inconsistent with the observed topography.

By counting the number of spikes in the echo tail, Senior and Siegel conclude that there are only about 20 to 30 principal reflecting regions which contribute (at any one time) to the major portion of the echo. This seems a rather narrow interpretation of the results. There is no evidence to suggest that if observations were made with say $\frac{1}{4}$ microsec. pulses, 3 or 4 spikes would not be seen where Hey and Hughes now see one. Further, the autocorrelation functions observed by Hey and Hughes suggest that many scattering centres are contributing to the echoes observed at all ranges from the leading edge (including the echo at the leading edge which also shows fading). The weakness of Senior and Siegel's analysis probably lies in their assumption that the leading edge echo observed at 2 microsec. pulses is, in fact, due to a single scatterer and does not consist of several reflected components. The most recent experimental observations made by Hughes (1960) at the Royal Radar Establishment near Malvern contradict Senior and Siegel's assumption, and thus it seems probable that their analysis is not justified, and can only be applied to observations made with shorter pulses.

Hargreaves (1959) has considered the experimental results from a statistical viewpoint. He first distinguished between reflection and diffraction at an irregular surface as follows.

Reflection by an Irregular Surface

The radio waves when intercepted by the Moon are almost plane, and hence if the surface is smooth over areas which include several Fresnel zones, specular reflection will take place. This will occur at each of these smooth areas, and the reflected power will be distributed over angles equal to twice that of their surface gradients. If the mean gradient of these undulations is ψ_0, then the reflected power will be distributed over an average angle to the normal θ_0 given by $\theta_0 = 2\psi_0$.

Diffraction by an Irregular Surface

If the surface irregularities are much smaller than the Fresnel zones, a diffraction treatment becomes necessary. Suitable theory has been developed (see Ratcliffe, 1956) for the study of irregularities in the Earth's ionosphere. Thus consider a plane surface where there are height fluctuations about the mean with a standard deviation h, and where the correlation coefficient $\gamma(d)$, which relates the height variations to the horizontal distance in the plane, follows a Gaussian law $\gamma(d) = \exp\left(-d^2/2d_0{}^2\right)$. Here d_0 is the structure size, being the value of d for which $\gamma(d) = 0 \cdot 61$. When plane waves of length λ are incident on this surface, the phase corrugations which appear in the reflected wave front will have a standard deviation given by $\phi = 4\pi h/\lambda$ radians. The modulation is said to be shallow if $\phi < 1$ radian, and the structure size l_0 in the reflected wave is then the same as d_0. Where the modulation is deep ($\phi > 1$) a smaller structure $l_0 = d_0/\phi$ is observed in the receding wave. Bowhill (1957) showed that, at a great distance from the surface, the power associated with the initial phase variations of the wave becomes equally shared between phase and amplitude fluctuations both of which have a mean value $\phi/\sqrt{2}$. Also the linear structure size in the wave front will appear the same whether phase or amplitude variations are observed. The apparent angular power spectrum is the Fourier transform of the spatial correlation coefficient $\gamma(d)$ and can be represented as $P(\theta) = \exp\left(-\theta^2/2\theta_0{}^2\right)$, where $\theta_0 = \lambda/2\pi l_0$ for small θ_0. Thus shallow modulation gives an angular power spectrum whose width is $\theta_0 = \lambda/2\pi d_0$, and for deep modulation $\theta_0 = \phi\lambda/2\pi d_0 = 2h/d_0$. These formulae are rigorously true for irregularities extending in one dimension only, but have been found numerically close to calculations for the two-dimensional case.

Hargreaves now considers the lunar surface. This appears to impose deep modulation on the reflected signals. Hence the small irregularities distribute the power over $\theta_0 = 2h/d_0$ and the large smooth areas over an angle $\theta_0 = 2\psi_0$. Since for the Moon the first Fresnel zone is $1 \cdot 4$ km in radius at $\lambda = 2 \cdot 5$ m, 300 m at $\lambda = 10$ cm and about $1 \cdot 5$ m for the wavelength of light, it is evident that both mechanisms operate and, in fact, give about the same angular power distribution, i.e. $\psi_0 \simeq h/d_0$ (Longuet-Higgins, 1957). Thus the observed angular power spectrum is determined both by the average gradient of the surface over a few Fresnel zones in area and also by the diffraction within these areas depending upon the average gradient of the smaller scale irregularities.

The result of Evans (1957a) that $P(\theta) \propto \cos^{30}\theta$ is approximated by a Gaussian, where $\theta_0 = 0.18$ radian. Hence $h/d_0 \leqslant 0.09$ and $\psi_0 \leqslant 5°$. This means that the average gradients of the surface sampled in areas a few kilometres across are not steeper than 1 in 10.

X. The Lunar Ionosphere

It can be argued that the smooth nature of the surface of the Moon observed at radio wavelengths arises as the result of the presence of a critically dense lunar ionosphere. The mechanism invoked is the production of a dense ionosphere in close proximity to the surface, due to the action of the incident ultraviolet and cosmic ray radiation. As electrons are emitted from the surface, the Moon rapidly acquires a net positive charge, so that it becomes increasingly difficult for electrons to escape completely. Thus the incident energy simply maintains a dense ionosphere close to the surface.

The arguments which can be advanced against this hypothesis as an explanation of the radar results are as follows:

1. The observed values of ρg (see Table I) are all a factor of 10 too small.

2. Some variation of the ionization density might be expected to occur with the variation of the phase of the Moon. Thus, at certain wavelengths, the density would drop below the critical value. No marked variations in mean echo intensity have been observed over the lunar month.

3. An extremely high electron density ($\sim 10^{11}/\text{cm}^3$) would be required to explain the results at 10 cm.

4. To explain the observed fading characteristics, the ionisation would be required to follow the surface contours very closely. In this case the surface would appear little different from that which would be seen in the absence of ionization, with the exception that ρ would be unity.

5. The arguments advanced by Hargreaves show that it is unnecessary to postulate anything unusual about the lunar surface to explain the results satisfactorily.

6. If a dense lunar ionosphere were to exist then the microwave observations of the temperature of the lunar surface (see Mezger and Strassl, 1959) ought to show a much greater wavelength dependence than is observed, since the temperatures measured would be of the sky brightness reflected in this ionosphere, and not of the actual surface.

XI. Conclusion

The results of many experiments carried out in the wavelength range 3 to 0.1 metres indicate that the surface of the Moon is smooth and undulating with average gradients of the order of 1 in 10, and on the average only about 10% of the surface is covered with small objects which are below the optical limit of resolution. The reflected signals are in many respects similar to those observed from aircraft over dry sandy terrestrial deserts at normal incidence. The measurement of the reflection coefficient for the surface material is complicated by the fact that the observed signals suffer marked intensity variations due to interference from many scattering regions. If, however, it is assumed that the r.m.s. signal level provides a proper measure of the reflection coefficient, the average value obtained from many experiments is $\rho \approx 0\cdot06$. This corresponds to a dielectric constant of $k_1 \approx 2\cdot72$ which is similar to that observed for dry sandy soils on the surface of the earth.

References

Bateman, R., and Smith, W. (1953). "*Q.S.T.*" **37**, 11.

Bauer, S. J., and Daniels, F. B. (1958). *J. Geophys. Res.* **63**, 439.

Bauer, S. J., and Daniels, F. B. (1959). *J. Geophys. Res.* **64**, 1371.

Bay, Z. (1946). *Hung. Acta Phys.* **1**, 1.

Blevis, B. C. (1957). *Nature, Lond.* **180**, 138.

Bowhill, S. A. (1957). *J. Atmos. Terr. Phys.* **11**, 91.

Browne, I. C., Evans, J. V., Hargreaves, J. K., and Murray, W. A. S. (1956). *Proc. Phys. Soc. Lond.* B **69**, 901.

De Witt, J. H., and Stodola, E. K. (1949). *Proc. Instn Radio Engrs*, **37**, 229.

Edison, A. R., Moore, R. K., and Warner, B. D. (1959). University of New Mexico, Albuquerque Engineering Experimental Station, *Technical Report EE–24*.

Evans, J. V. (1956). *Proc. Phys. Soc. Lond.* B **69**, 953.

Evans, J. V. (1957a). *Proc. Phys. Soc. Lond.* B **70**, 1105.

Evans, J. V. (1957b). *J. Atmos. Terr. Phys.* **11**, 259.

Evans, J. V., Evans, S., and Thomson, J. H. (1959). "International Astronomical Union Paris Symposium on Radio Astronomy", p. 8. Stanford University Press, Stanford.

Fricker, S. J., Ingalls, R. P., Mason, W. C., Stone, M. L., and Swift, D. W. (1958). Lincoln Laboratory Massachusetts Institute of Technology, *Technical Report No. 187*.

Grant, C. R., and Yaplee, B. S. (1957). *Proc. Instn Radio Engrs*, **45**, 976.

Green, P. (1959). Private communication.

Grieg, D. D., Metzger, S., and Waer, R. (1948). *Proc. Instn Radio Engrs*, **36**, 652.

Hanbury Brown, R., and Lovell, A. C. B. (1957). "The Exploration of Space by Radio", p. 15. Chapman & Hall, Ltd., London.

Hargreaves, J. K. (1959). *Proc. Phys. Soc. Lond.* B **73**, 536.

Hewish, A. (1951). *Proc. Roy. Soc.* **209**, 81.

Hewish, A. (1952). *Proc. Roy. Soc.* **214**, 494.

Hey, J. S., and Hughes, V. A. (1959). "International Astronomical Union Paris Symposium on Radio Astronomy", p. 13. Stanford University Press, Stanford.

Hughes, V. A. (1957). *Nature, Lond.* **180**, 1225.

Hughes, V. A. (1960). *Nature, Lond.* **186**, 873.

Kerr, F. J., and Shain, C. A. (1951). *Proc. Instn Radio Engrs*, **39**, 230.

Kerr, F. J., and Shain, C. A. (1957). *Nature, Lond.* **179**, 433.

Kerr, F. J., Shain, C. A., and Higgins, C. S. (1949). *Nature, Lond.* **163**, 310.

Kraus, J. D., and Ko, H. C. (1957). Electronics Research Directorate, Air Force Cambridge Research Centre AFCRC–TN–57–557.

Lawson, J. L., and Uhlenbeck, G. E. (1950 *a, b, c*). "Threshold Signals", pp. 47, 59, 199. McGraw-Hill, New York.

Leadabrand, R. L., Dyce, R. B., Fredriksen, A., Presnell, R. I., and Schlobohm, J. C. (1960). *Proc. Instn Radio Engrs*, **48**, 932.

Longuet-Higgins, M. S. (1957). *Phil. Trans.* **A 250**, 20.

Markov, A. V. (1958). *Astr. Zhurnal U.S.S.R.* **25**, 172.

Mezger, P. G., and Strassl, H. (1959). *Planetary Space Sci.* **1**, 213.

Mofensen, J. (1946). *Electronics*, **19**, 92.

Murray, W. A. S., and Hargreaves, J. K. (1954). *Nature, Lond.* **173**, 944.

Pettit, E., and Nicholson, S. B. (1930). *Astrophys. J.* **71**, 102.

Pettengill, G. (1960). *Proc. Instn Radio Engrs*, **48**, 933.

Ratcliffe, J. A. (1956). *Rep. Prog. Phys.* **19**, 188.

"Reference Data for Radio Engineers" (1955). 3rd ed., Stratford Press, Inc., New York.

Russell, H. N., Dugan, R. S., and Stewart, J. Q .(1945). "Astronomy": 1. "The Solar System". Ginn, Boston.

Senior, T. B. A., and Siegel, K. M. (1959). "International Astonomical Union Paris Symposium on Radio Astronomy", p. 29. Stanford University Press. Stanford.

Senior, T. B. A., and Siegel, K. M. (1960). *J. Res. Nat. Bur. Stand.* **64**D, 217.

Smith, F. G. (1952). *J. Atmos. Terr. Phys.* **2**, 350.

Sulzer, P. G., Montgomery, G. F., and Gerks, I. H. (1952). *Proc. Instn Radio Engrs*, **40**, 361.

Thomas, A. B. (1949). *Aust. J. Sci.* **11**, 187.

Trexler, J. H. (1958). *Proc. Instn Radio Engrs*, **46**, 286.

Webb, D. H. (1946). *Sky & Telesc.* **5**, 3.

Winter, D. F. (1956). Electronic Research Directorate, Air Force Cambridge. Research Centre, AFCRC–TR–56–106.

Yaplee, B. S., Bruton, R. H., Graig, K. J., and Roman, N. G. (1958). *Proc. Instn Radio Engrs*, **46**, 293.

CHAPTER 13

Origin and History of the Moon†

HAROLD C. UREY

I. Introduction... 481
II. Origin of the Lunar craters................................. 482
III. The Imbrium Collision...................................... 484
IV. Time of Formation of the Lunar Surface........................ 489
V. The Figure of the Moon..................................... 491
VI. The Heat Balance of the Moon............................... 495
VII. Density and Composition of the Moon.......................... 505
VIII. The Chemical Composition of the Surface Regions................. 510
IX. The Origin of the Moon.................................... 513
X. Conclusions.. 521
References... 521

I. Introduction

We do not know how the Moon originated, nor do we know how the solar system as a whole acquired its present configuration. However, certain evidence in regard to these questions exists; and if we gain satisfaction in exploring these bits of information available and trying to secure more evidence, then it is interesting to review the problem of the origin and possible history of our satellite and its relation to the Earth and the solar system.

In beginning the discussion of the internal structure, origin and evolution of the Moon, it is well to summarize the types of evidence available to us and, particularly, the interdependence of the lines of reasoning to be applied to the subject. The high mountains on its surface show that the subsurface regions are not plastic at the present time, nor have they been so at any time since the mountains were formed. However, the validity of this statement in turn depends on our conclusions in regard to the origin of the mountains; if they are folded mountains as on the Earth, and if extensive differentiation by lava flows has occurred, then the irregularities could be supported by low-density rocks below the mountains as is true in the case of the Earth. It is concluded in this chapter that the mountains have largely fallen into their present positions and that they do not have low-density roots.

† The author is grateful to the Yale University Press for permission to draw rather heavily at times on the revised chapter on the Moon from his book, "The Planets", to be published by Yale University Press.

The existence of high mountains requires a high degree of rigidity in the outer parts of the Moon. If the Moon has uniform density throughout, or at least varying only with the distance from the centre, then the deep interior of the Moon must have considerable rigidity since its shape is not an equilibrium one under its own gravitational field and that of the Earth, and under the centrifugal force due to its rotation on its axis and in its orbit. If the density varies with latitude and longitude, it is possible to account for the irregular shape even if the deep interior does not have great rigidity. These conditions on the rigidity in turn place limitations on the distribution of radioactive substances and on the past thermal history of the Moon. The low density of the Moon and its apparently low concentration of iron in its general composition lead to interesting conclusions in regard to its origin. Also, an interpretation of the surface features cannot be made without considering the thermal history. Since the Moon is a small body as compared to the Earth, volcanism cannot have been as great on the Moon as it is now or has been in the past on the Earth, but only detailed calculations can give us quantitative estimates of differences to be expected.

It is quite obvious that all these interdependent conditions make the arguments and conclusions difficult to present in a logical way without anticipating throughout the discussion conclusions which are presented later. It is concluded that the Moon was accumulated at low temperatures with only local or temporary melting, and that it has retained a high rigidity since its formation; that the surface features were mostly formed by collisions of objects with its surface; that lavas resulted from high-energy collisions with its surface and are not the result of subsurface melting as is true for the Earth; and that the surface features were mostly formed during a short period of time very early in its history.

II. Origin of the Lunar Craters

The lunar craters are mostly circular in outline with a high wall surrounding them, and in the case of many of the larger ones, with a central mountain peak. They vary in size from the limit of visibility, i.e. about 1 km in diameter to the great crater Clavius which is 236 km in diameter. The interiors are often partially filled with a smooth gray material. (The Wargentin crater is filled to the brim in this way). The rims and central peaks have rather gentle slopes as is true for most of the lunar mountains (see Chapter 12). The smallest ones appear to be very similar to terrestrial meteor craters. In general the craters are wide and shallow as compared to their depths. Some of the smaller craters occur along fissures as, for example, in the area west of Copernicus, and these as well as some others must be due to processes originating within the Moon.

Galileo first observed these craters in 1610 and since that time they have generally been regarded as of volcanic origin. In 1873, Proctor suggested that they were due to collisions of meteoric bodies, and since that time the argument as to their nature has continued. Baldwin (1949) discussed this subject in great detail and gave many references to the literature.   His discussion showed that most of the craters must be due to collisions of massive objects.   This was the conclusion of Gilbert (1893) who discussed many features of the craters, their random distribution if allowance is made for the great collisions that produced the maria (see Section III), and their markedly different forms as compared to terrestrial volcanoes, especially when the absence of erosion is considered.[†] The medium sized craters are distributed in the smooth maria and in the rugged land areas at random, though the larger craters are not found within the maria but in some cases do lie in the edges of the circular maria. (This latter point will be discussed later in another connection [Section IV]).

In considering the question of the meteoritic or plutonic origin of craters, it is well to begin with the question of energy sources required to produce these objects. In some way large amounts of energy were concentrated in very limited areas distributed at random over the surface. Comparisons with the Earth are difficult because of its greater size and obviously greater activity. Calderas result in localized positions of the Earth and at least in some cases are due to explosions of a violent kind. Melted silicates are able to dissolve considerable quantities of water and, as they crystallize, water pressure increases until an explosion can occur (Cotton, 1952). Such an origin for lunar craters requires that the Moon should have many volcanic forms such as those now found on the Earth, except that they should be more numerous, since in the absence of erosion as on the Moon, they would be preserved. No such abundance of typical volcanoes is present on the Moon.[‡] The random distribution with respect to area and the type of formation on which they occur are best explained by the collision hypothesis. Collisions of many kinds depending on the mass, velocity

---

† Near the centre of the Moon's disk several large craters are approximately in a line in a north-south direction, and it is often maintained that this indicates some non-random effect. However, this is the only prominent case of this kind and it is probably only the chance event to be expected.

‡ Gilbert noted this and other competent students have agreed with him.

and chemical composition of the colliding object and the character of the local surface could have occurred on the Moon, and such colliding objects could have supplied adequate sources of energy in the localized areas. The smaller craters are similar to known terrestrial meteorite craters, but we know of no terrestrial collisional craters with which to compare the larger ones, and it is not possible to estimate the exact forms to be expected for these larger craters. In particular the central peaks may be due to the rebound of the colliding object (as suggested by Gilbert), or of the lunar surface, but it is not at all impossible that some local melting occurred and produced some temporary volcanic effect. Some of these peaks have small craters at their summits which may be due to subsequent collisions of small objects, or to some detailed result of the large collision, or to the possible temporary volcano.

It is concluded that the craters are due for the most part to the random fall of objects on the lunar surface and hence it follows that the crater walls are not supported by low-density roots as is true for terrestrial mountains. The craters are supported by the physical strength of the underlying rocks.

III. The Imbrium Collision†

The structure of Mare Imbrium gives unequivocal evidence in regard to the origin of this mare and the whole region is most informative in regard to the origin of the surface features of the Moon. Figure 1 shows a photograph of the region in which foreshortening has been removed. Two circular areas are present: the larger one outlines the neighbouring mountain scarp while the smaller outlines a ring of mountain peaks; there are no mountain peaks within the smaller circle. It will be noted that mountain ridges radiate from the direction of this inner circle; this inner circle lies just in front of Sinus Iridum. The entire pattern is most probably due to a single event. At some time in the past,

† The Imbrian system was discovered by Gilbert in 1893 but has been rediscovered—apparently independently—by others since then. Delmotte (1914) described this system. The region was mapped by Lamech (1933) and by Darvey (1933). The latter author placed the position of the collision in Mare Imbrium south of the shore line between Plato and Pr. Laplace, instead of immediately before Sinus Iridum. The present writer believes this location to be improbable. The collision site would be close to, or superimposed upon the Straight mountains, Pico and Piton, and thus origins of these features subsequent to the collision would be required. The text gives reasons for the preferred location of the collision. Baldwin (1949) also discusses this Imbrian collision without knowing of previous work.

Much delay in understanding the structure and origin of the lunar surface has resulted from this repetitive discovery of important lunar features. It is to be hoped that the future will witness more careful cognizance and recognition of prior work such as has been and is practised in other fields of science.

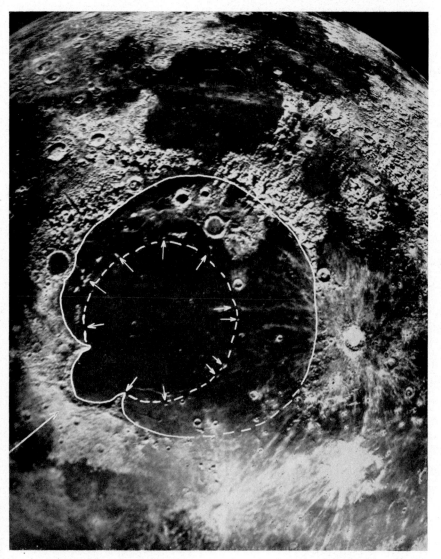

FIG. 1.   Region of Mare Imbrium.

this region of the Moon was covered with large and small craters similar to the southern land areas. An object approached at a low angle in the direction of the arrow, gouged out Sinus Iridum and bored a deep hole within the region of the small circle, raised a wavelike structure all around the region and sprayed out some of its substance and some of that of the Moon in a great fan of radiating mountain ridges, some of which extend some 1500 or 2000 km from the collision area. Subsequently the wave settled partly and broke at the shore line, that is, at the larger circle in the picture. Craters in the immediate region were largely destroyed. The object was somewhat less in diameter than the distance between the Laplace and Heraclides promontories at either side of Sinus Iridum, i.e. 230 km. Gilbert, from an estimate of the amount of material in the neighbourhood, estimated it as 100 miles, and Urey, from the evidence given here, as 200 km.†

Arguments have been advanced to the effect that the colliding object destroyed the sea wall of a large crater of which Sinus Iridum is the remnant, but this requires an exact superposition of two rare events, namely, the large collision that produced the Sinus Iridum crater and the second much larger collision which destroyed it, and this, while possible, is highly improbable. Gilbert first recognized these features except for the relation of Sinus Iridum to the pattern.

The craters within the large crater as well as Plato on the northern shore, are all post mare, as are probably the craters anywhere near the mare shores. Great masses of silicates presumably formed the Alps, the Haemus, Caucasus, and Carpathian mountains and other ridges in Oceanus Procellarum. The Alpine Valley at the northwest of the mare owes its existence to this event; it is probably a groove ploughed out by a high density nickel-iron missile. Other grooves through the walls of Ptolemaeus and Alphonsus and in these mountainous regions are almost certainly due to missiles from this collision. The object probably arrived at subsonic velocities, i.e. less than about 5 or 6 km per sec, for otherwise the object would have buried itself before the top part of the object would have received a signal that contact had been made. Deceleration in the vertical direction was necessary in order that the iron-nickel and silicate masses could be deflected in a nearly horizontal direction. The energy of the object assuming a diameter of 200 km, a density of $3 \cdot 5$ g cm^{-3} and a velocity of $2 \cdot 4$ km sec^{-1}, i.e. the escape velocity of the Moon, was 4×10^{32} ergs, and

---

† A. C. Charters has recently reported on small scale experiments which would indicate that these estimates may be too high, though scaling from laboratory collisions to such large ones introduces great uncertainty.

hence it is not surprising that premare craters would have been destroyed and that the walls of Ptolemaeus are very low as compared to other craters of similar size. (An approach of the object at an angle to the vertical requires that the velocity be somewhat greater than the escape velocity). The existence of silicate ridges and grooves due to nickel-iron bodies indicates that the colliding object contained both kinds of material in the top part. It is interesting to note that no mountainous masses lie on Mare Serenitatis and that there are no large craters in Mare Serenitatis or the collision area of Mare Imbrium (see Section IV).

Sabaneyev (1953) has made many experiments on the fall of soft objects into layers of soft material and finds that the lunar craters must have been formed by the fall, for the most part, of objects from the vertical direction, and that, therefore, these objects arrived at about the escape velocity of the Moon in agreement with the characteristics of the Imbrium collision.

The other circular maria, namely, Serenitatis, Crisium, Nectaris and Humorum, were produced most probably by the collision of other objects. Any unsymmetrical characteristics of the maria are not nearly so evident as are those associated with Mare Imbrium, and hence it may be supposed that the objects fell more nearly from the vertical. The flooded maria, that is, Fecunditatis, Tranquilitatis, Oceanus Procellarum and Nubium, and other smooth areas such as the various bays and filled craters, were probably produced by secondary processes such as the flow of lava from the collision maria, or as the result of finely divided material splashed from these maria or carried by some temporary atmosphere.

Gilbert believed that the maria were composed of melted silicates produced by the energy of the colliding bodies and that this liquid was sprayed over the region near the centre of the Moon's disk. Baldwin maintained that lava from the Moon's interior released by the Imbrium collision flowed over Oceanus Procellarum, Mare Nubium and the maria to the west as well. Gold (1955) has suggested that dust produced by light and particle erosion has flowed over the Moon to produce the smooth areas, and Urey (1956) has suggested that both melted silicates and dust or sandy material were produced by the great collisions and that a temporary atmosphere carried these materials to great distances. Kuiper (1959) maintains that an accreted crust floated on melted silicates below and that the melted silicates rose into areas where the crust was destroyed by the great collisions and in this way formed the maria.

The energy of the great collisions, even if the velocities were subsonic, is quite sufficient to produce some melting, even though a process of such magnitude cannot be reliably estimated in detail. Some energy would surely be lost as seismic energy and would be dissipated as heat throughout the Moon. If volatile substances were present in the colliding object or the lunar surface, a large spray of melted or finely divided solids would be produced and a substantial dust cloud could have been present. In complicated problems of this kind, direct observation would be much more satisfactory than theoretical calculations. Mare Tranquilitatis particularly looks like a lava flow from the region of Mare Serenitatis, because of its irregular border and the many partially flooded and distorted craters within the mare.

The mobile dust theory as a major and determining effect can hardly be correct. At the present time craters with high walls stand in the maria, and the Straight Wall in Mare Nubium is another example. Also, all the many fissures and ridges in the smooth areas should have been levelled and filled if mobile dust were present. Yet Gold's argument, that the smooth material within and between the craters in the land areas can hardly be the result of melted silicates oozing up all over this area, is convincing. Some dusty or sandy or gravelly material may cover these smooth areas, even though underneath the material is solidified lava.

Since liquid silicates as observed on Earth are less dense than the solids in contact with them, it is doubtful indeed that any large masses of liquid silicates could be retained beneath a solid crust for more than brief periods of time. In fact, natural moonquakes should liberate liquid of this kind without any collisions to initiate the process: this should be true particularly with respect to the assumption of a crust accreted from cosmic dust of mean cosmic composition floating on liquids below, since the solids should normally be more dense than the liquids. The hypothesis that a layer of melted material underlay the present visible surface at the time it was formed, makes it difficult to understand how the high mountains were supported. Unless these mountains have a low density for some reason which is not obvious, they should have settled into the lunar surface in a brief period, a point recognized by Gilbert two-thirds of a century ago.

Many of the mountainous masses near Mare Imbrium fell on the lunar surface and there is no reason to believe that this material was of lower density than the general body of the Moon. We conclude that at the time at which the maria and mountains were formed the Moon was sufficiently cold to have had a sufficiently high rigidity to support the mountains and inequalities of the maria, and that it has had such a low temperature ever since that time.

IV. Time of Formation of the Lunar Surface

Certain details of the lunar surface lead to the conclusion that the great collisions occurred within a surprisingly short period of time (Urey, 1952), and this is important from the standpoint of the origin of the Moon.

The region of Maria Imbrium and Serenitatis contains many ridges radiating from the collision area of Mare Imbrium: this is particularly true of the southern shore of Mare Serenitatis. Also, such ridges definitely oriented relative to the collision area and of a delicate appearing structure, are located in the smooth area connecting the two maria. If Mare Imbrium had been formed first, then the collision which produced Mare Serenitatis should have destroyed these ridges or covered them with debris from this collision. We conclude that the opposite was true: namely, that Mare Serenitatis is older. But in this case it is necessary to explain the absence of ridges from the Imbrian collision on the surface of Mare Serenitatis. The obvious explanation is that the mare was still molten when the Imbrian collision occurred.

Also, the collision maria have no large craters on their interiors, though their shores often have large craters which are evidently post-mare in time of origin. (This statement is true only for the collision area of Mare Imbrium. It is evident that the shelf area between the two circles of Fig. I does have such large craters.) Though these could happen by chance, they furnish supporting evidence for the conclusion reached from the Serenitatis-Imbrium relationships, namely, the maria were still molten when the intense bombardment stopped.

These facts imply a very short time between the two collisions that produced Maria Serenitatis and Imbrium, and in other cases a short period of time during which most of the bombardment of the lunar surface occurred. Calculations on the time of solidification are difficult because some frothy pumice-like material of low thermal conductivity could have covered the newly-formed Mare Serenitatis. Urey (1952, pp. 36, 37) estimated that the time for solidification under 100 metres of pumice-like material floating on a pool 10 km in depth could have been as long as 100,000 years. The time is proportional to the depth of the pool and to the thickness of the insulating layer. The calculated time is likely to be a maximum. Urey also calculated the cooling times for the freshly solidified maria. Table I gives the calculated cooling times from the formula for cooling of a plane surface,

$$\frac{T - T_0}{T_m - T_0} = \mathrm{Erf}\left(\frac{x}{2}\sqrt{\frac{K}{t}}\right),$$

where T is the temperature at distance x below the surface at time t.

T_0 is the temperature of the surroundings T_m the melting temperature, assumed to be 1500°C and constant throughout the mass, and K is the thermal diffusivity taken as $0·005$ sec cm^{-2}. Times would be greater if the surface were covered with an insulating layer. It is evident that within a relatively short period of time the whole pool would become cool in the surface region, though it would probably be

TABLE I

Loss of Temperature of Molten Lava, $T_m - T$, As Function of x and t

	t (years)					
x (metres)	125	500	2,000	8,000	32,000	128,000
100	170	640	1040	1290	1390	1430
200	2·2	170	640	1040	1290	1390
400	0	2·2	170	640	1040	1290
800	0	0	2·2	170	640	1040
1600	0	0	0	2·2	170	640
3200	0	0	0	0	2·2	170
6400	0	0	0	0	0	2·2
$(\delta T/\delta x)x = 0$ (in °C. cm^{-1})	0·189	0·0945	0·0472	0·0236	0·0118	0·0059

too plastic to support high mountainous masses for 10^5 years or more. However, such masses sinking into the plastic layer might well leave some surface irregularity as tell-tale evidence of the process. Such irregularities are not obvious; at least indicating that the processes occurred while the pools were still liquid. We conclude that the intense bombardment probably occurred within a total time of less than 10^5 years.

This short time is readily explained as due to the capture of the Moon by the Earth during the terminal stage for the formation of the Earth by the capture of solid objects (Urey, 1960). It can be expected that at some stage the Earth had a number of objects of varying sizes moving in orbits in its vicinity. The introduction of a massive object such as the Moon into an orbit of the same dimensions would strongly perturb the orbits of smaller objects so that they would collide with the Earth or Moon or escape from the system. It has proved to be very difficult to conclude on the basis of modern satellite calculations that any satellite orbit moving in the neighbourhood of the Moon's orbit would be stable for a large number of periods about the Earth. Also, such collisions with the Moon would occur with the escape velocity of the Moon or slightly larger in accordance with the conclusion in the preceding section in regard to the fall of the Imbrian planetesimal.

V. The Figure of the Moon

The irregular shape of the Moon and its importance from the standpoint of lunar history has been discussed by Urey (1951, 1952). Jeffreys (1959 a, b) has recently reviewed the pertinent data relative to the lunar ellipticities. Briefly, the calculated values for these ellipticities are as follows:

$$\frac{C-A}{C} = 5\frac{M}{m}\frac{a^3}{c^3} \quad \text{and} \quad \frac{C-B}{C} = \frac{5}{4}\frac{M}{m}\frac{a^3}{c^3},$$

where C is the moment of inertia about the lunar axis, A about an axis pointing toward the Earth, and B about the third axis; M and m are the masses of the Earth and Moon respectively, a is the radius of the Moon and c the Earth-Moon distance. These equations are derived on the assumption that the Moon has a uniform density with respect to its latitude and longitude, and that the density varies only slightly with radius. The surface of the Moon—or rather of the selenoid—is a spherical harmonic of second order with major axes,

$$a\left(1+\frac{25}{12}\frac{M}{m}\frac{a^3}{c^3}\right), \quad a\left(1-\frac{10}{12}\frac{M}{m}\frac{a^3}{c^3}\right), \quad a\left(1-\frac{25}{12}\frac{M}{m}\frac{a^3}{c^3}\right).$$

The theoretical values of the two ellipticities are $3 \cdot 75 \times 10^{-5}$ and $0 \cdot 94 \times 10^{-5}$ respectively.

The observed values of the first of these quantities can be calculated from the orbital characteristics from the formula,

$$\theta_0 = \frac{3i\beta}{(1+\mu)(2\mu+\mu^2-3\beta)}\sqrt{(1+\mu+\tfrac{1}{2}\mu^2)},$$

where θ_0 and i are the inclination of the lunar equator and orbit to the ecliptic, respectively, and μ is the ratio of the lunar period to the period of the precession of the node. The numerical values are well known, i.e. $\theta_0 = 1°32'1$, $i = 5°8'33''$ and $\mu = 0 \cdot 004019$. The calculated value of β, which is $C-A/B$ and is nearly equal to $C-A/C$, is $0 \cdot 000629$. This is a reliable value and it is $16 \cdot 8$ times the calculated value. The value of $(C-B)/C$ can be secured only from the Moon's physical libration in longitude and because of the very difficult observations, is not well known. It is necessary to observe the movement of a crater near the centre of the Moon's disk relative to the eastern or western limb, and due to the surface irregularities the results are not reliable and agreement between observers is not secured.

Jeffreys (1959a, 165 ff., 1959b) reviews these and suggests that $0 \cdot 67$ based on work of Yakovkin is the best value for the ratio $(C-B)/(C-A)$

whose theoretical value is 0·25. The observations indicate that there is definite disagreement between the observed and theoretical values for this ratio and, hence, that the shape of the Moon disagrees with the theory for any distance between the Earth and the Moon. The theory predicts a difference of 64 metres between the polar radius and the radius directed toward the Earth, and the observations indicate that the difference is somewhat more than one kilometre, and that the difference between the radius perpendicular to the polar radius and that toward the Earth is only slightly less than the latter. In this case, the difference in stress at the centre of the Moon as calculated by Jeffreys (1959a, p. 389) for a body having a free surface,

$$r = a[1 + \epsilon(\tfrac{1}{3} - \cos^2 \theta)]$$

is

$$\frac{32}{95}g\rho a\epsilon,$$

where g is the surface force of gravity, GM/a^2, and ρ is the density. With $a\epsilon$ equal to 1 km this gives 19 bars stress difference between the polar direction and that toward the Earth. This indicates that there must be considerable strength in the deep interior of the Moon now and that this has been true ever since this irregular shape has existed. It is surprising that a large object such as the Moon under stresses due to tides and thermal stresses due to unequal heat changes, would not be able to adjust in shape by one kilometre and thus relieve the stress. But if it has not done so, it surely indicates considerable strength in the deep interior and probably that no melting has occurred.†

Another explanation for the irregular shape has been offered by Urey, Elsasser and Rochester (1959). They suggest that the density of the Moon varies with angular position, i.e. highest density at the pole and least in the direction toward the Earth. They show that there will be no stress at the Moon's centre if the density distribution follows the equation

$$\frac{\delta}{\delta_0} = 1 - \beta P_2(\cos \theta) - \gamma P_2(\sin \theta \cos \phi)$$

---

† Jeffreys (1959a, p. 202) seems to believe that the Moon is strong enough to sustain this pressure on the basis of a comparison with surface rocks of the Earth. However, these rocks to a depth of 100 km probably do not approach the temperatures in the deep lunar interior and thus should be much stronger than the lunar interior. In fact, his arguments, when allowance is made for probable temperature differences as discussed below, probably support the view that the lunar interior could not support the calculated stress differences.

and the surface the equation

$$\frac{a}{a_0} = 1 + \tfrac{19}{20}\beta P_2(\cos\theta) + \tfrac{19}{20}\gamma P_2(\sin\theta\cos\phi),$$

where δ_0 is the mean density, a_0 is the radius of a sphere having the lunar volume, θ is the angle measured from the line to the Earth, and ϕ is the azimuth measured from the perpendicular to the line to the Earth and the pole.† β and γ are constants determined from the observed ellipticities. (This is not the configuration for which the potential energy is a minimum, but surely approximates it sufficiently well considering the uncertainty of the data). It is easily shown that

$$\frac{C-A}{C} = \tfrac{9}{8}\beta \quad \text{and} \quad \frac{C-B}{C} = \tfrac{9}{8}\gamma,$$

and these must equal the non-tidal part of the observed quantities. Then β and γ are $5 \cdot 3 \times 10^{-4}$ and $3 \cdot 6 \times 10^{-4}$ respectively. (The authors used a somewhat smaller value for $(C-A)/(C-B)$, namely, $0 \cdot 050$ and hence secured a slightly smaller value for γ). These authors also showed that a surface loading could not be used to account for the observations, provided that there is no stress at the centre of the Moon. In this case great strength is not required at any point in the Moon. For a moon having this variation of density to be converted to one of uniform density with angular position, the more dense regions must sink to the interior and the less dense must flow over the more dense material, or some high density constituent, e.g. iron-nickel etc., must settle out of the general mass. It requires much less strength to prevent such reorganization processes than it does to prevent a simple readjustment of the shape of the entire Moon as required if the Moon has a uniform density. If the density varies with angular position, then the Moon could not have been generally melted at any time in its history.

Surface elevations have been studied for many years. Baldwin (1949) recalculated the data of Saunder and of Franz secured by observing the librations of small craters and found evidence for a decreasing lunar radius as the limbs are approached. There is considerable irregularity in the data and the least square solutions cannot be regarded as very precise. Du Fresne (1956) studied this same data and concluded that there is considerable variation in elevation over small distances even in the maria. In this case smooth curves are not justified, but the present data do not justify any estimate in regard to contour lines.

---

† P_2 (cos θ) and P_2 (sin θ cos ϕ) are spherical harmonies and equal $(\tfrac{3}{2}\cos^2\theta - \tfrac{1}{2})$ and $(\tfrac{3}{2}\sin^2\theta\cos^2\phi - \tfrac{1}{2})$ respectively.

Occultations of stars give evidence in regard to the irregularities at the limb as shown by Brouwer (1952), and Watts (1958) has made an extensive study of the limb regions and has concluded that very great irregularities exist even up to differences of elevation of some 10 km. Such differences show that the outer parts of the Moon have greater strength than these parts of the Earth have at the present time. Thus the terrestrial regions covered quite recently by glaciers are rising within some tens of thousands of years. Haskell (1935, 1936) has estimated the viscosity of the Earth from the rate of rise and finds 10^{22} poise. This calculation is approximate only since solids do not flow as liquids, but a comparison may be valuable none the less. Haskell concludes that the time for nearly complete disappearance of an irregularity is given by

$$\tau = \frac{20\eta}{\delta g l},$$

where η is the viscosity, δ the density, g the force of gravity and l the distance between the depressed and elevated regions. Watts finds that the D'Alembert Mountains and Mare Orientale some 500 km apart on the eastern limb have a difference in elevation of 9·7 km. Substituting numerical values, the calculated time for the disappearance of this irregularity is found to be about 250,000 years. Even if Haskell's formula is not applicable, a difference of 9·7 km on the Moon is about equivalent to 5 km of ice on the Earth. The persistence of such an inequality requires that the outer parts of the Moon are now, and always have been since these inequalities were formed, more rigid and hence colder, than the outer parts of the Earth.

The maintenance of these great surface irregularities—such as the very low level of Mare Orientale—may be due to local accumulations of high-density materials, such as metallic iron-nickel below these depressed areas. In this case, the rigidity of the Moon must be sufficient to prevent the sinking of such masses through the silicates to the deep interior. Urey, Elsasser and Rochester (1959) showed that such masses near the lunar surface would not explain the anomalous ellipticities calculated from the moments of inertia.

It is difficult to decide in view of this evidence whether partial melting in the deep interior would result in the accumulation of pockets of lava and whether these would break through to the surface as great lava flows. The arguments here presented indicate that if they are lava flows they originated deep inside the Moon. It is probable that terrestrial lava flows of large size are part of the great mountain and continent building processes and these, in turn, are related to great convection currents in the mantle. For several reasons such processes have not occurred on the Moon and, hence, the lava flows probably have not come from the interior (Dietz, 1946; Urey 1953). Recently, another line of evidence has come from the first view of the rear side of the Moon. It has very limited maria as compared with the hemisphere facing the Earth, and it is difficult to understand why lava from the interior should not be approximately uniformly distributed over the surface. Pockets of liquid should accumulate under all parts of the surface and would hardly flow horizontally for great distances before breaking through to the surface.

It is likely that such conclusions will not be generally accepted until samples of the lunar surface are investigated. If the maria are filled with lava from the interior, they will have the composition of basalt throughout their mass. If they are the result of the great collisions, their composition will probably approximate that of the chondritic meteorites with only local or superficial basaltic material present in limited amounts.

VI. The Heat Balance of the Moon†

The preceding paragraphs give considerable evidence that the Moon was formed at a low temperature, but calculations in regard to its thermal history are important. First attempts on this problem were made by Urey (1951), but the fundamental data secured since completely invalidate the calculations made at that time, though the conclusions remain much the same.

† The writer's attempts to solve this problem have had a chequered history, as data altered in the last 10 years. (1) In 1950 (Urey, 1951) the solution was attempted using an age of 3 AE, a potassium concentration of 0·20% and scanty data on uranium and thorium, though it was approximately correct (Davis, (1947, 1950); Arrol, Jacobi and Paneth (1942). It was concluded that a uniform distribution of the radioactive elements was consistent with a rigid Moon and that an originally melted Moon was not. (2) In 1955 (Urey, 1955) the age of the meteorites and presumably the Moon had changed to 4·5 AE, the concentration of potassium to ~823 ppm (Edwards and Urey, 1955; Edwards, 1955; Ahrens, Pinson and Kearns, 1952) and the concentrations of uranium and thorium first reported for a single meteorite greater than other values by a factor of ten (Chackett, Golden, Mercer, Paneth and Reasbeck, 1950) were apparently confirmed by Patterson (1955). These concentrations were inconsistent with the known thermal characteristics of the Earth and hence the writer assumed that the meteorites were not the average material of the Earth and Moon and assumed a constant correction factor. Also, the writer accepted too uncritically an estimate of melting point elevation of silicates with pressure which was much too high (Urey, 1957, p. 53). This gave a consistent temperature history for the Moon and Earth (Urey, 1955, 1957). (3) In 1956 Hamaguchi, Reed and Turkevich (1957) revised the previous values for the uranium concentration, and Bate, Huizenga and Potrax (1959) revised the thorium data to lower values by about a factor of ten: this made the previous arbitrary revision of the

[footnote continued on page 496

It seems most probable that the concentration of radioactive substances in the Moon is that of the primordial material from which the planets were made. It is far less certain that this is true of the materials of the meteorites. Possibly the potassium concentration in the chondrites is higher than its concentration in the Moon.

At present the content of potassium, uranium and thorium in the chondritic meteorites are estimated to be: K, 823 ppm; U, $1 \cdot 14 \times 10^{-8}$ g/g; Th, $3 \cdot 96 \times 10^{-8}$ g/g.†

The concentration of potassium in the achondrites is lower by about a factor of 2. Also the variations in the potassium, rubidium and cesium concentrations show that some separative process of the alkalis has been effective and hence the concentrations cannot be taken as certain.

The radioactive constants for potassium, thorium and uranium are given in Table II and the heat production and temperatures to be expected in completely insulated chondritic matter are given in Table III. (A specific heat of $1 \cdot 25$ joules per gram is used for chondritic matter

† See H. Hamaguchi, G. W. Reed, and A. Turkevich, *Geochim. et Cosmoch. Acta*, **12**, 337 (1957); G. L. Bate, J. R. Huizenga, and H. A. Potrax, (1959); G. Edwards, *Geochim. et Cosmoch. Acta*, **8**, 285 (1955); G. Edwards and H. C. Urey, Ibid. **7**, 154 (1955); L. H. Ahrens, W. H. Pinson, and M. M. Kearns, Ibid. **2**, 229 (1952); P. W. Gast, *Geochim. et Cosmoch, Acta*, **19**, 1 (1960). The average of the Edwards and Urey determinations for potassium are 863 ppm. Arbitrarily this was revised by the writer to 823 ppm because J. Geiss found that there was a small systematic error in the previous work which at the time was estimated by the writer as about 40 ppm. The value used does not have the precision indicated, but the calculations have been made using this value and, if readers disagree with this value, corrections can be made. At the time of writing no more reliable value for the average concentration is available.

Footnote continued from page 495]

meteoritic data unnecessary (Urey, 1956). It was found that the thermal balance of the Earth is consistent with the concentrations of the radioactive elements. No revision of calculations was made since little change in conclusions regarding the Moon resulted from the revised data. (4) Boyd and England (1958) and Le Comte and Birch (1959) have shown that diopsite and albite melting points increase by $10 \cdot 3$ and $11 \pm 2°C$ respectively per 1000 bars of pressure, which is considerably less than was previously assumed and hence melting points in the interior of the Moon are probably less than previously assumed. Today, considerable variation in the concentrations of uranium in certain chondritic meteorites has been observed. Also the achondrites have lower concentrations of potassium and higher concentrations of uranium than do the chondrites. Considerable variation in the concentrations of the alkali metals, Rb and Cs, are observed in the chondrites, and these parallel smaller variations in the potassium concentrations (Webster, Morgan and Smales, 1958). These data indicate that there is no certainty that the concentrations of the radioactive elements observed in the meteorites are necessarily the same as the mean concentrations in the Moon and hence the present calculations may require further revision in the future. Also the melting conditions on the lunar interior are uncertain because of the limited data available and also because the content of water is crucial to any estimate. Possibly some progress has been made during the last ten years, but the changing data have made and still make all conclusions doubtful.

TABLE II

Nuclide	Heat Energy per g atom MeV	joule per g × 10⁻¹⁰	Half Life AE	Decay Constant AE⁻¹
K^{40}	0·71	0·171	1·27	0·546
Th^{232}	39·8	1·655	13·9	0·0499
U^{235}	45·2	1·856	0·713	0·972
U^{238}	47·4	1·922	4·51	0·1537

The energy data are from Birch (1954). More recent data for K^{40} would indicate that the heat energy may be 0·70 MeV. The K^{40} half life is slightly larger than that given by Wetherill (1957).

More recent data on the half life of U^{238} give 4·49 AE, but the calculations have been made using 4·51 AE for this constant. No important difference in conclusions would result from the use of the revised data.

in estimating the temperature). These data give the total heating that can be expected on the basis of these abundances of the elements.

In estimating the heat balance of the Moon, various assumptions in regard to initial temperatures and the distribution of the radioactive elements can be made. It now appears reasonable to assume an age of the Moon equal to the measured ages of the meteorites, namely, 4·5 AE, or possibly slightly greater than this. The non-equilibrium shape of the Moon indicates that it is highly rigid at the present or that it has an irregular distribution of density within its body; the latter condition can hardly obtain if the Moon was once completely melted. The former explanation requires that the past thermal history should be such that high rigidity can exist in the Moon, at the present time and in the outer parts, ever since the large surface features were established. It is the purpose of the present discussion of the thermal

TABLE III

Heat generation in meteoritic materials.

Nuclide	Concentration ppm	dE/dt at present Ergs g⁻¹ yr⁻¹	Total E in joules per g of chondritic meteorite generated since the specified aeons ago			
			4·5	5·0	5·5	5·5 From to 4·5
K^{40}	0·100	0·94	1828	2455	3280	1452
Th^{232}	0·0396	0·32	165	186	207	42
U^{235}	$8·22 \times 10^{-4}$	0·01	120	195	319	299
U^{238}	0·1132	0·33	217	252	289	72
Total		1·60	2330	3088	4095	1765
Temperature			1864	2470	3276	1412

history to establish, if possible, some limitations on the initial lunar temperatures.

Two initial temperature conditions will be explored. (1) The Moon was completely melted 4·5 AE ago and during solidification some concentration of the radioactive elements near the surface took place. The calculations show that *all* the radioactive elements must be in the surface regions in this case. (2) The Moon was formed at low temperatures. In this case it will be shown that the deep interior may be completely melted; also, a grossly uniform distribution of the radioactive elements must be assumed. If the concentrations of the radioactive elements are not lower than they are in the meteorites, general melting throughout the Moon would occur, if the time of formation was further than 4·5 AE in the past, and the mathematical development is not applicable. Following any thermal development to an earlier time does not appear to be possible.

The pressure within the Moon assuming constant density throughout is,

$$P = \tfrac{2}{3}\pi G\rho^2 a^2\left(1 - \frac{r^2}{a^2}\right)\text{dynes cm}^{-2} = 47000\left(1 - \frac{r^2}{a^2}\right)\text{bars.}$$

Using this equation, it is possible to estimate the melting points of a few substances as a function of depth. Strong (1959) has determined the elevation of the melting point of iron at 96,000 atm (97,300 bars) to be 190° ± 20° C. Hence the melting point of iron at the centre of the Moon under a pressure of 47,000 bars is 92° C higher than its melting point 1808° K, i.e. 1900° K or 1627° C. (The linear interpolation is satisfactory over the small range of pressure.) The data on silicates are limited and have been reviewed by MacDonald (1959) who has derived constants for the Simon empirical equation for diopsite and albite, using the data of Boyd and England (1958) and Le Comte and Birch (1959). His formulae give melting point elevations of 489° C and 405° C for diopsite and albite respectively. Using linear extrapolations, the elevation in both cases is about 500° C at 47,000 bars pressure. Using data for the entropy and volume changes on melting for olivine, Urey (1952) estimated the elevation of its melting point as 220° C, using the data of Bowen and Schairer (1935).

A mixture of substances does not melt at a constant temperature but initial melting may begin at about 1100° C in the absence of water, and thus the temperature of initial melting would follow the formula,

$$T_i = 1100 + 500\left(1 - \frac{r^2}{a^2}\right).$$

The temperature for final melting is difficult to estimate, but possibly the formula,

$$T_f = 1600 + 200\left(1 - \frac{r^2}{a^2}\right)$$

gives a reasonable approximation. The corresponding formula for the melting point for iron-nickel alloy is approximately

$$T_m = 1500 + 92\left(1 - \frac{r^2}{a^2}\right).$$

These formulae will be used to estimate the state of melting within a Moon heated from low temperatures by radioactive heating.

The course of solidification of an initially completely melted Moon is not easily and certainly estimated. Since solid silicates are more dense than their liquids and the first minerals to crystallize have the highest melting points and also higher densities than the lower melting species in general, we expect that the Moon would solidify from the centre outwards. Any metallic iron would sink to the centre. Olivines would crystallize and settle to the centre, but complete separation from intercrystalline liquid might not occur because of the low gravitational field near in the lunar interior. Also, ferrous iron concentrates in the liquid phase and this would result in a liquid approaching that of the solid in density in some regions and complete separation would be unlikely. Finally, the outer parts would solidify at some 1100° C. If water were present, it would concentrate near the surface and the final melting point would be considerably less. The temperature would vary from 1100° C at the surface or somewhat below the surface to 2000° C, i.e. 1800° C the melting point of olivine containing some 15% of ferrous oxide, plus 200° C due to the increased pressure. The radioactive elements concentrate in the residual liquid and would be present in higher concentrations near the surface but would hardly be removed quantitatively from the deep interior. In considering the case of the completely melted Moon, we shall assume a temperature for the freshly solidified Moon following the formula,

$$T = 1100 + 900\left(1 - \frac{r^2}{a^2}\right).$$

The differential equation for the change in temperature due to surface cooling with constant coefficient of heat conduction and uniform heating by radioactive elements is,

$$\frac{\partial T}{\partial t} = K\left(\frac{\partial^2 T}{\partial r^2} + \frac{2}{r}\frac{\partial T}{\partial r}\right) + \sum Q_i e^{-\alpha_i t},$$

where K is the the thermal diffusivity equal to $k/\rho c$, where k is the thermal conductivity; ρ, the density; c, the specific heat; and the Q_i is the rate of temperature rise due to the i-th radioactive element at time $t = 0$. The solution of this equation is,

$$T(r, t) = T_1 + T_2 + T_3,$$

where

$$T_1 = \sum_i \sum_{n=1}^{\infty} \frac{Q_i}{\alpha_i - K(n\pi/a)^2} \frac{2(-1)^n}{n\pi} \frac{a}{r} \sin\left(n\pi\frac{r}{a}\right) \times$$

$$[\exp(-\alpha_i t) - \exp(-Kn^2\pi^2 t/a^2)],$$

$$T_2 = -T_{0a} \sum_{n=1}^{n=\infty} \frac{2(-1)^n}{n\pi} \frac{a}{r} \sin\left(n\pi\frac{r}{a}\right) \exp(-Kn^2\pi^2 t/a^2),$$

and

$$T_3 = -\Delta T \sum_{n=1}^{\mu=\infty} \frac{12(-1)^n}{(n\pi)^3} \frac{a}{r} \sin\left(n\pi\frac{r}{a}\right) \exp(-Kn^2\pi^2 t/a^2).$$

Here T_1 gives the temperature above the surroundings due to the radioactive elements; T_2 is the temperature due to cooling from an initial temperature of T_0 throughout; and T_3 is that due to the term $\Delta T(1 - r^2/a^2)$ in the initial temperature formula. The Q_i's can be calculated from the formula,

$$Q_i = \frac{E_i}{c} \frac{dm_{i0}}{dt} = \frac{E_i}{c} \alpha_i m_{ip} \exp(\alpha_i t),$$

where E_i is the energy per gram of the ith nuclide, m_{i0} and m_{ip} are the masses of the ith nuclide per gram of meteorite initially and at present respectively, c is the specific heat of meteoritic matter and is assumed to be constant at $1 \cdot 25$ joules per gram and t is taken as $4 \cdot 5$ AE. The values of the Q_i's calculated from the data of Tables II and III are: K^{40}, $27 \cdot 68$; Th^{232}, $1 \cdot 039$; U^{235}, $2 \cdot 987$; and U^{238}, $1 \cdot 693$, all multiplied by 10^{-15} degrees centigrade per second.

Figures 1 and 2 show the variations of total temperature with time and radius for the two values of the thermal diffusivity, assuming an initial cold Moon at $0°$ C and uniform distribution of the radioactive

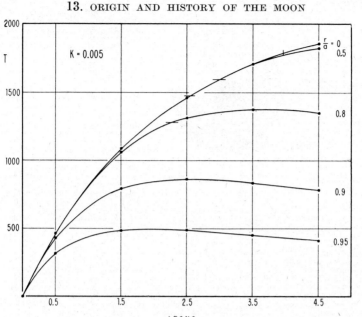

FIG. 2. Temperature within a Moon which was initially at 0° C throughout, calculated with $K = 0.005$. The horizontal lines across the curves for r/a equal to 0, 0·5 and 0·8 indicate the times of initial melting. The vertical line shows the time of complete melting.

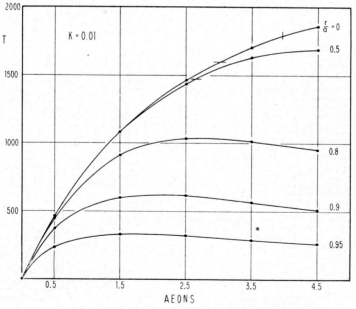

FIG. 3. This is similar to Fig. 1, except that $K = 0.01$.

elements. Table IV gives the contributions of each nuclide to the temperature at different radii and the assumed melting points at various

TABLE IV

	Present Temperatures (°C) of a Cold Moon at 0°C 4·5 AE Ago									
	K = 0·005					K = 0·010				
r/a	0·0	0·5	0·8	0·9	0·95	0·0	0·5	0·8	0·9	0·95
Initial Melting Temperature	1600	1475	1280	1195	1145	1600	1475	1280	1195	1145
Complete Melting Temperature	1800	1750	1672	1638	1621	1800	1750	1672	1638	1621
Temp. rise in 4·5 AE due to individual nuclide K^{40}	1462	1438	1052	600	313	1462	1326	739	391	196
Th^{232}	132	131	101	63	36	132	123	79	45	24
U^{235}	96	88	61	33	17	96	83	42	21	10
U^{238}	174	170	133	85	47	174	160	99	57	29
Total	1864	1827	1347	78	1413	1864	1692	959	514	259
	Present Temperatures (°C) of a Moon Solidified 4·5 AE Ago									
	K = 0·005					K = 0·010				
	No radioactive elements in the interior									
Initial Temperature	2000	1775	1424	1271	1187	2000	1775	1424	1271	1187
Residual Temperature T_2	1098	1052	608	311	153	1071	872	392	189	91
Residual Temperature T_3	772	549	222	108	52	645	437	169	80	38
Total Temperature	1870	1601	830	419	205	1716	1309	561	269	129
	With ½ of radioactive elements in the interior									
	2802	2514	1503	809	411	2645	2154	992	526	259

depths. If the thermal diffusivity is 0·005 partial melting of the silicates even at r/a equal to 0·8 would have begun over 2 AE ago. But if the thermal diffusivity is 0·01, no melting of silicates would have occurred at r/a equal to 0·8 but melting at r/a equal to 0·5 would have begun nearly 2 AE ago. Considerable melting of silicates on the deep interior is indicated on these models unless the abundances of the radioactive elements—and particularly potassium—used are too high.

Figures 4 and 5 show plots of calculated temperatures of a Moon initially at the melting point as estimated above. These curves show how slowly an object as large as the Moon, even with all the radioactive elements concentrated in the surface, would lose its temperature in the deep interior. Even out to half its radius with K equal to 0·01 which can reasonably be expected to be a maximum value, the temperature would fall by only 500° C in 4·5 AE. With some of the radioactive elements retained in the interior, the deep interior would cool even less rapidly or would rise in temperature depending on the amounts of

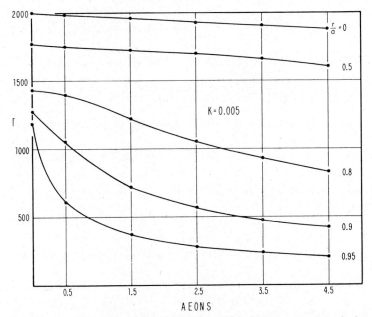

FIG. 4. Temperatures within a Moon which solidified 4·5 aeons ago calculated with $K = 0.005$. The initial temperatures are taken from the assumed melting point curve.
$$T = 1100 + 900(1 - r^2/a^2)$$

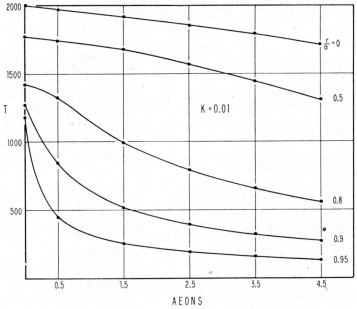

FIG. 5. This is similar to Fig. 3, except that $K = 0.01$.

these elements present in the interior. Table IV also lists the assumed melting temperatures and the calculated temperatures after 4·5 AE for two cases: (1) with no radioactive elements in the interior, and (2) with one-half of the assumed average content of these elements distributed uniformly throughout the body of the Moon. In the latter case, much melting out to half the radius should have occurred. The mean temperatures of an initially cold Moon (0° C) at the present time using 0·005 and 0·01 for the thermal diffusivities, are found to be 1100° C and 930° C respectively. Using a volume coefficient of expansion of 3×10^{-5} or a linear coefficient of 1×10^{-5} shows that the Moon should have expanded by about 1% of its radius of 1738 km, which is equivalent to an increase in circumference by $\sim$100 km. Many cracks and crevices are observed in many places and especially in the smooth areas, but whether the width of such crevices makes up 1% of the total distances is difficult to decide. Silicates have little tensile strength and, hence, the fissures should be narrow and numerous rather than wide and few in number.

MacDonald (1959) has made machine calculations of the lunar temperature and has included radiative transfer of heat energy. He has used a slightly lower concentration for potassium and a slightly higher specific heat: both have the effect of lowering the temperatures. His results are very similar to those given above. His central temperature for a Moon initially at 0° C is 1780° C, i.e. about one hundred degrees less than that given here. It is evident that the inclusion of radiative transfer makes but a slight difference on the calculated temperatures. He has considered the change in radius to be expected with time, and finds that the radius of an initially cold Moon would have increased mostly during the first 2 AE of its history and that since that time the change has been small. He also has made calculations for a Moon initially at 600° C throughout. Melting of silicates on the deep interior would occur in this case. All models show that metallic iron-nickel would be melted in the deep interior, but we have no evidence at present as to whether the Moon has a metallic core.

Since the temperature does not change uniformly with time throughout the Moon as illustrated by Figs. 2 and 3, stresses will be built up in the lunar interior and hence moonquakes should occur. MacDonald estimates this energy as about 4×10^{24} ergs per year, and thus some considerable lunar seismic activity can be expected.

Allan and Jacobs (1956) using the formulae given above with the T_3 term omitted, have considered the thermal histories of bodies of varying sizes and conductivities and with varying distributions of the radioactive substances. Their results are similar to those given here and those published previously. Their calculations give much detailed data on variations of temperatures with time and radii of such objects.

If the Moon solidified from the molten state, re-melting and lava flows must have occurred until all the radioactive elements were transferred to the surface. After this the Moon could cool down and become rigid. If this occurred previous to 4·5 AE ago, the irregular shape of the Moon can be understood on the basis of this model. Such a complete transfer of potassium, thorium and uranium to the Earth's surface has not occurred according to all estimates, and the assumption that it did occur in the early history of the Moon seems improbable.

In the case of the initially cold Moon, it seems almost certain that partial melting of silicates in the deep interior has occurred. It is possible, as mentioned previously, that we have over-estimated the concentrations of the radioactive elements. Even a decrease of 15% in these concentrations would result in sufficiently lower temperatures so that partial melting would not occur or be very slight at least. Thus it is possible that the irregular shape would be maintained by the strength of the materials. Also, a cold Moon could have accumulated with some variation in density throughout and the alternative explanation for the non-equilibrium shape would be possible.

The Moon probably accumulated at low temperatures, but any specific assumption as to the value of this temperature can hardly be substantiated with any confidence. Higher initial temperatures in the outer parts would make only slight changes in the present temperatures.

VII. Density and Composition of the Moon

The most important evidence regarding the composition of the Moon is derived from the interpretation of its low mean density. This low density has furnished the principal argument for the suggestion made by George Darwin that the Moon was derived from the outer parts of the Earth. In view of the evidence that the terrestrial planets vary in density when calculated to low temperatures and pressures, it seems more reasonable to suppose that the low density of the Moon is related to this more general characteristic of the terrestrial planets. Some years ago Urey (1952, 1956) suggested that the Moon's composition approximated more nearly to that of the primordial than does that of any other planetary body.

Also, it is generally supposed at the present time that the chondritic meteorites furnish approximate samples of such primordial material. However, they are not of uniform composition and hence some fractionation processes have modified their compositions. Two prominent groups have been identified by Urey and Craig (1953), though other groups in addition to these were recognized by Prior. Yavnel (1958) also has suggested other groups. We have no way of recognizing which, if any, of these groups represent the primordial composition. If some group could be recognized as having the proper physical characteristics and precisely the same composition, such a group *might* have accumulated from unfractionated primordial matter. Some years ago, the writer thought that the carbonaceous chondrites might constitute such a group. Analytical data for many of the elements indicate considerable but not exact constancy of composition but the data for sodium, potassium and uranium do not.

Abundance tables for the elements have been constructed assuming that the chondritic meteorites do constitute an approximate sample of primitive matter (Suess and Urey, 1956, 1958), and these tables have been used very advantageously in constructing theories for the origin of the elements. It is usually supposed that the Sun has this primitive composition, except that its composition has been modified by nuclear reactions since the planets were separated from it.

The density of the Moon at low pressures and ordinary terrestrial temperatures can be calculated by estimating the mean temperature and pressure and using reasonable values for the coefficients of expansion and compressibility. The mean temperatures can be estimated from the data given in the preceding section and from the calculations of MacDonald. The differences between the different models are not large and a mean value of $1100°$ C can be used. Even if the centre of the Moon is partly melted, little change in the calculations would result. Only if much of the Moon were melted would the calculated density be changed significantly; as shown in Section VI, this is improbable. The mean pressure is equal to $\frac{4}{15}\pi\rho^2 Ga^2$. Using numerical values this gives 19,100 bars.

The coefficients of expansion, α, and compressibility, β, of olivine are $3\cdot3 \times 10^{-5}$ and $7\cdot9 \times 10^{-7}$ respectively, and the mean density at $0°$ C and zero pressure, δ_0, can be calculated from the formula,

$$\delta = \delta_0 - 19,100\alpha + 1100\beta,$$

and this gives δ_0 equal to $3\cdot41$ g cm^{-3}. Using the values for α and β of enstatite, i.e. $2\cdot76 \times 10^{-5}$ and $10\cdot1 \times 10^{-7}$ respectively, gives $3\cdot38$ g cm^{-3} for this mean density. The low and high iron groups of Urey and Craig contain an average of $22\cdot33\%$ and $28\cdot58\%$ of iron respectively, and the respective calculated densities are $3\cdot574$ and $3\cdot761$ g cm^{-3}. (The observed mean densities are slightly less due probably to the presence of voids in these objects.) We calculate the amount of metallic iron which must be removed from a high iron group meteorite, in order that the density of the residue shall have the calculated densities of the Moon from the equation,

$$\frac{100}{3 \cdot 761} - \frac{x}{7 \cdot 86} = \frac{100 - x}{\delta_0(\text{Moon})} \quad .$$

If δ_0 (Moon) equals $3 \cdot 41$ g cm^{-3}, x equals $16 \cdot 48$ and this leaves $12 \cdot 10$ g of iron in $83 \cdot 52$ grams of the residue. The atomic ratio of iron to silicon in the Moon is $0 \cdot 35$ instead of $0 \cdot 85$ in the high iron group meteorites.

At the pressures existing in the Moon, the aluminium and sodium could be partially in jadeite rather than feldspars; this would result in smaller ratios of iron to silicon. The calculations can be made using the low iron group instead of the high iron group. The results of various calculations of this kind are given in Table V, taken from Urey (1959). A rough mean of all such calculations would indicate that if the Moon has the composition of the chondritic meteorites except for a lower concentration of iron, then the atomic ratio of iron to silicon is about $0 \cdot 25$ or $0 \cdot 30$.

Other explanations for the low density of the Moon as compared to the meteorites can be given. Thus we may calculate the water content of the lunar rocks which is necessary to lower the meteoritic densities to that of the Moon. Some 2–3% of water is required. Since water lowers the melting point of silicates, one would expect that extensive and persistent lava flows would have occurred on the Moon were this the true situation. Though a somewhat different concentration of water than that characteristic of the Earth and meteorites may exist in the lunar surface, such an extreme difference seems improbable.

The presence of graphite would also lower the density of chondritic material and simple calculations indicate that some 7–11% of graphite depending on various other factors would suffice. A lesser percentage of carbonaceous compounds would be sufficient, but in this case the reactions with iron oxide would produce water, and similar doubts arise in this case as in that when water was supposed to be present. Ringwood (1959) has suggested that the reduction of iron and silicon oxides by carbon has caused the high density of the Earth. Possibly the Moon is an object containing high concentrations of carbon which has not progressed through the reduction process. It is true that iron oxide and graphite would not react appreciably for long periods of time at low temperatures, but, at present, temperatures within the Moon should be sufficiently high for such reactions to occur. According

to approximate thermodynamic calculations for the reactions between
ferrous oxide and carbon, the pressure of carbon monoxide in the deep
interior at the present time should be about 10^4 bars and thus is less
than the over-burden pressure. It does not appear to be possible to

TABLE V

Comparison of the density of the Moon with calculated densities of meteoritic matter

Part 1		
	Observed	Calculated
1. Density of low-iron-group chondrites	3·51	3·574
2. Density of high-iron-group chondrites	3·66	3·761
3. Low-iron group with albite converted to jadeite and SiO_2 in $MgSiO_3$		3·653
†4. Density of Moon at low temperature and pressure: $\beta = 7\cdot9 \times 10^{-7}$, $\alpha = 3\cdot3 \times 10^{-5}$, $t = 1100°$ C (olivine)		3·41
5. Required iron content of (3) in order to have density (4)		
a. Iron present as Fe and FeS		10·78
b. Iron present as FeO		11·52
6. Cosmic abundance of Fe(Si = 10^6) (5a)	$2\cdot44 \times 10^5$	
(5b)	$2\cdot65 \times 10^5$	
Part 2 (Using other constants)		
‡4′. Density of Moon at low temperature and pressure: $\beta = 10\cdot1 \times 10^{-7}$, $\alpha = 2\cdot76 \times 10^{-5}$, $t = 1100°$ C (enstatite)		3·382
5′. Required iron content of (3) in order to have density (4′), removing FeO and FeS		9·11
6′. Cosmic abundance of Fe(Si = 10^6)	$1\cdot95 \times 10^5$	
7. Suess-Urey abundance of iron	6×10^5	
8. Aller solar abundance	$1\cdot4 \times 10^5$	

  † The values of α and β are those for forsterite and are taken from *Geol. Soc. Amer. Spec. Pap.*, 36, 33 and 36.

  ‡ The value of β is that for enstatite, and the value of α is the mean of augite and diopsite taken from *Geol. Soc. Amer. Spec. Pap.*, 36, 32 and 57.

eliminate the possibility that large amounts of graphite may account
for the low density. The very black mountainous areas west of
Copernicus which are part of the radiating system from Mare Imbrium,
may be due to carbonaceous material and may lend some support for
this suggestion.

Solar abundance data for the Sun (Aller, 1958) indicates a lower
abundance for iron relative to silicon and many other elements considerably less than that required by chondritic meteorite analyses.
Iron is regarded as the element whose abundance in the Sun is most
reliably estimated. This evidence supports to some extent the view
that the Moon is a primitive object containing the solar proportion of

iron and that this proportion is considerably less than that found in the chondritic meteorites. It is interesting to note that recent studies on the origin of the elements indicate that the iron abundance should be lower than that given by the chondritic meteorites (Cameron, 1959; Burbidge, Burbidge, Fowler and Hoyle, 1957). It will be most interesting to learn that evidence relative to this point can be learned when samples of the lunar surface become available, since this question bears on the problem of the origin of the solar system and the synthesis of the elements.

Another possible line of attack on this problem may be through a consideration of the ratio of the moment of inertia to the product of the mass and the square of the radius, G/Ma^2, which is 0·4 for a sphere of uniform density. Jeffreys (1959b, p. 159) estimates this quantity as 0·3971, assuming a surface density of 3·28 g cm^{-3} and internal density increasing to 3·41 g cm^{-3} at the centre. A quite different model giving a similar result can be constructed. The temperatures calculated in Section VI indicate that melting of iron sulphide and metallic iron-nickel should have occurred in the deep interior out to a radius somewhat in excess of $0·5a$, provided that the Moon began its history as a cold body. If the troilite and metallic phase from this limited volume are concentrated at the centre, the value of G/Ma^2 will be but slightly different from 0·4, since the contribution to the moment of inertia is proportional to the fifth power of the radius, and hence the outer parts contribute overwhelmingly to this quantity.

If the Moon was once generally melted, all the troilite and metal are concentrated at the centre. Assuming that the Moon consists of three concentric regions of densities, 3·3, 4·84, and 8·0 g cm^{-3}, all at low pressures and temperatures with a mean density of 3·41 g cm^{-3} and taking the iron sulfide as 5·77%, i.e. its percentage in the low iron group chondrites (Urey and Craig, 1953), the relative weight percentages and volumes of the three regions, the radii of the concentric shells and the ratio, G/Ma^2, can be easily calculated. The values, if temperature and pressure differences are included, will not be significantly different. The values so calculated are as follows:

	Per Cent Weight	Per Cent Volume	Radii of Shells (Lunar radius = 1)
Metal	2·36	1·01	0 − 0·216
Troilite	5·77	4·06	0·216 − 0·370
Silicate	91·85	94·93	0·370 − 1·000

The calculated value of G/Ma^2 is 0·3885, which is less than to Jeffreys' value secured from a very different model. It is evident that a much smaller core due to only a partial melting of the Moon would produce only a small deviation from the value for the uniform sphere.

If the composition is assumed to be constant and the temperature and pressure vary as calculated above (Section VI), an unstable condition exists with lower density at the centre of the Moon and the ratio, G/Ma^2, is greater than 0·4, though the deviation from this value would be small; namely, 0·1% or less. Whether such an unstable condition would persist throughout the time since the Moon was formed, is difficult to say, but if an observational value for this ratio could be secured with a reliability in the third significant figure, it should be possible to decide whether the Moon has a nearly uniform composition and, indeed, whether it has ever been generally melted.

VIII. The Chemical Composition of the Surface Regions

The physical properties of a thin layer of the lunar surface are known from the cooling curves observed during an eclipse as seen by Pettit (1935, 1940). Wesselink (1958) has derived a theory for such a cooling curve and a fit of the calculated to the observed curve gives a value for the product of the thermal conductivity, density and specific heat, $K\rho c$, of $1·2 \times 10^{-6}$ in calories and c.g.s. units.

Jaeger and Harper (1950) have shown that Pettit's data are not in agreement with a surface in which only one layer of uniform composition is present. The first part of the cooling curve fits their calculation for a substance with the constant, $K\rho c$, equal to $0·94 \times 10^{-6}$ cal^2 cm^{-4} sec^{-1}(°C)$^{-2}$ but the umbral part of the curve does not agree with the calculated values using this constant. They secure agreement using a layer 0·17 cm thick having this value for the constant, $K\rho c$, superimposed on material having a value of 10^{-4} for this constant. Gilvarry (1958) has extended this study to Pettit's observations on 27th October, 1939, eclipse and concludes that both the mountains and smooth areas are covered with highly insulating materials.

Piddington and Minnett (1949) have measured the intensity of the 24,000 megacycle lunar radiation and from this they estimate the temperature of the new Moon at 145° K and of the deeper layers as 234° K. A number of other studies have been made using the emission of wavelengths from 0·8 to 75 cm (Mezger and Strassl, 1959). Estimated mean temperatures range from 180° to 250° K. The subsurface temperatures probably lie in this range. No variation in temperature with a lunation is observed from the longer wavelengths, since such radiation originates well below the surface. All measurements indicate that the surface is covered with a thin highly insulating layer with $K\rho c$ equal to about 10^{-6}.

These observed data have been compared to observations by Smoluchowski (1910) on quartz particles of variable diameters at pressures down to 0·05 mm Hg. The value of K decreases nearly linearly with pressure and diameter of particles according to his measurements. Smoluchowski's values of $K\rho c$ for quartz particles of 0·09 and 0·26 mm diameters at 0·05 mm Hg pressure are 0·6 and $1\cdot4\times10^{-6}$ cal^2 cm^{-4} sec^{-1}(°C)$^{-2}$ respectively. Since the pressure at the lunar surface is smaller than 0·05 mm Hg, the diameters of the particles should be larger than those given. The evidence indicates that the lunar surface is covered with material of similar thermal properties to those of quartz particles a few tenths of a millimetre in diameter in high vacuum. Wesselink (1958) from an approximate theoretical calculation concluded that the grains may be 0·3 mm in diameter.

From the polarization of light reflected from the lunar surface, Wright (1927) concluded that it was covered by dust, high in silica such as pumice or granite. Lyot (1929) concluded from the variation of polarization of light with angle of reflection that the surface was covered by a brown volcanic ash. Different lunar areas polarize the light somewhat differently. It is often suggested that the ash layer has been formed by meteorites falling on the surface.

The action of light and high energy particles has almost certainly produced a superficial layer of material different from any natural material on the Earth's surface, so that studies of the polarization and absorption of light cannot be expected to identify the lunar surface materials. Sytinskaya (1957) has studied the brightness-colour diagrams of the Moon and many terrestrial materials and found no agreement between those of the Moon and any terrestrial material. We may conclude that we have no definitive evidence in regard to the chemical composition of the surface materials of the Moon.

The arguments previously presented indicate that the maria can hardly consist of lava originating from shallow depths beneath the lunar surface, because of the difficulties of accounting for the support of the high mountains.

On the other hand, lava originating from great depths is not excluded by this argument. In this case the materials of the collision maria are more basaltic or granitic in composition than are the mountainous areas and this should be true of the shallow maria as well. It is difficult to understand the origin of the smooth materials in the craters unless we postulate a deep pipe hundreds of kilometres long leading into each flooded area. Also, radioactive melting should have been uniform with respect to all directions; and, hence, approximately uniform flooding over the entire surface should have occurred. This is not true, particularly at the polar regions and the rear hemisphere as compared to the middle of the lunar disk. It should be noted that the thermal calculations (Section VI) are in accord with limited melting in the deep interior at the present time.

If the maria consist of lava produced by the great collisions, its composition should represent some average of the compositions of the original lunar surface and that of the colliding object. The pools of lava would solidify by the crystallization of the olivines which would sink to the bottom of the pool, then of more acid fractions, and finally of a surface consisting of basaltic and possibly approximate granitic composition. Gilbert believed that the neighbouring smooth areas were produced by splashes of material from these collision areas in some cases. This material should have solidified quickly and be more uniform in composition. Maria Tranquilitatis and Nubium and Oceanus Procellarum should have this composition, while Maria Imbrium, Crisium, Nectaris, Humorum and Serenitatis should consist of solidified deep pools. In general, the shallow areas should consist of the more average materials and the deep areas of the differentiated ones. As pointed out above, such materials may contain a certain amount of metallic iron-nickel, since such material produced the great grooves in the lunar surface. Evidently the large objects producing some of this may be very finely divided and the great smooth areas may be similar to chondritic meteorites in composition and physical structure.

The marked difference in albedo between the mountainous areas and the maria can reasonably be ascribed to differences in chemical composition, or physical state, or both. Superimposed on many features, both in the maria and mountainous areas, are the rays which become very bright when the Sun is high. These are evidently a fine dust of bead-like objects† produced during the collisions that in turn produced the ray craters and are entirely superficial in character and for present purposes may be ignored. The walls of the craters reflect sunlight at times of a low Sun while neighbouring smooth planes do not. At high Sun they appear as bright rings superimposed on a darker background. The ridges of the Imbrian system have a similar appearance in many ways. Some of these materials may have come from the colliding object while others might be from the original lunar surface and, hence, might well have different chemical composition. One would expect that materials nearer the collision site would be more probably

† One is reminded of the reflecting beads of the familiar road signs.

from the original lunar surface since such materials must have been accelerated from a stationary condition, while materials from the colliding object must have been decelerated and hence should have travelled further from the collision site. Lunar photographs do not indicate any very marked difference in appearance of the near and distant Imbrian ridges. West of Copernicus and along the southern shore of Mare Tranquilitatis are a number of patches of very black mountainous regions all belonging to the radiating Imbrian system. They merge rather continuously into other ridges of the lighter and more usual gray colour. Probably this dark material is of different chemical composition from the other material, though very minor differences in composition and physical state can make marked differences in colour.† Dark terrestrial rocks owe this characteristic mostly to the presence of iron, manganese and titanium, of which iron is the most abundant element. Small craters of very symmetrical shape in the mountainous regions and the maria often have differences in the degree of dark colour in qualitative agreement with differences in colour of the neighbouring regions. Thus the small craters in the dark mountainous area on the western shore of Sinus Aestuum appear to be very dark as compared with others in the lighter areas. The evidence in this instance favours the view that there is some difference in chemical or physical properties or both that is more than superficial in character. On the other hand, the small craters within Mare Imbrium do not appear to be of a significant difference in shade as compared to craters in neighbouring regions. Possibly visual observations directed to detection of such differences or quantitative measurements might give positive results on this question. In the minds of many people, including the present writer, there is a preference for the view that the so-called land areas of the Moon may have a more acidic composition than the maria, but there seems to be no definite evidence either to confirm or to disprove this view. The prejudice for this view probably has its origin in our definite knowledge in regard to the land areas and sea bottoms of the Earth and the analogy may be quite inapplicable. In fact, if the view that the maria are due to lava from the interior is true, it may well be that the maria have the more acid composition.

IX. The Origin of the Moon

It is not possible to state unequivocally just in what way the Moon originated. We can only recount the various hypotheses that have

---

† Black and white chondrites often have apparently identical composition and it is well known that heating a white chondrite in vacuum will cause it to become approximately as dark as a black chondrite.

been advanced together with the various lines of evidence which support or argue against these various suggested origins.

In general, three types of hypotheses have been advanced. (1) The Moon was removed from the Earth by tidal action. (2) The Moon and the Earth originated as a double planet in one gaseous cloud. (3) The Moon was captured by the Earth some time after each were essentially completely formed with their present sizes and masses.

The suggestion that the Moon broke off from the Earth was made by Sir George Darwin on the basis of his extensive mathematical studies of the tides. He pointed out that if the Moon were combined with the Earth, the combined angular momentum would require that the combined mass rotate with a four-hour period and thus the period of the solar tides would be two hours: this is approximately the period of free oscillation of the Earth. It was suggested that a resonance resulted and that the height of the tide increased until a mass separated from the Earth and became the Moon. The theory explained the low density of the Moon as compared to that of the Earth since it would not include a portion of the metallic core of the Earth.

This theory assumes that in some way an Earth was formed and only after this origin did tidal friction become active. Thus without some physical theory for the origin of the combined Earth-Moon, this theory is incomplete. Since the theory was put forward, Moulton, Jeffreys and others have made extensive studies on this problem, and at present all agree that it does not represent a physically possible mechanism of origin. If the Earth was solid, very rapid dissipation of the energy of the resonance tide into heat would occur; if the Earth was liquid one wonders how it secured and retained a high temperature. Jeffreys also found that in this case dissipation of the energy would occur before the amplitude became great enough to produce a separation of the Moon. Nölke (1934) pointed out that the newly-separated Moon would produce a tidal effect that would return the Moon to the Earth since its period would be less than the rotational period of the Earth and hence it would be retarded in its rotation. We can conclude definitely that the Moon was not removed from the Earth.

The second class of theories, namely, the double planet origin, is not generally associated with any particular author. There are two general possibilities in this case: first, it may be assumed that the Earth and Moon accumulated within a protoplanet; in this case accumulation must have occurred at very high temperatures. Eucken (1944) has shown from chemical arguments that iron would condense first as temperatures fell, followed by the silicates, and he suggested that this process accounted for the core of the Earth. It would be assumed then that the Moon accumulated somewhere in this gaseous mass. If this occurred deep in the interior, it would also have accumulated at high temperatures, and the reason for the absence of a large amount of metallic iron in its interior as indicated by its density is far from obvious; if it accumulated in the colder outer parts, it probably would have been lost when the great mass of gas was dissipated. The apparently insurmountable obstacle to this process is that there appears to be no way for the gases of higher atomic and molecular weight than helium to have left the earth so completely as they have (Urey, 1951). When large amounts of gas were present there may have been considerable rotation which would promote the loss of gas, but finally in this process a minor fraction of this gas would be left, say, for example, some 5% of the Earth's mass as a cosmic mixture of H_2, He, CH_4, NH_3, H_2O, Ne, etc. The gravitational field and velocity of rotation would be about that of the present Earth and no loss of the heavier gases could occur. In this case some hundred times as much carbon and nitrogen should be present as there is now, and the amount of neon should have been comparable to the amounts of these gases. There seems to be no answer to this line of reasoning except that the gases all left very completely before the solid materials of the Earth accumulated, i.e. they were lost while the solid materials were widely separated in space. This leads to the second possibility, namely, that the Earth and Moon each accumulated from solid objects moving together in a large group. In this case the Earth and Moon should have accumulated similar amounts and types of material, i.e. silicate, metal, etc., and their densities when corrected for pressure should be similar, which is not the case. The Moon is most peculiar in this respect, for its composition is different from that of the meteorites and terrestrial planets. There seems to be no acceptable mechanism for accounting for the properties of the Moon and Earth on the assumption that they accumulated within a protoplanet of approximately primitive composition, or that they accumulated as a double planet from a "globular cluster" of solid objects.

The capture hypothesis has been mentioned repeatedly in recent years. In this case the Moon was accumulated elsewhere—this accumulation must be considered later—and then was captured by the Earth. It is supposed that many objects of lunar size and smaller were captured to form the terrestrial planets, and the Moon, by a very special chance, was captured by a close approach to the Earth so that the relative energy was dissipated as heat through tidal action. It is also possible that capture occurred through some three-body mechanical effect. Either process should be a rare occurrence but possibly during the time of accumulation of the planets when many objects were being captured, it is not unreasonable to suppose that one such object may have been captured in this way. The evidence for a short time period for many of the lunar collisions and the explanation offered in Section IV, is in accord with this origin. In this case the Moon had some separate origin from the Earth and other terrestrial planets, and this separate origin must account for its different density and composition. Implicit in this suggestion is the requirement that the Moon is a more ancient body than are the Earth and other terrestrial planets.

Four suggestions to account for the varying densities of the Moon and terrestrial planets have been offered.

(1) Ramsey (1948, 1949) has suggested that the high-density core of the Earth is due to the existence of silicates in a very high-density metallic form at the pressures existing at and below the core boundary. On this basis there is no difference in composition of the Earth and Moon. This point of view is held by a number of students of the Moon and planets. Recently Levin (1958) has again maintained this position. In this case the Moon and the Earth accumulated near each other from similar materials.

However, it is necessary on the basis of present evidence to conclude that Mercury is a very special object. Its very high density of $5 \cdot 0$ g cm^{-3} or more cannot be explained in this way because of its small mass and hence comparatively low pressures on its interior. Some fractionation of the high and low density material is necessary. Also the Moon, as shown in Section VII, contains less iron than the meteorites. The density of Mars might be regarded as consistent with materials of meteoritic composition but not those of the Moon by any reasonable estimates on the basis of our present evidence. If increased concentrations of iron must be assumed in order to account for the density of Mercury, Mars and the meteorites, there seems to be no good reason for trying desperately to account for the Earth's core by assuming high density modifications of silicates for which there is no other evidence at the present time.

(2) Urey (1951) suggested that objects embedded in a protoplanet were heated to high temperatures and partly volatilized. The silicates floating on the surfaces of these objects were evaporated more than the metallic fraction which sank below the surface. Subsequently, all the gases and volatilized silicates were blown out of the proto-planets by light or particle radiation from the Sun, leaving residues of objects of variable composition which then accumulated into the respective planets. The Moon could have been a particularly large object whose composition was only slightly changed by this process.

Hence it was assumed that the Moon has more nearly the primitive composition, and as we have seen in Section VII, it appears at present to agree more nearly with the composition of the Sun.

(3) Urey (1956, 1958) suggested that many objects of lunar mass plus the normal proportions of gaseous materials, i.e. about 300 times the present mass of the Moon, accumulated in the plane of the ecliptic due to gravitational instability. Lunar-sized objects accumulated within these gas masses. The gases were dissipated and collisions broke up the solid objects, producing great masses of finely divided silicates which were driven into interstellar space with the gases leaving objects with somewhat increased proportions of metal; these masses accumulated into the planets. The Moon remained as one primary object that by chance was not destroyed or accumulated into a planet and was captured by the Earth. If the Moon accumulated from small particles within such a gas mass, its density would be constant with respect to angular position and its irregular shape could not be due to such a variation of density as suggested by Urey, Elsasser and Rochester (1959). They estimated that it accumulated from some 29,000 objects having masses of $2 \cdot 4 \times 10^{21} g$, though, as they emphasized, this is only one model for its accumulation. However, as will be mentioned later, it may have captured some high density objects during its accumulation in a gas mass and in this case the variation of density with angular position could occur. Also, this might explain the higher concentration of iron relative to the Sun that is needed to account for its density (Section VII).

The accumulation of a lunar-sized object within a gas mass having approximately solar composition could occur under a great variety of conditions of temperature and pressure.† Using the calculations of Emden for polytropic gas spheres estimates of temperature and pressure can be given (see Eddington, 1930). These estimates do not include the effect of a high density mass at the centre but since material of lunar or terrestrial composition makes up only some $0 \cdot 30\%$ of solar matter, no great error can be made in calculations assuming that the matter is entirely gaseous. The tables for γ ($= C_p/C_v$) equal to $1 \cdot 5$ or polytropic index equal to 2 an approximation to a cosmic ratio of H_2 and He, i.e. $1 \cdot 6$ to $\cdot 41$ (Suess and Urey, 1958) the central temperature is readily estimated as

$$T_0 = 1 \cdot 16 \times 10^{-15} M/R, \ °K,$$

† This was mentioned by Urey (1956) in connection with the origin of the meteorites, but its specific application to the origin of the Moon was not given. The numerical values given here do not agree with those given previously because estimates of the composition of solar matter have been revised.

where R is the radius of the gas sphere in centimetres. The central pressure is found to be

$$P_0 = 1 \cdot 09 \times 10^{-7} M^2 / R^4 \text{ dynes cm}^{-2}.$$

With R equal to 10^{10} cm, $M = 2 \cdot 2 \times 10^{28}$g, $T_0 = 2620°$ K and $P_0 = 5000$ bars and values of these quantities are easily calculated for other values of R. Hence, an accumulation of the Moon in such a gas mass could have taken place under a great variety of conditions. It may have been at low or high temperatures and pressures, with small or large amounts of water or hydrocarbons being condensed, and these conditions may have changed during the accumulation as contraction occurred due to radiation of energy or to loss of gasses to space. (The temperature is proportional to the first power and the pressure to the second power of the mass.)

These high temperatures may have produced the melting in meteoritic material. But also the heating by radioactive elements, as proposed by Goles, Fish and Anders (1960), may have been important in such processes and such heating could probably be included in this model (see below under (4)).

This postulated course of events does not make the Moon an unusual object during its formation. It is different from many other objects assumed to have been present only in that it was one of a number that were preserved from collisional break-up, and in that it was captured in a very special orbit and not into the body of the Earth.

(4) Ringwood (1959) and MacDonald and Knopoff (1958) have proposed that the variation in density of the Moon and terrestrial planets is due to differing states of reduction of the elements in these objects, particularly the elements iron and silicon. Ringwood proposed that carbon was the essential reducing agent. If this reduction occurred within the Earth, we are again faced with the difficulty of losing carbon oxides into space (Urey, 1960). This process is possible only if the reduction occurred on objects not larger than about lunar size, for otherwise the gases cannot be lost. In this case, the Moon is an object which for some reason did not go through this intense reduction process and was subsequently captured by the Earth. MacDonald and Knopoff assume that oxygen was lost under high pressure and therefore this must have occurred within the Earth. It is difficult to understand how high pressure is maintained while oxygen escapes and how the oxygen left the Earth. Ringwood's suggestion seems more plausible but leaves unsolved problems† (Urey, 1960). In particular, it suggests

† Present estimates of the density of Mercury require that non-volatile compounds be lost from the planet even if the reduction process proceeded to an extreme extent.

that the Moon may contain a large amount of carbon which for some reason has not reacted with its iron and silicon oxides.

Recently, Goles, Fish and Anders (1960) have proposed that the melting required for the formation of the minerals of the meteorites was produced by heat from short-lived radioactive elements remaining from the synthesis of the elements: such sources of energy could supply the heat for Ringwood's carbon reduction process. However, it is difficult to understand the properties of the Moon on the basis of these proposals: they require that objects accumulated at a proper time after the synthesis of the elements, so that a proper residual radioactivity was present; then these objects were melted with reduction of the iron and silicon oxides. The gases produced, CO and CO_2, then escaped and the objects so produced were accumulated into the terrestrial planets. But we must now explain how the Moon avoided this heating process for if it had been heated, its density should be comparable to that of the planets estimated at low pressures and to the density of the meteorites. However, this outline of events requires that the Moon has had some very special history.

The most probable source of heat is Al^{26} with a half life of $7 \cdot 5 \times 10^5$ years. If the objects that subsequently formed the Earth accumulated a few million years before the Moon accumulated, sufficient heat for melting could be available for these objects and yet only a small amount of heat would be produced in the Moon. The Moon would thus be a very special object on this ground in addition to being a very special one because of its capture by the Earth in a close orbit. The suggestion of radioactive sources of heat for any melting or high temperature chemical reactions during the formation of the solar system requires that the accumulation process occurred very quickly after the general synthesis of the elements, i.e. some ten million years or less, or that processes of element synthesis occurred during the process of formation of the solar system. It is far from clear that either assumption is reasonable, though in the present state of our knowledge, such processes can hardly be excluded.

Possibly we may try to modify both the proposals of Ringwood, namely, that the heating process took place in lunar-sized objects instead of within the Earth, and those of Goles et al., namely, that objects of lunar size instead of asteroidal size or smaller, accumulated. Thus, objects may have accumulated over some ten or more millions of years. The early ones became heated intensely, others formed later somewhat less and still others formed still later were heated very little. The Moon by chance is one of the latter objects which also by chance was captured by the Earth in a very special orbit late in its history of accumulation. However, this accumulation of the Moon must have been predominantly from the primordial dust cloud and not from previously processed materials which had been through the intense heating and fractionation process, for otherwise the density of the Moon and terrestrial planets would be similar.

It is difficult to suggest any reasonable mechanism for such a selective process of accumulation. If we combine these ideas with the accumulation of lunar masses, as suggested by Urey, a solution may be possible. The solar nebula may have broken up into such masses differing in size to a considerable degree and these may have developed toward the accumulation of solid objects within the gaseous masses at different velocities. In this case they all had primitive compositions but some advanced to a stage with a compact object at the centre at different times, thus supplying the conditions for producing the different chemical composition of the terrestrial planets and the Moon. As mentioned above, some accumulation of high density objects may account for the apparently higher concentration of iron in the Moon, as compared to the astronomical value for the Sun.

It has often been assumed that the Moon and all other planetary objects were accumulated at high temperatures without any adequate source of the high temperatures being specified. The recent literature continues to contain references of this kind. For example, various suggestions for an age of the Moon of 5 to 5·5 AE have appeared in the recent literature (cf., e.g. Kuiper, 1959), though the source of heat was not clearly specified. Recently, Reynolds (1960) has found anomalously large concentrations of Xe^{129} in meteorites and this must be due to the radioactive decay of I^{129}. If this persisted from a synthesis of the elements 5·5 AE ago up to even 4·7 AE ago, it persisted through about 50 half lives of I^{129} and during this time it would have decayed by a factor of about 10^{15}: this is such a large factor that the nebula would have been predominantly I^{129} at 5·5 AE ago. The Moon could not have accumulated such a long time ago. However, if it accumulated even a modest time after the last contribution to the synthesis of the elements, considerable heat from such elements may have been available and complete melting could have occurred. In this case the irregular distribution of density with angular position as suggested by Urey, Elsasser and Rochester (1959) (Section V) could not occur, for sinking of the more dense regions would have occurred until uniformity in density with angular position was established; hence the irregular shape must be supported only by its physical strength. The calculations on the heat balance show how difficult it is to secure the required rigidity in an originally melted Moon. It does not appear to be impossible but the radioactive elements must be concentrated at the surface almost quantitatively in marked contrast to the observed situation in the case of the Earth.

X. Conclusions

The Moon accumulated independently of the Earth and represents a more primitive object than the terrestrial planets. Its composition is more nearly that of the Sun and the original solids in the primitive dust cloud. The planets were modified in composition during their formation in the direction of having a higher concentration of metallic iron or silicon or both. The Moon was captured by the Earth early in the history of the solar system, probably during the terminal stage of the Earth's growth from lunar- and asteroidal-sized objects. Shortly after its capture by the Earth it was intensively bombarded for a short period of time. The objects which fell on the Moon at that time were satellites of the Earth and fell with moderate velocities.

Since that time a limited number of objects have fallen on the Moon with high velocities from interplanetary space. Some volcanic effects in which craters of different dimensions than those characteristic of the Earth are present on the Moon. The great plains of the Moon probably are at least partly lava flows from the deep interior, or were produced by the energy of the great collisions. Dust, gravel, rubble may also have been produced by the same collisions and by light and high energy particle erosion.

These conclusions will be made more certain or will be modified by knowledge gained by the direct exploration of the Moon in the years immediately in the future. It is well to remember that we do not know how the Moon originated. There is available some evidence in regard to the question but much more is needed before conclusions can be reached which will be generally accepted.

References

Ahrens, L. H., Pinson, W. H., and Kearns, M. M. (1952). *Geochim. et Cosmoch. Acta*, **2**, 229.

Allan, D. W., and Jacobs, J. A. (1956). *Geochim. et Cosmoch. Acta*, **9**, 256.

Aller, L. H. (1958). *Handb. Phys.* **51**.

Arrol, W. J., Jacobi, R. B., Paneth, F. A. (1942). *Nature, Lond.*, **149**, 235.

Baldwin, R. B. (1949). "The Face of the Moon". Univ. Chicago Press.

Bate, G. L., Huizenga, J. R., and Potrax, H .A. (1959). *Geochim. et Cosmoch. Acta*, **16**, 88.

Birch, F. (1954). "Nuclear Science", Chapter 5. (H. Faul, ed.),

Bowen, N. L., and Schairer, J. F. (1935). *Amer J. Sci.* 29, 151.

Boyd, F. R., and England, J. (1958). *Yearb. Carnegie Instn.*, **57**, 173.

Brouwer, D. (1952). See H. C. Urey, "The Planets", p. 24, Yale University Press.

Burbidge, E. M., Burbidge, G. R., Fowler, W. A., and Hoyle, F. (1957). *Rev. Mod. Phys.* **29**, 547.

Cameron, A. G. W. (1959). *Astrophys. J.* **129**, 676. See also Burbidge, G. R. (1960) *ibid.* **131**, 2, 519, and Cameron, A. G. W. (1960) *ibid.* **131**, 2, 521.

Chackett, K. F., Golden, J., Mercer, E. R., Paneth, F. A., and Reasbeck, P. (1950). *Geochim. et Cosmoch. Acta*, **1**, 3.

Cotton, C. A. (1952). "Volcanoes as Landscape Forms", Chapter 16. Whitcomb & Tombs, London.

Darvey, M. (1933). *Bull. Soc. Astr. Fr.*, 452–457.

Davis, G. L. (1947, 1950). *Amer J. Sci.* **245**, 677; **248**, 107.

Delmotte, G. (1914). *Bull. Soc. Astr. Fr.*, 1914, 41–44, and 1923 "Recherches Selénographiques". Blanchard, Paris.

Dietz, R. S. (1946). *J. Geol.* **54**, 359.

Du Fresne, E. R. (1956). *Astrophys. J.* **124**, 638.

Eddington, A. (1930). "The Internal Constitution of Stars", p. 79 ff. Cambridge Univ. Press.

Edwards, G. (1955). *Geochim. et Cosmoch. Acta*, **8**, 285.

Edwards, G., and Urey, H. C. (1955). *Geochim. et Cosmoch. Acta*, **7**, 154.

Eucken, A. (1944). *Nachr. Akad. Wiss. Göttingen*, Pt. 1, pp. 8, 9.

Gast, P. W. (1960). *Geochim. et Cosmoch. Acta*, **19**, 1.

Gilbert, G. K. (1893). *Bull. Phil. Soc. Wash.* **12**, 241–292. This paper will be republished in the near future by the American Philosophical Society of Washington.

Gilvarry, J. J. (1958). *Astrophys. J.* **127**, 751.

Gold, T. (1955). *Mon. Not. R. Astr. Soc.* **115**, 585.

Goles, G. G., Fish, R. A., and Anders, E. (1960). *Astrophys. J.* In press.

Hamaguchi, H., Reed, G. W., and Turkevich A. (1957). *Geochim. et Cosmoch. Acta*, **12**, 337.

Haskell, N. A. (1935). *Physics*, **6**, 265; (1936) *ibid.* **7**, 56.

Jaeger, J. C., and Harper, A. F. A. (1950). *Nature, Lond.* **166**, 1026.

Jeffreys, H. (1959a). "The Earth", 4th ed. Cambridge Univ. Press.

Jeffreys, H. (1959b). *Mon. Not. R. Astr. Soc.* **118**, 14.

Kuiper, G. P. (1959). *J. Geophys. Res.* **64**, 1714.

Lamech, F. (1933). "Carte du réseau rectiligne de la Lune". Toulouse.

Le Comte, P., and Birch, F. (1959). Private communication.

Levin, B. J. (1958). *Voprosy Kosmog.* **6**, 56.

Lyot, B. (1929). *Ann. Obs. Paris-Meudon*, **8**, Fasc. I.

MacDonald, G. J. F., (1959). *J. Geophys. Res.* **64**, 1996 ff.

MacDonald, G. J. F., and Knopoff, L. (1958). *Geophys. J.* **1**, 284.

Mezger, P. C., and Strassl, H. (1959). *Planet. Space Sci.* **1**, 213 ff. and references there given.

Moulton, F. R. (1908). *Publ. Carnegie Instn*, No. 107.

Nölke, F. (1934). *Gerlands Beitr. Geophys.* Bd. 41, Heft 1.

Patterson, C. (1955). *Geochim et Cosmoch. Acta*, **7**, 151.

Pettit, E. (1935, 1940). *Astrophys. J.* **81**, 17; **91**, 408.

Piddington, J. H., and Minnett, H. C. (1949). *Aust. J. Sci. Res.* A2, 63.

Ramsey, W. H. (1948, 1949). *Mon. Not. R. Astr. Soc.* **108**, 406; (1949) *Mon. Not. R. Astr. Soc. Geophys. Suppl.* **6**, 409.

Reynolds, J. H. (1960). *Phys. Rev. Lett.* **4**, 351.

Ringwood, A. E. (1959). *Geochim. et Cosmoch. Acta,* **15**, 257.

Sabaneyev, P. F. (1953). *Moscow, Byull. Vsesoyuz. Astronomo-Geodezicheskogo Obshchestva,* No. 13 (20), pp. 7–20.

Smoluchowski, M. (1910). See "International Critical Tables," **2**, 315.

Strong, H. M. (1959). *J. Geophys. Res.* **64**, 653–659.

Suess, H. E., and Urey, H. C. (1956). *Rev. Mod. Phys.* **28**, 53; (1958) *Handb. Phys.* **51**, 296 ff.

Sytinskaya, N. N. (1957). Leningrad University Scientific Notes. "Works of the Astronautical Observatory", **17**, 74.

Urey, H. C. (1951). *Geochim. et Cosmoch. Acta,* **1**, 207.

Urey, H. C. (1951). *Geochim. et Cosmoch. Acta,* **1**, 255 ff.

Urey, H. C. (1952). "The Planets". Yale Univ. Press.

Urey, H. C. (1953). *Proc. Nat. Acad. Sci. Wash.* **39**, 933.

Urey, H. C. (1954). *Astrophys. J. Suppl.* No. 6. **1**, 147.

Urey, H. C. (1955). *Proc. Nat. Acad. Sci. Wash.,* **41**, 127.

Urey, H. C. (1956). *Proc. Nat. Acad. Sci. Wash.,* **42**, 889.

Urey, H. C. (1956). *Astrophys. J.* **124**, 625.

Urey, H. C. (1956). *Observatory,* **176**, 232.

Urey, H. C. (1957). "Progress in Physics and Chemistry of the Earth", Vol. 2. pp. 46–76.

Urey, H. C. (1958). Hugo Mueller Lecture. *Proc. Chem. Soc. Lond.* p. 67.

Urey, H. C. (1959). *J. Geophys. Res.* **64**, 1721.

Urey, H. C. (1960). *Geochim. et Cosmoch. Acta,* **18**, 151.

Urey, H. C. (1960). *Astrophys. J.* In press.

Urey, H. C. and Craig, H., (1953). *Geochim. et Cosmoch. Acta,* **4**, 36.

Urey, H. C., Elsasser, W. M., and Rochester, M. G. (1959). *Astrophys. J.* **129**, 842.

Watts, C. B. (1958). Private communication and address before the Amer. Assn. Adv. Sci. in Washington, D.C.

Webster, R. K., Morgan, J. W., and Smales, A. A. (1958), *Geochim. et Cosmoch. Acta,* **15**, 150.

Wesselink, A. J. (1958), *Bull. Astr. Insts. Netherlds,* **10**, 352.

Wetherill, G. W. (1957), *Science,* **126**, 545.

Wright, F. E. (1927). *Proc. Nat. Acad. Sci. Wash.* **13**, 535.

Yavnel, A. A. (1958). *Meteoritika,* No. 15, pp. 115–135.

Author Index

Italic numbers indicate pages on which complete references are to be found.

A

Abbot, C. G.   214, 215, *226*, 388, 389, *404*

Adams, J. C.   18, 20, *25*, 80, *96*

Ahrens, L. H.   495, 496, *521*

Airy, G. B.   18, *25*

Akabane, K.   420, *427*

Albritton, A.   307, 314, 315

Albritton, C. C.   307, 315, *351, 352*

Allan, D. W.   504, *521*

Aller, L. H.   508, *521*

Alter, Dinsmore   301, *351*

Al'tshuler, L. V.   319, *351*

Anders, E.   518, 519, *522*

Anderson, E. M.   301, *351*

Arago, F.   132, *159*, 244

Arrol, W. J.   495, *521*

Ashbrook, J.   279, *281*

"Asterios", (August and Heinrich Thiersch)   287, *358*

Atkinson, R. d'E.   31, *58*, 259, *281*

B

Bagg, T. C.   409, *428*

Baldwin R. B.   274, *281*, 286, 287, 316, 323, 349, *351*, 483, 484, 493, *521*

Banachiewicz, Th.   29, 30, 48, 50, 53, *58*, 249, *281*

Barabashev, N. P.   122, *128, 129*, 132, *159*

Barantseva, M.   *128*

Barbier, D.   211, 224, *226*

Barringer, D. M.   310, 321, *351*

Bate, G. L.   495, 496, *521*

Bateman, R.   449, *478*

Bauer, E.   202, *226*

Bauer, S. J.   449, *478*

Bay, Z.   429, 447, *478*

Beals, C. S.   307, *351*

Beck, C. W.   311, *351*

Beer, W.   167, *226*, 241, 242, 252, *281*, 323, *351*

Belkovich, I. V.   47, 57, *58*, 246, 247, 251, *281, 282*

Bemmelen, R. W. van   291, *351*

Bennett, A. L.   117, *128*

Bentz, A.   312, *351*

Beringer, R.   419, *427*

Bessel, F. W.   46, *58*

Birch, F.   496, 497, 498, *521, 522*

Birkhoff, G.   342, *351*

Bjork, R. L.   317, *351*

Blackhall, J.   274, *281*

Blagg, M. A.   251, *282*

Blevis, B. C.   439, *478*

Bond, W. C.   100, *128*

Boon, F.   307, 314, 315

Boon, J. D.   307, 315 *351, 352*

Borough, H. C.   418, *428*

Bouška, J.   200, 206, *226, 227*

Bowen, E. G.   204, *277*

Bowen, N. L.   498, *521*

Bowhill, S. A.   476, *478*

Boyd, F. R.   311, *352*, 496, 498, *521*

Bracewell, R. N.   *428*

Branco, W.   287, 288, 312, 313, *352*

Brazhnik, M. I.   319, *351*

Brock, B. B.   315, *352*

Brooks, C. E. P.   219, *227*

Brosinsky, A.   164, 167, *227*

Brouwer, D.   22, *25*, 84, *96*, 494, *522*

Brown, E. W.   2, 7, 14, 16, 18, 20, 21, *25*, 34, *58*, 81, *96*

Browne, I. C.   443, 449, 450, 451, 452, 470, *478*

Bruton, R. H.   24, *25*, 436, 439, 455, 459, *479*

Bucher, W. H.   314, 315, *352*

Buchanan, R.   165, *227*

Bülow, Kurd von   288, 349, *352*

Buettner, K.   146, *159*

Bullrich, K.   *128*

Burbidge, E. M.   509, *522*

Burbidge, G. R.   509, *522*

Byers, F. M. Jr.   295, *357*

C

Cabannes, J.   195, 202, *227*
Cailleux, A.   139, 140, *159*
Calder, W. A.   *128*
Calvisius, S.   162, *227*
Cameron, A. G. W.   509, *522*
Carpenter, J.   286, *356*
Cassini, J. D.   167, *227*
Chackett, K. F.   494, *522*
Chambers, G. F.   163, *227*
Chandon, E.   47, *58*
Chauvenet, W.   165, *227*
Chao, E. C. T.   310, 312, *352, 357*
Charters, A. C.   342, *352*
Christie, W. H. M.   125, *128*
Cimino, M,   192, 211, 212, *227*
Clairaut, A. C.   8, *25*
Clemence, G. M.   66, *96*
Coates, R. J.   420, *427*
Condon, E. U.   63, *96*
Conley, J. M.   418, *428*
Conway, R. G.   420, *428*
Cotton, C. A.   292, *352*, 483, *522*
Cowell, P. H.   22, *25*
Craig, H.   506, 509, *523*
Craig, K. J.   24, *25, 479*

D

Daguerre, L. J. M.   244
Dahmer, Georg   288, *352*
D'Alembert, J.   8, *25*
Daly, R. A.   289, 315, *352*
Damoiseau, M. C. T.   8, *25*
Dana, J. D.   286, *352*
Daniels, F. B.   449, *478*
Danjon, A.   105, *128*, 190, 202, 217, 218, *226, 227*
Darton, N. H.   292, *352*
Darvey, M.   484, *522*
Darwin, G. H.   92, *96*
Daubrée, Auguste   295, *352*
Davis, G. L.   495, *522*
Davis, W. M.   285, *352*
Dehm, Richard   312, *352, 357*
Delaunay, C. E.   9, 20, *25*
Delmotte, G.   484, *522*
Denisse, J. F.   420, *427*

De Sitter, W.   20, *25*, 88, *97*
De Witt, J. H.   429, 447, *478*
Dicke, R. H.   419, *427*
Dietrich, G.   90, *97*
Dietz, R. S.   289, 314, *353*, 495, *522*
Dorn, Paul   311, *353*
Dobson, G. M. B.   196, *227*
Dollfus, A.   134, 136, 137, 138, 139, 140, 143, 144, 150, 151, 152, 155, 156, 157, *159*
Doodson, A. T.   71, 72, 75, *97*
Doublet, E.   163, *227*
Draper, J. W.   244
Dubois, J.   188, 216, 222, *227, 229*, 392, 394, 395, 396, *404*
Dufay, J.   195, *227*
Dufour, C.   208, *227*
Du Fresne, E. R.   493, *522*
Dugan, R. S.   440, *479*
du Séjour, D.   164, *229*
Dyce, R. B.   460, 462, 464, 467, *478*

E

Ebert, H.   288, *353*
Eddington, A. S.   517, *522*
Edison, A. R.   455, *478*
Edwards, G.   495, 496, *522*
Einarsson, Trausti   291, *353*
Élie de Beaumont, J. B. A. L. L.   286, *353*
Elsasser, W. M.   93, *98*, 492, 494, 517, 520, *523*
Elsmore, B.   224, *227*
England, J. L.   311, *352*, 496, 498, *521*
Ensley, E.   *128*
Epstein, P. S.   413, *427*
Ericsson, John   289, *353*
Eropkin, D. J.   225, *227*
Escher, B. G.   288, 291, *353*
Eucken, A.   514, *522*
Euler, L.   9, 10, 13, *25*, 32
Evans, G. L.   311, *357*
Evans, J. V.   443, 449, 450, 451, 452, 453, 454, 457, 461, 470, 477, *478*
Evans, S.   457, 461, *478*

F

Fabry, Ch.   *128*, 174, *227*
Fairchild, H. L.   289, *353*
Fastie, W.   401, *404*

Faye, H. A.   288, *353*
Fedoretz, V.   118, *128*
Ferguson, G. M.   307, *351*
Feshbach, H.   66, *97*
Fessenkov, V. G.   *128*, 172, *227*
Fielder, G.   265, *281*
Finch, R. H.   298, *354*
Firth, C. W.   295, *353*
Fischer, F.   249
Fish, R. A.   518, 519, *522*
Fisher, W.   219, *227*
Forbes, V. S.   288, *353*
Fortini, T.   211, *227*
Fowler, W. A.   509, *522*
Fraas, E.   313, *352*
Franz, J.   46, *58*, 247, 249, 251, *281*
Frechen, J.   291, *354*
Fredriksen, A.   460, 462, 464, 467, *479*
Freedland, M. V.   58, *58*
Fresa, A.   192, *227*
Fricker, S. J.   436, 438, 439, 442, 443, 458, *478*
Frisch, Cr.   164, *227*
Fujinami, S.   261, *281*

G
Galbraith, F. W.   290, *353*
Galilei, Galileo, 231, 233, 251, *281*, 483
Garstang, R. H.   *428*
Gascoine, S. C. B.   109, *130*
Gast, P. W.   496, *522*
Gaubil, A.   162, *227*
Geoffrion, A.   411, *427*
Gerks, I. H.   449, *479*
Gerstlauer, K.   312, *353*
Giamboni, L. A.   335, *353*
Gianuzzi, M. A.   211, *227*
Gibson, J. E.   420, 421, *427*
Gifford, A. C.   316, *353*
Gilbert, G. K.   286, 307, 341, 346, 349, *353*, *354*, 483, 484, *522*
Gilvarry, J. J.   316, *354*, *428*, 510, *522*
Glasstone, Samuel   334, *354*
Gold, T.   487, *522*
Golden, J.   495, *522*
Goles, G. G.   518, 519, *522*
Goodacre, Walter,   241, 286, *353*
Goetz, K.   112, 195
Gold, T.   146, *159*
Gotz, P.   *227*

Gotz, W.   *128*
Gouy, J.   141, *159*
Graff, K.   *128*
Graig, K. J.   436, 439, 455, 459, *479*
Grant, C. R.   455, *478*
Green, J.   288, 323, *354*
Green, P.   440, 445, 446, *478*
Greenstein, J. L.   203, *227*
Grieg, D. D.   440, 444, *478*
Griggs, D. T.   329, *354*
Groves, G. W.   78, 83, 90, 93, *97*
Gruithuisen, F. von P.   285, *354*
Günther, Siegmund   288, *353*
Güssow, K.   100, *129*
Guth, V.   192, 206, 207, *227*, *228*

H
Habibullin, S. T.   47, 57, *58*
Hack, J. T.   295, *354*
Hall, A. L.   315, *354*
Halley, E.   62, 80, *97*
Hamaguchi, H.   495, 496, *522*
Hanbury Brown, R.   437, *478*
Hannay, J. B.   288, *354*
Hansa, M.   204, *227*
Hansen, P. A.,   10, 11, 13, 20, *25*, 34, *58*
Hardy, C. T.   307, 311, *354*
Hargreaves, J. K.   443, 449, 450, 451, 452, 460, 470, 475, *478*, *479*
Harper, A. F. A.   418, *427*, 510, *522*
Hartmann, J.   164, 168, 179, *227*
Hartwig, E.   47, *58*, 247, 281
Haskell, N. A.   494, *522*
Hayn, F.   33, 34, 38, 41, 43, 45, 46, 49, 53, 55 57, *59*, 246, 247, 261, *281*
Heath, T.   163, *227*
Heiskanen, W.   89, *97*
Hepperger, J.   164, 172, *227*
Herbst, W. A.   300, *355*
Herschel, F. J. W.   100, *129*, 240
Herschel, W.   252, *281*, 285, *354*
Hevelius, J.   252, *282*
Hewish, A.   224, *227*, 460, *478*
Hey, J. S.   460, 461, 462, 475, *478*
Heyden, F. J.   211, *227*
Higgins, C. S.   448, *479*
Hill, G. W.   5, 10, 13, 17, 20, *25*, *26*
Hill, J. E.   316, *353*
Hoag, A.   225, *227*

Holt, P, H.   300, *355*
Hooke, Robert   285, *354*
Hopmann, J.   251, *282*
Hopmann, Michael   291, *354*
Horrix, Wilhelm   311, *356*
Hoyle, F.   509, *522*
Hubbert, M. K.   284, 299, *354*
Hughes, R. F.   318, *358*
Hughes, V. A.   436, 460, 461, 462, 475, *478, 479*
Huizenga, J. R.   495, 496, *521*
Humboldt, Alexander von   286, *354*
Humphreys, G. W.   179, *228*

I

Ina, T.   261, *281*
Ingalls, R. P.   436, 438, 439, 442, 443, 458, *478*
Inghram, M. G.   347, *356*
Ives, H. E.   316, *354*

J

Jacobi, R. B.   495, *521*
Jacobs, J. A.   504, *521*
Jaeger, J. C.   413, 417, 418, *427, 428*, 510, *522*
Jaggar, T. A. Jr.   298, *354*
Jahns, R. H.   290, 295, *354*
Jeffreys, H. 22, *26*, 57, *59*, 75, 82, 89, 92, *97*, 288, *354*, 491, 492, 509, *522*
Jönsson, A.   34, 43, *59*
Joesting, H. R.   315, *354*
Johnson, H.   *129*
Johnston, R. G.   409, *428*
Jones, H. Spencer   21, 22, *26*, 57, *59*, 82, 84, 88, *97*
Judd, J. W.   291, *355*

K

Kaiser, H.   *129*
Kant, I.   285, *355*
Kariaguina, Z.   109, *129*
Karpoff, Roman   307, *355*
Kawai, S.   261, *281*
Kearns, M. M.   495, 496, *521*
Keenan, P. C.   *129*
Kerr, F. J.   436, 438, 439, 440, 448, *479*
King, E. S.   *129*
King, P. B.   314, *354*

Kirch, A.   206, *228*
Knetsch, Georg   291, *354*
Knopoff, L.   518, *522*
Ko, H. C.   434, *479*
Koebke, F.   200, *228*
Kolesnikov-Svinareve, V. I.   339, *356*
Kopal, Z.   250, 264, *282*
Korner, M.   411, *427*
Koziel, K.   30, 33, 34, 38, 41, 47, 48, 49, 50, 51, 52, 53, 54, 55, 56, 57, *59*, 246, 247, *282*
Kosik, S. M.   168, 200, *228*
Kozyrev, N. A.   216, 217, *228*, 393, 392, *405*
Kranz, Walter   313, *355*
Kraus, J. D.   434, *479*
Krejči-Graf, Karl   288, *355*
Krieger, J. N.   245
Kristenson, H.   261, *282*
Kron, G. E.   109, *129*
Krupnikov, K. K.   319, *351*
Kühl, A.   199, *228*
Kuiper, G. P.   93, *97*, 287, 303, 326, 332, 345, 349, *355*, 487, 520, *522*

L

Lafay, A.   141, *159*
Lagrange, J. L.   27, *59*
Lahire, P.   167, *228*
Lalande, J. F.   167, *228*
Lambert, F.   167, *228*
Lambert, J. J.   241
Lamech, F.   484, *522*
Landau, A.   307, *351*
Landerer, J. J.   132, *159*
Langley, S. P.   407, *427*
Langren, M. F.   163, *228*
La Paz, L.   311, *351*
Laplace, P. S. 8, 21, *26*, 27, *59*, 75, 80, *97*, 175, *228*
Lawson, J. L.   434, 451, 452, *479*
Leadabrand, R. L.   460, 462, 464, 467, *479*
Le Comte, P.   496, 498, *522*
Ledenev, B. N.   319, *351*
Lee, W. T.   294, *355*
Legentil, G. J. H.   167, *228*
Lemonnier, P. C.   167, *228*
Leonard, F. C.   307, *355*
Le Roux, E.   420, *427*

Levin, B. J. 516, *522*
Link, F. 176, 179, 180, 186, 188, 192, 193, 195, 199, 200, 201, 202, 203, 205, 206, 207, 209, 211, 214, 215, 216, 219, 223, 224, 225, *226*, *227*, *228*, 385, 386, 400, 401, *405*
Linková, Z. 199, 200, 205, *228*
Loewy, M. 245
Lohrmann, W. G. 241
Longuet-Higgins, M. S. 476, *479*
Lord, J. O. 311, *355*
Lovell, A. C. B. 437, *478*
Lubbock, J. W. 9, *26*
Lyot, B. 132, 133, 141, 142, 145, 150, 155, 156, 158, *159*, 510, *522*

M

MacDonald, G. J. F. 62, 70, 73, 75, 76, 77, 84, 88, *97*, 498, 504, 518, *522*
MacDonald, T. L. 274, 275, *282*
Machin, K. E. 224, *228*
McMath, R. R. 252, 268, *282*
McKnight, E. T. 315, *355*
MacRobert, T. M. 91, *97*
Mädler, J. H. *226*, *228*, 241, 242, 252, *281*, 323, *351*
Madsen, B. M. 310, *352*
Markov, A. V. *129*, 457, *479*
Markowitz, W. 77, *97*
Marshall, R. K. 289, *355*
Martynov, D. Y. 108, *129*
Mason, W. C. 436, 438, 439, 442, 443, 458, *478*
Matheson, G. L. 300, *355*
Matoušek, Otakar 288, *355*
Maunder, E. W. 218, *228*
Mayer, T. 238, 239
Melchior, P. 89, *97*
Mercer, E. R. 495, *522*
Merrill, G. P. 316, *355*
Metzger, S. 440, 444, *478*
Meydenbauer, A. 287, *356*
Mezger, P. G. 420, 421, *427*, 477, *479*, 510, *522*
Miller, Ephraim *356*
Minnett, H. C. 417, 418, 424, *426*, 510, *522*
Mintz, Y. 77, *97*
Mitra, S. K. 198, *228*
Mofensen, J. 446, *479*

Mohorovičič, Stepan 288, *356*
Molengraaff, G. A. F. 315, *353*
Montgomery, G. F. 449, *479*
Moore, P. A. 286, *359*
Moore, R. K. 455, *478*
Morgan, J. W. 496, *523*
Morse, P. M. 66, *97*
Moulton, F. R. 316, *356*, *522*
Müller, G. 298, *356*
Muncey, R. W. 418, *427*
Munk, W. H. 62, 70, 73, 75, 76, 77, 78, 83, 84, 88, 90, *97*
Murray, W. A. S. 443, 449, 450, 451, 452, 470, *478*, *479*

N

Nasmyth, J. H. 286, *356*
Nathan, Hans 312, *356*
Naumann, H. 47, 57, *59*
Nazarenko, V. A. 339, *356*
Nefediev, A. A. 47, 56, 57, *59*, 246, 247, *282*
Nel, L. T. 315, *356*
Nevill, E. N. 286, *356*
Newcomb, S. 20, 22, *26*
Nicholson, S. B. 109, *129*, 407, 411, *428*, 440, 457, *479*
Nikonova, E. 109, *129*
Nölke, F. 514, *522*

O

Odé, Hans 299, *356*
Öhman, Y. 134, *159*
Oppolzer, Th. 163, 166, *228*
Ordoñez, Ezequiel 294, *356*
Orlova, N. S. 120, 126, *129*
Öpik, E. *129*
Ower, L. H. 288, *356*

P

Paetzold, H. K. 196, 197, 199, *228*, 229
Palmén, E. 206, *229*
Paneth, F. A. 495, *521*, *522*
Pannekoek, A. 174, *229*
Parenago, P. *128*
Pariiskii, N. N. 89, *97*
Parsons, W. 132, *159*
Patterson, C. C. 347, *356*, 494, *522*

Pawsey, J. L.   *428*
Peal, S. E.   289, *356*
Pecora, W. T.   312, *356*
Perret, F. A.   291, 300, *356*
Petrie, R. M.   252, 268, *282*
Pettengill, G.   439, 443, 463, 466, 467, *479*
Pettit, E.   109, *129*, 215, *229*, 407, 411, 412, *428*, 440, 457, *479*, 510, *522*
Pickering, E. C.   112, *129*
Pickering, W. H.   *129*, 286, 288, 303, *356*
Piddington, J. H.   419, 420, 426, *428* 510, *522*
Pingré, P.   *229*
Pingré-Bigourdan, J.   163, *229*
Pinson, W. H.   495, 496, *521*
Plana, J.   8, *26*
Plouff, Donald   315, *354*
Poincaré, H.   16, *26*
Poisson, S. P.   9, *26*
Poldervaart, Arie   288, 323, *354*
Potrax, H. A.   495, 496, *521*
Prantle, E.   163, *229*
Presnell, R. I.   460, 462, 464, 467, *479*
Proctor, Mary   287, *356*
Proctor, R. A.   186, *229*, 287, *356*
Puiseux, P.   47, *59*, *129*, 245, 261

Q

Quiring, Heinrich   289, *356*

R

Rackham, T. W.   275, *282*
Radau, R.   10, 20, *26*
Radlova, L. N.   *129*
Ramanathan, R. R.   206, *229*
Ramsey, W. H.   516, *522*
Ratcliffe, J. A.   476, *479*
Raynard, A. G.   186, *229*
Reasbeck, P.   495, *522*
Reaves, G.   192, *229*
Reck, Hans   290, *357*
Reed, G. W.   495, 496, *522*
Reich, Hermann   311, *357*
Reiche, Parry   294, *357*
Reuss, J. D.   163, *229*
Reuter, Lothar   *357*

Reynolds, J. H.   520, *522*
Riccioli, J. B.   162, *229*
Ringwood, A. E.   507, 518, *523*
Roach, C. H.   295, *357*
Rochester, M. G.   93, *98*, 492, 494, 517, 520, *523*
Roman, N. G.   436, 439, 455, 459, *479*
Rosenberg, H.   112, *129*
Rosse, Lord   132, *159*, 407, *428*
Rougier, G.   101, 102, 103, 104, 107, 121, *129*, 188, 214, *229*, 388, *405*
Routh, E. J.   *97*
Rozet, M. le Capitaine   *357*
Russell, H. N.   101, 107, *129*, 440, *479*
Russell, I. C.   295, *356*
Rutherford, L. M.   244

S

Sabaneyev, P. F.   487, *523*
Sacco, Federico   288, *357*
Sakharov, V. N.   339, *357*
Salomonovich, A. E.   420, *427*
Sauer, Adolf   312, *357*
Saunder, S. A.   241, 249, *282*
Saussure, M.   172, *229*
Sawyer, H. E.   252, 268, *282*
Schairer, J. F.   498, *521*
Schlobohm, J. C.   460, 462, 464, 467, *479*
Schmidt, J. F. J.   167, *229*, 241, 243, 252, *282*, 323, *357*
Schoch, C.   162, *229*
Schoenberg, E.   105, *129*
Schröder, Jöachim   312, *357*
Schröter, J. H.   241, 252, *282*
Schrutka-Rechtenstamm, G. von.   57, *59*, 247, 249, 251, 274, *282*
Schureman, P.   71, 91, *97*
Schwarz, E. H. L.   289, *356*, *357*
Scrope, G. P.   286, 295, *357*
Secchi, A.   132, *159*
Seeger, C. L.   420, *428*
Seeliger, H.   164, 172, 177, 199, *229*
Sellards, E. H.   311, *357*
Senior, T. B. A.   469, 470, 473, *479*
Shain, C. A.   436, 438, 439, 440, 448, *479*
Shaler, N. S.   289, *357*
Sharonov, V. V.   119, 123, *129*, *130*

Shoemaker, E. M. 294, 295, 307, 310, 312, 315, 318, 319, 320, 321, 332, 333, 350, *352, 357, 358*
Shorthill, R. W. 418, *428*
Siegel, K. M. 469, 470, 473, *479*
Simeons, G. 288, *358*
Sinton, W. M. 409, 410, 411, 418, 420, 421, 424, *427, 428*
Široký, J. 391, *405*
Smales, A. A. 496, *523*
Smart, W. M. 65, 66, 79, 94, *97*
Smith, F. G. 224, *228*, 437, *479*
Smith, M. 219, *229*
Smith, S. P. 298, *358*
Smith, W. , 449, *478*
Smoluchowski, M. 416, *428*, 511, *523*
Spencer, L. J. 289, 307, *358*
Spitzer, L. 158, *159*
Spurr, J. E. 288, *358*
Stair, R. 409, *428*
Staude, N. *128*
Stearns, H. T. 295, 298, *358*
Stebbins, J. 109, *129*
Stehn, C. E. 291, *358*
Sterneck, R. V. 89, *98*
Stewart, J. Q. 440, *479*
Stodola, E. K. 429, 447, *478*
Stone, M. L. 436, 438, 439, 442, 443, 458, *478*
Strassl, H. 420, 421, *427*, 477, *479*, 510, *522*
Stratton, F. J. M. 46, *59*
Strong, H. M. 498, *523*
Strong, J. 409, *428*
Struyck, N. 162, *229*
Stutzer, H. O. 311, *357*
Suess, Eduard 287, 288, 345, 349, *358*
Suess, F. E. 288, *358*
Suess, H. E. 506, *523*
Sulzer, P. G. 449, *479*
Švestka, Z. 189, 204, 206, 209, 219, *227, 229*
Swift, D. W. 436, 438, 439, 442, 443, 458, *478*
Sytinskaya, N. 119, *129, 130*, 511, *523*

T

Takeuchi, H. 75, *98*
Taylor, G. I. 22, *26*, 89, *98*
Tchekirda, A. T. 122, *128*

Teller, Edward 329, *353*
Thomas, A. B. 439, *479*
Thomas, A. P. W. 298, *358*
Thomson, J. H. 457, 461, *478*
Tilghman, B. C. 310, *358*
Tilton, G. R. 347, *356*
Tomkins, H. G. 289, *358*
Treibs, Walter 312, *358*
Trexler, J. H. 452, 455, 456, 457, 458, *479*
Troitsky, B. S. 420, *428*
Tschunko, H. F. A. 117, *130*
Tsesevich, V. P. 210, *229*
Turkevich, A. 495, 496, *522*
Turner, G. 274, 277, *282*

U

Uhlenbeck, G. E. 434, 451, 452, *479*
Urey, H. C. 93, *98*, 223, *229*, 287, 349, *358*, 487, 489, 490, 491, 492, 494, 495, 496, 498, 505, 506, 507, 509, 515, 516, 517, 518, 520, *522, 523*

V

Vahsvik, K. N. 295, 298, *358*
van Bemmelen, J. 291
van de Waerden, B. L. 23, *26*
van Diggelen, J. 120, 126, *128*, 264, *282*
van Woerkom, A. J. J. 22, *26*
Vassy, E. 222, *229*
Vaucouleurs, G. de 217, *229*
Verbeek, R. B. M. 291, *358*
Very, F. W. 407, *428*
Veryl, G. 298, *355*
Viete, Gunter 288, 294, *359*
Vigroux, E. 121, *130*, 197, *229*
Vinogradova, E. *128*

W

Waer, R. 440, 444, *478*
Wagner, P. A. 296, *359*
Walker, M. F. 192, *229*
Warner, B. D. 455, *478*
Wasiutyński, Jeremi 289, *359*
Watts, C. B. 57, *59*, 246, *282*, 494, *523*
Webb, D. H. 446, *479*
Webster, R. K. 496, *523*
Wegener, Alfred 286, 289, *359*

2M*

Weimer, Th. 47, 53, 59, 251, 261, 282
Weinek, L. 245
Werner, E. 311, 359
Wesley, W. H. 251, 282
Wesselink, A. J. 130, 413, 428, 510, 511, 523
Westerhout, G. 420, 428
Wetherill, G. W. 497, 523
Whipple, F. L. 318, 359
Whipple J. A. 244
Whitwell, T. 261, 282
Wichmann, M. 46, 59
Wilkins, H. P. 243, 286, 359
Williams, Howel 290, 291, 313, 359
Willis, D. G. 299, 354
Wilson, C. W. 314, 359
Winter, D. F. 431, 440, 479
Wirtz, C. 130, 212, 229
Witkowski, J. 223, 229
Wolf, R. 163, 229
Wolff, F. L. von 288, 359

Wood, R. W. 130
Woolard, E. W. 78, 79, 98
Woolley, R. v. d. R. 109, 130
Wright, F. E. 130, 134, 141, 142, 159, 289, 323, 359, 511, 523

Y

Yakovkin, A. A. 40, 47, 54, 57, 58, 59, 246, 247, 251, 282
Yaplee, B. S. 24, 25, 436, 439, 455, 459, 478, 479
Yavnel, A. A. 506, 523

Z

Zabidarov, E. I. 339, 356
Zacharov, I. 204, 227, 229
Zelinskaya, M. R. 420, 428
Zhuchikhim, V. I. 319, 351
Zinner, E. 108, 130
Zoellner, F. 101, 130
Zwicky, F. 225, 229

Subject Index

A

Absorption coefficients 424, 425
Aerosols 222
Alphonsus 248, 302, 364, 365
  central peak of 370, 372, 373
  red glow in 378
  spectrograms of 366–68, 374–77
Alps, lunar 268, 361
Ambiguity function 446
Apennines, lunar 268
Archimedes 146
Ariadadeus 302
Aristarchus 122, 272
  luminescence in 394
Aristillus 345
Artificial Satellites 23
Ash, volcanic 144, 145
  polarization from 154
Ashen light 100, 148, 150
  selective polarization of 151
Astronautics 186
Atmosphere
  attenuation of flux dueto 171
  ozone in 196
  rocket soundings in 176
Atmospheric extinction 118
Atomic clocks 23
Aufsturz-hypothese 288, 289

B

Balloon observations 152, 197
Barycentre, of Earth–Moon system 3–5
Basalt 123, 141
  absorption coefficient of 425
Bistatic Radar 442
Blasenhypothese 287, 288
Bohemian Basin 286
Boltzmann's constant 433
Brown's tables 2, 5, 23, 96

C

Calderas 290, 291, 383, 483
Cape Heraclides 486

Cape Laplace 486
Carpathian Mountains, lunar 337, 349
Carbon reduction process 519
Cassini, J. D.
  three laws of 27, 31, 32
Cassiopeia 433
Cat's Eye Photometer 105, 190, 191
Chondrites 496
  black 513
  carbonaceous 506
  high iron group 508
  low iron group 508, 509
  white 513
Clavius 268, 269, 272, 482
Cloudiness and Earth's shadow 206
  (see Eclipses)
  and isophotes 207
Coesite 310, 312
Cometary heads, spectra of 372, 374
Co-ordinates 63
  see also elliptical, equatorial, geo-
    graphic, rotating co-ordinates
Copernicus 273, 302
  ejecta trajectories from 329, 335
  ray system of 304, 305, 335
Coronograph 149, 156, 157
Cosmic rays 477
Crater chains 340
Craterlets 250
Craters, ice hypothesis of 289
  random distribution of 483
  of elevation 286
  volcanic origin of (see also Maars)
    285
Crystal Eigenfrequencies 424
Cygnus 431

D

d'Alembert Mountains 494
Deserts, terrestrial 478
Diabases 142
Diamond Head (maar) 295
Diatremes 295

533

Dielectric constant 470
  for dry terrestrial rock 431
Doppler broadening 451, 452, 465
Doppler shift 434, 438, 439, 443, 447
Dorpat observatory 47, 56
  heliometric observations at 53, 57
Dyadic 66
  rotation dyadic 64

E

Earth,
  brightness of 153
  convection currents in 495
  density of 507, 516
  equatorial radius of 24
  erosion of 281
  non-sphericity of 10, 20, 61
  plastic deformation of 73
  rotation of 22, 67, 68, 76, 81–83, 92, 438
  tidal deformation of 75
  tidal friction of 21, 62, 63
Earthlight 221, 222
Ebert's Rule 268, 274
Eclipses, lunar 161, et seq.
  and Earth's atmosphere 162
  and spherical shape of Earth 162
  brightness of 217, 218, 220
  classical theory of 162
  frequency of 164
  future eclipses 166–7
  photometry of 171
Eclipse shadow 179, 206
Eclipse temperatures 411–413, 416
Eifel Maars 292
Eifel Plateau 291, 301, 302
Ejecta, smothering effects of 328
  trajectories 329
Elliptical co-ordinates 168
Engelhardt observatory 47
Equatorial bulge 63
Equatorial co-ordinates 240
Eratosthenes 327
Eratosthenian age 348
Eulerian angles 33
Excitation functions 77
Extinction coefficient 425

F

Fastie–Ebert system 401
Feldspars, in lunar rocks 507
Filters, optical 117, 121, 122, 191, 409
Fissures 301
Flux density 430–432
Fraserburgh, radio telescope 463
Fraunhofer lines 216
  intensity of in lunar spectrum 390
Fresnel's laws 135
Fresnel Reflection loss 422, 425
Fresnel zones 439, 475, 476
Full Moon, brightness of 99, 374

G

Gases, from lunar interior 159
  luminescence of 362
Gaussian law 476
Geographic axes 70, 75, 76
Geographic co-ordinates 71
Geographic latitude 194, 196, 198
Geographic pole 76
Geologic and lunar time scale 347
Geyser 300
Gezeiten-hypothese 287, 288
Gja 302
Gauges in lunar surface 326, 344
Granite 123, 141, 510
Graphite 505
Gravimetric observations 88, 89
Great Empirical term 22, 87
Grimaldi 121, 122
Gruithuisen 285

H

Haute Provence observatory 121
Hawaii 286
Heliometer 46, 47, 54, 57, 246, 249
Hell plain 268, 270
High absorbing layer 199, 200, 210
Hill-top craters 274
Hopi Buttes (maars) 295, 297, 300, 301
Hydraulic fracturing 299
Hydrodynamic flow 343
Hyginus 279, 302, 303, 306
Hyginus N. 359, 360
Hypervelocity experiments 342

I

Igneous rocks, thermal conductivity of 147
Imbrian system 346, 347
Infra-red measurements 417, 421
Infra-red photography of Moon 363
International lux constant 108
Ionosphere 436, 437, 449, 476
    lunar ionosphere 477
Ionospheric refraction 448
Irish sea 89
Isotropic radiator 430
    Moon, as 447
Isotropic re-radiation 439
Isotropic reflector 432

J

Jadeite 505
Jangle U. experiment 315, 320, 325, 330, 333
Jodrell Bank, experimental station 403, 449, 452, 457
Johnson-Morgan photometric system 109
Julian century 20
Jupiter, atmosphere of 225
    perturbations produced by 35

K

Katmai valley 382
Kepler (crater) 272
Keplerian motion 5
Kilauea 298
Kilimanjaro 275
Kimberlite pipes 296, 345
Kirchoff's law 422
Krakatoa 274, 291

L

Lambert's laws of reflection and scattering 113, 114, 125, 440, 443, 444, 449, 451–54, 462, 467–69
Lapilli 292
Latitude, selenographic 28
Lava 141, 142
    lunar lava 377
    terrestrial lava 507, 512
Leonids 223
Lephrites 142
Lichens 127

Limb-darkening theory 452–4
Limestone 123
Limit of resolution 478
Line depth method 391–94, 404
Linné 124, 144, 223, 361, 362
Lommel-Seeliger law of reflection and scattering 114, 115, 440, 444, 449, 451–454, 462, 467
Love numbers 72, 73, 76
Love operators 73
Lowell observatory 409, 421
Luminescence, lunar 215, 216
    and eclipses (which see) 209
    fluctuations in 396
    intensities of 395
    spectra of (see line depth method also) 396
Lunar atmosphere 154, 224
    density of 155, 156
Lunar cracks 112, 117, 482
Lunar crescent, positive limb of 116
Lunar crust, layering of 338
Lunar details, apparent brightness of 119
    colour brightness diagram 123
Lunar domes 277, 289, 303, 346
Lunar dust, thickness of 148, 418
Lunar ellipsoid 46
Lunar ephemeris, improved 24
Lunar luminous constant 110
Lunar mountains 117, 122, 255, 265, 490
Lunar photography 244
Lunar photographic atlas 245
Lunar surface, indicatrices of reflection 126, 127
Lunar temperatures 408, et seq.
Luni-solar camera 118

M

Maars 288–292, 300, 321–324, 350, 351
Magma 289, 299
Magmatic rocks 125
Magnetites 142, 475
Mare Crisium 121, 122
Mare Frigoris 122
Mare Imbrium 276, 287, 346, 484, 485, 487
    see also Imbrian system.
    ridges on 489

Mare Nubium 268
Mare Orientale 494
Mare Serenitatis 134, 268, 487
 pumice on 489
Mare Tranquilitatis 121, 277, 278
Mars, density of 516
Maser 432
McMath-Hulbert observatory 252
Mercury 148
 density of 516
Messier 144
Meteor Crater, Arizona 307–311, 313,
 316, 317, 319–321, 325, 332, 345
Meteorites, as catalysers for rain 204
Meteorites, chondritic (see also chon-
 drites) 494, 505–507, 509, 512
Meteorite craters 316
Meteoritic bombardment 124
Meteoritic iron 310
Micrometeorites 203, 345
Moon, absolute stellar magnitude of
 106
 albedo of 431
 a rigid body 32
Moon, as smooth reflector 440
 as wavelength converter (see also
 Luminescence) 385
 brightness of various parts of 111,
 112, 127
 celestial latitude and longtitude of 64
 colour of 110, 122
 curve of polarization for 132, 133
 distance from Earth 24, 433
 effect of solar attraction on rotating
 Moon 46
 far side of 267
 figure of 54
 geocentric coordinates of 30
 global brightness of during eclipse
 193
 integral brightness of 103, 108
 integral brightness and phase angle
 of 100, 104
 magnetic field of 393
 maps of 234–237, 240, 242
 isothermal maps of 410, 411
Moses Rock, diatreme 302
Mösting, A. 47, 49, 56, 247–9
 selenographic co-ordinates of 48,
 50, 51, 53

Mount Huygens 275
Mount McKinley 275
Mount Wilson observatory 327
Mule's Ear diatreme 297

N
Nautical Almanac 257, 258
Nilahue, maar 298, 300
Nuclear craters 319, 334
Nuclides 500
Nutation 61, 62, 65, 69, 78
 free nutation 79
 forced nutation 80

O
Occultations, of stars 494
Oceanus Procellarum (see also Procel-
 larian system) 134, 303
Odessa crater 311, 315, 320
Odessa observatory 223
Olivine 497, 504, 510
Osculating element 94–95
Ozone
 absorption coefficients of 198
 amount of ozone in atmosphere 196
Ozone
 distribution of ozone from eclipse
 results 197
Ozone layer 195, 220
 light absorption in 194, 221
 Variations of ozone with geographi-
 cal latitude 196, 198

P
Parasitic light 189–192
Paris observatory 47, 261
Penumbra 193, 194, 210–213
Peridotites 142
Phlegraean fields 286, 295
Photometer, photographic 192
 Pickering's shadow photometer 101
 Zöllner's polarizing visual photo-
 meter 101
Photomultiplier, tri-alkali 400
Pic-du-Midi observatory 149, 156, 245,
 252
Piton 275–7
Planetesimal accretion 287
Planets, atmosphereless 413
Plato 122, 124

Polar wandering 70
Polaris 113, 118
Polarization 133 et seq.
  elliptical 133
  from granular absorbing substances 137
  from light and dark parts of Moon 150
  from powdered glass 138
  from powders of small absorbing grains 143
  from sugar 136
  from transparent sand 140
  from volcanic ash 145
  from yellow sand 139
  negative polarization 143
Polytropic gas spheres 517, 518
Porphyry 141
Post detector bandwidth 447
Post detector signal to noise ratio 448
Potassium 505, 506
Power spectrum 454, 465
  radio frequency 451
  echo 452, 457
Precession 61, 62, 65, 69, 78, 80
Procellarian system 347–350
Proclus 121
Ptolemy 248
Pulvermaar 295
Pulse length, echo amplitude versus 472, 473
Pumice 291
  heat conductivity of 383
Punch bowl maar 295

Q

Quartz-sandstone 136

R

Radar echoes 429, 450, 458–49
  amplitudes of 447
  fading of 448
  frequency functions of 455
  intensity of 460
  power of 436
  power spectrum of 446
  time function of 446
Radar, over dry sandy terrestrial deserts 455
  techniques to measure Moon's distance 24

Radio waves
  ionospheric absorption of 437
  refraction of 436
Rankine-Hugoniot conditions 329
Rays, lunar 325, 326, 337
  formation of 335
Ray patterns, of Pickering, Proclus, and Tycho 343, 344
Rayleigh atmosphere 172, 203, 206, 220, 221
Rayleigh's law 451, 468
Rayleigh scattering 115, 316
Reactor diode parametric amplifier 430
Receiver bandwidth 434
Receiver noise factor 432
Rectangular co-ordinates 13, 14, 168
Red Mesa diatremes 297
Reflection coefficient 431
Regiomontanus 274
Regiomontanus A 274
Rieskessel 311, 313, 320
Rotating co-ordinates 14
Rotating rectangular co-ordinates 18

S

Saint Augustine's and Kimberley Mines 296
Scattering cross section 471–473
Schollen und Schuppen zone 312, 313, 315, 333
Schröter's rule 268, 274
Schröter's valley 144
Schröter's visual scale 111
Schwabian Alb. 311
Seeliger's sector 200
Selenographic co-ordinates 28, 168
Selenoid
  mean-selenoid 251
  deviation from sphere 260, 491
Shadow increase (see also Eclipses) 167, 170
Shadow terminator 187
Sidereal time 81
Sierra Madera 314, 315, 348, 350
Soda Lake Maar 295
Solar constant, variations in 388, 389
Solar corona 387
Solar disk, limb-darkening of 178

Solar nebula   520

Spectrometers, photoelectric   399, 400
    photographic   398

Specular reflection   474

Spherical polygionometry   52

Stadius   302

Stefan-Boltzmann constant   414

Steinheim basin   313, 321

Stellar magnitudes, visual system   108

Straight Wall   144, 279, 280, 366, 488

Strasbourg observatory   56, 101

Strato-volcano   303

Swan resonance series   369

Suevit   312, 313

Sun, apparent angular diameter of 262
    colour temperature of   379
       high energy electromagnetic and corpuscular radiation from 371, 385
    radio waves from   437, 438

Sweep frequency   434

T

Tashkent observatory   113, 117, 122

Teapot Ess crater   315, 320, 325

Tektites   127

Tensional wave   318

Terrestrial albedo   222

Terrestrial atmosphere, refraction in 175
    scattering of light in   188
    structure of   177
       variations of terrestial atmosphere with geographical latitude (see also Eclipses)   185

Theophilus   268, 271, 302

Thermal inertia, of basalt, granite, pumice   413

Thermopiles   407
    calibration of   408

Thorium   505

Tidal deformation, of Earth   70, 75

Tidal dissipation, of energy within Earth   62, 92, 93

Tidal forces, of Moon   91

Tidal period, internal oscillations of 89

Tidal perturbation   71

Tide, bodily   88, 96

Tide, ocean   88, 89

Tides, origin of   514

Tides, sidereal tides   83

Topocentric co-ordinates of moon   30

Transmitter pulses   435

Triesnecker   302

Troitite   509

Troposphere   204, 436

Tuffs   126

Tycho   272

U

Ubehebe   292

Ultra-violet radiation on Moon   477

Umbra, during lunar eclipse   165

Umkehr-effect   195

United States Army Signals Laboratory   446

United States Naval Research Laboratory   24, 261

Universal time   81

Upheaval dome   315

Uranium   505, 506

V

Venus, atmosphere of   225
    keplerian orbit of   19
    transit of   186

Vesuvius   300

Vorries   312

Vredefort dome   315, 321, 350

Vulkanhypothese   287, 288

W

Wargenin   482

Wauen Namus crater   294

Wood patch   122

Wrinkle-ridges   264

X

X-rays   213

Y

Yerkes observatory   121

Yucca Flat   315

Z

Zuñi Salt Lake crater   292–294, 302